ECLECTIC EDUCATIONAL SERIES

RAY'S™ NEW TEST EXAMPLES IN ARITHMETIC

BY

B. O. M. De BECK, A.M.

Originally published by
Van Antwerp, Bragg & Co.

This edition published by

1000 East Huron Street, Milford, Michigan 48042

ISBN 0-88062-057-9
Printed in the United States of America

PRESENT PUBLISHER'S PREFACE

We are honored and happy to bring to you the classic Arithmetics by Joseph Ray. In the 1800s these popular books sold more than any other arithmetics in America, in fact over 120,000,000 copies. Now with this reprinting, they are once again available for America's students.

Ray's Arithmetics are organized in an orderly manner around the discipline of arithmetic itself. They present principles and follow up each one with examples which include difficult problems to challenge the best students. Students who do not master a concept the first time can return to it later, work the more difficult problems, and master the concept. Thus in these compact volumes is a complete arithmetic course to study in school, to help in preparing for ACT and SAT tests, and to use for reference throughout a lifetime.

In order to capture the spirit of the original Ray's, we have refrained from revising the problems and prices. Only a few words have been changed, as we felt it wise. Thus students will have to rely on their arithmetic ability to solve the problems. Also the charm of a former era lives on in this reprinting. Flour and salt are sold by the barrel, kegs may contain tar, and postage stamps cost 3¢ each. Through this content, students learn social history of the 1800s in a unique, hands-on manner at the same time they are mastering arithmetic.

The series consists of four books ranging from Primary Arithmetic to Higher Arithmetic, as well as answer keys to accompany them. We have added a teacher's guide to help today's busy teachers and parents.

We wish to express our appreciation to the staff of the Special Collections Library at Miami University, Oxford, Ohio, for its cooperation in allowing us to use copies of their original Ray's Arithmetics.

George M. Mott, President
MOTT MEDIA, INC.

PREFACE

This revised and enlarged edition of Test Examples is now respectfully presented to the teachers of our country.

It is confidently believed that it will furnish them the necessary number and variety of exercises essential to successful instruction in arithmetic.

While the difficulties likely to be encountered in school and ordinary business will be found here presented, all mere puzzles have been carefully excluded.

No example has been introduced which the average pupil can not solve without assistance, and no solid progress can be expected unless this is required.

The examples in each article have been carefully graded, the first few being suited to very young pupils, while the last half would furnish work for advanced pupils, whose time is limited.

Attention is called to examples occurring in pairs, where a slight variation in statement changes the nature of the problem.

In each article the number of examples presented is made to depend upon the difficulty and importance of the particular subject presented.

B. O. M. De BECK.

Cincinnati,
December, 1883.

CONTENTS

TEST EXAMPLES.

NOTATION.

ARTICLE 11.

Numbers to be Written:

1. Nineteen. Ninety. Ninety-nine.
2. Five hundred and two.
3. Three hundred and sixty-seven.
4. Nine hundred. Nine hundred and twenty.
5. Four thousand and seven.
6. Four thousand and seventy.
7. Four thousand and seventy-seven.
8. Nine thousand six hundred and five.
9. Eight thousand four hundred and twenty.
10. Seven thousand six hundred and fifty-four.
11. Ten thousand. Ten thousand and ten.
12. Forty thousand and seventeen.
13. Fourteen thousand and seventy.
14. Eighty-seven thousand.
15. Twelve thousand and forty-one.
16. Ninety-one thousand two hundred.
17. Sixty thousand three hundred and forty.
18. Sixteen thousand three hundred and fourteen.
19. Fifty-five thousand and fifty-five.

20. Ninety thousand nine hundred and one.

21. Forty-eight thousand and six.

22. Eleven thousand seven hundred.

23. Thirty thousand and thirty.

24. Twenty-one thousand one hundred and seven.

25. Eighty thousand and eight.

26. Sixty-nine thousand four hundred and seventy.

27. Seventy thousand two hundred and eighty.

28. Fifty thousand six hundred.

29. Nineteen thousand nine hundred and twenty-three.

30. Two hundred and twenty-five thousand seven hundred and ninety-one.

31. Two hundred and five thousand seven hundred and one.

32. Six hundred and eighty thousand.

33. Three hundred thousand and eighty.

34. Eight hundred and four thousand nine hundred.

35. One hundred and nine thousand.

36. Four hundred thousand nine hundred.

37. Five hundred thousand and thirty-one.

38. Seven hundred and five thousand five hundred and seven.

39. Four hundred thousand and ninety.

40. Two hundred thousand two hundred and two.

41. Nine hundred and eleven thousand and twenty.

42. One hundred and eighty-seven thousand and thirty.

43. One hundred and eighty-seven thousand and three.

44. Six hundred thousand three hundred and twenty.

45. One hundred and two thousand and three.

46. Nine hundred and eighty-seven thousand.

47. Eight hundred thousand and one.

48. Seven hundred and seventy thousand seven hundred.

49. Six hundred and sixty thousand and sixty.

50. Four hundred thousand one hundred and fifty-seven.

51. Seven million seven hundred thousand seven hundred.

52. Nine million four hundred thousand.

53. Eight million five hundred.

54. Twenty million two hundred and twenty thousand five hundred.

55. Sixty million nine hundred and five thousand.

56. Sixty million nine hundred thousand and five.

57. Four hundred million and ninety.

58. Forty million and two hundred.

59. Thirty-eight million five thousand and sixty.

60. Twenty million two thousand two hundred.

61. Ninety-nine million and nine.

62. Fifteen million fifty thousand and fifteen.

63. Fifty million fifteen thousand and fifty.

64. Seventy million and four.

65. Thirty-four million and fifty-six thousand.

66. Fifty-six million and thirty-four.

67. One hundred and forty million two thousand eight hundred.

68. One hundred and forty million and eight hundred.

69. Two hundred million five thousand and sixty.

70. Five hundred million and eight.

71. Six billion six hundred million seven thousand and thirty.

72. Forty billion seven hundred thousand two hundred and three.

73. One hundred billion nine hundred and thirty three.

74. Thirty trillion forty billion fifty million and sixty.

75. Sixty nine billion and four thousand.
76. Eighty billion and ninety.
77. Sixteen trillion six hundred million.
78. Forty trillion two million and three hundred.
79. Thirteen trillion two hundred billion.
80. Forty trillion fourteen thousand.

In the following examples, Th. *stands for thousand,* M *for million,* B *for billion,* Tr. *for trillion.*

81. Write 69 B. 43 M. 319.
82. Write 41 Tr. 17 Th. and 60.
83. Write 48 B. 90 Th.
84. Write 300 Tr. 200 M. and 94.
85. Write 175 B. 13 M. 299.
86. Write 99 Tr. 308.
87. Write 167 Tr. 44 M. 273 Th.
88. Write 409 Tr. 93 M. and 7.
89. Write 900 Tr. 9 Th. 900.
90. Write 375 Tr. 2 M.

NUMERATION.

Article 12.

Copy, separate into periods, and read:

23	4000	10000	524358	7564219
223	2309	34000	409126	6000628
500	6008	57900	600888	32400070
809	8054	74210	347000	136629000
890	3456	97526	200014	8029504962
731	5790	20064	870900	90900009

713	2090	43009	166060	4800080008
444	9307	69200	900089	77000009452
440	7114	80005	763005	526300004
506	4017	79046	225200	30300013003
310	8006	30749	840096	9243000000
687	3680	68802	400002	16700054
1600	9502	40200	680400	66055000500
1750	4008	50060	304006	300000936420
1904	6789	10208	560230	840005400
2378	5200	29847	708020	67760800008
3095	7440	91006	940094	10101010101
5120	1005	80770	709000	40005000600
8700	8060	65030	120502	897065403210
7040	6463	60007	402029	19901990199
4001	2008	48016	290000	678900000257
6802	5083	89119	607080	8040050006
2094	1240	53647	550406	900000700001
9530	3402	10203	803590	61100065084

456780993	26375	13700687319
7654019000	123456789	378483852468
69952468308	87654321	22670000007000
2600800430	3000192	6200900004
83004251007	40090283	100010001018
10083682645	29700370	93724561427
967013750	100560460	5720000902
380080545802	406000557	2237000888005
72000974094	73990646	432666000456
80000303080	1462739	58079529000
954270738900	800002824	8076530900700
3000160069	99033910	74040850770
76544599823	123774105	199055805630
500000922356	60005298	9365704004060

ADDITION.

Article 19.

(1)	(2)	(3)	(4)	(5)	(6)
444	476	743	622	208	748
233	340	385	387	759	677
342	546	614	494	437	386
531	784	286	365	666	974
124	937	367	938	384	953
345	542	894	673	759	379

(7)	(8)	(9)	(10)	(11)
5834	3948	4567	1357	6429
2345	5678	8912	9246	7531
768	1234	3456	8135	8642
4367	9999	7891	7924	9753
9843	7654	2345	6813	6767
6438	3467	6789	5897	8345

(12)	(13)	(14)	(15)	(16)
94073	47356	75319	86427	43214
9846	29356	86426	98574	67785
78468	31663	54687	89758	89376
93785	73548	34387	67896	97644
49679	46659	67496	9523	35975
3492	54762	78588	84376	68796
78685	8658	92738	63527	82768

(17)	(18)	(19)	(20)
473826	483736	765432	754218
584937	736475	198765	765432
695346	859648	432198	109876
746578	365439	765432	543210
677365	449563	987654	987654
485956	658757	321987	321098
345567	512934	654321	765432

(21)	(22)	(23)	(24)
864268	798386	946738	234567
975319	837654	784293	376674
876543	425262	367564	456953
234567	667788	852381	716364
426453	445599	177539	168478
777777	374859	796142	579797
638904	465768	265498	923564
135246	556677	437651	437675

(25)	(26)	(27)	(28)
4538762	4321763	5847354	6756453
7465477	3419844	7356819	1237634
5632850	4553735	9868943	7468515
6783219	9676756	8675478	3189743
7546578	6789427	9756986	4581524
2613695	8252178	3868314	6453635
8843617	7843439	7444267	7684813
4684653	5586865	9565479	9792354
6795876	8638274	8947548	2316615
4777656	4871847	4798716	9875243

(**29**)	(**30**)	(**31**)	(**32**)
8968548	7945	54	7694746
5637225	6723987	7483	887
6096	1496959	4565572	9769938
2375867	58964	4860	985398
9144636	7	438333	47879
6813405	8877898	9873865	4473767
82277	5693887	5687	6838438
1146	836836	798476	689989
3450014	8869	9929	8971524
8129982	9779853	6549590	7318

33. 7467 + 8938 + 5489 + 6756 + 4887 = what?

34. 57364 + 76528 + 79525 + 55772 + 98769 = what?

35. 49586 + 48659 + 39745 + 87685 + 92367 = what?

36. 58737 + 62914 + 13579 + 24682 + 98765 = what?

37. 4359 + 78768 + 90000 + 85076 + 19467 = what?

38. 37648 + 58459 + 39393 + 78978 + 89789 = what?

39. 76543 + 87654 + 98765 + 34567 + 45678 = what?

40. 12398 + 77665 + 99887 + 88776 + 66554 = what?

41. 73842 + 15693 + 17369 + 82456 + 48597 = what?

42. 49386 + 59487 + 69489 + 76563 + 86465 = what?

43. 76834 + 893584 + 4678 + 59356 + 5968 + 4938 = what?

44. 3456 + 34567 + 345678 + 3456789 = what?

45. 7654 + 987 + 9876 + 98765 + 987654 + 876543 + 8765 + 87654 = what?

46. Add 37590, 4856, 938, 4675, 12834, 2753, and 492.

47. Add 3962, 9623, 2639, 6293, 3269, 9326, 2963, and 6392.

48. Add 6783, 75, 4938, 6, 3974, 7788, 48395, and 568.

49. Add 29, 2967, 96, 9672, 67, 6729, 72, 7296, 79, and 796

50. Add 67, 8945, 5873, 88, 6377, 24, 5891, 53, and 492.

51. Add fifty thousand and twenty-six; sixteen thousand two hundred; nine thousand and ninety-four; 47396; twenty-seven thousand six hundred and seven; 84759; ninety-three thousand and nineteen, and 6733.

52. Add 289564; ninety-four thousand six hundred and eight; 763268; 56921; nine hundred thousand and forty; sixteen thousand eight hundred and seven, and 5698.

53. A man owned seven houses, costing as follows: $5860, $4575, $9560, $12750, $6788, $3500, and $7388. What was the cost of all?

54. The following passengers were carried on a railway: Monday, 2567; Tuesday, 894; Wednesday, 1388; Thursday, 3146; Friday, 1098; Saturday, 3834; and Sunday, 675. How many were carried during the week?

55. Eight men weigh as follows: 168 pounds, 195 pounds, 108 pounds, 187 pounds, 136 pounds, 205 pounds, 154 pounds, and 172 pounds. What is the weight of all?

56. In a city the inhabitants numbered as follows: Americans 57465, Germans 32903, Irish 7588, English 4995, Italians 2893, Colored 2566. How many in all?

57. The membership in four churches was as follows: in the first, 295 men and 330 women; in the second, 107 men and 95 women; in the third, 240 men and 277 women; and in the fourth, 150 men and 148 women. How many members in all?

58. A well was sunk through loam 3 feet, gravel 19 feet, clay 24 feet, sand 5 feet, and limestone 29 feet. How deep is the well?

59. What is the sum of all the numbers under 100, whose ten's figure is 7?

60. Find the total weight of 12 bales of hay, weighing as follows: 467, 388, 491, 417, 373, 402, 333, 412, 309, 383, 417, and 398 pounds.

61. A farmer raises 850 bushels of corn, 720 of oats, 560 of wheat, 236 of rye, 13 of millet, 390 of barley, and 78 of buckwheat. How much grain has he in all?

62. Five clerks receive $1275 apiece, and four others $960 apiece. What are their total wages?

63. The pupils in a school are classed as follows: A grade, 77 boys and 69 girls; B grade, 105 boys and 99 girls; C grade, 148 boys and 153 girls; D grade, 195 boys and 196 girls; and E grade, 219 boys and 231 girls. How many pupils in the school?

64. A planing mill sells the following quantities of lumber: pine, 19680 feet; oak, 7845 feet; poplar, 12098 feet; cherry, 2780 feet; ash, 9860 feet; walnut, 5947 feet; maple, 1439 feet; beech, 610 feet; and sycamore, 439 feet. How many feet in all?

65. In a school 340 children are 6 years old, 297 are 7 years, 258 are 8 years, 227 are 9 nine years, 196 are 10 years, 145 are 11 years, 128 are 12 years, 91 are 13 years, 67 are 14 years, and 48 are older. How many pupils in the school?

66. A lady spent as follows: for muslin, 87 cents; calico, 95 cents; flannel, 175 cents; tape, 7 cents; buttons, 15 cents; thread, 25 cents; needles, 5 cents; silk, 280 cents; table cloth, 375 cents; and napkins, 250 cents. Find the amount of her bill.

67. Spent in a market as follows: for beef, 89 cents; chicken, 65 cents; turnips, 13 cents; carrots, 7 cents; oranges, 15 cents; apples, 35 cents; radishes, 10 cents; potatoes, 34 cents; butter, 45 cents; eggs, 56 cents; and beans, 30 cents. How much did I pay for all?

68. A commenced business with $9278, and gained $346; B with $7866, and gained $963; C with $12390, and gained $2240; and D with $1862, and gained $16. How much were the four then worth?

69. A factory makes in a week 960 chairs, 40 sofas, 68 lounges, 93 settees, 38 sideboards, 29 bureaus, 165 wash-stands, 82 wardrobes, 326 tables, 120 desks, and 5 black-boards. How many articles in all?

70. A steamer on a trip carried the following: iron, 475 tons; flour, 76 tons; cotton, 84 tons; coffee, 45 tons; sugar, 119 tons; barley, 84 tons; paper, 9 tons; lumber, 173 tons; rice, 17 tons; corn, 45 tons; cheese, 22 tons; and other articles, 36 tons. What was the weight of the cargo?

71. Write 58487 ten times and add.

72. A vessel sailed per day as follows: 204 miles, 78 miles, 137 miles, 99 miles, 136 miles, 196 miles, 312 miles, 273 miles, 301 miles, and 264 miles. Find the length of the trip.

73. Find the sum of all the numbers between 48 and 60.

74. Eight barrels of salt weighed respectively 372, 401, 294, 277, 336, 348, 299, and 363 pounds. Find the weight of all.

75. A has $450; B $7 more than A. How many have both?

76. A owns 320 acres of land; B, 120 more than A; and C, 100 more than B. How many acres have the three?

77. I lost $68, $23, and $254, and then had $77. How much had I at first?

78. A merchant paid during the year for rent, $1500; repairs, $205; book-keeper, $1500; clerks, $3200; fuel, $205; freight, $688; gas, $1018; advertising, $274; dray-age, $290; taxes, $360; and little expenses, $164. Find his total expenses.

79. The rooms of a school-house contained 63, 61, 59, 57, 55, 53, 51, 49, 47, and 45 pupils respectively. How many pupils in all?

SUBTRACTION.

Article 26.

1. From 4368 take 2634.
2. From 56789 take 9876.
3. From 33333 take 4040.
4. From 303030 take 222222.
5. From 5263743 take 2281429.
6. From 34567890 take 12345678.
7. From 34567890 take 1234567.
8. From 43216723 take 9013861.
9. From 29345678 take 2934587.
10. From 2009988 take 1838899.
11. From 60000254 take 5000169
12. From 222333444 take 22334455
13. From 367890000 take 724.
14. From 8245673432 take 7345582604.
15. From 99009900 take 88088088
16. From 90008000 take 2765094
17. From 21222324 take 12223242
18. From 3067543581 take 9364.
19. From 189640054 take 99999999.
20. From 880088007 take 80059920.
21. Take 47563 from 128290.
22. Take 1357924 from 4297531.
23. Take 98700563 from 100987285.
24. Take 7654083 from 23582467.
25. Take 7654083 from 235824674.
26. Take 30047582 from 40100000.
27. Take 235643218 from 524870042.
28. Take 3242526272 from 4252621222.
29. Take 123456789 from 987654321.
30. From four million and sixty take 239734.

31. From 59 billion and 30 thousand take 9 million 527 thousand 235.

32. 34000527 — 8370263 = what?

33. 200003000 — 5604037 = what?

34. 37360000 less 29504574 = what?

35. How much greater is 234568001 than 42734056?

36. How much less is 2980752 than 3009527?

37. From 1 unit of the eighth order take 5432187.

38. What number must be taken from five million and five to leave five thousand five hundred?

39. What number must be added to 3723489 to make ten million?

40. What is the difference between 3802764 and 3890609?

41. 39 million less 7800973 = what?

42. What is the difference between 8200969 and 7040080?

43. From 17 million 14 thousand take 9 million 99 thousand 900.

44. From 1 trillion take 560000900384.

45. From forty billion sixty million take 7 billion 328 million 9 thousand and 87.

46. A house cost $4000, and was sold at a loss of $968. How much was received for it?

47. A house was sold for $3425, at a gain of $956. Find the cost.

48. I had $843, and gave away all except $96. How much did I give away?

49. A man had 320 acres, of which 47 acres were woodland. How much was cleared?

50. Washington was born in 1732, and died in 1799. How old was he when he died?

51. In what year was a man born, who died in 1875 at the age of 86?

52. Commenced business with $18420, and quit with $16975. How much did I lose?

53. Commenced with $29080, and lost $2364. How much had I left?

54. After gaining $2972, I had forty thousand dollars. With what sum did I commence?

55. A man agrees to build 4270 feet of fence; after completing 1909 feet, how much remains to be built?

56. A published 40000 copies of a book, and sold 37036. How many remain unsold?

57. I had $1807 in bank, and gave a check for $250. How much was in bank after the check was paid?

58. Sold goods at an advance of $12500, and my expenses were $3750. What was my real gain?

59. At an election Brown received 1013 votes and Jones 834 votes. What is Brown's majority over Jones?

60. Floods occurred in the Ohio River in the years 1832 and 1883. How many years between the two?

61. A treasurer received $507320, of which he paid out $498078. How much has he still?

62. From 2004 take 668 twice.

63. Subtract 3728 three times from 12000.

64. Find the excess of 40789 over 30978.

65. From 100000308 take 15700890 four times.

Addition and Subtraction.

66. $453 + 268 + 2000 - 983 = ?$

67. $2500 + 2145 - 485 - 3485 = ?$

68. $489 + 625 - 873 + 341 = ?$

69. $3250 - 2409 + 1783 - 999 = ?$

70. $10000 - 2733 - 2789 - 2648 = ?$

71. $11111 - 2844 - 2557 + 129 = ?$

72. From 2701 take the difference between 2701 and 897.

73. From 2700 take the sum of 598 and 697.

74. I had $2365; I received $2138 for a house, and paid away $3980. How much have I left?

75. A farmer had 300 acres of tilled land, 725 acres of pasture, and 409 acres of woodland; he sells 987 acres. How much has he now?

76. From the sum of 3456 and 6546 take the difference between 10000 and 1001.

77. From the sum of 4783 and 5984 take their difference.

78. A city contained 47850 inhabitants; 1372 moved in, and 679 moved away; 948 were born, and 473 died. How many did it then contain?

79. Had in bank $2125; deposited $267, and afterwards drew out $415 and $290. How much is left in bank?

80. Bought 4 hogsheads of sugar containing 1183, 1211, 1170, and 1293 pounds, and then filled and sold 3 barrels, each containing 219 pounds. How much is left?

81. Sold, the first year, $8760 worth of goods; the next year $2698 more than the first. How much was that for two years?

82. Williams & Co. gained $4200 the first year, $3850 the second year, and then had $30000. What was their capital at first?

83. Had $20880; gained $1706 the first year, and enough the second year to make my capital $25000. What did I gain the second year?

84. A firm owed me $3800; I bought from them $12000 of goods, paying them $5000 cash, and giving them a note for balance due them. What was the amount of the note?

85. A is worth \$4750; B \$988 more than A; C \$47 less than B; and D \$50 less than A. How much have all together?

86. A man died leaving property worth \$60000 to be divided among his widow, two sons, and three daughters; each son received \$9870, and each daughter \$7890. How much remains for the widow?

MULTIPLICATION.

ARTICLE 31.

1. 326 × 5 = ?
2. 734 × 6 = ?
3. 459 × 7 = ?
4. 386 × 8 = ?
5. 597 × 6 = ?
6. 678 × 4 = ?
7. 5678 × 8 = ?
8. 9768 × 7 = ?
9. 7678 × 5 = ?
10. 8986 × 9 = ?
11. 5846 × 7 = ?
12. 6967 × 8 = ?
13. 783419 × 3 = ?
14. 605628 × 7 = ?
15. 577237 × 8 = ?
16. 409846 × 7 = ?
17. 391055 × 6 = ?
18. 732364 × 5 = ?
19. 694573 × 9 = ?
20. 806782 × 7 = ?
21. 798990 × 8 = ?
22. 680401 × 6 = ?
23. 474692 × 5 = ?
24. 696283 × 8 = ?
25. 467670984 × 8 = ?
26. 288076589 × 7 = ?
27. 668948078 × 9 = ?
28. 701539548 × 11 = ?
29. 933697658 × 10 = ?
30. 845786793 × 8 = ?
31. 457868839 × 9 = ?
32. 766854729 × 7 = ?
33. 870896697 × 9 = ?

34. 287 × 23 = ?
35. 493 × 22 = ?
36. 391 × 24 = ?
37. 465 × 34 = ?
38. 386 × 25 = ?
39. 472 × 26 = ?
40. 951 × 35 = ?
41. 587 × 36 = ?
42. 958 × 37 = ?
43. 6254 × 42 = ?
44. 3873 × 47 = ?
45. 6485 × 43 = ?
46. 3129 × 58 = ?
47. 7654 × 69 = ?
48. 8397 × 42 = ?
49. 6549 × 83 = ?

50. 2386 × 94 = ?
51. 786 × 97 = ?
52. 458 × 69 = ?
53. 6083 × 48 = ?
54. 769 × 316 = ?
55. 846 × 527 = ?
56. 846 × 906 = ?
57. 938 × 238 = ?
58. 938 × 709 = ?
59. 776 × 483 = ?
60. 987 × 904 = ?
61. 3456 × 895 = ?
62. 4567 × 786 = ?
63. 5678 × 607 = ?
64. 6789 × 568 = ?
65. 7894 × 409 = ?

66. Multiply 8945 by 645.
67. Multiply 48075 by 376.
68. Multiply 6908 by 489.
69. Multiply 629075 by 3089.
70. Multiply 738306 by 4605.
71. Multiply 923874 by 3837.
72. Multiply 8877655 by 4657.
73. Multiply 1357986 by 5783.
74. Multiply 4378078 by 6329.
75. Multiply 2468642 by 3759.

76. What cost 93 horses at $75 apiece?

77. What cost 75 horses at $93 apiece?

78. How many yards of thread on 84 spools, holding 196 yards each?

79. What will 9568 bushels of wheat cost, at 127 cents a bushel?

80. A butcher sells 2657 pounds of beef, daily, for 93 days. Find the total amount sold.

81. A book contains 288 pages; and each page, 840 ems. How many ems in the book?

82. What is the total capacity of 46 freight cars, each holding 14260 pounds?

83. What will it cost to grade 257 miles of road at $385 a mile?

84. How many links in 289 chains, each chain having 743 links?

85. A horse can draw a load of 1423 pounds. How much could 85 horses draw?

86. A company of soldiers contains 85 men. How many men in 67 companies?

87. A lot is 287 feet front, and worth $162 for each front foot. What is the lot worth?

88. If 2347568 gallons of water pass a certain point in a river in one hour, how many gallons will pass in 48 hours?

89. How far will a star go in 75 days, if it goes 1267893 miles per day?

90. A barrel of flour contains 196 pounds. Find the weight of 472 barrels.

91. What must be paid for grading a railroad 327 miles long, at $1237 a mile?

92. How many peach trees can be planted on 179 acres, each acre having 256?

93. If a seine contains 4365 yards of twine, how many yards will be required for 483 seines?

94. What will be the weight of 96 horses, estimating them at 1387 pounds apiece?

95. If the circulation of a library is 24306 volumes daily, how many would that be in 297 days?

96. If 829 men could dig a canal bed in 248 days, how many men would be required to complete the work in one day?

ARTICLE 32.—*Case I.*

1. 47384 × 63 = ?
2. 60872 × 132 = ?
3. 346891 × 77 = ?
4. 7205674 × 27 = ?
5. 889793 × 72 = ?
6. 426312 × 44 = ?
7. 3784931 × 45 = ?
8. 6292558 × 96 = ?
9. 3490175 × 66 = ?
10. 768793 × 35 = ?
11. 453312 × 42 = ?
12. 673944 × 108 = ?
13. 483576 × 64 = ?
14. 363108 × 144 = ?
15. 273733 × 88 = ?
16. 903465 × 81 = ?
17. 693197 × 48 = ?
18. 843839 × 84 = ?
19. 783571 × 55 = ?
20. 932186 × 56 = ?

ARTICLE 33.—*Case II.*

1. 28734 × 1000 = ?
2. 49865 × 100 = ?
3. 6200945 × 1000 = ?
4. 384503 × 10000 = ?
5. 468357 × 100 = ?
6. 40050008 × 1000 = ?
7. 40070893 × 100000 = ?
8. 37088900 × 1000 = ?
9. 26893845 × 10000 = ?
10. 34779267 × 100 = ?
11. 48596023 × 100000 = ?
12. 76540063 × 1000 = ?

ARTICLE 34.—*Case III.*

Multiply:

1. 590 by 45.
2. 4732 by 730.
3. 66450 by 6600.
4. 38700 by 40800.
5. 96050 by 39000.
6. 483200 by 79610.
7. 738512 by 4850000.
8. 400400 by 640800.
9. 5008 by 50790.
10. 60904 by 384000.
11. 706004 by 80400000.
12. 209800 by 606600.
13. 345678 by 78050000.
14. 46003 by 90020.
15. 97623 by 5648000.
16. 87410 by 809300.
17. 53820 by 256700000.
18. 6767600 by 4760000.
19. 948372 by 138200.
20. 21101 by 6095000.

SHORT DIVISION.

ARTICLE 41.

Divide:

1. 45678936 by 3.
2. 43218765 by 5.
3. 9999992660 by 7.
4. 807006935 by 5.
5. 392919096 by 8.
6. 987652308 by 4.
7. 987652308 by 6.
8. 111111111 by 9.
9. 222222222 by 6.
10. 21026838 by 3.
11. 74060259 by 7.
12. 76587692 by 4.
13. 723645000 by 8.
14. 876543210 by 9.
15. 9876543215 by 7.
16. 346800270 by 5.
17. 6001674864 by 3.
18. 3031674804 by 6.
19. 345680528 by 4.
20. 759274400 by 8.
21. 39291993 by 9.
22. 876543210 by 6.
23. 392919096 by 4.
24. 123456128 by 8.
25. 350364075 by 5.
26. 5555558400 by 7.
27. 618170472 by 9.
28. 617180742 by 6.
29. 1001002002 by 3.
30. 406052983 by 7.

31. Find one fourth of 3738392.
32. Find one eighth of 7360576.
33. Find one third of 26688111.
34. Find one ninth of 28880109.
35. Find one sixth of 45500196.
36. What is one fifth of 56009800?
37. What is one seventh of 54985448?
38. What is one ninth of 23401881?
39. What is one fourth of 23601880?

40. Four men earn $2968: how much is that for each of them?

41. How many 6-pound balls will be required to weigh 7644 pounds?

42. How many hats can be bought for $2075, at $5 apiece?

43. In one week there are 7 days: how many weeks in 8429435 days?

44. A man earns $972 in 6 months: how much is that per month?

45. A car can go 8 miles in an hour: how long will it take it to go 4560 miles?

46. How many 5-gallon jugs can be filled from 2520 gallons of molasses?

47. $3450 was raised among some merchants, each paying $6: how many were there?

48. Five passenger cars can carry 360 persons: how many is that for each car?

49. Eight stoves weigh 2792 pounds: what is the weight of each?

50. A railroad train can go 3003 miles in 7 days: how far is that each day?

51. How long will it take a man to earn $896, if his wages are $7 a week?

52. How many blank books can be made from 5552 sheets of paper, if each book contains 8 sheets?

53. A man dying left $16814 to be equally divided among 7 children: what was the share of each?

54. A bar of soap weighs 4 pounds: how many bars will be required to weigh 9996 pounds?

55. At $6 a day, how many days will be required to earn $1638?

56. How many sashes, of six panes each, can be filled from 7776 panes of glass?

57. If the Government pays $9256320 of debt in 9 months, how much would that be per month?

58. If 125616 soldiers were divided equally into 8 divisions, how many soldiers would that be for each division?

59. How many sixes would it take to make 16008?

LONG DIVISION.

ARTICLE 42.

Divide:

1. 84878 by 31.
2. 223686 by 51.
3. 328233 by 71.
4. 220867 by 41.
5. 898716 by 91.
6. 356500 by 92.
7. 380398 by 82.
8. 675000 by 72.
9. 241552 by 62.
10. 309557 by 43.
11. 1674123 by 33.
12. 6582564 by 83.
13. 3766110 by 94.
14. 2997592 by 74.
15. 4832460 by 54.
16. 1362768 by 44.
17. 3323232 by 36.
18. 3323232 by 48.
19. 1009827 by 27.
20. 1501305 by 39.
21. 4141387 by 59.
22. 38739176 by 19.
23. 45806266 by 902.
24. 18757711 by 611.
25. 48512520 by 713.
26. 16379005 by 421.
27. 45000000 by 338.
28. 15349839 by 771.
29. 36517449 by 893.
30. 11998679 by 197.

31. Divide 240158529 by 6201.
32. Divide 292246250 by 4138.
33. Divide 37021447680 by 9085.
34. Divide 100200300400 by 8251.
35. 234567891000 ÷ 3456 = ?
36. 345678912000 ÷ 4567 = ?
37. 456789123000 ÷ 5678 = ?

38. At 47 cents apiece, how many hammers can be bought for 18565 cents?

39. How many cars, each 24 feet long, can be placed upon a track 3744 feet long?

40. If 986 pounds is a load for one horse, how many horses will be required to carry 493986 pounds?

41. What will one horse cost, if the bill for 293 horses is $89365?

42. How many sewing machines, at $65 each, can be bought for $4225?

43. If a foundry consume 428 bushels of coal in a day, how long will 121980 bushels last?

44. A man traveled 5341 miles in 109 days: how far was that each day?

45. How many years would be required to pay a debt of $2004002154, if $13013001 are paid yearly?

46. A turnpike was constructed at a cost of $2765 per mile, and the total cost was $215670: how long was the road?

47. Divide 57 million 114 thousand and 57 by 19019.

48. If 56 pounds of rye make a bushel, how many bushels would be required to weigh 93744 pounds?

49. 83 iron columns weigh 764264 pounds: find the weight of each.

50. By what number must 706126 be divided to give 89 for a quotient?

51. By what number must 4328 be multiplied, so that the product may be 8331400?

52. If a short-hand writer can write 125 words in a minute, how long will he require to write 13375 words?

53. What was the length of one piece of cloth, if 193 pieces measured 36477 yards?

CONTRACTIONS IN DIVISION.

ARTICLE 43.—*Case I.*

Divide:

1. 4524 by 24.

2. 455364 by 36.

3. 372518 by 32.

4. 2736595 by 45.

5. 4728392 by 48.

6. 1168384 by 56.

7. 13413501 by 27.

8. 3742015 by 28.

9. 27253746 by 18.

10. 47351850 by 25.

11. 11111111 by 42.

12. 3579135 by 63.

ARTICLE 44.—*Case II.*

1. Divide 47389256 by 1000.
2. Divide 367854001 by 100.
3. Divide 27000008746 by 10000.
4. Divide 1234567892 by 100.
5. Divide 3704605504 by 1000.
6. Divide 9897969594 by 100000.
7. Divide 130027005 by 100.
8. Divide 123843658 by one thousand.
9. Divide 44872362592 by one million.
10. Divide 5000700040 by ten thousand.
11. Divide 37264839527 by ten.
12. Divide 43 million by one hundred.
13. Divide 12345654321 by one thousand.
14. Divide 754000000000400 by one billion.
15. Divide 47638592143 by ten thousand.

ARTICLE 45.—*Case III.*

1. Divide 472956 by 40.
2. Divide 124578013 by 140.
3. Divide 56789324 by 8000.
4. Divide 3438725382 by 1900.
5. Divide 263341058 by 470.
6. Divide 738495262 by 4050.
7. Divide 3213213313 by 8800.
8. Divide 345456567 by 3400.
9. Divide 765472384 by 107000.
10. Divide 9236453400000 by 7200.
11. Divide one billion by 706700.
12. Divide 397 billion by 97 thousand.
13. Divide 56784935867 by 3050600.
14. Divide 999999999 by 90990.

ARTICLE 49.—*Promiscuous Examples.*

1. Bought 60 cows at \$33 apiece, and 47 at \$28 apiece: what was the total cost?

2. What cost 47 hogsheads, each containing 48 gallons of molasses, at 65 cents a gallon?

3. Had 96 horses; 3 died, and the others were sold at \$150 apiece. What sum was received for them?

4. A man having \$10000, kept \$307, and with the rest bought land at \$27 an acre. How many acres did he buy?

5. Multiply the sum of 209 and 390 by their difference.

6. Two men had \$8550 apiece; one bought cows at \$38 each, the other cows at \$45 each. How many more did the first buy than the second?

7. Eighty-seven horses were sold at \$155 apiece, and the money invested in mules at \$93 apiece. How many mules were bought?

8. Four times 1728 are how many less than 10000?

9. Raised 65 bushels of potatoes on each of 85 acres of land; used 180 bushels, and sold the remainder at 63 cents a bushel. How much was received for them?

10. Four men were in partnership, having in all \$8560; the first had \$2140, the second \$3076, and the third and fourth had equal sums. How much had each of the latter?

11. 66 horses were bought at \$127 apiece; sold one third at \$125 apiece, and the remainder at \$135 apiece. What was my gain on all?

12. I have a lot 65 feet front, worth \$175 per front foot; if I trade for a farm of 126 acres, worth \$90 an acre, how much cash should I receive?

13. Divide 312×273 by $312 - 273$.

14. Forty-eight men can build a bridge in 187 days; how many must be employed to build it in 176 days?

15. Seventy-three horses eat 101835 pounds of hay in 93 days; how much was that daily for each horse?

16. A man borrows $6000, and pays $400 a year for the use of it; how much should he pay back at the end of 4 years?

17. What sum will be received for 137 acres of land, which cost $75 per acre, and were sold at a gain of $49 per acre?

18. What sum will be received for 354 acres of land, which cost $29 per acre, and were sold at a gain of $94?

19. A man received a legacy of $8273; he paid $131 expenses, and with the remainder bought bonds at $118 apiece; how many did he buy?

20. If a sewing machine is worth $45, how many sewing machines must be traded for 117 watches at $65 apiece?

21. How much must be paid for 45 turkeys, so that 95 cents may be gained by selling them at 87 cents apiece?

22. The dividend was 39 times 552, and the divisor 299: find the quotient.

23. Bought 882 acres of woodland; after clearing one ninth of it, I sold the cleared land at $18 an acre, and the woodland at $11 an acre. How much did I receive in all?

24. If a number will contain 322 ninety-six times, how many times will it contain 69?

25. Bought 48 cows at $32 apiece, and 20 horses at $100 apiece; sold them so as to gain $200. What did I receive for them all?

26. A banker buys 52 shares of stock for $5824; for how much must he seil them to gain $8 a share?

27. Bought 293 hogsheads of sugar at $58 apiece; for how much must I sell it to gain $7?

28. A pile of lumber weighing 39039 pounds lost one seventh of its weight in drying: what did it then weigh?

29. How many 20-gallon casks can be filled from 395 barrels of molasses of 48 gallons each?

30. Sold 47 wagons at $50 apiece, and after buying a farm had $495 left. What was the cost of the farm?

31. What number must be multiplied by 47 to make the product equal to the difference between 987 and 11797?

32. What number must be divided by 73 to make the quotient equal to the sum of 456 and 2893?

33. Spent $8880 for horses at $74 apiece; 23 died: how many remain?

34. If 93 horses cost $19158, how many can be bought for $79310?

35. Bought hogs for $893, and sold them at $11 apiece, gaining $9; how many did I buy?

36. Of what number is 526 both divisor and quotient?

37. If 36 men earn $6912 in 12 weeks, how much does each earn per week?

38. How often is one fourth of one thousand contained in one fifth of one million?

39. After selling 68 cows, at $42 apiece, how much must I borrow if I wish to buy 209 hogs at $14 apiece?

40. Sold 923 yards of my cloth at $4 a yard, and the remainder at $5 a yard, and received in all $5222. How many yards had I at first?

41. If 47 men, in 58 weeks, can dig 215354 yards of ditch, how many yards can 29 men dig in 47 weeks?

42. If an army of 23479 men consume 2653127 pounds of food in a month, how many pounds would be required per month after 4839 men have been killed?

43. Bought 356 acres for $2848, and sold at $11 per acre: how much did I gain?

44. 59375 yards of bunting were bought to make a certain number of flags, 19 yards being intended for each; if 5 yards more are needed for each flag, how much more bunting must be bought?

45. Received $5850 for 18 months' rent; the rent was then raised $20 per month. What was the rent for the next 12 months?

46. A car will carry 11700 pounds; what is the weight of a boat-load of wheat which lacks 250 pounds of filling 23 cars?

47. If an acre of ground will produce 52 bushels of turnips or 70 bushels of potatoes, how many bushels of potatoes can be raised on a farm that will produce 9100 bushels of turnips?

48. What number exceeds one ninth of 3096 as much as one eighth of 3096 exceeds one tenth of 3690?

49. Bought land for $8370, and sold it at $31 an acre, losing $248. How many acres were there?

50. A man having $25725, kept one third, and invested the remainder in land at $49 per acre: how many acres did he purchase?

51. Bought 135 mules at $115 apiece; sold one fifth of them at a gain of $18 apiece, and the others at a gain of $16 apiece. What was my total gain?

52. A man has a farm of 260 acres; on each acre he can raise 35 bushels of oats, worth 93 cents a bushel, or 130 bushels of potatoes, worth 24 cents a bushel. How much more would he realize from oats than from potatoes?

53. From 8 times 7317 take 9 times 5328, and divide the result by the difference between one eighth of 504 and one ninth of 1008.

UNITED STATES MONEY.

Article 53.

Write the following sums:

1. Thirteen dollars ninety-three cents.
2. Eighty-seven dollars forty-nine cents and three mills.
3. Twenty-nine dollars and eight cents.
4. One hundred and fifty-seven dollars and fifty cents.
5. Nine dollars nine cents and nine mills.
6. Twelve dollars and two mills.
7. Five hundred dollars and ten cents.
8. Two hundred dollars and three mills.
9. Ninety-nine dollars and ninety cents.
10. Ninety dollars and ninety-nine cents.

Read the following:

$ 73.38	$ 34.20	$ 96.011	$ 309.806
$ 73.028	$457.02	$ 49.102	$4561.25
$ 70.328	$ 2.909	$600.888	$ 3.092
$ 45.006	$ 6.099	$100.16	$ .59
$ 74.05	$ 5.005	$116.03	$ 739.11
$300.10	$ 88.10	$ 11.603	$ 46.03
$ 59.00	$393.25	$821.018	$1000.97

Article 55.—*Reduction of United States Money.*

1. Reduce $93 to cents.
2. Reduce 800 cents to dollars.
3. Reduce 46 cents to mills.
4. Reduce 187 mills to cents.
5. Reduce 76 dimes to cents.
6. Reduce $45 to mills.
7. Reduce 3009 mills to dollars.
8. Reduce $89.17 to cents.
9. Reduce $700 to cents.

10. Reduce \$10000 to mills.

11. Reduce 4 dollars 4 cents 4 mills to mills.

12. Reduce \$467.02 to cents.

13. Reduce \$467 to cents.

14. Reduce \$83 and 9 mills to mills.

15. Reduce 123000 mills to dollars.

ARTICLE 56.—*Addition of United States Money.*

1. What is the sum of 19 dollars 85 cents; 43 dollars and 79 cents; 76 dollars and 21 cents; 58 dollars and 15 cents; and 29 dollars and 75 cents?

2. Add \$74.19, \$15.01, \$46.28, \$9.60, \$17.81, \$25.72, \$9.93, and \$7.46.

3. \$7.007 + \$70.70 + \$7.07 + \$77.77 + \$777.77 + \$99.00 + \$4.683 + \$500 = ?

4. A man owes A \$750, B \$99.65, C \$427.80, D \$3.47, E \$697.29, F 50 dollars, and G 45 cents. What is his total indebtedness?

5. A man bought 2 coats, costing \$7.50 and \$18; 2 vests, costing \$3.20 and \$7.80; 2 pairs of pants, costing \$4.60 and \$9; 2 hats costing \$1.85 and \$5.50; and 3 shirts costing \$1.75, \$1.75 and \$3. What did he pay for all?

6. I paid for digging cellar, \$59.75; for limestone masonry, \$195.40; for freestone, \$168.90; for brick-work, \$897.60; for carpenter work, \$528.65; for tin roof, \$179; for iron work, \$40.60; for plastering, \$237.85; for painting, \$153.70; for plumbing, \$67.60; for gas-fitting, \$39; and for lightning-rods, \$78.90. How much did these items cost?

7. Bought a farm for \$2750, a horse for \$127.50, a cow for \$53.60, mules for \$286, sheep for \$69, hogs for \$268.90, a wagon for \$60.85, harness \$55.60, and plows, harrows, etc., \$186.40. How much did I pay for all?

ARTICLE 57.—*Subtraction of United States Money.*

1. From $120.63 take $87.29.

2. Take $39.82 from $90.15.

3. Take $76.09 from $100.

4. $1025 — $800.80 = ?

5. $90 less 90 cents = ?

6. $78.15 less $15.78 = ?

7. How much must be taken from $1000 to leave $690.09?

8. A man commenced business with $16208, and lost $1069.40; how much had he then?

9. How much must a man invest, so that after gaining $1690.18 he may have $8008?

10. From $2000 take $739.84 twice.

11. A man owes $529.60, and has $900; how much will he have after paying his debts?

12. A man has $429.13, and owes $600; after paying his money, how much will he still owe?

ARTICLE 58.—*Multiplication of United States Money.*

1. Multiply $8.293 by 24.

2. Multiply $9.835 by 36.

3. Multiply $43.75 by 84.

4. Multiply $8.008 by 65.

5. Multiply $9.12 by 60.

6. Multiply $27.008 by 400.

7. Multiply $29.632 by 750.

8. Find 39 times $.636.

9. What is 891 times 13 cents 6 mills?

10. $87, 3 cents × 3000 = ?

11. $68, 5 mills × 560 = ?

12. What cost 49 barrels of flour at $6.75 a barrel?

13. What cost 67 acres of land at $159.60 an acre?

14. What must be given for 34 horses at $88.40 each?

15. What cost 54 yards of grading at $7.282 per yard?

16. What must be given for 89 hogs at $8.34 apiece?

17. What cost 956 gallons of vinegar at 12 cents a gallon?

18. What will be paid for 526 quarts of berries at 22 cents a quart?

19. Sold 351 sheep at $2.50 apiece; how much did I receive for them?

20. What cost 5000 tickets at 18 cents apiece?

21. What cost 42357 yards of calico at 8 cents a yard?

22. What cost 4500 bolts at 6 mills each?

23. How much will a man earn in 57 days at $2.25 a day?

24. What cost 40 boxes of starch, containing 33 pounds each, at $.075 per pound?

25. If a soldier receives a pension of $1.75 per month, how much will 38 receive in 19 months?

26. What cost 40 boxes of candy, 40 pounds each, at 40 cents a pound?

27. What cost 808 bales of cotton, containing 465 pounds each, at 3 cents 6 mills per pound?

28. What cost 87 boxes of eggs, each containing 72 dozen, at $.125 per dozen?

29. What cost 9388 papers of pins, each containing 30 dozen pins, at 2 mills per dozen?

30. What will the glass cost for 8 houses, each containing 8 rooms, each room having 4 windows, and each window 4 panes, at 37 cents 5 mills per pane?

31. A man has 10 casks of stove polish, containing 425 pounds each; each pound will fill 6 papers, sold at 5 cents a paper. How much will be received for the entire amount?

32. What cost 40 bundles of paper, containing 2 reams each, each ream weighing 60 pounds, at 8 cents 3 mills per pound?

33. What cost 708 boxes of tomatoes, each containing 24 cans of 2 pounds each, at 11 cents a pound?

34. Find the cost of 82 boxes of calico, each box containing 40 bolts, and each bolt 30 yards, at $.066 per yard.

35. Find the amount received for 5 blocks of building lots, each block containing 12 lots, each lot being 25 feet front, the whole being sold at $8.75 per front foot.

36. What will be the wages of 240 men, employed 17 days, of 10 hours each, at 17 cents 5 mills per hour?

Article 59.—*Division of United States Money.*

1. Divide $49.50 cents by 33 cents.

2. Divide $393.75 by 75 cents.

3. Divide $200 by 32 cents.

4. Divide $333 by 45 cents.

5. Divide $1186.98 by $2.71.

6. Divide $3677.94 by $5 and 4 mills.

7. Divide $1608.88 by 33 cents 8 mills.

8. Divide $2162.45 by 30 cents 5 mills.

9. How much muslin, at 13 cents a yard, can be bought for $23.66?

10. How many sheep, at $3.75 apiece, can be bought for $600?

11. How many needles, at 3 mills apiece, can you buy for $19.38?

12. At $1.25 an acre, how much land can you buy for $995?

13. How many apples, at 1 cent 5 mills each, must be sold to realize $3?

14. How many planes, costing 85 cents each, can be bought for $129.20?

15. How many 20-cent tickets must be sold to make the receipts $500?

16. Divide $99.48 by 4.

17. Divide $95.004 by 7.

18. Divide $326.36 by 8.

19. Divide $436.032 by 9.

20. Divide $389 by 25.

21. Divide $440.44 by 77.

22. Divide $1500.496 by 491.

23. Divide $4226.427 by 603.

24. Nine horses cost me $1025.01; find the cost of each.

25. Sold 43 bushels of peaches for $120.40; how much was that per bushel?

26. $528.44 was divided equally among 11 heirs; find the share of each.

27. What must I charge per bushel for apples, so as to realize $526.50 for 2340 bushels?

28. 144 penknives cost $90; how much was that apiece?

29. 900 pounds of cheese cost $49.50; how much did one pound cost?

30. 600000 pounds of cotton cost $45000; how much is that per pound?

31. If 40 horses cost $5318, what would 76 horses cost?

32. If 38 men earn $1136.20 in 26 days, what is each man's daily wages?

33. If grape settings sell at $3.50 per hundred, how much is that apiece?

34. What cost 750 pickles at $1.20 per hundred?

35. If 16 chests of tea sell for $460.80, at 60 cents a pound, how many pounds in each chest?

ARTICLE 60.—*Promiscuous Examples.*

1. Paid for land, $970.50; for buildings, $1963.60; for horses, $180.75; for cattle, $217.50; for seeds, $29.50; for tools, $36.40; for harness, $82.50; for provisions, $200; and for hogs, $319.25. Find the total expenditure.

2. What cost 5 sofas, at $13.75 each, and 7 lounges, at $4.60 each?

3. Gave $108 for 45 yards of cloth, which I sold for $116.10; find my gain per yard.

4. A dealer bought peaches at $2.50 a bushel; how many bushels must he sell, at a profit of 70 cents a bushel, to receive $144?

5. What cost 1750 picture cards at $1.40 a hundred?

6. I saved $104.52 in 6 months; if my salary was $80 a month, what were my expenditures each month?

7. I saved $130.56 in 8 months; if my expenses were $80 a month, what was my monthly salary?

8. What cost 3700 papers at $2.20 a hundred?

9. A company owes $120000, and its assets amount to $30780; the deficit is collected from 15000 shares of stock. How much is that on each share?

10. How much will be left from a hundred dollar bill after spending the following amounts: $3.60, $11.17, 50 cents, $1.96, $6.40, $8.33, $29.08, and 98 cents.

11. A contractor agrees to grade a road for $14000; he pays a foreman $5 a day, for 80 days; 25 cart drivers $2.25 a day, for 75 days; and 83 laborers $1.30 a day for 77 days. Find his profit.

12. Sold 29 horses for $1914, losing $159.50; what did each cost?

13. Sold a farm of 46 acres for $3000, gaining $7.10 per acre; what did the farm cost?

14. What will I save in 14 months, if I earn $75 each month, and spend $39.25 per month?

15. I worked 13 weeks at $13.75 per week, and saved $58.50 during that time; what were my weekly expenses?

16. How many dimes in $40?

17. How many half-eagles in $1080?

18. How many 3-cent pieces should be given for 240 eagles?

19. How many 5-cent pieces should be given for 720 quarter-eagles?

20. If a man had one of each of the gold coins, how many quarter-dollars could he get for them?

21. Invested $4329 in cattle at $18.50 a head, and sold them at $23.08 a head; what was my gain?

22. Bought a house for $3300; made some repairs, and sold it for $4250, gaining $487.75. What was the cost of the repairs?

23. How many days, of 11 hours each, must a man work to earn $499.07, at 13 cents an hour?

24. Bought 40600 pounds of sugar for $2639, and sold it at a gain of 5 mills per pound; what was my gain?

25. Bought 15600 pounds of coffee for $5850, and sold it for $6162; how much was my gain per pound?

26. Bought rice for $3573; sold it for 5 cents per pound, gaining 5 mills per pound; how many pounds did I buy?

27. What cost 2468 pounds of butter, on which $86.38 was gained by selling it at 30 cents a pound?

28. Forty barrels of coal oil were bought for $241; how much was gained by selling at 15 cents a gallon, there being 50 gallons in each barrel?

29. Fifty barrels of molasses cost $1152, at 48 cents a gallon; how many gallons in each barrel?

30. A team pays $1.75 for toll, at the rate of 25 cents for 10 miles; how far does it go?

31. The expenses of a church festival were $237.52, and the gain was $701.98; how many 25-cent tickets had been sold?

32. A worked 47 days, at $2.55 per day; B worked 4 days longer than A, but received only the same amount. How much did B earn per day?

33. Find the cost of 40 boxes, each containing 24 cans, and each can holding 6 pounds of canned peaches, boxes costing 25 cents each, cans 5 cents each, and peaches 4 cents per pound.

Find the amount of the following bills:

34.	35	yards	Muslin,	at	$0.12	per yard.
	47	do	Calico,	"	.08	do.
	23	do	Delaine,	"	.16	do.
	13	do	Alpaca,	"	.35	do.
	21	do	Silk,	"	1.05	do.
	10	do	Satin,	"	1.25	do.
	7	do	Velvet,	"	2.40	do.
35.	4	pounds	Tea,	at	$1.15	per pound.
	7	do	Coffee,	"	.32	do.
	15	do	Sugar,	"	.13	do.
	20	do	Beef,	"	.09	do.
	17	do	Ham,	"	.12	do.
	12	do	Cheese,	"	.15	do.
	19	do	Starch,	"	.09	do.
36.	400	feet	Pine,	at	$0.025	per foot.
	720	do	Poplar,	"	.03	do.
	560	do	Walnut,	"	.07	do.
	875	do	Oak,	"	.02	do.
	94	do	Beech,	"	.045	do.
	120	do	Cedar,	"	.06	do.

REDUCTION.

Article 63.—*Dry Measure.*

1. Reduce 4 bu. 3 pk. 2 qt. 1 pt. to pints.

2. Reduce 9 bu. 2 qt. 1 pt. to pints.

3. Reduce 18 bu. 3 pk. 1 pt. to pints.

4. Reduce 36 bu. 3 qt. to pints.

5. Reduce 89 bu. 2 pk. to quarts.

6. Reduce 4789 pt. to bushels.

7. Reduce 5766 qt. to bushels.

8. Reduce 99 bu. 3 pk. 7 qt. 1 pt. to pints.

9. Reduce 583 bu. 1 pt. to pints.

10. Reduce 123456 pt. to bushels.

11. Reduce 4933 pk. to pints.

12. Reduce 25616 bu. to pints.

13. Reduce 25616 pt. to bushels.

14. Reduce 12345 qt. to pecks.

15. Reduce 7 million bushels to quarts.

Article 64.—*Liquid Measure.*

1. Reduce 38 gal. 3 qt. to pints.

2. Reduce 1025 gi. to gallons.

3. Reduce 87634 gal. to pints.

4. Reduce 93 gal. 2 qt. 1 pt. to gills.

5. Reduce 23867 pt. to gallons.

6. Reduce 8642 gal. to gills.

7. Reduce 99 gal. 3 qt. 2 gi. to gills.

8. Reduce 3732 gills to quarts.

9. Reduce 73 gal. 3 qt. 1 pt. 1 gi. to gills.

10. How many gallons in 33033 cubic inches?

11. How many cubic inches in 500 gallons?

12. A vessel measures 52206 cubic inches; how many gallons would it hold?

Article 65.—*Avoirdupois Weight.*

1. Reduce 3 T. to pounds.
2. Reduce 5 T. 13 cwt. to pounds.
3. Reduce 9 T. 1 cwt. 50 lb. to pounds.
4. Reduce 7 T. 19 cwt. 99 lb. to pounds.
5. Reduce 13 T. 13 lb. to pounds.
6. Reduce 4 T. 17 cwt. to ounces.
7. Reduce 3 T. 20 lb. 5 oz. to ounces.
8. Reduce 12945 lb. to tons.
9. Reduce 98400 lb. to tons.
10. Reduce 876543 lb. to tons.
11. Reduce 38742 T. to ounces.
12. Reduce 160080 oz. to tons.
13. Reduce 71 T. 17 cwt. 71 lb. to pounds.
14. Reduce 711771 lb. to tons.
15. Reduce 40000000 oz. to tons.
16. Find the weight of 375 balls weighing 32 pounds each.
17. Find the weight of 3000000 candles weighing 3 ounces each.
18. Find the weight of 3456 20-pound cannon balls.
19. Reduce 15999999 oz. to tons.
20. What is the weight of 357 boxes of alum, weighing 56 pounds each?

Article 66.—*Long Measure.*

1. Reduce 49 yd. 2 ft. 9 in. to inches.
2. Reduce 53 yd. 7 in. to inches.
3. Reduce 41 mi. 200 rd. to rods.
4. Reduce 77 yd. 2 ft. to inches.
5. Reduce 4953 mi. to rods.
6. Reduce 5678 in. to yards.

7. Reduce 38257 rd. to miles.

8. Reduce 498 yd. 11 in. to inches.

9. Reduce 373845 rd. to miles.

10. Reduce 39601 in. to yards.

11. Reduce 39601 mi. to rods.

12. Reduce 39601 rd. to miles.

ARTICLE 67.—*Square Measure.*

1. Reduce 7 A. 100 sq. rd. to square rods.

2. Reduce 3 sq. mi. 300 A. to square rods.

3. Reduce 19 sq. mi. 19 A. 19 sq. rd. to square rods.

4. Reduce 18 sq. yd. 8 sq. ft. 118 sq. in. to square inches.

5. Reduce 39 sq. mi. 90 sq. rd. to square rods.

6. Reduce 99 sq. yd. 99 sq. in. to square inches.

7. Reduce 50000000 sq. mi. to square rods.

8. Reduce 1 billion square inches to square yards.

ARTICLES 68 AND 69.—*Rectangles.*

Find the area of the following:

1. A floor 18 ft. long and 15 ft. wide.

2. A carpet 27 ft. long and 22 ft. wide.

3. A platform 80 ft. long and 16 ft. wide.

4. A pavement 40 ft. long and 9 feet wide.

5. A ceiling 36 ft. long and 20 ft. wide.

6. A lot 72 rd. long and 60 rd. wide.

7. A farm 80 rd. long and 76 rd. wide.

8. A field 100 rods square.

Find the cost of the following:

9. The carpet in example 2 at $1.30 a sq. yd.

10. The pavement in example 4 at 30 cents a sq. yd.

11. The farm in example 7 at $17.75 per A.

12. The platform in example 3 at 3 cents per sq. ft.

13. A farm extends along the road 60 rods; how wide must it be to contain 45 A.?

14. A road is 3 rods wide; how long must it be to contain 120 A.?

15. A farm is 100 rods long and 96 rods wide; how much wheat will it produce at the rate of 13 bushels to the acre?

16. A roof 100 feet long requires 300 square yards of roofing; how wide is it?

17. A floor is 40 feet long and requires 120 square yards of carpet; how wide is it?

ARTICLE 70.—*Solid or Cubic Measure.*

1. Reduce 3483648 cu. in. to cubic yards.

2. Reduce 3 cu. yd. 300 cu. in. to cubic inches.

3. Reduce 746496 cu. in. to cubic yards.

4. Reduce 9856 cu. ft. to cords.

5. Reduce 11 C. 111 cu. ft. 1111 cu. in. to cubic inches.

6. How many cubic yards in a cellar 40 feet long, 18 feet wide, and 9 feet deep?

7. How many cords in a wood-pile 120 feet long, 8 feet high, and 4 feet wide?

8. How many cubic yards of masonry in a stone pier 320 feet long, 36 feet wide, and 12 feet thick?

9. What will be the cost of a breakwater 900 feet long, 6 feet thick, and 12 feet high, at $2.75 per cubic yard?

10. Find the cost of a pile of wood 40 feet long, 40 feet wide, and 8 feet high, at $3.75 a cord.

11. How many inch cubes of lead can be cast from a mass 3 feet long, 1 foot high, and 2 feet wide?

12. Find the cost of digging a ditch 12 feet wide, 6 feet deep, and 285 feet long, at $.75 a cubic yard.

ARTICLE 71.—*Time Measure.*

1. Reduce 3 da. 2 hr. 30 min. to seconds.
2. Reduce 11 weeks to minutes.
3. Reduce 3 wk. 3 da. 3 hr. 3 min. 3 sec. to seconds.
4. Reduce 9 wk. 9 hr. to seconds.
5. Reduce 43 da. 43 sec. to seconds.
6. Reduce 777600 sec. to weeks.
7. Reduce 45678 min. to days.
8. Reduce 87500 days to seconds.
9. Reduce 72000 min. to weeks.
10. How many minutes in the year 1890?
11. How many minutes in the last three months of the year?
12. How many seconds in February, 1889?
13. How many seconds in 5 leap years?
14. Reduce 3 common years to hours.
15. A clock ticks 120 times in a minute; how many ticks will it make in the year 1892?
16. Reduce 19 wk. 5 da. 21 hr. 20 min. to minutes.

ARTICLE 73.—*Miscellaneous Tables.*

1. Reduce 17 lb. 10 oz. 16 pwt. to grains.
2. Reduce 18 lb. 18 gr. to grains.
3. Reduce 24 lb. 11 oz. 19 pwt. 23 gr. to grains.
4. Reduce 87340 gr. to pounds.
5. Reduce 50660 pwt. to pounds.
6. Reduce 31275 lb. to pennyweights.
7. Reduce 15 thousand gr. to pounds.
8. Reduce 4 lb. 4 oz. 4 gr. to grains.
9. Reduce 10 lb. 10 pwt. to grains.
10. Reduce 3 ℔ 9 ℥ 3 ʒ 1 ℈ 14 gr. to grains.
11. Reduce 9 ℔ 3 ʒ 2 ℈ to scruples.

12. Reduce 14 ℔ 7 ℥ 7 gr. to grains.

13. Reduce 45677 gr. to pounds.

14. Reduce 3478 ʒ to pounds.

15. Reduce 12345 ℈ to pounds.

16. Reduce 7 Cong. to f. ℥.

17. Reduce 3 O. 2 f. ℥ to minims.

18. Reduce 71 Cong. 3 f. ʒ to f. ʒ.

19. Reduce 4 ft. 6 in. to lines.

20. Reduce 5 feet to hands.

21. Reduce 17 leagues to miles.

22. Reduce 16 spans to yards.

23. In 17 hands how many feet?

24. In 20 yards how many spans?

25. Reduce 52 spans to hands.

26. Reduce 80 paces to fathoms.

27. Reduce 75 hands to fathoms.

28. Reduce 25 chains to rods.

29. Reduce 37°, 37′, 37″ to seconds.

30. Reduce 19°, 19″ to seconds.

31. Reduce 37864″ to degrees.

32. Reduce 450° to seconds.

33. How many things in 30 dozen?

34. How many things in 15 gross?

35. How many things in 5 great gross?

36. Reduce 15 score to dozens.

37. Reduce 360 score to gross.

38. What cost 12 kegs of nails at 6 cents a pound?

39. What cost 12 barrels of flour at 3 cents a pound?

40. What cost 12 barrels of pork at 8 cents a pound?

41. What cost 12 casks of lime, at 6 mills per pound?

42. What cost 1872 rings at 80 cents a gross?

43. What cost 7 great gross of needles, at 3 cents a dozen?

44. What cost 7 great gross of pins at 3 cents a gross?

45. What cost 9 gross of braces, at 7 cents apiece?

46. What cost 18 quires of drawing paper at 4 cents a sheet?

47. How many sheets of paper in 6 bundles?

48. A ream of paper will make how many 8vo. leaves?

49. Three reams of paper will make how many 12mo. pages?

50. How many reams of paper will be required for 3000 octavo books of 320 pages each?

Article 74.—*Promiscuous Examples.*

1. Reduce 49 yd. 2 ft. to inches.

2. Reduce 7 lb. 3 pwt. to grains.

3. Reduce 174528 sq. in. to square yards.

4. Reduce 12500″ to degrees.

5. Reduce 504000 cu. in. to cubic yards.

6. Reduce 3 ℔ 7 ℥ 2 ℈ to grains.

7. Reduce 863990 sec. to weeks.

8. Reduce 3329 pt. to bushels.

9. Reduce 14 great gross to dozens.

10. Reduce 7 T. 13 cwt. to pounds.

11. Reduce 3734 in. to yards.

12. Reduce 15 cords to cubic inches.

13. Reduce 5678 pt. to gallons.

14. Reduce 1016064 lb. flour to barrels.

15. Reduce 5400 scores to gross.

16. Reduce 3456 bu. to quarts.

17. Reduce 39750 pwt. to pounds.

18. Reduce 14 T. 14 lb. to ounces.

19. Reduce 23 gallons to f. ℥.

20. Reduce 333360 min. to weeks.

21. Reduce 7599 pt. to gallons.

22. Reduce 435670 sq. rd. to square miles.

23. Reduce 240 mi. to rods.
24. Reduce 78 gal. 3 qt. 1 pt. to pints.
25. Reduce 19 wk. 20 sec. to seconds.
26. Reduce 310 mi. 310 rd. to rods.
27. Reduce 49600 oz. to T.
28. Reduce one million sec. to weeks.
29. Reduce 384 cu. yd. to cords.
30. Reduce 5350 lb. to grains.
31. Reduce 12345 qt. to bushels.
32. Reduce 13 common years to minutes.
33. Reduce 12 cu. yd. 23 cu. ft. to cubic inches.
34. Reduce 39 T. 39 lb. to pounds.
35. Reduce 8 ℔ 8 ℥ 8 gr. to grains.
36. Reduce 46 sq. yd. 2 sq. ft. 36 sq. in. to sq. in.
37. Reduce 9876 pt. to gallons.
38. Reduce 10000 in. to yards.
39. Reduce 1284 pt. to bushels.
40. Reduce 11 ℥ 7 ʒ 2 ℈ to grains.
41. Reduce 5 sq. mi. 5 sq. rd. to square rods.
42. Reduce 162 C. to cubic yards.
43. Reduce 26 reams to 16mo. leaves.
44. Reduce 47580″ to degrees.
45. Reduce one million pt. to gallons.
46. Reduce 3500 gr. to ℥.
47. Reduce 6399 pt. to bushels.
48. Reduce 24 reams to sheets.
49. Reduce 793863 sq. in. to square yards.
50. Reduce one million oz. to tons.
51. Reduce 79 yd. 11 in. to inches.
52. Reduce 19 C. 1600 cu. in. to cubic inches.
53. Reduce 704000 sq. rd. to square miles.
54. Reduce 137 bu. 3 pk. to pints.
55. Reduce 5 wk. 5 da. 15 hr. 55 sec. to seconds.
56. Reduce 13 mi. 130 rd. to rods.

57. Reduce 1600 barrels of pork to pounds.

58. Reduce 30 T. 1 cwt. to ounces.

59. Reduce 217728 cu. in. to cubic yards.

60. Reduce 6920 pt. to gallons.

61. Reduce 10 great gross to scores.

62. Reduce 456789 oz. to tons.

63. Reduce ten thousand pt. to bushels.

64. Reduce 14° 23″ to seconds.

65. Reduce 4720 qt. to gallons.

66. Reduce one million sq. in. to square yards.

67. Reduce 6732 in. to yards.

68. Reduce 5280 minims to f. ℥.

69. Reduce 565 bu. 1 pt. to pints.

70. Reduce 3456000 sec. to weeks.

71. Reduce 3456000 12mo. pages to reams.

72. Reduce 288000 oz. to tons.

73. Reduce 387 A. 100 sq. rd. to square rods.

74. Reduce 17 leagues to rods.

75. Reduce 87 cu. yd. 25 cu. ft. to cords.

76. What cost 35 bushels of apples at 18 cents a peck?

77. What cost 13 bushels of salt at 3 cents a pint?

78. How much iron will be required to make 1000 4-oz. spikes?

79. How much milk will be needed to fill 80 dozen pint bottles?

80. A man's expenses are $1.17 a day; how much is that for July?

81. How many rings, weighing 6 pwt. each, can be made from 3 lb. of gold?

82. 414 gallons of cider were put in bottles containing 3 gills each; how many dozen bottles were required?

83. Find the cost of a pile of wood 40 feet long, 8 feet wide, and 8 feet high, at $3.75 per cord.

84 What cost 20 bushels of apples at 20 cents a peck?

85. A lawn 120 feet long, and 54 feet wide, was sodded at a cost of 19 cents per square yard; what was the total cost?

86. 561 pounds of iron were made into horse-shoes weighing 6 ounces each; how many were made?

87. How many 3-grain pills can be made from 5℥ of quinine?

88. If sound moves 1124 feet per second, how long will it be in passing over 39340 yards?

89. How many bottles, holding 1 pt. 3 gi. each, can be filled from 168 gallons?

90. A comet moves 40″ per day; how far will it move in 120 days?

91. What cost a carpet 21 feet long and 15 feet wide, at $1.75 per square yard?

92. How many pounds in 480 dozen boxes of baking powder holding 15 ounces each?

93. How much silver will be required to make 10 dozen spoons, each weighing 15 pwt.?

94. How many cords of wood can be cut on 25 acres, at the rate of 72 cubic feet to a square rod?

95. If bottles hold 1 pt. 2 gi. each, how many dozen bottles can be filled from 126 gallons?

96. How many sashes, each 3 yd. 1 ft. long, can be cut from 200 yards of silk?

97. 500 bushels of peaches were packed in baskets, each holding 3 pk. 1 qt.; how many baskets were required?

98. A paper containing 2 ℥ 1 ℈ of medicine was divided into pills weighing 5 grains each, which were sold at 2 cents apiece; how much was received for it?

99. If 25 sq. rd. produce 1 bushel of wheat, how many bushels can be raised on a square mile?

100. If a weaver can weave 10 sq. ft. of carpet in an hour, how many sq. yd. can he weave in 15 days, working 12 hours per day?

101. How many plates, each weighing 2 lb. 8 oz., would be required to weigh 7 tons?

102. What cost 3 lb. 4 oz. of gold plate, at $.95 per pwt.?

103. Three cwt. of indigo was put up in ounce papers; how many dozen papers would that give?

104. A cistern containing 3003 gallons is emptied by a pipe carrying 1 gal. 1 gi. per minute; how long will it take to empty it?

105. A boy walks a rod in 3 seconds; how long will he be in walking 15 miles?

106. At 5 cents a pint, how many bushels of strawberries can be bought for $20?

107. A publisher issued an edition of 5000 12mo. books of 288 pages each; how many reams of paper were required?

108. If a pint of water weigh one pound, how many gallons will be required to make a weight of 8 tons?

109. What cost 13 yards of antique lace, at $20 per inch?

110. What sum will be received for 57 bushels of apples, at 24 cents per peck?

111. What will be the cost of fencing a field 180 rods long and 56 rods wide, at 75 cents per rod?

112. Three ounces and two drams of medicine was divided into powders weighing 13 grains each; how much would be received for the powders, at 15 cents apiece?

113. Fifteen bushels of cherries cost $33.60; how much is that per pint?

114. How much will a man earn in 9 weeks, at $2.25 per day?

115. A ship sails 10′ 30″ per hour; how many days will it take to sail 28°?

116. What will milk cost, to fill 40 dozen bottles, holding 3 gills each, at $2.50 a gallon?

117. A block of stone is 8 ft. long, 8 ft. wide, and 8 ft. thick; how much will it weigh if a cu. ft. weighs 625 lbs?

118. Find the cost of 300 bushels of oysters, at 12 cents per peck.

119. If a railway train can go 22 miles 160 rods in 1 hour, how long will it require to go 1710 miles?

120. What cost 9 tons of hay, at 9 mills per pound?

121. A tank will hold 1000 gallons of water; how many cubic feet in it?

122. A steel plate is 2 feet long and 16 inches wide, and weighs 2 ounces to each square inch; what is it worth, at $0.075 per pound?

123. A man's income being $1.33 every hour, what will it be in the year 1895?

124. What cost 375 fathom of rope, weighing 2 pounds per foot, at 5 cents 5 mills per pound?

125. How many score in 30 great gross?

126. Sold berries at 6 cents a pint, and realized $15.12; how many bushels were sold?

127. What cost 400 gallons of molasses, at 7 ct. a pint?

128. How many rings, weighing 6 ounces each, can be made from 141 pounds of iron?

129. How many plates, weighing 6 ounces each, can be made from 141 pounds of silver?

130. Wheat weighs 60 pounds per bushel; find the cost of 30720 pounds, at 90 cents a bushel.

131. What will be the cost of paving a street 2700 feet long, and 40 feet wide, at $0.72 per square yard?

132. If a machine will peg a shoe in 4 minutes, how many dozen will it peg in 6 days of 10 hours each?

133. A cistern containing 480 gallons of water has two leaks: from one, 3 gills run out per minute; from the other, 13 gallons per hour. How much will be left in the cistern at the end of 8 hours?

134. 550 bushels of corn were bought at 44 cents a bushel, and retailed at 14 cents a peck; how much was gained?

135. How long would it take a tortoise to crawl a league, moving 4 rods an hour and 15 hours a day?

136. A man eats 2 lb. 3 oz. daily; how many weeks would 2 T. 9 cwt. last him?

137. A had 150 barrels of flour; B had the same weight of beef; how many barrels would it fill?

138. How many bags, of 2 bu. 2 qt. each, will be required to contain 2145 bushels of wheat?

139. How long would it take to build a road 86 mi. 20 rd. long, if 1 mi. 20 rd. can be made in a day?

140. What cost 256 cubic yards of wood, at $3.17 a cord?

141. If 3 bu. 2 pk. of berries cost $8.40, how much is that per quart?

142. A man poured 48 gallons of milk into bottles containing 1 qt. 1 pt. each, and sold them at 60 cents per bottle; how much did he receive?

143. How many gallons of essence will be required to fill 40 gross of bottles, each to contain 1 fluid ounce?

144. How many labels, 2 in. long and 1 in. wide, can be cut from 6 sheets of paper, each 4 ft. wide and 8 ft. long?

145. If 1 bu. 1 pk. of peaches cost $3, what will 1 bushel cost?

146. Twenty-four sheets were folded in 12mo.; how many sheets would be required to make as many quarto leaves?

COMPOUND NUMBERS.

ARTICLE 75.—*Addition of Compound Numbers.*

1. Add together 4 bu. 2 pk. 5 qt.; 17 bu. 3 pk. 1 qt.; 9 bu. 2 pk. 6 qt.; 16 bu. 3 pk. 5 qt.; 5 bu. 1 pk. 3 qt.; 2 bu. 7 qt.; 1 pk. 2 qt.; and 3 bu. 3 qt.

2. Add together 199 bu. 2 pk.; 83 bu. 3 pk.; 65 bu. 1 pk.; 88 bu. 2 pk.; 100 bu. 2 pk.; 116 bu. 1 pk.; 134 bu. 3 pk.; and 111 bu. 2 pk.

3. 27 gal. 3 qt. 1 pt. + 27 gal. 2 qt. 1 pt. + 27 gal. 1 qt. 1 pt. + 27 gal. 1 pt. + 27 gal. 3 qt. + 27 gal. 2 qt. + 27 gal. 1 qt. = ?

4. 3 T. 17 cwt. 60 lb. + 5 T. 15 cwt. 70 lb. + 4 T. 90 lb. + 9 T. 19 cwt. 99 lb. + 7 T. 16 cwt. + 5 cwt. 92 lb. = ?

5. 15 gal. 1 pt. + 16 gal. 1 qt. + 17 gal. 1 qt. 1 pt. + 18 gal. 2 qt. + 19 gal. 1 pt. + 20 gal. 3 qt. + 21 gal. 1 pt. + 22 gal. 3 qt. 1 pt. = ?

6. Find the sum of 7 cwt. 29 lb.; 9 cwt. 40 lb.; 16 cwt. 67 lb.; 13 cwt. 28 lb.; 12 cwt. 71 lb.; 10 cwt. 60 lb.; 3 cwt. 33 lb.; and 16 cwt. 72 lb.

7. 29 gal. 2 qt. 1 pt. + 29 gal. 2 qt. 1 pt. + 29 gal. 2 qt. 1 pt. + 29 gal. 2 qt. 1 pt. + 29 gal. 2 qt. 1 pt. + 29 gal. 2 qt. 1 pt. = ?

8. Find the sum of 7 yd. 2 ft. 11 in.; 4 yd. 1 ft. 7 in.; 12 yd. 2 ft. 5 in.; 9 yd. 1 ft. 1 in.; 12 yd. 1 in.; 15 yd. 1 ft. 5 in.; 6 yd. 7 in.; and 10 yd. 1 ft. 11 in.

9. Add together 7 yd. 2 ft.; 7 yd. 2 in.; 6 yd. 1 ft. 7 in.; 4 yd. 11 in.; 9 yd. 2 ft. 6 in.; 3 yd. 3 in.; 12 yd. 2 ft.; and 6 yd. 10 in.

10. 75 A. + 75 sq. rd. + 76 A. 76 sq. rd. + 77 A. 77 sq. rd. + 78 A. 78 sq. rd. + 72 A. 72 sq. rd. + 119 A. 140 sq. rd. = ?

11. 7 sq. yd. 7 sq. ft. 77 sq. in. + 8 sq. yd. 8 sq. ft. 88 sq. in. + 22 sq. yd. 22 sq. in. + 49 sq. yd. 4 sq. ft. 48 sq. in + 39 sq. yd. 96 sq. in. = ?

12. Find the sum of 3 sq. mi. 300 A.; 7 sq. mi. 500 A.; 4 sq. mi. 444 A.; 2 sq. mi. 222 A.; 10 sq. mi. 229 A.; and 5 sq. mi. 555 A.

13. 27 cu. yd. 26 cu. ft. + 26 cu. yd. 25 cu. ft. + 25 cu. yd. 24 cu. ft. + 24 cu. yd. 23 cu. ft. + 23 cu. yd. 22 cu. ft. + 22 cu. yd. 21 cu. ft. = ?

14. 25 C. 17 cu. ft. + 25 C. 1700 cu. in. + 25 C. 117 cu. ft. 1170 cu. in. + 252 C. 1717 cu. in. + 28 C. 127 cu. ft. + 19 C. 127 cu. ft. 1727 cu. in. = ?

15. 3 da. 13 hr. 20 min. + 7 da. 17 hr. 27 min. + 3 da. 13 hr. 33 min. + 6 da. 23 hr. + 4 da. 6 hr. 56 min. + 11 da. 11 hr. 11 min. + 19 da. 19 hr. 59 min. = ?

16. 5 da. 59 min. + 5 da. 58 min. + 5 da. 57 min. + 5 da. 56 min. + 5 da. 55 min. + 5 da. 54 min. + 5 da. 53 min. = ?

17. 4 lb. 9 oz. 12 pwt. + 6 lb. 7 oz. 18 pwt. + 3 lb. 10 oz. 10 pwt. + 5 lb. 11 oz. + 2 lb. 11 pwt. + 6 lb. 6 oz. 16 pwt. + 13 lb. 13 pwt. = ?

18. 2 ʒ 2 ℈ 10 gr. + 7 ʒ 19 gr. + 5 ʒ 1 ℈ 16 gr. + 5 ʒ 10 gr. + 2 ʒ 2 ℈ 1 gr. + 5 ʒ 1 ℈ 4 gr. = ?

19. 5 ℥ 3 ʒ 2 ℈ + 4 ℥ 2 ʒ 1 ℈ + 7 ℥ 2 ℈ + 7 ʒ 2 ℈ + 2 ℥ 4 ʒ 1 ℈ + 3 ℥ 5 ʒ 2 ℈ + 7 ʒ 1 ℈ + 7 ℥ 1 ℈ = ?

20. 4 score and 6 + 3 score and ten + 4 score and 8 + 4 score and 9 + 2 score and 18 + 3 score and 12 = ?

21. 14° 35′ 23″ + 17° 49′ 49″ + 26° 30′ 10″ + 30° 59′ 1″ + 7° 24′ 48″ + 13° 29′ 50″ + 9° 59″ = ?

22. 8° 15′ 28″ + 6° 28′ 29″ + 7° 30′ 30″ + 11° 44′ 32″ + 13° 31′ 31″ + 13° 30′ 31″ = ?

23. 3 cong. 7 O. 11 f. ℥ + 5 cong. 4 O. 9 f. ℥ + 7 cong. 7 O. 7 f. ℥ + 9 cong. 5 f. ℥ + 7 cong. 7 O. + 5 O. 15 f. ℥ = ?

24. 2 f. ℥ 4 f. ʒ 20 ♏ + 3 f. ℥ 5 ʒ 40 ♏ + 7 f. ℥ 3 f. ʒ 40 ♏ + 6 f. ℥ 2 f. ʒ 20 ♏ = ?

25. Seven barrels of coal oil were gauged as follows: 49 gal. 3 qt.; 51 gal. 2 qt.; 48 gal. 3 qt.; 55 gal. 2 qt.; 52 gal. 2 qt.; 53 gal. 1 qt.; and 50 gal. 2 qt. How much in all?

26. How much wood in 5 piles, containing respectively 25 C. 87 cu. ft.; 56 C. 112 cu. ft.; 39 C. 41 cu. ft.; 43 C. 16 cu. ft.; and 88 C. 88 cu. ft.?

27. Eggs were packed in 6 boxes: 29 doz. and 7; 40 doz. and 10; 35 doz. and 5; 60 doz. and 10; 38 doz. and 9; and 52 doz. and 7. How many dozen in all?

28. Find the weight of 8 hogsheads of sugar, weighing as follows: 11 cwt. 83 lb.; 12 cwt. 46 lb.; 11 cwt. 55 lb.; 12 cwt. 19 lb.; 13 cwt. 1 lb.; 12 cwt. 52 lb.; 11 cwt. 93 lb.; and 12 cwt. 51 lb.

29. A farmer planted 17 A. 100 sq. rd. in wheat, 21 A. 120 sq. rd. in oats, 30 A. 50 sq. rd. in corn, 13 A. 60 sq. rd. in potatoes, 7 A. 40 sq. rd. in sorghum, and 11 A. 110 sq. rd. in broom-corn. How much land had he in cultivation?

30. A vessel sailed 13 da. 7 hr. to the first port, and stopped there 2 da. 20 hr; then 25 da. 20 hr. to the second port, and stopped there 3 da. 23 hr.; then 40 da. 5 hr. to the third port, and stopped there 2 da. 19 hr.; then 60 da. 16 hr. to the starting point. How long was the voyage?

31. A railroad train traveled as follows: 14 mi. 125 rd. to first station; 9 mi. 77 rd. to second; 16 mi. 62 rd. to third; 31 mi. 35 rd. to fourth; 11 mi. 83 rd. to fifth; and then 18 mi. 98 rd. to its destination. What was the length of the trip?

32. Set down 3 da. 13 hr. 39 min. 26 sec. seven times, and then add them.

ARTICLE 76.—*Subtraction of Compound Numbers.*

1. From 40 bu. take 20 bu. 3 qt.

2. 39 bu. 1 pk. 1 qt. — 19 bu. 3 pk. 3 qt. = ?

3. From 100 gal. take 49 gal. 3 qt. 2 gi.

4. From 353 gal. 1 pt. take 203 gal. 3 qt.

5. From 3 T. 13 cwt. 23 lb. take 1 T. 18 cwt. 5 lb.

6. From 1 T. 1 cwt. 1 lb. 1 oz. take 11 cwt. 11 lb. 11 oz.

7. From 47 mi. 180 rd. take 23 mi. 250 rd.

8. From 16 yd. 2 ft. 1 in. take 9 yd. 1 ft. 2 in.

9. 81 yd. 6 in. — 18 yd. 8 in. = ?

10. From 9 sq. mi. 100 A. take 4 sq. mi. 370 A.

11. 39 sq. yd. 4 sq. ft. 44 sq. in. — 21 sq. yd. 7 sq. ft. 89 sq. in. = ?

12. From 300 sq. mi. 300 A. 100 sq. rd. take 100 sq. mi. 300 A. 150 sq. rd.

13. From 36 cu. yd. 10 cu. ft. 800 cu. in. take 8 cu. yd. 19 cu. ft. 900 cu. in.

14. Take 18 C. 1500 cu. in. from 81 C. 1478 cu. in.

15. 5 hr. 6 min. 22 sec. — 2 hr. 20 min. 20 sec. = ?

16. From 7 wk. 6 da. 5 hr. 4 min. 3 sec. take 3 wk. 4 da. 5 hr. 6 min. 7 sec,

17. Take 9 lb. 7 oz. 16 pwt. from 15 lb. 3 oz. 3 pwt.

18. 5 ℔ 4 ℥ 3 ʒ 1 ℈ — 2 ℔ 6 ℥ 6 ʒ 2 ℈ = ?

19. From 14° 7′ 10″ take 9° 18′ 30″.

20. From 19 reams take 12 reams 4 quires.

21. From 3 gross 4 dozen take 1 gross 8 dozen.

22. From 1 O. 3 f. ℥ 2 f. ʒ take 13 f. ℥.

23. If 25 bu. 3 pk. 2 qt. have been sold from 40 bu. of peanuts, what quantity is left?

24. A farmer has 450 bu. of potatoes; if he sells 273 bu. 2 pk. what quantity will he have left?

25. The time between two cities by steamer is 2 wk. 2 hr.; by railroad, 5 da. 19 hr.; how much time is gained by the railroad route?

26. From a tank containing 327 gal. 2 qt. 1 pt., 10 gal. 3 qt. 1 pt. leaked out; how much remains?

27. If a tract of 36 A. 120 sq. rd. be cut from a farm of 120 A., how much will be left?

28. A quantity of pig iron, weighing 17 T. 5 cwt. 48 lb., was melted to make stove castings, which, when cast, weighed 17 T. 1 cwt. 90 lb.; how much metal was lost in the work?

29. From a pile of wood containing 106 C. 105 cu. ft., there was taken away a boat load of 87 C. 120 cu. ft.; how much remained?

30. A cart weighed 13 cwt. 80 lb., and, after being filled with coal, weighed 3 T. 11 cwt. 90 lb.; what was the weight of the coal?

31. A ship was 13° 7′ 20″ from a port, and sailed 4° 43′ 40″ toward it; how far from the port was it then?

32. How much will be left of a mass of medicine weighing 1 ℔ 1 ʒ., after 7 ℥ 5 ʒ 2 ℈ 10 gr. have been made into pills?

33. A boat laden with 750 T. 60 lb. was sunk, and 473 T. 90 lb. of the freight was saved; how much was lost?

34. The regular time between two cities was 100 hr. 10 min., and the train arrived 3 hr. 52 min. ahead of time; how long had it taken to make the run?

35. A man contracted to deliver 100 C. of wood, and has only 78 C. 96 cu. ft.; how much does he lack?

36. A man having 89 bu. 1 pk. of clover seed, sold 37 bu. 3 pk. to each of his two brothers; how much has he remaining?

37. From 30 days subtract 5 da. 12 hr. 19 minutes three times.

ARTICLE 77.—*Time between two dates.*

1. Money was borrowed May 18, 1882, and returned Jan. 6, 1884; how long had it been kept?

2. The battle of Monmouth was fought June 28, 1778, and the battle of Antietam September 17, 1862; what time elapsed between the two events?

3. Washington was born February 22, 1732, and died December 14, 1799; at what age did he die?

4. The pilgrims landed December 21, 1620; how long was that before the Declaration of Independence, July 4, 1776?

5. What time elapsed between the surrender at Yorktown, October 19, 1781, and the signing of the treaty of peace, September 3, 1783?

6. A child born December 3, 1876, commenced school August 27, 1883; at what age was that?

7. How old was Washington at the battle of Monmouth? (See examples 2 and 3.)

8. What time elapsed from the battle of Lexington, April 19, 1775, to the firing on Fort Sumter, April 12, 1861?

ARTICLE 78.—*Time in days between two dates.*

1. Find the number of days from Aug. 5 to the second day of the next December.

2. How many days from Nov. 15, 1871, to Jan. 18, 1872?

3. How many days from Oct. 20, 1877, to Mar. 15, 1878?

4. How many days from Jan. 12, 1880, to Oct. 15, 1880?

5. How many days from June 5 to Dec. 25?

6. A servant was hired May 18, and discharged November 29; for how many days should she be paid?

7. How many days from Apr. 6, 1875, to Apr. 1, 1876?

8. Corn was planted April 18, and was ripe September 27; how many days was that?

Article 79.—*Multiplication of Compound Numbers.*

1. 3 bu. 2 pk. 5 qt. 1 pt. × 8 = ?
2. 7 gal. 3 qt. 1 pt. 3 gi. × 8 = ?
3. 3 cwt. 27 lb. 8 oz. × 10 = ?
4. 5 yd. 2 ft. 7 in. × 11 = ?
5. 3 sq. yd. 7 sq. ft. 72 sq. in. × 6 = ?
6. 7 cu. ft. 700 cu. in. × 10 = ?
7. 3 oz. 7 pwt. 10 gr. × 24 = ?
8. 3 ℥ 2 ℈ 12 gr. × 60 = ?
9. 3 gal. 1 pt. 1 gi. × 72 = ?
10. 2° 10′ 20″ × 36 = ?
11. 3 quires 10 sheets × 120 = ?
12. 3 mi. 190 rd. × 77 = ?
13. 13 hr. 24 min. 36 sec. × 99 = ?

14. What will be the weight of 27 castings, 1 T. 12 cwt. 42 lb. each?

15. If an acre will produce 6 bu. 3 pk. 5 qt. of wheat, how much can be raised on 20 acres?

16. If a stream flows 17 yd. 2 ft. 8 in. in a minute, how far would that be in an hour?

17. If a square rod produces 7 qt. 1 pt. of strawberries, what quantity could be raised on 1 A.?

18. A steamer makes a trip in 1 da. 5 hr. 19 min.; what time would be required for 20 trips?

19. If a quart of berries can be picked in 14 min. 20 sec., how long would it take to pick 1 pk.?

20. If a herd of cattle consumes 9 T. 3 cwt. 18 lb. daily, how much fodder would be required for the month of November?

21. If 34 sq. yd. 8 sq. ft. 60 sq. in. of flooring are required for one floor, how much will be needed for 14 floors?

22. If 1 qt. of seed will produce 1 bu. 1 pk. 1 qt. of grain, how much grain will 1 bu. of seed produce?

Article 80.—*Division of Compound Numbers.*

1. Divide 32 bu. 1 pk. 3 qt. by 9.

2. Divide 1 T. 9 cwt. 80 lb. 8 oz. by 8.

3. Divide 22 yd. 2 ft. by 6.

4. Divide 8 sq. yd. 4 sq. ft. 16 sq. in. by 10.

5. Divide 2 da. 15 hr. 12 min. by 18.

6. Divide 3 oz. 11 pwt. 16 gr. by 20.

7. Divide 2 ℥ 6 ʒ by 12.

8. Divide 225 gal. 3 qt. 1 pt. 2 gi. by 30.

9. Divide 238 yd. 1 ft. by 33.

10. Divide 67 sq. yd. by 54.

11. Divide 230 da. 13 hr. 20 min. by 100.

12. Divide 19 cu. yd. 9 cu. ft. 864 cu. in. by 19.

13. A man raised 237 bu. 3 pk. 2 qt. of raspberries on 10 A.; how much was that per acre?

14. If 19 jars would contain 103 gal. 3 qt. 1 pt. 1 gi., what would one contain?

15. If 11 cwt. 79 lb. 12 oz. of sugar be packed in 12 kegs, how much will each contain?

16. One hundred cu. yd. of earth are to be hauled away in 18 carts; how much will that be for each?

17. A glacier moved 43 yd. in 701 da. 13 hr. 22 min.; how long did it take to move 1 yd.?

18. A planet moved 13° 30′ 50″ in 25 days; what would be the average motion per day?

19. Fifteen equal bins contain 3740 bu. 2 pk. 4 qt. of wheat; how much is in each?

20. A steamer goes 183 mi. 144 rd. per day; how far is that per hour?

21. In 7 days, of 10 hours each, a furnace will turn out 242 T. 18 cwt. of blooms; how much is that per hour?

22. A gardener raised 275 bu. of beets on an acre of ground; what was the yield per square rod?

LONGITUDE AND TIME.

Articles 81 and 82.

Find the differences in time, corresponding to the following differences in longitude:

1. 40°.
2. 33° 20′.
3. 36° 17′.
4. 69° 51′.
5. 100° 10′.
6. 49° 13′ 30″.
7. 66° 45″
8. 70° 17′ 15″.
9. 99° 9′.
10. 111° 51′ 30″.
11. 58° 58′ 15″.
12. 97° 53′.

Find the differences in longitude, corresponding to the following differences of time:

13. 11 hr. 17 min. 13 sec.
14. 6 hr. 59 min. 17 sec.
15. 10 hr. 10 min. 10 sec.
16. 7 hr. 17 min. 27 sec.
17. 15 hr. 14 min. 29 sec.
18. 4 hr. 45 min. 10 sec.
19. 5 hr. 29 min. 25 sec.
20. 47 min. 47 sec.

21. A man travels east 29°; will his watch be fast or slow then, and how much?

22. A boat sails 47° west; how much will her chronometer gain or lose on the time at the point reached?

23. A team travels eastward 45′ a day; will its day be lengthened or shortened, and how much?

24. What is the difference of time between two places whose longitudes are 29° east, and 54° west?

25. When it is 7 o'clock A. M. at a place in 93° west longitude, what is the time at another place in 39° west longitude?

26. When it is 7 o'clock A. M. at a place in 107° east longitude, what is the time at another place in 40° east longitude?

27. When it is 11 o'clock A. M. at a place in 40° west longitude, what is the time at another place in 70° east longitude?

28. When it is 3 o'clock P. M. at a place in 3° east longitude, what is the time at another place in 68° west longitude?

29. When it is 6 o'clock A. M. in 90° east longitude, what is the time in 90° west longitude?

30. What is the difference of time between two places, one in 37° 35′ east longitude, the other in 47° 10′ west longitude?

FACTORING.

Article 87.

Find the Prime Factors:

1. Of 51.
2. Of 52.
3. Of 62.
4. Of 63.
5. Of 72.
6. Of 75.
7. Of 76.
8. Of 120.
9. Of 132.
10. Of 168.
11. Of 196.
12. Of 198.
13. Of 204.
14. Of 207.
15. Of 252.
16. Of 561.
17. Of 882.
18. Of 828.
19. Of 2662.
20. Of 3087.
21. Of 4356.

ARTICLE 88.

What Prime Factors are common to:

1. 60 and 80?
2. 90 and 120?
3. 80 and 120?
4. 135 and 180?
5. 126 and 210?
6. 324 and 432?
7. 324 and 594?
8. 264 and 638?
9. 462 and 819?
10. 385 and 595?
11. 363 and 1419?
12. 48, 72, and 84?
13. 78, 104, and 143?
14. 192, 252, and 348?
15. 64, 104, 144, and 376?
16. 135, 180, 210, and 375?
17. 144, 168, 192, and 240?
18. 117, 143, 286, and 390?
19. 126, 196, 238, and 266?
20. 187, 231, 275, and 308?
21. 147, 210, 315, and 364?
22. 384, 486, 324, and 510?

ARTICLE 89.—*Greatest Common Divisor.*

Find the Greatest Common Divisor:

1. Of 48 and 84.
2. Of 40, 60, and 90.
3. Of 117 and 171.
4. Of 889 and 560.
5. Of 124 and 600.
6. Of 390 and 702.
7. Of 392 and 637.
8. Of 770 and 891.
9. Of 873 and 378.
10. Of 656 and 1066.
11. Of 980 and 2401.
12. Of 3003 and 21000.
13. Of 1008 and 1584.
14. Of 1296 and 2304.
15. Of 16983 and 18574.
16. Of 243, 324, and 432.
17. Of 56, 84, and 126.
18. Of 80, 120, and 180.
19. Of 468, 648, and 864.
20. Of 675, 945, and 1053.
21. Of 980, 2002, and 15001.
22. Of 289, 391, and 493.
23. Of 288, 387, and 486.
24. Of 3375, 8205, and 15000.
25. Of 81, 135, 450, and 780.
26. Of 63, 144, 216, and 297.
27. Of 1120, 960, 888, and 666.

ARTICLE 90.—*Least Common Multiple.*

Find the Least Common Multiple:

1. Of 8, 12, 16, and 20.
2. Of 9, 12, 16, and 20.
3. Of 12, 16, 20, and 24.
4. Of 16, 20, 25, and 40.
5. Of 36, 42, 48, and 54.
6. Of 24, 30, 42, and 28.
7. Of 60, 66, 30, and 36.
8. Of 21, 35, 55, and 84.
9. Of 16, 18, 20, and 22.
10. Of 16, 18, 20, and 30.
11. Of 16, 18, 20, and 24.
12. Of 18, 20, 24, and 36.
13. Of 24, 54, 84, and 144.
14. Of 121 and 122.
15. Of 221 and 323.
16. Of 169 and 325.
17. Of 343 and 735.
18. Of 150, 225, and 375.
19. Of 100, 200, and 300.
20. Of 14, 24, 44, and 42.
21. Of 143 and 175.
22. Of 143 and 176.
23. Of 12, 16, 24, 36, and 72.
24. Of 30, 36, 48, 64, and 80.
25. Of 18, 26, 54, and 78.
26. Of 576, 384, 288, 768, and 256.
27. Of 8, 9, 10, 11, and 12.
28. Of 45, 75, 81, 72, and 54.
29. Of 245, 343, 441, and 98.
30. Of 123, 205, 287, and 246.

ARTICLE 91.—*Cancellation.*

1. How often is 12 contained in 4 times 27?

2. Divide 18×21 by 14×9.

3. In 16 times 18 how many times 12?

4. How often is 6×8 contained in 16×18?

5. How many score in 12×25?

6. How many flower-beds 4 feet long and 3 feet wide, can be made from a plat 36 feet long and 18 feet wide?

7. Divide $8 \times 9 \times 10 \times 12$ by $3 \times 4 \times 5 \times 6$.

8. Sold six dozen tumblers at 8 cents apiece, and spent the money for yarn at 18 cents a pound; how many pounds did I receive?

9. How many barrels of sugar, at $15 a barrel, will pay for 18 hogs, at $20 apiece?

10. Divide $18 \times 20 \times 24 \times 32$ by $27 \times 16 \times 40$.

11. How many lots 5 feet square can be cut from a lot 30 feet square?

12. Divide $18 \times 17 \times 16 \times 15$ by $2 \times 3 \times 4 \times 5 \times 6$.

13. A quantity of iron will make three hundred 30-lb. castings; how many 25-lb castings will it make?

14. Twenty reams of paper, of 20 quires each, and each quire 24 sheets, and each sheet making 24 pages, were made into books containing 160 pages each; how many dozen books would there be?

15. How many hundred blocks 3 in. long, 2 in. wide, and 1 in. thick, can be made from a block 5 ft. long, 3 ft. wide, and 5 in. thick?

FRACTIONS.

ARTICLE 103.—*Reduction of Integers to Fractions of given Denominators.*

Reduce:

1. 14 to sevenths.
2. 23 to elevenths.
3. 7 to twenty-thirds.
4. 63 to eighteenths.
5. 90 to ninths.
6. 31 to thirty-seconds.
7. 3 to fifty-sixths.
8. 26 to eighths.
9. 315 to ninths.
10. 200 to twelfths.
11. 37 to eighteenths.
12. 34 to fortieths.
13. 14 to twentieths.
14. 27 to thirteenths.
15. 31 to sixteenths.
16. 67 to twenty-seconds.
17. 19 to ninetieths.
18. 81 to twenty-ninths.

ARTICLE 104.—*Case II.*

Reduce the following to Improper Fractions:

1. $15\frac{7}{8}$.
2. $19\frac{5}{7}$.
3. $99\frac{1}{9}$.
4. $73\frac{1}{10}$.
5. $36\frac{8}{15}$.
6. $42\frac{11}{18}$.
7. $176\frac{2}{7}$.
8. $19\frac{1}{19}$.
9. $28\frac{17}{18}$.
10. $45\frac{5}{22}$.
11. $73\frac{8}{73}$.
12. $29\frac{3}{100}$.
13. $272\frac{8}{11}$.
14. $396\frac{4}{27}$.
15. $562\frac{3}{14}$.
16. $100\frac{1}{100}$.
17. $682\frac{11}{16}$.
18. $129\frac{14}{41}$.
19. $29\frac{4}{111}$.
20. $21\frac{1}{19}$.
21. $73\frac{73}{99}$.

ARTICLE 105.—*Case III.*

Reduce the following to Integers or Mixed Numbers:

1. $\frac{457}{6}$.
2. $\frac{368}{8}$.
3. $\frac{1239}{7}$.
4. $\frac{1239}{10}$.
5. $\frac{4710}{13}$.
6. $\frac{2617}{15}$.
7. $\frac{4618}{19}$.
8. $\frac{2468}{17}$.
9. $\frac{3753}{23}$.
10. $\frac{739}{22}$.
11. $\frac{5647}{14}$.
12. $\frac{3973}{26}$.
13. $\frac{4140}{18}$.
14. $\frac{4678}{33}$.
15. $\frac{3003}{77}$.
16. $\frac{9876}{100}$.
17. $\frac{3402}{42}$.
18. $\frac{1234}{15}$.
19. $\frac{7630}{35}$.
20. $\frac{12345}{23}$.
21. $\frac{4678}{97}$.

ARTICLE 106.—*Case IV.*

1. Reduce $\frac{4}{11}$ to thirty-thirds.
2. Reduce $\frac{5}{12}$ to sixtieths.
3. Reduce $\frac{3}{8}$ to fortieths.
4. Reduce $\frac{4}{5}$ to thirty-fifths.
5. Reduce $\frac{17}{20}$ to hundredths.

Reduce the following fractions:

6. $\frac{8}{9}$ to a fraction whose denominator is 126.
7. $\frac{16}{21}$ " " " " " 105.
8. $\frac{12}{13}$ " " " " " 156.
9. $\frac{17}{19}$ " " " " " 171.

Reduce the following fractions:

10. $\frac{17}{20}$ to a fraction whose denominator is 280.
11. $\frac{14}{23}$ " " " " " 345.
12. $\frac{17}{28}$ " " " " " 336.
13. $\frac{15}{29}$ " " " " " 464.
14. $\frac{17}{32}$ " " " " " 416.
15. $\frac{27}{38}$ " " " " " 1368.
16. $\frac{81}{88}$ " " " " " 7744.
17. $\frac{73}{80}$ " " " " " 4560.
18. $\frac{13}{212}$ " " " " " 3604.
19. $\frac{29}{273}$ " " " " " 1911.
20. $\frac{179}{197}$ " " " " " 6698.

ARTICLE 107.—*Case V.*

Reduce the following to their Lowest Terms:

1. $\frac{144}{169}$.
2. $\frac{84}{126}$.
3. $\frac{405}{705}$.
4. $\frac{567}{1001}$.
5. $\frac{407}{999}$.
6. $\frac{407}{990}$.
7. $\frac{803}{876}$.
8. $\frac{9200}{12075}$.
9. $\frac{1625}{3055}$.
10. $\frac{1234}{4319}$.
11. $\frac{1681}{1763}$.
12. $\frac{999}{1350}$.
13. $\frac{3456}{4356}$.
14. $\frac{3465}{4356}$.
15. $\frac{945}{1785}$.
16. $\frac{1296}{1620}$.
17. $\frac{2345}{3685}$.
18. $\frac{3468}{5202}$.
19. $\frac{1950}{4050}$.
20. $\frac{3025}{7744}$.
21. $\frac{4001}{5001}$.

ARTICLE 108.—*Case VI.*

Reduce the following to Least Common Denominators:

1. $\frac{2}{3}, \frac{1}{4}, \frac{3}{5}$.
2. $\frac{4}{5}, \frac{5}{6}, \frac{8}{9}$.
3. $\frac{3}{8}, \frac{3}{4}, \frac{3}{7}$.
4. $\frac{4}{9}, \frac{7}{10}, \frac{8}{15}$.
5. $\frac{2}{5}, \frac{3}{10}, \frac{4}{15}, \frac{9}{20}$.
6. $\frac{7}{8}, \frac{7}{12}, \frac{7}{16}, \frac{7}{24}$.
7. $\frac{9}{10}, \frac{7}{12}, \frac{9}{20}, \frac{7}{24}$.
8. $\frac{4}{15}, \frac{5}{24}, \frac{7}{30}, \frac{9}{40}$.
9. $\frac{13}{20}, \frac{13}{40}, \frac{13}{60}, \frac{13}{80}$.
10. $\frac{9}{14}, \frac{9}{22}, \frac{9}{26}$.
11. $\frac{7}{9}, \frac{5}{6}, \frac{3}{4}, \frac{3}{8}, \frac{5}{12}$.
12. $\frac{3}{25}, \frac{7}{20}, \frac{9}{10}, \frac{11}{50}$.
13. $\frac{3}{4}, \frac{1}{6}, \frac{7}{9}, \frac{11}{12}, \frac{1}{3}$.
14. $\frac{1}{2}, \frac{1}{12}, \frac{1}{22}, \frac{1}{32}$.

15. $\frac{3}{10}$, $\frac{11}{20}$, $\frac{5}{12}$, $\frac{7}{8}$.
16. $\frac{1}{12}$, $\frac{4}{9}$, $\frac{5}{16}$, $\frac{13}{18}$.
17. $\frac{4}{15}$, $\frac{5}{18}$, $\frac{7}{10}$, $\frac{1}{6}$.
18. $\frac{4}{15}$, $\frac{5}{18}$, $\frac{7}{10}$, $\frac{1}{16}$.
19. $\frac{3}{8}$, $\frac{5}{18}$, $\frac{9}{28}$, $\frac{7}{48}$.
20. $\frac{11}{15}$, $\frac{7}{10}$, $\frac{2}{3}$, $\frac{5}{6}$.
21. $\frac{2}{9}$, $\frac{3}{10}$, $\frac{2}{7}$, $\frac{3}{11}$.
22. $\frac{5}{8}$, $\frac{7}{9}$, $\frac{7}{16}$, $\frac{7}{18}$.
23. $\frac{2}{11}$, $\frac{2}{33}$, $\frac{3}{22}$, $\frac{3}{44}$.
24. $1\frac{2}{3}$, $1\frac{3}{4}$, $1\frac{5}{6}$, $1\frac{7}{12}$.
25. $2\frac{4}{5}$, $\frac{7}{15}$, $3\frac{3}{10}$, $\frac{11}{20}$.
26. $\frac{11}{12}$, $\frac{15}{16}$, $\frac{17}{18}$, $\frac{23}{24}$.
27. $\frac{4}{7}$, $\frac{4}{8}$, $\frac{4}{9}$, $\frac{4}{10}$.
28. $\frac{13}{16}$, 2, $\frac{13}{24}$, $\frac{13}{36}$, $\frac{13}{48}$.
29. $\frac{17}{20}$, $\frac{18}{21}$, $\frac{9}{14}$, $\frac{17}{18}$, $\frac{11}{12}$.
30. $\frac{4}{9}$, $\frac{3}{8}$, $5\frac{5}{6}$, $\frac{7}{4}$, $8\frac{11}{12}$.

Article 110.—*Addition of Fractions. Case I.*

Add the following fractions:

1. $\frac{7}{18}$, $\frac{12}{18}$, $\frac{15}{18}$, $\frac{14}{18}$.
2. $\frac{5}{12}$, $\frac{7}{12}$, $\frac{11}{12}$, $\frac{9}{12}$.
3. $\frac{13}{24}$, $\frac{14}{24}$, $\frac{15}{24}$, $\frac{16}{24}$.
4. $\frac{18}{36}$, $\frac{21}{36}$, $\frac{24}{36}$, $\frac{27}{36}$.
5. $\frac{11}{48}$, $\frac{12}{48}$, $\frac{13}{48}$, $\frac{14}{48}$.
6. $\frac{4}{77}$, $\frac{13}{77}$, $\frac{18}{77}$, $\frac{9}{77}$.
7. $\frac{53}{80}$, $\frac{63}{80}$, $\frac{73}{80}$, $\frac{23}{80}$.
8. $\frac{24}{72}$, $\frac{27}{72}$, $\frac{18}{72}$, $\frac{32}{72}$.
9. $\frac{12}{84}$, $\frac{16}{84}$, $\frac{21}{84}$, $\frac{28}{84}$.
10. $\frac{56}{112}$, $\frac{63}{112}$, $\frac{64}{112}$, $\frac{34}{112}$.
11. $\frac{72}{120}$, $\frac{80}{120}$, $\frac{96}{120}$, $\frac{27}{120}$.
12. $\frac{75}{144}$, $\frac{85}{144}$, $\frac{95}{144}$, $\frac{105}{144}$.
13. $\frac{47}{160}$, $\frac{48}{160}$, $\frac{49}{160}$, $\frac{50}{160}$.
14. $\frac{77}{180}$, $\frac{87}{180}$, $\frac{97}{180}$, $\frac{107}{180}$.

Article 111.—*Case II.*

Add the following quantities:

1. $\frac{5}{16}$, $\frac{5}{6}$, $\frac{5}{12}$.
2. $\frac{16}{21}$, $\frac{17}{28}$, $\frac{19}{42}$, $\frac{15}{56}$.
3. $\frac{7}{12}$, $\frac{7}{8}$, $\frac{7}{9}$, $\frac{7}{18}$.
4. $\frac{14}{15}$, $\frac{17}{18}$, $\frac{13}{45}$, $\frac{11}{30}$
5. $\frac{6}{7}$, $\frac{5}{8}$, 4, $\frac{3}{4}$.
6. $\frac{5}{11}$, $\frac{7}{12}$, $\frac{8}{13}$.
7. $\frac{4}{27}$, $\frac{11}{18}$, $\frac{19}{72}$, $\frac{17}{36}$.
8. $\frac{2}{3}$, $\frac{3}{4}$, $\frac{4}{5}$, $\frac{5}{7}$.
9. $\frac{2}{3}$, $\frac{3}{4}$, $\frac{4}{5}$, $\frac{5}{8}$.
10. $4\frac{7}{8}$, $3\frac{2}{3}$, $8\frac{1}{2}$, $6\frac{3}{4}$.
11. $5\frac{1}{5}$, $6\frac{1}{6}$, $8\frac{1}{8}$, $10\frac{1}{10}$.
12. $12\frac{1}{2}$, $16\frac{2}{3}$, $29\frac{1}{6}$, $40\frac{1}{4}$.
13. $38\frac{7}{8}$, $38\frac{7}{12}$, $38\frac{7}{9}$, $38\frac{7}{18}$.
14. $123\frac{1}{4}$, $135\frac{1}{6}$, $147\frac{1}{8}$, $156\frac{1}{3}$.
15. $725\frac{1}{3}$, $87\frac{3}{4}$, $93\frac{7}{8}$, $591\frac{5}{6}$.
16. $\frac{4}{5}$, $\frac{3}{8}$, $\frac{5}{6}$, $\frac{5}{8}$, $\frac{1}{6}$.
17. $\frac{4}{9}$, $\frac{5}{8}$, $\frac{2}{5}$, $\frac{5}{9}$.
18. $1\frac{1}{3}$, $1\frac{1}{4}$, $1\frac{1}{6}$, $1\frac{1}{8}$, $1\frac{1}{12}$.
19. $2\frac{2}{3}$, $2\frac{3}{4}$, $2\frac{5}{6}$, $2\frac{7}{8}$, $2\frac{11}{12}$.
20. $1\frac{3}{8}$, $1\frac{5}{9}$, $2\frac{2}{3}$, $7\frac{3}{8}$.
21. $3\frac{1}{2}$, $2\frac{1}{3}$, $3\frac{1}{4}$, $4\frac{1}{3}$.
22. $\frac{3}{16}$, $\frac{3}{20}$, $\frac{5}{16}$, $\frac{5}{24}$, $\frac{7}{12}$, $\frac{7}{8}$.

23. $1\frac{2}{3}$, $1\frac{3}{4}$, $1\frac{5}{6}$, $1\frac{1}{8}$, $1\frac{5}{12}$.
24. $6\frac{1}{2}$, $6\frac{2}{3}$, $7\frac{1}{4}$, $7\frac{1}{3}$, $8\frac{3}{8}$.
25. $16\frac{1}{3}$, $17\frac{3}{4}$, $8\frac{11}{12}$, $7\frac{5}{12}$, $4\frac{7}{12}$.
26. $1\frac{1}{3}$, $1\frac{2}{5}$, $1\frac{4}{15}$, $1\frac{5}{18}$, $1\frac{7}{9}$.
27. $\frac{6}{7}$, $\frac{5}{8}$, $\frac{3}{4}$, $\frac{3}{14}$.
28. $234\frac{2}{7}$, $236\frac{3}{8}$, $238\frac{1}{4}$, $239\frac{1}{9}$.
29. $12\frac{4}{5}$, $124\frac{5}{6}$, $1\frac{3}{8}$, $17\frac{1}{4}$, $18\frac{1}{3}$.
30. $1\frac{2}{5}$, $1\frac{5}{6}$, $1\frac{7}{8}$, $11\frac{1}{3}$, $19\frac{11}{40}$.

ARTICLE 113.—*Subtraction of Fractions. Case I.*

1. From $18\frac{15}{16}$ take $5\frac{5}{16}$.
2. $47\frac{17}{20} - 23\frac{11}{20} = ?$
3. $29\frac{15}{18} - 21\frac{7}{18} = ?$
4. $24\frac{17}{20} - 15\frac{9}{20} = ?$
5. $91\frac{5}{6} - 19\frac{2}{6} = ?$
6. $42\frac{19}{20} - 31\frac{7}{20} = ?$
7. $23\frac{7}{16} - 14\frac{11}{16} = ?$
8. $193\frac{17}{18} - 34\frac{11}{18} = ?$
9. $39\frac{17}{24} - 29\frac{19}{24} = ?$
10. $100\frac{14}{25} - 80\frac{21}{25} = ?$
11. $38\frac{17}{27} - 26\frac{26}{27} = ?$
12. $237\frac{1}{80} - 37\frac{21}{80} = ?$
13. $327\frac{11}{24} - 184\frac{16}{24} = ?$
14. $168\frac{15}{36} - 93\frac{19}{36} = ?$
15. $299\frac{1}{8} - 11\frac{5}{8} = ?$
16. $73\frac{18}{35} - 47\frac{11}{35} = ?$
17. $400 - 47\frac{3}{5} = ?$
18. $736 - 367\frac{18}{49} = ?$
19. $19\frac{7}{100} - 7\frac{19}{100} = ?$
20. $365 - 37\frac{11}{100} = ?$
21. $423\frac{18}{23} - 237 = ?$
22. $146\frac{17}{32} - 92\frac{19}{32} = ?$
23. $1473\frac{7}{8} - 597\frac{3}{8} = ?$
24. $573\frac{109}{120} - 294\frac{47}{120} = ?$

ARTICLE 114.—*Case II.*

1. From $\frac{2}{3}$ take $\frac{5}{8}$.
2. From $\frac{5}{7}$ take $\frac{6}{11}$.
3. From $\frac{11}{12}$ take $\frac{9}{10}$.
4. From $\frac{7}{18}$ take $\frac{3}{16}$.
5. From $\frac{4}{5}$ take $\frac{5}{12}$.
6. From $\frac{19}{20}$ take $\frac{7}{15}$.
7. From $\frac{17}{18}$ take $\frac{7}{12}$.
8. From $\frac{8}{7}$ take $\frac{7}{8}$.
9. From $\frac{13}{16}$ take $\frac{13}{20}$.
10. From $\frac{7}{11}$ take $\frac{7}{12}$.
11. From 6 take $2\frac{7}{12}$
12. From $6\frac{5}{8}$ take $2\frac{11}{12}$.
13. From $1\frac{7}{9}$ take $\frac{17}{28}$.
14. From $15\frac{3}{16}$ take 8.
15. From $8\frac{1}{3}$ take $7\frac{1}{7}$.
16. From $13\frac{18}{19}$ take $5\frac{7}{18}$.
17. From $6\frac{7}{11}$ take $\frac{17}{20}$.
18. From 800 take $147\frac{13}{21}$.
19. From $728\frac{1}{2}$ take $149\frac{15}{28}$.
20. From $24\frac{17}{48}$ take $19\frac{19}{40}$.
21. From $48\frac{17}{24}$ take $26\frac{19}{25}$.
22. From $432\frac{7}{8}$ take $329\frac{9}{10}$.
23. From $16980\frac{5}{6}$ take $7991\frac{8}{11}$.

ARTICLE 115.—*Multiplication of Fractions.*

Multiply together:

1. $\frac{7}{8}$, $\frac{9}{10}$.
2. $\frac{5}{12}$, $\frac{8}{15}$.
3. $\frac{15}{28}$, $\frac{14}{25}$.
4. $\frac{49}{80}$, $\frac{40}{63}$.
5. $\frac{33}{50}$, $\frac{17}{55}$.
6. $\frac{15}{14}$, $\frac{21}{10}$.
7. $\frac{7}{8}$, $\frac{4}{9}$, $\frac{6}{21}$.
8. $\frac{3}{5}$, $\frac{11}{12}$, $\frac{25}{22}$.
9. $\frac{2}{3}$, $\frac{8}{9}$, $\frac{15}{56}$.
10. $\frac{6}{11}$, $\frac{26}{21}$, $\frac{33}{13}$.
11. $\frac{18}{7}$, $\frac{20}{9}$, $\frac{28}{11}$.
12. $3\frac{4}{7}$, $2\frac{2}{5}$.
13. $5\frac{1}{3}$, $5\frac{1}{4}$, $5\frac{1}{5}$.
14. $2\frac{2}{7}$, $3\frac{3}{8}$, $4\frac{4}{9}$.
15. $5\frac{1}{2}$, $5\frac{1}{3}$, $5\frac{1}{4}$.
16. $4\frac{2}{5}$, 6, $3\frac{2}{11}$.
17. $35\frac{3}{5}$, 9.
18. $\frac{5}{7}$, 150, $6\frac{3}{10}$.
19. $325\frac{5}{8}$, $10\frac{2}{3}$.
20. $13\frac{3}{4}$, $13\frac{3}{4}$.
21. $1562\frac{1}{2}$, $1562\frac{1}{2}$.
22. $3\frac{1}{4}$, $3\frac{1}{5}$, $3\frac{1}{6}$.
23. 8, $7\frac{2}{3}$, 5.
24. $4\frac{4}{7}$, $5\frac{5}{8}$, $5\frac{5}{9}$, $3\frac{1}{2}$.
25. $5\frac{1}{3}$, $6\frac{1}{4}$, $7\frac{1}{5}$, $8\frac{1}{6}$.
26. $\frac{6}{35}$, 6, $4\frac{2}{3}$, $5\frac{5}{9}$.
27. $\frac{11}{12}$, $3\frac{1}{2}$, $1\frac{1}{5}$, $2\frac{2}{5}$.
28. $8\frac{8}{9}$, $3\frac{3}{4}$, 7, $3\frac{3}{5}$.
29. $2\frac{2}{3}$, $2\frac{2}{5}$, $2\frac{2}{9}$, $2\frac{2}{11}$.
30. 7, $7\frac{1}{2}$, 8, $8\frac{1}{2}$, 9.
31. 8, $8\frac{1}{3}$, $8\frac{2}{3}$, 9.
32. $\frac{4}{15}$, $3\frac{1}{7}$, $3\frac{1}{8}$, $3\frac{1}{9}$, 6.

ARTICLE 116.—*Fractional Parts of Integers.*

1. What is $\frac{7}{11}$ of 100?
2. What is $\frac{9}{5}$ of 87?
3. What is $\frac{31}{32}$ of 80?
4. What is $\frac{14}{45}$ of 70?
5. What is $\frac{8}{91}$ of 9?
6. What is $\frac{13}{30}$ of 43?
7. What is $\frac{18}{19}$ of 18?
8. What is $\frac{14}{27}$ of 72?
9. What is $\frac{11}{120}$ of 17?
10. What is $\frac{53}{16}$ of 200?
11. What is $\frac{21}{25}$ of 120?
12. What is $\frac{16}{19}$ of 67?

ARTICLE 117.—*Compound Fractions.*

Reduce the following to Simple Fractions:

1. $\frac{3}{4}$ of $\frac{18}{19}$.
2. $\frac{5}{7}$ of $\frac{17}{20}$.
3. $\frac{4}{9}$ of $2\frac{1}{2}$.
4. $\frac{5}{8}$ of $13\frac{1}{3}$.
5. $\frac{17}{18}$ of $\frac{15}{28}$.
6. $\frac{11}{13}$ of $\frac{19}{15}$.
7. $\frac{4}{81}$ of $\frac{9}{20}$.
8. $\frac{14}{15}$ of $11\frac{1}{3}$.

9. $\frac{11}{3}$ of $\frac{14}{5}$.
10. $\frac{3}{100}$ of $\frac{4}{81}$.
11. $\frac{15}{26}$ of $11\frac{1}{7}$.
12. $\frac{3}{4}$ of $\frac{7}{8}$ of $10\frac{2}{3}$.
13. $\frac{5}{8}$ of $\frac{5}{9}$ of $13\frac{1}{5}$.
14. $\frac{3}{10}$ of $\frac{7}{5}$ of $24\frac{2}{7}$.
15. $\frac{16}{17}$ of $\frac{14}{15}$ of $\frac{3}{8}$ of $4\frac{2}{7}$.
16. $\frac{9}{16}$ of $\frac{25}{36}$ of $\frac{7}{4}$ of $3\frac{3}{5}$.
17. $\frac{5}{12}$ of $\frac{5}{6}$ of $\frac{4}{15}$ of $\frac{9}{13}$.
18. $\frac{27}{32}$ of $\frac{14}{21}$ of $\frac{20}{3}$ of $6\frac{2}{7}$.
19. $\frac{19}{30}$ of $\frac{7}{11}$ of $\frac{6}{28}$ of $\frac{33}{38}$.
20. $\frac{13}{16}$ of $\frac{8}{9}$ of $\frac{5}{3}$ of $4\frac{4}{5}$.
21. $\frac{19}{50}$ of $\frac{15}{90}$ of $\frac{7}{5}$ of $4\frac{2}{3}$.
22. $\frac{3}{4}$ of $\frac{5}{6}$ of $\frac{16}{21}$ of $5\frac{1}{4}$.
23. $\frac{3}{11}$ of $\frac{4}{7}$ of $\frac{5}{9}$ of $\frac{11}{13}$ of $18\frac{1}{5}$.
24. $\frac{11}{9}$ of $\frac{14}{6}$ of $\frac{5}{22}$ of $130\frac{1}{2}$.
25. $\frac{15}{28}$ of $\frac{15}{32}$ of $\frac{16}{25}$ of $4\frac{4}{5}$.
26. $\frac{11}{20}$ of $\frac{18}{13}$ of $\frac{17}{9}$ of $17\frac{1}{3}$.
27. $\frac{16}{33}$ of $\frac{14}{27}$ of $\frac{11}{21}$ of $\frac{9}{19}$ of 90.
28. $\frac{5}{14}$ of $\frac{18}{29}$ of $\frac{21}{25}$ of $\frac{7}{9}$ of $6\frac{1}{4}$.

ARTICLE 118.—*Miscellaneous Examples.*

Find the cost :

1. Of $3\frac{3}{4}$ lb. of sugar, at $8\frac{1}{3}$ ct. a lb.
2. Of 5 yd. muslin, at $11\frac{1}{4}$ ct. a yd.
3. Of $7\frac{3}{4}$ lb. cheese, at $8\frac{1}{3}$ ct. a lb.
4. Of $312\frac{1}{2}$ lb. of brass, at $27\frac{1}{5}$ ct. a lb.
5. Of $4\frac{2}{3}$ yd. of fence, at \$$2\frac{2}{5}$ a yd.
6. Of $17\frac{1}{2}$ lb. of coffee, at \$$\frac{3}{8}$ a lb.
7. Of $2\frac{2}{5}$ mi. of road, at \$17200 a mi.
8. Of 18 bu. of potatoes, at \$$\frac{3}{5}$ a bu.
9. Of $38\frac{3}{4}$ lb. of steel, at $12\frac{1}{2}$ ct. a lb.
10. Of $6\frac{3}{4}$ lb. of rice, at $6\frac{2}{3}$ ct. a lb.
11. Of $13\frac{1}{3}$ oz. of copper wire, at $7\frac{1}{2}$ ct. an oz.
12. Of 4728 lb. of pork, at $3\frac{3}{4}$ ct. a lb.
13. From $\frac{1}{2}$ of $17\frac{1}{3}$ take $\frac{1}{3}$ of $17\frac{1}{2}$.
14. To $\frac{3}{4}$ of $5\frac{2}{3}$ add $\frac{4}{7}$ of $5\frac{3}{4}$.
15. Multiply $\frac{4}{5}$ of $7\frac{1}{3}$ by $\frac{3}{4}$ of $7\frac{1}{5}$.
16. How far can a boat move in $6\frac{3}{5}$ hours, at the rate of $13\frac{1}{2}$ miles per hour?

17. What cost $8\frac{1}{5}$ T. of hay, at \$$16\frac{2}{3}$ a T.?

18. A man owning $47\frac{1}{2}$ A. of land, sold $\frac{3}{5}$ of it; how many acres has he remaining?

19. A man had $25\frac{5}{6}$ cords of wood, and burned $\frac{5}{8}$ of it; how much remains?

20. What cost 8000 torches at $\frac{1}{5}$ ct. each?

21. What would be the value of $\frac{2}{7}$ of a farm of $58\frac{1}{3}$ acres, at \$$7\frac{1}{2}$ an acre?

22. A man earned \$$7\frac{1}{2}$ a week, for $6\frac{5}{6}$ weeks, and saved $\frac{1}{4}$ of his wages; how much did he save?

23. An iron bar was $8\frac{1}{4}$ feet long; $\frac{1}{5}$ of it being broken off, the remainder was sold for $2\frac{1}{2}$ ct. a lb. How much was received for it, the weight being $8\frac{1}{3}$ lb. per foot?

24. A had $57\frac{1}{3}$ acres; B, $49\frac{1}{5}$ acres; each gave the other $\frac{1}{3}$ of his own land; how much more had A then than B?

ARTICLE 119.—*Division of Fractions.*

1. Divide $\frac{7}{8}$ by $\frac{3}{4}$.

2. Divide $\frac{3}{4}$ by $\frac{7}{8}$.

3. Divide $9\frac{1}{4}$ by $6\frac{1}{6}$.

4. Divide $18\frac{1}{3}$ by $2\frac{3}{4}$.

5. Divide $17\frac{7}{9}$ by $\frac{5}{6}$.

6. Divide $\frac{3}{8}$ by 20.

7. Divide $4\frac{1}{4}$ by $4\frac{1}{5}$.

8. Divide $19\frac{3}{10}$ by $3\frac{3}{5}$.

9. Divide $2\frac{1}{5}$ by $5\frac{1}{2}$.

10. Divide $13\frac{1}{13}$ by $4\frac{1}{4}$.

11. Divide $27\frac{1}{2}$ by $1\frac{4}{7}$.

12. Divide $2\frac{2}{9}$ by $8\frac{1}{3}$.

13. Divide $19\frac{1}{5}$ by $4\frac{4}{11}$.

14. Divide $18\frac{3}{7}$ by $4\frac{3}{10}$.

15. Divide 180 by $3\frac{5}{7}$.

16. Divide $\frac{2}{5}$ by 25.

17. Divide 800 by $\frac{8}{17}$.

18. Divide $15\frac{9}{11}$ by $4\frac{1}{7}$.

19. Divide $18\frac{5}{9}$ by $13\frac{1}{3}$.

20. Divide $7\frac{1}{7}$ by $1\frac{1}{4}$.

21. Divide $3\frac{1}{3}$ by $4\frac{1}{5}$.

22. Divide 675 by $1\frac{4}{5}$.

23. Divide $39\frac{1}{10}$ by $4\frac{1}{4}$.

24. Divide $396\frac{1}{3}$ by $4\frac{1}{6}$.

25. Divide $13\frac{1}{5}$ by $47\frac{2}{3}$.

26. Divide $8\frac{4}{5}$ by 400.

27. Divide $67\frac{3}{8}$ by $3\frac{1}{7}$.

28. Divide $6\frac{2}{3}$ by $11\frac{1}{9}$.

29. Divide 44589 by $39\frac{5}{9}$.

30. Divide $347\frac{1}{3}$ by $123\frac{5}{8}$.

31. What cost 1 egg, at $17\frac{1}{2}$ ct. a dozen?

32. If 7 men earn $\$243\frac{1}{2}$, what will each man's share be?

33. A farm of $287\frac{3}{4}$ acres was divided among 5 children; what would be the share of each?

34. How much silk could be bought for $\$\frac{1}{4}$, at $3 a yard?

35. If $4\frac{1}{2}$ lb. cheese cost 80 ct., find the cost of 1 lb.

36. At $4\frac{3}{10}$ ct. a lb., how many pounds of rice can be bought for 75 ct.?

37. How much coffee, at $37\frac{1}{2}$ ct. a pound, can be bought for 10 ct.?

38. How many apples, at $\frac{1}{3}$ ct. each, can be bought for 15 cents?

39. How much saffron, at $16 an ounce, can be bought for $\$\frac{2}{3}$?

40. If $1\frac{1}{3}$ oz. of quinine cost $\$4\frac{1}{4}$, how much is that per ounce?

41. At $\$2\frac{2}{5}$ per day, how many days must a man work to earn $\$22\frac{1}{2}$?

42. How much must a man charge per hour to receive $\$1\frac{3}{5}$ for $9\frac{1}{2}$ hours?

43. How many yards of muslin, at $6\frac{2}{9}$ ct. a yd., can be bought for 80 ct.?

44. If $2\frac{2}{5}$ lb. of butter cost $\$1\frac{1}{4}$, how many pounds can be bought for $\$4\frac{1}{2}$?

45. A man chops $14\frac{1}{2}$ C. in $4\frac{3}{5}$ da.; how long will it take him to chop $23\frac{1}{5}$ C.?

ARTICLE 120.—*To find what part one number is of another.*

1. $7\frac{1}{2}$ is what part of 20?

2. $16\frac{2}{3}$ is what part of $62\frac{1}{2}$?

3. $\frac{4}{7}$ is what part of 28?

4. $4\frac{2}{5}$ is what part of $5\frac{1}{13}$?

5. $7\frac{3}{10}$ is what part of $10\frac{3}{7}$?
6. $8\frac{3}{4}$ is what part of 105?
7. $19\frac{5}{7}$ is what part of $30\frac{2}{3}$?
8. $84\frac{6}{7}$ is what part of $90\frac{3}{4}$?
9. What part of 102 is $4\frac{1}{4}$?
10. What part of $77\frac{7}{9}$ is $3\frac{4}{7}$?
11. What part of $91\frac{2}{3}$ is $13\frac{3}{4}$?
12. What part of $19\frac{4}{5}$ is $3\frac{6}{7}$?
13. $\frac{4}{5}$ of $16\frac{2}{3}$ is what part of $\frac{5}{9}$ of $34\frac{2}{7}$?
14. $\frac{7}{8}$ of $33\frac{1}{2}$ is what part of $\frac{3}{4}$ of $50\frac{1}{4}$?
15. $\frac{19}{20}$ of $\frac{19}{20}$ is what part of $\frac{3}{10}$ of $90\frac{1}{4}$?
16. $\frac{1}{30}$ of $30\frac{1}{3}$ is what part of $\frac{1}{10}$ of $20\frac{4}{5}$?

Article 121.—*Reduction of Complex Fractions.*

Reduce the following to Simple Fractions:

1. $\dfrac{4\frac{1}{2}}{5\frac{5}{7}}$.
2. $\dfrac{9\frac{1}{3}}{9\frac{4}{5}}$.
3. $\dfrac{17\frac{3}{5}}{24\frac{3}{4}}$.
4. $\dfrac{\frac{3}{8}}{15\frac{5}{7}}$.
5. $\dfrac{4}{19\frac{3}{11}}$.
6. $\dfrac{18\frac{5}{12}}{37\frac{2}{5}}$.
7. $\dfrac{13\frac{3}{5}}{4\frac{1}{4}}$.
8. $\dfrac{\frac{7}{8}}{19\frac{1}{3}}$.
9. $\dfrac{15\frac{3}{8}}{51\frac{2}{3}}$.
10. $\dfrac{8\frac{4}{7}}{84}$.
11. $\dfrac{69\frac{3}{8}}{95\frac{1}{7}}$.
12. $\dfrac{46\frac{1}{2}}{69\frac{3}{4}}$.
13. $\dfrac{23\frac{1}{3}}{75\frac{1}{4}}$.
14. $\dfrac{48\frac{4}{9}}{109}$.
15. $\dfrac{53\frac{4}{9}}{120\frac{1}{4}}$.

Article 122.

1. By what must $7\frac{1}{5}$ be multiplied, to give the product $20\frac{1}{4}$?

2. By what must $7\frac{1}{5}$ be divided to make the quotient $2\frac{1}{4}$?

3. How many pounds of sugar can be bought for $42\frac{1}{2}$ ct., at $9\frac{1}{3}$ ct. a lb.?

4. Bought $5\frac{3}{5}$ A. of land for \$77; what was the price per A.?

5. Divide $\frac{2}{3}$ of $\frac{5\frac{2}{5}}{7\frac{7}{8}}$ by $\frac{2}{5}$ of $\frac{3\frac{1}{7}}{4\frac{2}{5}}$.

6. I had $23\frac{3}{4}$ A. of land, and sold $\frac{5}{7}$ of it for \$1045; how much was that per A.?

7. If $2\frac{1}{2}$ yd. of cloth cost $\$3\frac{1}{2}$, how much can be bought for $\$4\frac{1}{2}$?

8. If $2\frac{1}{2}$ lb. of honey cost $\$\frac{3}{4}$, how much can be bought for $\$10\frac{1}{10}$?

9. How often will $\frac{5\frac{1}{4}}{2\frac{1}{3}}$ contain $\frac{2\frac{1}{4}}{5\frac{1}{3}}$?

10. A boy had $\$\frac{4}{5}$, and spent $\frac{2}{5}$ of it for cherries; how many straps, at $\$\frac{3}{50}$ each, can he buy with the balance of his money?

11. I am offered $14\frac{1}{3}$ A. for $\$103\frac{1}{5}$; I have only \$100; how many acres should I receive for my money?

12. Divide $\frac{3\frac{3}{7}}{8\frac{4}{5}}$ by $\frac{13\frac{1}{3}}{9\frac{3}{7}}$.

13. I had $\$43\frac{2}{10}$, which I paid for gold at $\$\frac{9}{10}$ a pwt.; I had the gold made into rings weighing $1\frac{1}{5}$ pwt. each; how many rings were made?

14. By what must $\frac{3\frac{8}{9}}{5\frac{3}{5}}$ be divided to make a quotient equal to $\frac{1\frac{1}{3}}{3\frac{3}{4}}$?

15. By what must 10 be multiplied, so that the product may be $\frac{1}{10}$?

16. I had $4\frac{4}{7}$ bl. of glue, and gave $\frac{1}{3}$ of my lot to my brother for $\$25\frac{3}{5}$; how much was that per bl.?

17. If $7\frac{7}{8}$ yd. of cloth cost $\$16\frac{4}{5}$, how many yards can be purchased for $\$28\frac{4}{9}$?

ARTICLE 123.—*Fractional Compound Numbers.*

1. How many yards in 24 rd.?

2. How many sq. yd. in 1 A.?

3. How many years in 14690 days?

4. What cost $14\frac{1}{6}$ lb. of coffee at 27 ct. a lb.?

5. Reduce 84 sq. rd. to sq. ft.

6. What cost $112\frac{3}{4}$ yd. of paving, at \$$8\frac{4}{5}$ per rod.?

7. A field is $37\frac{1}{3}$ rd. long, and $25\frac{1}{2}$ rd. wide; how many sq. rd. in it?

8. What cost 1463 yd. of telegraph wire, at 20 ct. a rod?

9. How much will 43560 sq. yd. of land cost at \$13.75 an acre?

10. What cost $51\frac{1}{2}$ bu. of wheat at $16\frac{1}{4}$ ct. a peck?

11. Reduce 12 yr. 300 da. to hr.

Find the cost of:

12. $17\frac{1}{2}$ yd. of silk, at $87\frac{1}{2}$ ct. a yd.

13. $37\frac{1}{2}$ bu. of potatoes, at $56\frac{2}{3}$ ct. a bu.

14. $26\frac{4}{5}$ yd. of tape, at $1\frac{1}{3}$ ct. a yd.

15. $6\frac{6}{7}$ oz. of pepper, at $4\frac{1}{4}$ ct. an oz.

16. $18\frac{1}{2}$ lb. of ham, at $10\frac{1}{4}$ ct. a lb.

17. $14\frac{1}{2}$ oz. of copper, at $2\frac{1}{4}$ ct. an oz.

18. Reduce 53000 ft. to mi.

19. Reduce 3 A. 120 sq. rd. to sq. yd.

20. Reduce 127512 in. to mi.

21. How many sq. in. in 3 A.?

22. A field $93\frac{1}{3}$ rd. long contains 7 acres; how wide is it?

23. How many steps 2 ft. 9 in. long must be taken in going 5 mi.?

24. A glacier moves $2\frac{1}{4}$ in. in a day; how long will it take it to move one mile?

ARTICLES 124 AND 125.—*Reduction to Lower Denominations.*

1. Reduce $\frac{3}{128}$ bu. to the fraction of a quart.
2. Reduce $\frac{7}{90}$ gal. to the fraction of a pint.
3. Reduce $\frac{1}{2000}$ cwt. to the fraction of an oz.
4. Reduce $\frac{1}{5000}$ A. to the fraction of a sq. yd.
5. Reduce $\frac{2}{135}$ cu. yd. to the fraction of a cu. ft.
6. Reduce $\frac{3}{1461}$ yr. to the fraction of a day.
7. Reduce $\frac{17}{400}$ lb. to the fraction of an oz (Iron).
8. Reduce $\frac{3}{1000}$ lb. to the fraction of a pwt.
9. Reduce $\frac{11}{480}$ ℥ to the fraction of a scruple.
10. Reduce $\frac{1}{104000}$ sq. mi. to the fraction of a sq. rd.
11. Reduce $\frac{3}{1000000}$ cu. yd. to the fraction of a cu. in.
12. Reduce $\frac{1}{90000}$ da. to the fraction of a sec.
13. Reduce $\frac{1}{8000}$ bu. to the fraction of a pt.
14. Reduce $\frac{11}{147000}$ wk. to the fraction of a min.
15. Reduce $\frac{12}{875}$ gal. to the fraction of a gill.
16. Reduce $\frac{19}{32}$ gal. to integers.
17. Reduce $\frac{7}{11}$ T. to integers.
18. Reduce $\frac{17}{18}$ mi. to integers.
19. Reduce $\frac{23}{24}$ A. to integers.
20. Reduce $\frac{5}{9}$ yr. to integers.
21. Reduce $\frac{7}{9}$ lb. Troy to integers.
22. Reduce $\frac{59}{60}$ gal. to integers.
23. Reduce $\frac{15}{16}$ ℥ to integers.
24. Reduce $\frac{15}{32}$ T. to integers.
25. Reduce $\frac{1}{880}$ mi. to integers.
26. Reduce $\frac{3}{100}$ of a degree to integers.
27. Reduce $\frac{1}{121}$ sq. mi. to integers.
28. Reduce $\frac{4}{5}$ chain to integers.
29. Reduce $\frac{25}{81}$ C. to integers.
30. Reduce $\frac{1}{5}$ O. to integers.
31. Reduce $\frac{37}{81}$ da. to integers.

ARTICLE 126.—*Reduction to Higher Denominations*

1. Reduce $\frac{4}{5}$ min. to the fraction of a day.
2. Reduce $\frac{1}{20}$ cu. ft. to the fraction of a cord.
3. Reduce $\frac{9}{8}$ sq. in. to the fraction of a sq. yd.
4. Reduce $\frac{32}{45}$ oz. to the fraction of a cwt.
5. Reduce $\frac{16}{19}$ pt. to the fraction of a gal.
6. Reduce $\frac{32}{5}$ pt. to the fraction of a bu.
7. Reduce $\frac{3}{10}$ gr. to the fraction of an oz.
8. Reduce $\frac{243}{16}$ cu. in. to the fraction of a cu. yd.
9. Reduce $\frac{36}{11}$ ℈ to the fraction of a pound.
10. Reduce $\frac{22}{3}$ yd. to the fraction of a mile.
11. Reduce $\frac{363}{400}$ sq. yd. to the fraction of a sq. mi.
12. Reduce $\frac{487}{5}$ hr. to the fraction of a year.
13. Reduce $\frac{25}{36}$ lb. to the fraction of a ton.
14. Reduce $\frac{11}{3}$ in. to the fraction of a chain.
15. Reduce $\frac{18}{7}$ gi. to the fraction of a gal.
16. Reduce $\frac{1}{16}$ qt. to the fraction of a bu.

ARTICLE 127.

1. What part of 1 mi. 10 rd. is 88 rd.?
2. What part of 2 bu. 1 qt. is 1 bu. 2 qt.?
3. What part of 9 C. is 16 cu. ft.?
4. What part of 39 lb. is 7 lb. 8 oz.?
5. What part of 1 wk. 5 da. is 1 da. 8 hr.
6. 3 A. 6 sq. yd. is what part of 9 A.?
7. 17 bu. 3 pk. 4 qt. is what part of 65 bu.?
8. 3 ʒ 1 ℈ is what part of 5 ℥ 2 ℈?
9. 8 yd. 1 ft. is what part of 5 rd. 1 yd.?
10. 2° 37′ 30″ is what part of 8° 45′?
11. What part is 5 gal. 1 gi. of 10 gal.?
12. What part is 3 doz. and 6, of a gross?
13. What part is 12 lb. 8 oz. of 2 T. 5 cwt.?

Article 128.

1. $\frac{5}{24}$ sq. yd. — $\frac{3}{8}$ sq. ft. = ?
2. $\frac{4}{5}$ C. + $\frac{4}{5}$ cu. yd. = ?
3. $\frac{3}{4}°$ — $\frac{4}{5}'$ = ?
4. $\frac{3}{7}$ lb. — $\frac{4}{7}$ oz. + $\frac{4}{7}$ pwt. = ?
5. $\frac{3}{8}$ T. — $\frac{4}{5}$ cwt. = ?
6. $\frac{4}{3}$ Cong. + $\frac{2}{3}$ O. = ?
7. $\frac{3}{5}$ mi. — $\frac{5}{9}$ rd. = ?
8. $\frac{8}{9}$ chain — $\frac{1}{4}$ pace = ?
9. $\frac{3}{4}$ wk. + $\frac{4}{9}$ da. + $\frac{3}{5}$ hr. = ?
10. $\frac{4}{5}$ bu. + $\frac{3}{5}$ pk. + $\frac{2}{5}$ qt. + $\frac{2}{5}$ pt. = ?
11. $\frac{4}{9}$ gal. + $\frac{4}{9}$ qt. + $\frac{4}{9}$ pt. + $\frac{4}{9}$ gi. = ?
12. $\frac{7}{12}$ T. + $\frac{5}{12}$ cwt. + $\frac{11}{12}$ lb. = ?
13. $\frac{3}{11}$ mi. + $\frac{4}{11}$ rd. + $\frac{1}{4}$ yd. + $\frac{1}{4}$ ft. = ?
14. $\frac{2}{9}$ ℥ + $\frac{4}{9}$ ʒ + $\frac{1}{3}$ ℈ = ?
15. $\frac{13}{28}$ C. + $\frac{17}{45}$ cu. yd. + $\frac{13}{35}$ cu. ft. = ?

Article 129.—*Promiscuous Examples.*

1. From $8\frac{1}{3}$ take $7\frac{7}{10}$.
2. Reduce $\frac{5}{22}$ sq. mi. to integers.
3. Add $3\frac{1}{3}$ to the difference between $4\frac{1}{4}$ and $6\frac{1}{6}$.
4. From $7\frac{7}{9} \times 6\frac{6}{7}$ take $6\frac{6}{7} \times 5\frac{5}{6}$.
5. Reduce $\frac{4}{9}$ to a fraction whose denominator is 126.
6. Reduce $\frac{9117}{13169}$ to its lowest terms.
7. Reduce $\frac{810}{900}$ to twentieths.
8. Find a number which multiplied by $8\frac{1}{3}$ gives 60.
9. What number divided by $4\frac{5}{7}$ gives $4\frac{5}{11}$?
10. From $\frac{7}{8} \div \frac{5}{4}$ take $\frac{3}{8} \div \frac{7}{4}$.
11. Reduce $\frac{7}{11}$ to a fraction whose numerator is 77.
12. What part of \$5 is $\frac{4}{5}$ of 5 cents?
13. Reduce $\frac{1}{7750}$ T. to the fraction of a pound.
14. \$$4\frac{1}{2}$ will buy $1\frac{2}{5}$ yd. of cloth; how much will $1\frac{2}{3}$ yd. cost?
15. Bought 3750 lb. of iron, at \$3.50 per cwt.; what is the amount of the bill?

16. A boy works 3 days at the rate of $\$5\frac{3}{4}$ a week; how much does he earn?

17. I have 55 A. of land, worth $\$17\frac{1}{2}$ an acre; B wishes to trade me 7 hogs, worth $\$7\frac{1}{3}$ each; what part of my land should be given for them?

18. Bought $32\frac{1}{2}$ T. of iron for \$1218.75; at that rate, what quantity can I buy for \$1000?

19. A man lost $\$13\frac{3}{4}$, and borrowed $\$57\frac{3}{5}$; he then had $\$106\frac{1}{2}$; what sum had he at first?

20. What number is as much greater than $15\frac{1}{2}$ as $15\frac{1}{2}$ is greater than $7\frac{5}{11}$?

21. A farmer raised 208 bu. 1 pk. of wheat, and sold 119 bu.; what part of his crop has he remaining?

22. A lady bought $35\frac{1}{4}$ yd. carpet for \$47; had she bought 6 yd. more, what would the bill have been?

23. A farm is worth \$5500, and A owns $\frac{5}{12}$ of it; what part of his share should A sell for \$825?

24. How much would a family consume in August, at the rate of 8 lb. 5 oz. daily?

25. $\frac{5}{7}$ of a certain number is $389\frac{1}{7}$; what is the number?

26. Multiply $4\frac{2}{5} \times 8\frac{1}{3}$ by $2\frac{2}{11} \times 3\frac{3}{8}$.

27. A farmer sold $\frac{4}{11}$ of his flock of geese, and has 14 dozen remaining; how many geese had he at first?

28. Reduce $\frac{7\frac{1}{3}}{8\frac{4}{5}}$, $\frac{11\frac{1}{3}}{12\frac{3}{4}}$, $\frac{7\frac{1}{2}}{12\frac{6}{7}}$, and $\frac{7\frac{1}{4}}{11\frac{3}{5}}$ to a common denominator.

29. Hats cost $\$3\frac{1}{3}$ apiece, but late in the season are sold at $\frac{4}{5}$ of the cost; how many can I then buy for \$48?

30. Sold a house for \$2373, which was $\frac{7}{9}$ of the cost; how much did I lose?

31. A lawyer collected \$18.80, and kept $\frac{3}{8}$ of it; how much did he pay over?

32. What number is that, to which, if you add $\frac{3}{8}$ of itself, the sum will be $82\frac{1}{2}$?

33. Find the value of a lot 88 ft. long and $49\frac{1}{2}$ ft. wide, at \$700 per acre.

34. $\frac{5}{6}$ of a farm are worth $\$3157\frac{1}{2}$; what are $\frac{8}{9}$ of it worth?

35. $53\frac{1}{3}$ yards of cloth cost me \$88; what will I lose by selling $8\frac{1}{2}$ yd. for \$10?

36. Three men found a sum of money, of which the first took $\frac{1}{5}$, and the second $\frac{5}{8}$, leaving the third man \$69.44; what was the sum found?

37. A expended \$347 for land, at $\$\frac{2}{5}$ an acre; and B, \$4243 for land, at $\$5\frac{1}{2}$ an acre; how many acres have both together?

38. What was the cost of 47 head of cattle, if \$47 was lost by selling 13 head for $\$26\frac{1}{2}$ apiece?

39. From a lot 100 rd. long and $72\frac{1}{2}$ rd. wide, was sold a lot 45 rd. long and 29 rd. wide; what part of the whole lot was sold?

40. A owns 405 A. 39 sq. rd., and B owns 391 A. 109 sq. rd.; how much land must A sell B, so that their farms may be of equal size?

ARTICLE 130.—*Practice.*

Find the cost of:

1. 450 lb. butter, at 25 ct. a pound.

2. 784 yd. muslin, at $6\frac{1}{4}$ ct. a yard.

3. 462 gal. vinegar, at $16\frac{2}{3}$ ct. a gallon.

4. 673 yd. delaine, at $62\frac{1}{2}$ ct. a yard.

5. 96 gal. milk, at $\$1.87\frac{1}{2}$ ct. a gallon.

6. 5726 lb. whiting, at $1\frac{1}{2}$ ct. a pound.

7. 538 bu. wheat, at $\$1.12\frac{1}{2}$ a bushel.

8. 788 yd. cloth, at $\$1.62\frac{1}{2}$ a yard.

9. 375 lb. cheese, at $8\frac{1}{3}$ ct. a pound.

10. 424 A. land, at $\$3.18\frac{3}{4}$ an acre.

11. 398 bu. barley, at 75 ct. a bushel.

12. 666 lb. feathers, at 33⅓ ct. a pound.

13. 78 C. wood, at $4.75 a cord.

14. 3786 lb. twine, at 16⅔ ct. a pound.

15. 5 gal. 3 qt. of vinegar, at $2.50 a gallon.

16. 17 yd. 2 ft. of paving, at $2.40 a yard.

17. 69 bu. 3 pk. of potatoes, at 68 ct. a bushel.

18. 4 lb. 11 oz. of honey, at 36 ct. a pound.

19. 3 hr. 45 min. work, at 40 ct. an hour.

20. 7 oz. 7 pwt. of silver, at 88 ct. an ounce.

21. 3 bu. 3 pk. of clover seed, at $3.60 a bushel.

22. 49 sq. yd. 6 sq. ft. of plastering, at 27 ct. a square yard.

23. 3 ℥ 2 ʒ 1 ℈ of quinine, at $3.60 an ounce.

24. 4 bu. 2 pk. 5 qt. of berries, at $3.20 a bushel.

25. 15 gal. 3 qt. 1 pt. 1 gi. of milk, at $1.92 a gallon.

26. 5 C. 96 cu. ft. of wood, at $4.40 a cord.

27. How many bushels of oats, at 37½ ct. a bu., can be bought for $7.87½?

28. How much cloth, at $2.12½ a yard, can be bought for $90.31¼?

29. What cost 18 lb. 12 oz. of coffee, at 33⅓ ct. a lb.?

30. Find the cost of 500 screws, at 36 ct. a gross.

31. Find the cost of 18 bu. 2 pk. of apples, at $.66⅔ a bushel.

32. What cost 40 rubbers, at 40 cents a dozen?

33. At $3.37½ an acre, how many acres of ground can be bought for $281.25?

34. What cost 5 bu. 2 pk. of strawberries, at 33⅓ ct. a quart?

35. A week's work is 6 da., of 10 hr. each; how much can a man earn in 4 da. 6 hr., if his weekly wages are $10.50?

36. Find the cost of 11 T. 940 lb. of hay, at $12 a ton.

DECIMAL FRACTIONS.

ARTICLE 135.—*Writing Decimals.*

Write the following Decimal Numbers:

1. 803 *thousandths.*
2. Fifty-one *thousandths.*
3. Nine *thousandths.*
4. Forty-six *ten-thousandths.*
5. Two hundred and one *ten-thousandths.*
6. 7735 *hundred-thousandths.*
7. 86 *hundred-thousandths.*
8. 3 *hundred-thousandths.*
9. Nine hundred and nineteen *thousandths.*
10. Nine thousand and twenty *ten-thousandths.*
11. Ten thousand and one *hundred-thousandths.*
12. Five thousand and sixty-seven *ten-thousandths.*
13. 381257 *millionths.*
14. 40703 *millionths.*
15. 2008 *millionths.*
16. 88 *millionths.*
17. 7 *millionths.*
18. Forty seven thousand and eighteen *millionths.*
19. Five hundred and fifty-five *millionths.*
20. Three hundred thousand and eight *millionths.*
21. Sixty-seven *millionths.*
22. Fifty-seven *tenths.*
23. 2406391 *ten-millionths.*
24. 65400 *ten-millionths.*
25. 49 *ten-millionths.*
26. 880004 *ten-millionths.*
27. 6 *ten-millionths.*
28. 31000722 *ten-millionths.*
29. Four hundred and eighty *hundredths.*

30. 14 *units* and 5 *hundredths.*
31. 3 *units* and 17 *thousandths.*
32. 3000 *units* and 4 *thousandths.*
33. 3004 *thousandths.*
34. 8354 *hundredths.*
35. One *unit* and one *millionth.*
36. One million *units* and one *millionth.*
37. Three hundred *millionths.*
38. Seven hundred *units* and seven *hundredths.*
39. 19 *billionths.*
40. 39704 *ten-billionths.*
41. 800004 *hundred-millionths.*
42. Eight thousand and five *tenths.*
43. Eight thousand *units* and five *ten-thousandths.*
44. 379000 *units* and 379 *thousandths.*
45. Fifty thousand and one *hundred billionths.*
46. $\frac{3}{10}$, $\frac{7}{100}$, $\frac{19}{1000}$, $\frac{483}{100}$, $\frac{39}{10000}$.
47. $\frac{88}{100}$, $\frac{903}{10000}$, $\frac{7}{1000}$, $\frac{21}{100000}$, $\frac{89}{10}$.
48. $5\frac{87}{100}$, $16\frac{8}{1000}$, $200\frac{17}{100}$, $30\frac{30}{100000}$.

Article 136.—*Reading Decimals.*

Read the following Decimal Numbers:

1. 4.18; 6.008; .0006; 36.036; 3.4075.
2. .702; .078; .02005; 50.09; .0006.
3. .00066; .30066; .00456; .000036.
4. .01; .016; .0162; .01624.
5. 4736.2; 3.8914; .356; 283.67.
6. 2000.20002; 304.0506; 7.24006.
7. .3703; 3.703; 37.03; 370.3.
8. 4.4; 4.04; 4.004; 4.0004.
9. .056; 30.07; .00009; .010203.
10. 45.0009; .005009; 60.016.
11. 37.03; 4638.9; 364.005.

12. .0102 ; .001002 ; .00010002.

13. 5.806 ; 50.4903 ; 6.8938.

14. 3700.0004 ; .3704 ; 3000.0704.

Change the following to Common Fractions:

15. .64 ; .165 ; .0375 ; .9375.

16. .024 ; .00008 ; .0000088.

17. .875; .4375; .15625.

18. .1024; .83875; .873642.

ARTICLE 141.—*Reduction of Decimals. Case III.*

Reduce the following to Common Fractions or Mixed Numbers:

1. .875.
2. .64.
3 .512.
4. .625.
5. .025.
6. .256.
7. .0025.
8. .2224.
9. .975.
10. .0084.
11. .1875.
12. .46875.
13. 4.045.
14. 26.18.
15. .0125.
16. 19.625.
17. 300.25.
18. 46.875.
19. 13.92.
20. 20.02.
21. .6875.
22. 14.01875.
23. 9.008.
24. .34375.

ARTICLE 142.—*Reduction of Decimals. Case IV.*

Reduce the following to Decimals:

1. $\frac{3}{8}$.
2. $\frac{9}{20}$.
3. $\frac{5}{16}$.
4. $\frac{11}{25}$.
5. $\frac{13}{50}$.
6. $\frac{15}{80}$.
7. $\frac{13}{32}$.
8. $\frac{17}{32}$.
9. $\frac{21}{16}$.
10. $\frac{3}{160}$.
11. $\frac{1}{800}$.
12. $\frac{17}{250}$.
13. $\frac{9}{500}$.
14. $\frac{137}{160}$.
15. $\frac{11}{640}$.
16. $\frac{61}{64}$.
17. $\frac{89}{50}$.
18. $\frac{50}{89}$.
19. $\frac{17}{71}$.
20. $\frac{28}{70}$.
21. $\frac{36}{48}$.
22. $\frac{49}{52}$.
23. $\frac{27}{200}$.
24. $\frac{13}{811}$.

ARTICLE 143.—*Addition of Decimals.*

1. Add 3.12; 41.3; 68.94; 39.77.

2. 18 and 54 hundredths + 19 and 5 tenths + 53 and 73 hundredths + 37 and 56 hundredths + 16 and 9 tenths = ?

3. 5 and 17 thousandths + 73 and 29 hundredths + 128 and 3 tenths + 94 and 983 thousandths + 26 and 71 hundredths + 271 and 7 tenths = ?

4. Add 413 thousandths; 413 ten-thousandths; 413 hundred-thousandths, and 413 millionths.

5. 25.7 + 6.009 + .4309 + 509.7 + 38.08 + 8.983 + 73.38 = ?

6. Add 46 and 89 thousandths; 60 and 894 thousandths; 8 and 946 thousandths; 9 and 468 thousandths; 89 and 46 thousandths; 460 and 89 thousandths, and 20.

7. Add 400.009; 40.09; 4.0009; 40.9; 400.09; 4.009; 100; and .002.

8. 738.84 + 388.47 + 884.73 + 847.38 + 473.88 + 59.99 + 59.099 + 99.59 = ?

9. Add 17.38; 18.37; 19.36; 20.35; 21.34; 22.33; 23.32; 24.31 and 25.3.

10. Write 395.4276 seven times and add.

11. Write 234.056 eight times and add.

12. Add 893 thousandths; 753 hundredths; 49 tenths; 3739 thousandths; 5 hundredths; 55 hundredths; 5500, and 127 thousandths.

13. 46.8 + 48.6 + 68.4 + 64.8 + 84.6 + 86.4 + 44.4 + 66.6 + 88.8 = ?

14. Add 74 and 8 ten-thousandths; 36 and 5-thousandths; 637 and 4 ten-millionths; 29 and 8 tenths; 3 and 8914 hundred-thousandths; 55 and 93 hundredths; 84 millionths, and 637 and 27306 ten-millionths.

ARTICLE 144.—*Subtraction of Decimals.*

1. From 47.378 take 19.89.

2. From 60.06 take 50.89.

3. From 48.937 take 13.0609.

4. From 300 take 46.875.

5. From 345.6789 take 88.88.

6. Take 8.76 from 234.372.

7. Take 23.9564 from 32.404.

8. Take 22.222 from 111.11.

9. Take 6.0008 from 22.93004.

Find the difference between the following:

10. 39.81 and 20.985.

11. 100.001 and 50.09.

12. 324.137 and 199.9994.

13. 64 thousandths and 64 hundredths.

14. From 147 and 39602 hundred-thousandths take 58 and 545986 millionths.

15. Take 73421 and 397 ten-thousandths from 124316 and 397 thousandths.

ARTICLE 147.—*Multiplication of Decimals.*

Multiply:

1. .643 by .89.

2. 3.56 by 62.5.

3. 7.875 by 94.

4. .125 by .126.

5. 48.76 by 48.75.

6. .03 by .02.

7. .744 by .125.

8. .0375 by .036.

9. 9.9 × .098.

10. 666. × 5.55.

11. .048 × .04375.

12. .9375 × 2400.

13. 7.39 × .0043.

14. .2502 × .0848.

15. 42.075 × 100.

16. 3.956 × 42.75.

17. Multiply 48 units and 75 hundredths by 6 units and 32 thousandths.

18. Multiply 893 thousandths by 893 ten-thousandths

19. Multiply 38400 by 19 units and 28 thousandths.

20. Multiply 27 thousand by 27 thousandths.

21. Multiply 78 and 125 thousandths by 1024.

22. Multiply 67 thousand 2 hundred by 67 and 2 hundredths.

23. Multiply 7936 ten-thousandths by 390 and 625 thousandths.

24. Multiply 6.625 by 14.32.

ARTICLE 150.—*Division of Decimals.*

Divide:

1. 5.845 by 3.5.

2. 9.4125 by 1.25.

3. .7614 by .36.

4. 2.875 by 1.15.

5. 4.752 by 198.

6. .897 by .06.

7. .897 by 260.

8. .7375 by .059.

9. 1287.7651 by 3.217.

10. 160 by .04.

11. 6.5667 by 31.27.

12. 17429.1 by .4251.

13. 3.1 by 3.2.

14. .004 by 160.

15. 8.91 by 1.98.

16. 1 by 16.

17. Divide 37 units and 37 thousandths by 4 units and 4 thousandths.

18. Divide 12 units and 12 hundredths by 16 units and 16 hundredths.

19. Divide 1 hundred by 1 hundredth.

20. Divide 208 millionths by 65 hundred-thousandths.

21. Divide 8.76 by 132.

22. Divide .9 by 2.99.

23. Divide .001 by 150.

24. Divide 27.5 by .28.

Decimal Compound Numbers.

Article 151.—*Reduction to Lower Denomination.*

1. Reduce .0125 bu. to the decimal of a pint.
2. Reduce .0273 gal. to the decimal of a pint.
3. Reduce .00043 T. to the decimal of a pound.
4. Reduce .0275 yd. to the decimal of an inch.
5. Reduce .0000075 sq. mi. to the decimal of a sq. rd.
6. Reduce .0000025 cu. yd. to the decimal of a cu. in.
7. Reduce .00001125 da. to the decimal of a second.
8. Reduce .00375 C. to the decimal of a cu. ft.
9. Reduce .000575 sq. yd. to the decimal of a sq. in.

Article 152.—*Reduction of Decimals to Integers.*

Find the value of the following, in Integers:

1. .4375 bu.
2. .4375 gal.
3. .15625 T.
4. .15625 mi.
5. .390625 sq. mi.
6. .7 C.
7. .38 yr.
8. .047 of a circle.

Article 153.—*Reduction to Higher Denominations.*

1. Reduce .352 pt. to the decimal of a bushel.
2. Reduce .48 gi. to the decimal of a gallon.
3. Reduce .648 sq. in. to the decimal of a sq. yd.
4. Reduce .5832 cu. in. to the decimal of a cu. yd.
5. Reduce .472 qt. to the decimal of a bushel.
6. Reduce .486 min. to the decimal of a day.
7. Reduce .4096 oz. to the decimal of a cwt.
8. Reduce .39 pt. to the decimal of a gallon.
9. Reduce .1296 sec. to the decimal of a day.
10. Reduce .015 pt. to the decimal of a bushel.

11. Reduce .13824 cu. in. to the decimal of a cord.

12. Reduce .17532 hr. to the decimal of a year.

13. Reduce .792 in. to the decimal of a mile.

14. Reduce 7.68 oz. to the decimal of a ton.

15. Reduce .17424 sq. in. to the decimal of an acre.

ARTICLE 154.—*Promiscuous Examples.*

1. Find the value of .05 da. in integers.

2. If 3.7 yards cost $10.36, what will 5.8 yards cost?

3. If 3.5 acres of land cost $430.43, how many acres could be bought for $614.90?

4. Find the cost of 4 bu. 3 pk. of oats, at 46 cents a bushel.

5. A man sold 55 gal. 1 pt. of milk, at $1.80 a gallon, and was paid in tea at 84 ct. a pound; how many pounds did he receive?

6. A field 40 rods wide contains 10 A. 80 sq. rd.; how long is it?

7. How much wood, at $2.90 a cord, can be bought for $105.125?

8. .4 mi. + .3 rd. + .7 yd. = ?

9. Find the value of .7475 T. in integers.

10. How much vinegar, at 24 ct. a gallon, can be bought for $7.77?

11. What cost 1000 cu. yd. of embankment, at the rate of $0.37 per cu. ft.?

12. Find the value of .234375 bu. in integers.

13. What cost 7227 feet of wire fence, at 14 ct. a rod?

14. A locomotive runs 17 mi. 32 rd. in an hour; how far will it run in 13 hr. 39 min.?

15. .1 yr. + .2 wk. + .3 da. + .4 hr. = ?

16. Reduce $\frac{4}{9}$ of $\frac{13\frac{1}{2}}{16}$ to a decimal.

17. 1.4 bu. — 3.7 pk. = ?

18. How much land, at $500 an acre, can be bought for $131.25?

19. .03 T. + .73 cwt. + .75 lb. =?

20. Find the cost of 7 lb. 7 oz. of silverware, at $1.20 an ounce.

21. How much cloth, at $1.44 a yd., must be given for 6 bu. 6 qt. of strawberries, worth $4.80 a bushel?

22. At 12½ ct. a pound, how much cheese can be bought for $19.81¼?

23. What cost 4350 lb. iron, at $2.80 a hundred pounds?

24. What cost 8764 pickles, at 75 ct. a hundred?

25. What cost 108 screws, at $1.08 per gross?

26. Find the value of .77 yr. in integers.

27. A locomotive runs 16 mi. 256 rd. per hour; how long will it be in running 154 mi. 280 rd.?

28. A man can earn 18¾ ct. per hour, and a boy 12½ ct.; how much will the man earn while the boy earns $4?

29. Grading a road cost $10312.50, at 62 ct. 5 m. per foot; how long is the road?

30. Find the value of a lot 70 rods square, at $20 an acre.

THE METRIC SYSTEM.

ARTICLE 156.—*Measures of Length.*

Reduce:

1. 394.5 Hm. to dm.
2. 93.64 m. to kilometers.
3. 1234.56 Dm. to Mm.
4. 987.65 Km. to Dm.
5. .34 m. to myriameters.
6. 74.6 Dm. to cm.
7. 83.7 Hm. to Mm.
8. .37 Mm. to meters.
9. 4600 Km. to dm.
10. 58000 cm. to Hm.
11. 374.5 Mm. to cm.
12. 67.25 Dm. to Km.
13. 8936.4 cm. to Dm.
14. .456 Km. to Hm.

ARTICLE 157.—*Metric Square Measure.*

Reduce:

1. 374680 m^2 to hektars.
2. 493.2 A. to centars.
3. 387.43 ca. to ars.
4. 387.43 m^2 to ars.
5. 43.875 A. to m^2.
6. .457 ca. to hektars.
7. 8973.4 m^2 to hektars.
8. 5839 A. to m^2.
9. 3843 ca. to hektars.
10. 3970 A. to centars.

ARTICLE 158.—*Measures of Capacity.*

Reduce :

1. 4800 cl. to liters.
2. 39.5 Dl. to centiliters.
3. 493.7 dl. to Hl.
4. 58.39 Hl. to centiliters.
5. .457 Dl. to liters.
6. 6.789 l. to centiliters.
7. 34.692 Hl. to Dl.
8. 42.789 dl. to liters.
9. 325.84 l. to hektoliters.
10. 4.7 dl. to dekaliters.
11. 3800 Hl. to deciliters.
12. 29.7 l. to dekaliters.
13. 468.3 cl. to hektoliters.
14. 38700 Dl. to deciliters.
15. 49 m^3 to liters.
16. 37282 cl. to m^3.
17. 678 l. to cubic meters.
18. .0303 m^3 to deciliters.

ARTICLE 159.—*Metric Weights.*

Reduce:

1. 6.5 Mg. to M. T.
2. 489.31 Dg. to mg.
3. .04653 Q. to Dg.
4. 654.3 Hg. to quintals.
5. 87 M. T. to kilograms.
6. .937 mg. to grams.
7. 123.456 Hg. to dg.
8. 873.4 dg. to Dg.
9. 88.736 Mg. to cg.
10. .0086 g. to quintals.
11. .0765 Kg. to M. T.
12. 3945 cg. to Hg.
13. 3.894 M. T. to grams.
14. 87300 Kg. to mg.
15. 89900 Dg. to Mg.
16. .00489 Q. to dg.
17. 4000 G. to Mg.
18. 12000000 mg. to Kg.
19. 9876541 dg. to quintals.
20. 34.56 Kg. to grams.
21. 48004800 cg. to Hg.
22. .09083 M. T. to mg.

ARTICLE 160.

Find the value of:

1. 40 meters.
2. 50 hektars.
3. 375 kilograms.
4. .6375 kilometers.
5. 13 tonneaux.
6. 93.75 sters.
7. 875 grams.
8. 500 cubic meters.
9. 625 square meters.
10. 37.5 ars.

Reduce:

11. 45 hektoliters to bu.
12. 100 inches to meters.
13. 100 mi. to kilometers.
14. 100 sq. yd. to m^2.
15. 100 acres to hektars.
16. 100 cu. yd. to m^3.
17. 48 sq. rd. to ars.
18. 18 T. to metric tons.
19. 454 bu. to hektoliters.
20. 66 gal. to liters.
21. 1 lb. 4oz. 1 pwt. 12 gr. to grams.
22. 3000 sq. ft. to m^2.
23. 56 bu. 3 pk. to Hl.
24. 2 ℔ 8 ℥ 1 ʒ 12 gr. to the metric system.

ARTICLE 161.—*Miscellaneous Examples.*

1. What cost 475 kilos of iron, at 4 ct. a pound?

2. What cost 6 hektometers of fence, at 15 ct. a foot?

3. What cost 40 sters of wood, at $6.25 per cord?

4. What cost 327 cubic meters of stone-work, at $5.30 per cubic yard?

5. Find the weight of a stone 4 m. long, 4 dm. wide, and 8 cm. thick, if a cubic meter weighs 3 cwt.

6. What cost a field 300 meters square, at $30 per ar?

7. What cost a pile of wood 8 m. long, 3 m. wide, and 1.5 m. high, at $1.30 per ster?

8. What must be paid for 17 quintals of wheat, at 5 ct. per kilo?

9. A field is 52 yd. wide and 92 yd. long; what is it worth, at $.35 per square meter?

10. A pile of stone is 109 ft. long, 36 ft. wide, and 9 ft. high; what is it worth at $3.80 per cubic meter?

11. Find the cost of 64.3 lb. of gold ore, at 45 ct. per gram.

12. Find the cost of a gold chain weighing 1929 grains, at 60 ct. a gram.

13. What would be the cost of 2 T. 15 cwt. 11 lb. 8 oz. of coal, at $5.60 per metric ton?

14. How long will it take a man to walk 31.0685 mi. if he can walk 6 kilometers in an hour?

PERCENTAGE.

ARTICLE 164.—*Case I.*

Find the following:

1. 28 % of 925.
2. 25 % of 624.
3. 23 % of 900.
4. $13\frac{1}{3}$ % of 744.
5. $16\frac{2}{3}$ % of 390.
6. $37\frac{1}{2}$ % of 8.8.
7. $2\frac{1}{2}$ % of 290.
8. $\frac{3}{10}$ % of 70.
9. $14\frac{2}{7}$ % of 1393.
10. 56 % of 750.
11. 5.6 % of 750.
12. $\frac{1}{9}$ % of 467.
13. 800 % of 800.
14. 900 % of $\frac{1}{900}$.

What is:

15. 22% of 1800 bu. corn?
16. 85% of 7 da.?
17. $\frac{1}{10}$% of $480?
18. 500% of 71 A.?
19. 53% of 3 T.?
20. 20% of 19 gal. 1 qt. 1 pt.?
21. 100% of 3 bu. 2 pk.?
22. $66\frac{2}{3}$% of 87 gal.?
23. $\frac{1}{2}$% of $\frac{1}{2}$?
24. $2\frac{2}{3}$% of $2\frac{1}{2}$?
25. $16\frac{2}{3}$% of $16\frac{2}{3}$?
26. 77% of 187.05?

Article 165.—*Case II.*

1. What per cent of 275 is 33?
2. What per cent of 48 is 36?
3. What per cent of 60 is 10.2?
4. What per cent of 800 is 600?
5. What per cent of 666 is 499.5?
6. What per cent of 350 is 56?
7. What per cent of 75 bu. is 33 bu.?
8. What per cent of 48 is 96?
9. What per cent of 56 is 560?
10. $172\frac{1}{2}$ is what per cent of 230?
11. 187.5 is what per cent of 150?
12. .5 is what per cent of 250?
13. 4 is what per cent of $17\frac{7}{9}$?
14. 2.3 is what per cent of $18\frac{2}{5}$?
15. .014 is what per cent of 70?
16. $29\frac{1}{5}$ is what per cent of 80?
17. 1 bu. 2 pk. is what per cent of 3 bu. 3 pk.?
18. 6 gal. 3 qt. is what per cent of 4 gal. 2 qt.?
19. What per cent of $\frac{7}{20}$ is $\frac{21}{40}$?
20. What per cent of 1 wk. is 4 da. 4 hr. 48 min.?

Article 166.—*Case III.*

1. 4.2 is 6% of what number?
2. 153 is 68% of what number?
3. $3\dot{1}5$ is $\frac{1}{2}$% of what number?
4. 6 is $3\frac{3}{7}$% of what number?
5. $14\frac{2}{5}$ is $4\frac{1}{2}$% of what number?
6. $7\frac{5}{7}$ is 150% of what number?
7. $43\frac{1}{3}$ is $11\frac{1}{9}$% of what number?
8. 35 is $46\frac{2}{3}$% of what number?

9. $1\frac{1}{3}$ is $\frac{1}{20}\%$ of what number?
10. 175 is 1000% of what number?
11. $45\frac{3}{8}$ is $18\frac{3}{4}\%$ of what number?
12. 3 bu. 3 pk. is 24% of what quantity?
13. 5 da. 5 hr. is 150% of what quantity?
14. 18 gal. is 96% of what quantity?
15. 18 T. 9 cwt. is $22\frac{1}{2}\%$ of what quantity?
16. 9 A. 40 sq. rd. is 40% of what quantity?

Article 167.—*Case IV.*

1. What number, increased by 30% of itself, equals 1690?

2. What number, diminished by 80% of itself, would give 80?

3. 777 is 40% greater than what number?
4. 777 is 40% less than what number?
5. 60 is 60% less than what number?
6. 60 is 60% more than what number?
7. What fraction, less $23\frac{1}{3}\%$ of itself, would equal $\frac{23}{40}$?
8. What number + 26% of itself, would equal $25\frac{1}{5}$?

9. What number, increased by 135% of itself, would give $15\frac{2}{3}$?

10. What number, diminished by $99\frac{1}{6}\%$ of itself, would leave 350?

11. What number, increased by $\frac{4}{5}\%$ of itself, would give 56?

12. Find a number which, added to $18\frac{3}{4}\%$ of itself, will give 36.1.

Article 169.—*Miscellaneous Examples.*

1. Sold a house for $1805, which was 5% less than the cost; find the cost.

2. In a grade of 560 pupils, 532 passed at examination; what % of the grade passed?

3. A farmer's wife had 20 dozen chickens, and $6\frac{2}{3}\%$ of them died; how many died?

4. A man had 140 hogs, which he sold at $8 apiece, and spent 32% of the money for sheep, at $2.80; how many sheep did he buy?

5. Sold a house for $1840, which was 15% more than the cost; what was the cost?

6. In a school of 950 pupils, 52% were girls; how many boys were there?

7. After 22% of a pole had been broken off by the wind, it was 117 feet high; how high was it at first?

8. A's farm is 30% of B's; if B has 160 A., how many acres has A?

9. A's farm is 30% of B's; if A has 180 A., how many acres has B?

10. A's farm is 30% of B's; if both together have 208 acres, how many has B?

11. A's farm is 30% of B's; if B has 280 acres more than A, how many has B?

12. An engine traversed 15% of a road in 18 hours, at the rate of 14 mi. 128 rd. per hour; what was the length of the entire road?

13. William is 4 ft. 7 in. high; his brother is 20% taller; what is the height of the latter?

14. A trade dollar weighs 420 grains, of which 10% is alloy; how much pure silver in 640 trade dollars?

15. The eagle contains 258 grains, of which 10% is alloy; how much alloy must be mixed with 12.9 oz. of pure gold for the coinage of eagles?

16. What will be the weight of the alloy in $1000 of gold coin?

17. What weight of pure gold must be mixed with 140 oz. Troy of alloy for coinage of gold coin?

18. 26% of a farmer's potatoes spoiled, and he still had 407 bushels of sound ones; how many bushels had he at first?

19. A ship's crew had provision for 18 weeks, but a storm destroyed 25% of it; how long would the remainder last them?

20. What number, less 40% of itself, would be equal to 40% of 930?

21. A man owed $60500; but, being unable to pay in full, settled for $44770; what % of his debt did he pay?

22. A publishing house sold 15% more books this year than last year; if the number this year is 52900 dozen, what was the number last year?

23. What number, increased by 120% of itself, would equal 803?

24. A tenant pays his landlord 3 pk. out of every 5 bu. he raises; what % is that?

25. 34000000 letters were posted, of which 170,000 were sent to the dead letter office; what % was that?

26. A field is 168 rods long, and its length is 40% greater than its breadth; find the area of the field.

27. A field is 168 rods long, and its breadth is 40% less than its length; find the area of the field.

28. A field is 168 rods wide, and its breadth is 40% less than its length; find the area of the field.

29. A farmer raised 450 bu. of oats the first year; the second year his crop was 20% greater than the first; and the third year, 25% less than the second; how many bushels did he raise in the three years?

30. I have 47 A. 40 sq. rd. of beech woods, which is 27% of my woodland; how many acres of timber have I in all?

31. Ore lost 32% in smelting, and 433 T. 10 cwt. of blooms were produced; how much ore was smelted?

Article 172.—*Commission.*

1. An agent sold a house for $3940, at $2\frac{1}{2}\%$ commission; what sum did he receive?

2. An agent sold a farm for $2750, at $1\frac{1}{5}\%$ commission; what sum did he send the owner?

3. The commission on $7500 sales amounted to $125; what was the % commission?

4. An agent sold a stock of groceries for $77500, and sent the owner $75640; what was his % commission?

5. A commission merchant sold goods at $2\frac{1}{2}\%$ commission, and sent the owner $2281.50; what commission did he retain?

6. An attorney collected a claim at $12\frac{1}{2}\%$ commission, and sent his principal $934.50; what was the amount of the claim?

7. I sold goods at auction, charging the owner 5%, and sent him $199.69; what was the amount of the sale?

8. Received $1300.50 to invest in starch, retaining my commission of 2%; what sum should I invest?

9. An agent received 5% commission for collecting 3 years' rent, and sent the owner $684; what rent was collected monthly?

10. A farmer allowed a drover 3% commission for selling his hogs, by which the drover realized $1455; what sum was sent the farmer?

11. A farmer allowed a drover 3% commission for selling his hogs, by which the farmer realized $1455; what sum did the drover retain?

12. Thompson sold for a refinery 45000 gal. molasses, at 62 ct. a gallon, and 127000 lb. sugar, at $12\frac{1}{2}$ ct. a lb.; what was his commission, at $\frac{1}{2}\%$?

13. A lawyer collected a debt of $750; he paid $14.60 expenses, and sent the creditor $724.15; what % commission did he charge?

14. Sent A $1025.10, which he invested in sugar, first deducting his commission, at 2%; sent B an equal sum, which he invested in flour, retaining $\frac{1}{2}$% commission; what was the difference in the two purchases?

15. A commission merchant, whose expenses were $7125, cleared $2127.25 profit in a year by selling goods at 2% commission; what was the amount of his sales?

ARTICLE 173.—*Trade Discount.*

1. Sold 47500 lb. of iron at $2.75 per cwt., 4% off for cash; what sum was received for it?

2. 500 cases of slates were sold; list price, $36 per case, with 60 and 60% off; what was realized?

3. Goods were bought at 10 and 10% off, for $688.50; what was the list price?

4. Goods were bought at 40, 10 and 2% off, for $1455.30; find the list price.

5. Goods were bought at 10, 2 and 40% off, for $1455.30; find the list price.

6. Bought goods at 5% off, and the discount was $16.30; what was the amount of the purchase?

7. Bought goods at 50, 10 and 2% off, and the discounts amounted to $167.70; what was the amount of the purchase?

ARTICLE 174.—*Profit and Loss.*

1. Goods costing $350 were sold at a gain of 12%; what was the gain?

2. Cost $750, gain $\frac{1}{2}$%; find the gain.

3. Cost $400, loss $7\frac{1}{2}$%; find the selling price.

4. Cost $625, loss $2\frac{2}{5}\%$; find the loss.

5. Selling price $308.70, gain 5%; find cost.

6. Cost $75, selling price $80.10; find the % of gain.

7. Cost $70, selling price $65.80; find the % of loss.

8. What % is lost by selling for $16 that which cost $20?

9. What % is gained by selling for $100 that which cost $80?

10. What % is gained on berries costing $3 per bu., and sold at 16 ct. per qt.?

11. What % is gained on indigo costing $45 a cwt., and sold at 5 ct. an oz.?

12. What % is gained on quinine costing $3 an oz., and sold at 2 ct. a grain?

13. What % is lost by selling for $84 that which cost $105?

14. What % is gained by selling for $105 that which cost $84?

15. Gained 60% by selling a cow for $60; what % would have been gained by selling her for $50?

16. Reducing the selling price 10 ct. reduced the gain 8%; find the original gain.

17. What % does the huckster gain, whose bushel-measure holds only 3 pk. 6 qt.?

18. If I sell 15 acres for as much as 18 acres cost, what % do I gain?

19. If I sell 18 acres for as much as 15 acres cost, what % do I lose?

20. Sugar was bought at $6\frac{7}{8}$ ct. a pound, and sold at $7\frac{1}{8}$ ct. a pound; what % was gained?

21. I gained $\frac{1}{2}\%$ by selling my farm for $1346.70; find the cost.

22. What was the cost of muslin, on which $11\frac{1}{9}\%$ was gained by selling it at $11\frac{1}{9}$ ct. per yd.?

23. Retaining my commission at 2%, how much can I invest in cotton for a manufacturer who sends me $8000?

24. Retaining my commission at 2%, what amount of cotton goods must I sell for the manufacturer so as to owe him $8000?

25. Bought $8000 worth of cotton; what sum must the manufacturer send me, my commission being 2%?

26. Sold $8000 worth of cotton goods; what sum must I send the manufacturer, my commission being 2%?

27. I gained 150% by selling silk at $1.50 a yard; what % would I gain by selling at $1.60 per yard?

28. A merchant sold molasses to a grocer, gaining 12%; the grocer retailed it for $4120.90, gaining 16%; what was the first cost to the merchant?

29. A bookseller gains 20% by selling a history for $2.10; if the publisher reduces his price 4%, what % will the bookseller then make if he sells at the same price as before?

30. I have a contract to deliver goods, and I gain 15% thereby; if the price to me is lowered 8%, how many % will my income be increased?

ARTICLE 175.—*Miscellaneous Examples.*

1. Jones had wheat costing $8000, which he sold to Smith at 8% profit; Smith afterward sold the wheat back to Jones for $8000; what % did Smith lose?

2. I bought goods at 40 and 40% off, paying for them $294.30; what was the list price?

3. Two farms were sold at $1800 each; one at a gain of 20%, the other at a gain of 25%; what was the difference in their cost?

4. If I sell $\frac{5}{8}$ of a farm for what $\frac{4}{5}$ of it cost, what % do I gain?

5. An architect charged $\frac{1}{2}\%$ for plans and specifications, and $1\frac{1}{4}\%$ for superintending the erection of a house; and he received in all, $151.20; what was the cost of the house, including his fees?

6. Two booksellers expended $3000 each for books, one at 25% off the list, the other at 20% off; if they sold at the list price, how much more did one receive than the other?

7. I buy goods at 20% off the list price; how many % can I take off the list price to gain 10%?

8. By selling at 25% off the list price, I gain 25%; what discount from the list price did I receive when buying?

9. A sells to B at 10% profit; B sells to C at 5% profit; if C paid $5336.10, what did the goods cost A?

10. I buy goods at 20 and 5% off the list price, and sell at 5% off the same list; what % do I gain?

11. What % will a grocer make in selling by using for a pound a weight of only $15\frac{1}{5}$ oz.?

12. What % will he lose, by using the same weight in buying?

13. How much above cost must I mark goods, so that I can take off 20%, and still gain 10%?

14. How much above cost must I mark goods, so that I can take off 10% and still gain 20%?

15. What % off the list must I receive, so that I can gain 12% by selling at 16% off the same list?

ARTICLE 177.—*Brokerage.*

1. Seventy-five shares were bought at par by a broker for an operator who paid $7515; what was the % of brokerage?

2. Bought 550 shares of stock, and my brokerage was $165; what was the %?

3. Bought 260 shares at $\frac{1}{4}\%$ brokerage, and afterwards sold them at $\frac{1}{5}\%$; what was my brokerage?

4. The brokerage on 820 shares of Michigan Southern stock was $82; what was the %?

5. Ninety-eight shares of O. and M. stock were sold at $\frac{1}{8}\%$ brokerage; what was received for selling them?

6. How many shares must be bought to make the brokerage $50, at $\frac{1}{5}\%$?

7. What is the brokerage on 8268 shares of Kentucky Central stock at $\frac{1}{6}\%$?

8. What must be paid a broker for buying 78 shares railroad stock, at $\frac{1}{3}\%$; 65 shares steamboat stock, at $\frac{1}{4}\%$; and 48 shares insurance stock, at $\frac{1}{2}\%$?

ARTICLE 178.—*Assessments and Dividends.*

1. What would be the assessment on 60 shares of mining stock, at $32\frac{1}{2}\%$?

2. An insurance company declares a dividend of $3\frac{3}{4}\%$; what will A receive, who owns 46 shares?

3. An assessment of $12\frac{1}{2}\%$ on turnpike stock realized $28000; how many shares were there?

4. What % must be assessed on 2500 shares of steamboat stock, to cover a loss of $75000?

5. What sum will the owner of 58 shares receive from a dividend of $4\frac{1}{2}\%$?

6. What assessment is made when the owner of 35 shares pays $90 more than the owner of 23 shares?

7. A $3\frac{1}{2}\%$ dividend being declared on 8000 shares of stock, $26320 were paid out; how much remained of unclaimed dividends?

8. A stock dividend of 8% was declared, after which the president had 378 shares; how many had he owned before the dividend was declared?

ARTICLE 179.—*Stock Values.*

1. What will be the cost of 40 shares of Reading R. R. stock, at $88\frac{7}{8}$?

2. What will I receive for 280 shares of Lackawanna, at $127\frac{3}{4}$?

3. What must be paid for 300 shares Chesapeake and Ohio, at $20\frac{1}{2}$, brokerage $\frac{1}{5}\%$?

4. How many shares St. Paul, at $104\frac{1}{8}$, brokerage $\frac{1}{8}\%$, can I buy for $5421?

5. My agent sold for me 720 shares Ohio and Mississippi at $$33\frac{1}{2}$, brokerage $\frac{1}{4}\%$; and with the money bought Wabash Pacific preferred, at $44\frac{3}{4}$, brokerage $\frac{1}{4}\%$; how many shares of the latter did I receive?

6. Bought Northern Pacific at $50\frac{3}{8}$, and sold at $50\frac{7}{8}$, and neither lost nor gained; what was the rate of brokerage?

7. Bought 450 shares of North Western at $133\frac{5}{8}$, brokerage, $\frac{1}{4}\%$; and sold at $133\frac{7}{8}$, brokerage $\frac{1}{4}\%$; what was my loss?

8. If gold is worth 102 in currency, what is currency worth in gold?

9. A broker buys Pacific Mail, at a brokerage of $\frac{1}{4}\%$, for which I pay $103750, including his brokerage, $625; what did he pay for that stock?

10. What sum in gold must I pay for $1440 currency, at $\frac{5}{8}\%$ discount?

11. What sum in currency must I pay for $1431 in gold, at $\frac{5}{8}\%$ premium?

12. How many shares, at 5% discount, must be given for 180 shares at 14% premium?

13. Invested $70225 in Canada Southern at 66, and sold at 68; find my gain, each brokerage being $\frac{1}{4}\%$.

ARTICLE 180.—*Stock Investments.*

1. I invest $12168 in 4% bonds, at 4% premium; what annual income will I receive from them?

2. A man bought Covington and Lexington stock at 20, and received 2% dividends annually; what % was that on his investment?

3. A capitalist invested $8214 in 4% bonds at 74; what income will that produce annually?

4. $19600 was invested in 3% bonds, giving an annual income of $840; at what rate were the bonds bought?

5. What income will arise from investing $5488 in 6% bonds at 112?

6. What income will be produced by investing $3000 in 3% bonds, at 30?

7. I had 450 6% bonds, which I sold at 112, and invested the proceeds in a 5% bond at 90; how much did I increase my income?

8. When gold declined from 137 to 120, how much less currency was received per annum for eighteen $500 6% bonds?

9. What must be paid for a 5% bond, to make a $6\frac{1}{4}$% investment?

10. What must be paid for $4\frac{1}{2}$% bonds to realize $7\frac{1}{2}$% income?

11. What must be paid for a 6% bond, to make a 5% investment?

12. What % of income is derived from U. S. 5% bonds costing 112, when gold is 105?

13. Five % mining bonds yield an income of $20\frac{5}{6}$% annually; at what rate were they bought?

14. How much less income will be obtained by investing $2185 in 4% bonds at 95, than in 5% bonds at 115?

INTEREST.

Article 183.—*Case I.*

Find the interest for One Year of:

1. \$500 at 9%.
2. \$750 at 6%.
3. \$72 at 10%.
4. \$3200 at $7\frac{1}{2}$%.
5. \$1950 at 14%.
6. \$5 at 11%.

Find the amount for One Year of:

7. \$585 at 4%.
8. \$75 at $6\frac{2}{3}$%.
9. \$8765 at $4\frac{4}{5}$%.
10. \$470 at 12%.
11. \$940 at $2\frac{1}{2}$%.
12. \$999 at 9%.

Find the interest of:

13. \$392.00 for 3 yr., at 6%.
14. \$137.50 for 6 yr., at $4\frac{4}{5}$%.
15. \$900.10 for 6 yr., at 5%.
16. \$3570.40 for 4 yr., at 10%.
17. \$876.50 for 8 yr., at $6\frac{1}{4}$%.
18. \$3888.20 for 6 yr., at $3\frac{1}{2}$%.

Find the amount of:

19. \$375.00 for 5 yr., at $6\frac{2}{3}$%.
20. \$894.50 for 4 yr., at 5%.
21. \$132.35 for 9 yr., at 4%.
22. \$9.45 for 3 yr., at 9%.
23. \$9000.00 for 10 yr., at 10%.
24. \$9.99 for 9 yr., at 9%.

Find the interest of:

25. \$270.00 for 2 mo., at 8%.
26. \$52.80 for 5 mo., at 5%.
27. \$1346.00 for 8 mo., at 9%.
28. \$876.52 for 11 mo., at $2\frac{1}{2}$%.
29. \$777.77 for 7 mo., at 7%.
30. \$300.06 for 8 mo., at $6\frac{2}{3}$%.

Find the amount of:

31. \$187.50 for 8 mo., at 9%.
32. \$945.00 for 10 mo., at 4%.
33. \$473.20 for 7 mo., at 5%.
34. \$586.20 for 9 mo., at $3\frac{1}{3}$%.
35. \$3948.80 for 8 mo., at $8\frac{3}{4}$%.
36. \$371.20 for 5 mo., at $6\frac{1}{4}$%.

Find the interest of:

37. \$600.00 for 20 da., at 9%.
38. \$825.00 for 12 da., at 6%.
39. \$347.50 for 24 da., at 5%.
40. \$72.00 for 15 da., at $6\frac{2}{3}$%.
41. \$1938.57 for 12 da., at $2\frac{2}{3}$%.
42. \$3847.21 for 11 da., at $3\frac{3}{4}$%.

Find the amount of:

43. \$4740.00 for 10 da., at 6%.
44. \$6.00 for 12 da., at 10%.
45. \$480.00 for 20 da., at 3%.
46. \$16200.00 for 16 da., at $9\frac{1}{9}$%.
47. \$387.50 for 9 da., at 8%.
48. \$474.63 for 11 da., at $7\frac{1}{5}$%.

Find the interest of:

49. \$600.00 for 2 yr. 5 mo., at 6%.
50. \$400.00 for 2 yr. 2 mo. 15 da., at $4\frac{1}{2}$%.
51. \$432.00 for 3 yr. 4 mo. 20 da., at 5%.
52. \$387.00 for 2 yr. 6 mo. 24 da., at 12%.
53. \$486.00 for 3 yr. 5 mo. 7 da., at 5%.
54. \$729.00 for 4 yr. 7 mo. 5 da., at $6\frac{2}{3}$%.
55. \$555.00 for 5 yr. 5 mo. 5 da., at 5%.
56. \$897.31 for 4 yr. 7 mo. 11 da., at 11%.

Find the amount of:

57. $400.00 for 3 yr. 6 mo., at 8%.
58. $720.00 for 4 yr. 5 mo., at 5%.
59. $750.00 for 3 yr. 2 mo. 15 da., at 4%.
60. $960.00 for 5 yr. 9 mo. 12 da., at 8%.
61. $471.50 for 3 yr. 7 mo. 12 da., at 5%.
62. $89.25 for 2 yr. 11 mo. 17 da., at 3%.
63. $1367.41 for 4 yr. 3 da., at 6%.
64. $3791.40 for 12 yr. 27 da., at 4%.

Find the interest of:

65. $360 from May 12, 1872, to July 20, 1877, at 7%.
66. $450 from July 25, 1880, to Nov. 2, 1884, at 4%.
67. $540 from Dec. 18, 1880, to May 28, 1881, at 8%.
68. $960 from May 29, 1883, to June 1, 1885, at 3%.
69. $1111.50 from Oct. 13, 1879, to May 28, 1888, at 4%.
70. $999.90 from June 8, 1878, to Dec. 1, 1881, at 8%.
71. $379.83 from March 3, 1878, to Oct. 16, 1886, at $3\frac{1}{3}$%.

Find the amount of:

72. $5200 from Sept. 21, 1873, to April 4, 1880, at 9%.
73. $540 from Oct. 21, 1865, to June 7, 1869, at 8%.
74. $480 from June 5, 1885, to Nov. 1, 1887, at 6%.
75. $600 from Nov. 27, 1801, to Aug. 6, 1803, at 3%.
76. $388.80 from July 7, 1883, to Feb. 15, 1885, at $6\frac{2}{3}$%.
77. $493.75 from June 7, 1882, to Jan. 1, 1883, at 5%.
78. $666.66 from July 21, 1881, to Dec. 20, 1883, at $7\frac{1}{2}$%.

ARTICLE 184.—*The Twelve Per Cent Method.*

Find the interest of One Dollar at 12% for:

1. 6 mo. 6 da.
2. 9 mo. 21 da.
3. 2 yr. 5 mo. 13 da.
4. 3 yr. 7 mo. 29 da.
5. 2 yr. 1 mo. 1 da.
6. 5 yr. 28 da.
7. 4 yr. 1 da.
8. 1 yr. 11 mo. 29 da.

Find the interest of One Dollar for:

9. 5 mo. 12 da., at 5%.
10. 8 mo. 12 da., at 10%.
11. 9 mo. 6 da., at 8%.
12. 9 mo. 10 da., at 9%.
13. 2 mo. 4 da., at 9%.
14. 9 mo. 9 da., at 3%.
15. 7 mo. 7 da., at 7%.
16. 4 mo. 1 da., at 6%.
17. 5 mo. 5 da., at 5%.
18. 17 da., at 6%.
19. 3 yr. 6 mo. at 4%.
20. 2 yr. 7 mo. 8 da., at 3%.
21. 1 yr. 4 da., at 8%.
22. 3 yr. 9 mo. 18 da., at 10%.
23. 7 yr. 5 da., at 6%.

Find the interest of:

24. $600.00 for 4 mo. 10 da., at 6%.
25. $720.00 for 2 yr. 5 mo. 15 da., at 5%.
26. $480.00 for 1 yr. 9 mo. 12 da., at 9%.
27. $216.00 for 7 yr. 2 mo. 24 da., at 5%.
28. $500.00 for 3 yr. 3 mo. 6 da., at 15%.
29. $360.00 for 7 yr. 7 mo. 7 da., at 7%.
30. $100.80 for 3 yr. 4 mo. 5 da., at 5%.
31. $297.60 for 3 yr. 1 mo. 15 da., at 6%.
32. $102.40 for 3 yr. 7 mo. 6 da., at 4%.
33. $105.60 for 3 yr. 3 mo. 3 da., at 4½%.
34. $487.50 for 5 yr. 6 mo. 1 da., at 3%.
35. $5000.00 for 12 yr. 1 mo. 10 da., at 8%.
36. $39.75 for 4 yr. 4 da., at 4%.
37. $7.75 for 9 mo., 19 da., at 5%.

Find the amount of:

38. $1296 for 2 yr. 6 mo. 15 da., at 5%.
39. $500.40 for 12 yr. 9 mo. 10 da., at 4%.
40. $840 for 3 yr. 12 da., at 7%.
41. $98.75 for 1 yr. 2 mo. 3 da., at 6%.
42. $5787.28 for 3 yr. 11 mo. 29 da., at 4%.
43. 30 cents for 30 years, at 30%
44. $387.45 for 3 yr. 1 da., at 4½%.

Find the interest of:

45. $390 from Aug. 15, 1870, to May 21, 1873, at 8%.

46. $5374 from May 21, 1870, to Aug. 15, 1874, at 6%.

47. $378.47 from Nov. 12, 1881, to April 6, 1884, at 7%.

Find the amount of:

48. $538.20 from Aug. 3, 1881, to Jan. 27, 1885, at 5%.

49. $588.30 from Oct. 19, 1870, to March 4, 1876, at 7%.

50. $47.38 from Dec. 5, 1790, to May 1, 1820, at $4\frac{1}{2}$%.

ARTICLE 185.—*Case II.*

Find the time in the following:

1. Principal $720, Interest $108.00, Rate 5%.

2. Principal $540, Interest $81.00, Rate 6%.

3. Principal $600, Interest $104.00, Rate 8%.

4. Principal $90, Interest $90.00, Rate 4%.

5. Principal $80, Interest $100.00, Rate 10%.

6. Principal $80, Amount $100.00, Rate 10%.

7. Principal $200, Amount $400.00, Rate 5%.

8. Principal $85, Interest $28.90, Rate 6%.

9. In what time will $750 amount to $760, at 6%?

10. In what time will $450, at 8%, earn $57.60 interest?

11. In what time will any principal double itself at 9%?

12. In what time will any principal, at 8%, increase one fourth?

13. In what time will any principal, at 6%, increase one fifth?

14. How long will it take $480 to amount to $840, at 6%?

15. How long will it take $75 to amount to $76, at 5%?

16. How long will it take $76 to amount to $95, at 4%?

17. How long will it take $76 to gain $95, at 4%?

18. In what time at 8%, will $1500 amount to $1737?

19. In what time will $550, at 8%, gain $81.40?

20. A man paid $3.50 for the use of $70 at 20%; how long had he had it?

ARTICLE 186.—*Case III.*

Find the rate per cent in the following:

1. Principal $400, interest $100, time 4 yr. 2 mo.

2. Principal $750, interest $95, time 1 yr. 7 mo.

3. Amount $315, interest $35, time 2 yr. 1 mo.

4. Amount $390, principal $360, time 1 yr. 8 mo.

5. At what per cent will any principal double itself in 12 years?

6. At what per cent will any principal increase one half in 10 years?

7. Lent $550 for 3 years, and received $682; what per cent was that?

8. At what per cent will any principal treble itself in 40 years?

9. At what per cent will $900 amount to $1000 in 1 yr. 4 mo. 20 da.?

10. A man charged $1 for the use of $40 for 1 month; what per cent was that?

11. A man charged $2 for the use of $50 for 20 days; what per cent was that?

12. Principal $990, interest $338.25, time 5 yr. 1 mo. 15 da.; find the rate.

13. $700, in 6 years, amounted to $847; find the rate per cent.

14. A $5000 U. S. bond has coupons for $50 every 3 months; what is the rate per cent?

15. A railroad mortgage bond for $500 has coupons for $11.25 every six months; what per cent did it pay?

16. A boy paid 1 cent for the use of $1 for 3 days; what rate per cent was that?

17. One loan increased one third in 3 years, another one fourth in four years; what was the difference of the rates?

18. How much must the rate be increased, to increase the interest of $560, in 4 years, $56?

19. The United States exchanged $200000000 of 6% bonds for new bonds, and saved $6000000 a year; what per cent did the new bonds bear?

20. A state owed $2600000 in 7% bonds, for which it gave new bonds, saving $65000 annnally; what rate per cent did the new bonds bear?

ARTICLE 187.—*Case IV.*

1. Interest $65, time 5 yr., rate 5%; find the principal.

2. What principal, in 4 years, at 7%, will produce $203 interest?

3. Interest $50, time 5 yr., rate 5%; find the principal.

4. What sum, in 3% bonds, will give an annual income of $735?

5. What sum, in $4\frac{1}{2}$% bonds, will yield $792 annually?

6. Interest for 5 yr. 5 mo. 13 da., at 8%, was $39.26; what was the principal?

7. Rate $4\frac{1}{2}$%, time 3 yr. 7 mo. 14 da., interest $117.36; find the principal.

8. Rate 8%, time 8 da., interest $8; find the principal.

9. What sum, at $3\frac{3}{4}$%, for 4 yr. 5 mo. 10 da., will gain $327.40?

10. What sum, at 6% interest, would gain $104.43 in 4 yr. 1 mo. 5 da.?

11. What principal will produce $613.70 interest in 10 yr. 10 da., at 10%?

12. The interest for 7 yr. 1 mo. 19 da., at 5%, is $128.45; what is the principal?

ARTICLE 188.—*Case V.*

1. What principal, in 4 yr., at 10%, will amount to $840?

2. What principal will amount to $880 in 2 yr., at 5%?

3. Rate 8%, time 3 yr. 6 mo. 20 da., amount $231.20; find the principal.

4. Amount $147.60, time 2 yr. 10 mo. 15 da., rate 8%; find the principal.

5. Amount $180, rate 5%, time 6 yr. 8 mo.; find the principal.

6. Amount $180, rate 10%, time 3 yr. 4 mo.; find the interest.

7. What sum at interest for 7 yr. 7 mo. 6 da., at $7\frac{1}{2}$%, will amount to $643.70?

8. What sum must I deposit in a savings bank, at 4%, so that at the end of 3 yr. 2 mo. 15 da. I can draw out $169.25?

9. What sum at interest 12 yr., at 12%, will amount to $481.90?

10. What principal will amount to $250.25 in 8 yr. 7 mo. 6 da., at 5%?

11. What principal would amount to $9409, in 540 yr., at 7%?

12. A loaned $990 for 6 yr. 8 mo., at 3%; what sum must B loan for 7 yr., at 5%, to realize the same amount that A does?

Article 190.—*Compound Interest.*

Find the amount, at compound interest, of:

1. \$400 for 2 yr., at 5%.

2. \$600 for 1 yr. 6 mo., at 10%.

3. \$409.60 for 3 yr., at $6\frac{1}{4}$%.

4. \$500 for 3 yr., at 8%.

Find the compound interest of:

5. \$640 for 5 yr., at 4%.

6. \$640 for 4 yr., at 5%.

7. \$500 for 2 yr. 2 mo., at 6%.

8. \$1562.50 for 4 yr., at 8%.

9. Find the interest of \$2000 for 2 yr. at 8% compound interest, payable semi-annually.

10. Find the compound interest of \$125 for 1 yr. 8 mo., at 8%.

11. Find the compound interest of \$250 for 2 yr., at 6%, payable semi-annually.

12. What is the amount of \$1000 for 1 yr. at 4% compound interest, interest payable quarterly?

13. What is the difference between simple and compound interest on \$1000, for 3 yr., at 4%?

14. What is the difference between simple and compound interest on \$1000, for 4 yr., at 3%?

Article 191.—*Annual Interest.*

1. No interest having been paid, find the amount due in 3 yr. on a note of \$500, with interest at 6%, payable annually.

2. What would be the amount of the above note, if the interest were payable semi-annually?

3. What would be the interest of $750, for 5 yr., at 6%, annually, no interest having been paid?

4. Interest having been paid for 3 yr., find the amount due on a note for $900, for 7 yr., at 4%, payable annually.

5. A note was given May 15, 1884, for $1500, with 6% interest, payable annually; what was due on this note May 15, 1889?

6. What would have been the interest on the above note Aug. 15, 1887?

7. If the interest on the above note had been paid for 3 yr., what would have been due on the note Oct. 30, 1890?

8. If the interest on the above note had been paid for 2 yr., what would be the interest due on it Dec. 10, 1888?

Article 192.—*Partial Payments.*

1. A note of $500 is dated Oct. 1, 1870. Int., 8%. Indorsed Oct. 1, 1872, $130; Oct. 1, 1874, $100. What was due Oct. 1, 1875?

2. A note of $500 is dated Oct. 1, 1870. Int., 8%. Indorsed Oct. 1, 1872, $30; Oct. 1, 1874, $200. What was due Oct. 1, 1875?

3. A note of $600 is dated Jan. 1, 1865. Int., 6%. Indorsed March 1, 1866, $30; April 1, 1867, $40; May 1, 1868, $100. What was due Jan. 1, 1870?

4. A note of $600 is dated Jan. 1, 1865. Int., 6%. Indorsed April 1, 1866, $30; March 1, 1867, $40; May 1, 1868, $100. What was due Jan. 1, 1870?

5. A note of $800 is dated May 18, 1880. Int., 5%. Indorsed March 24, 1881, $84; July 24, 1881, $42.50; June 4, 1882, $91; Oct. 4, 1883, $34. What was due Jan. 1, 1884?

6. A note of $500 is dated Sept. 19, 1870. Int., 4%. Indorsed June 10, 1871, $10; Oct. 10, 1871, $10; March 19, 1872, $40; Aug. 19, 1872, $38. What was due Feb. 13, 1874?

7. A note of $960 is dated June 23, 1880. Int., 4½%. Indorsed July 8, 1881, $50; July 23, 1882, $50; Aug. 8, 1883, $100; Jan. 1, 1884, $15. What was due June 28, 1884?

8. A note of $875 is dated May 5, 1877. Int., 6%. Indorsed Oct. 12, 1878, $50; July 13, 1879, $100; May 23, 1880, $30; June 16, 1881, $300. What was due Nov. 29, 1881?

ARTICLE 193.—*Mercantile Rule.*

1. A note of $400 is dated Dec. 16, 1882. Indorsements: March 4, 1883, $50; May 28, 1883, $50; Aug. 10, 1883, $50; Oct. 22, 1883, $50. What was due Dec. 4, 1883, interest at 6%?

2. A man owed $325 from Jan. 1, 1879. He paid March 1, 1879, $40; April 1, 1879, $40; May 1, 1879, $80; July 1, 1879, $80; Dec. 1, 1879, $80. What was due Jan. 1, 1880, reckoning 6% interest?

3. A man borrowed $600 July 1, 1881, and paid $100 on the first day of each succeeding month in that year. What was due Jan. 1, 1882, interest at 6%?

4. Borrowed $187.50 May 13, 1884. Paid $30 July 30, 1884; $35 Aug. 12, 1884; $40 Oct. 3, 1884; $50 Dec. 17, 1884; and $40 Feb. 1, 1885. What was due May 1, 1885, interest at 12%?

5. Borrowed $110 Jan. 1, 1882, and paid $10 on the first day of each succeeding month in the year. What was due Jan. 1, 1883, interest at 6%?

DISCOUNT.

ARTICLE 196.—*Bank Discount. Case I.*

Find the date when due, bank discount, and proceeds of:

1. A note of $400, dated July 8, payable in 60 days, and discounted at 6%.

2. A note of $450, dated March 18, payable in 90 days, and discounted at 8%.

3. A note of $400, dated April 18, payable in 90 days, and discounted at 9%.

4. A note of $520, dated June 16, payable in 90 days, and discounted at $4\frac{1}{2}$%.

5. A note of $540, dated June 16, payable in 3 months, and discounted at 6%.

6. A note of $80, dated Feb. 24, 1879, payable in 60 days, and discounted at 9%.

7. A note of $180, dated Jan. 15, 1881, payable in 90 days, and discounted at 4%.

8. A note of $480, dated May 19, payable in 5 months, and discounted at 3%.

9. A note of $320, dated Sept. 13, payable in 4 months, and discounted at $4\frac{1}{2}$%.

10. A note of $810, dated Jan. 16, 1883, payable in 100 days, and discounted at 8%.

11. A note of $89.40, dated July 19, payable in 40 days, and discounted at 5%.

12. A note of $13.93, dated Aug. 18, payable in 6 months, and discounted at 7%.

13. A note of $399.99, dated Oct. 16, payable in 50 days, and discounted at 10%.

14. A note of $1122.33, dated Dec. 18, 1879, payable in 90 days, and discounted at 7%.

Find the date when due, time of discount, bank discount, and proceeds of:

15. A note of $400, dated May 18, 1880, payable in 6 months, and discounted Aug. 21, 1880, at 6%.

16. A note of $500, dated July 26, 1870, payable in 90 days, and discounted Aug. 5, 1870, at 12%.

17. A note of $450, dated Jan. 19, 1880, payable in 3 months, and discounted Feb. 16, at 4%.

18. A note of $720, dated Oct. 14, 1875, payable in 90 days, and discounted Nov. 21, 1875, at 5%.

19. A note of $360, dated May 19, 1877, payable in 3 months, and discounted June 26, 1877, at 4%.

20. A note of $360, dated May 19, 1877, payable in 90 days, and discounted June 26, 1877, at 4%.

21. A note of $783.29, dated April 22, 1875, payable in 80 days, and discounted June 3, 1875, at 9%.

22. A note of $400, dated Dec. 16, 1883, payable in 4 months, with interest at 6%, and discounted Feb. 13, 1884, at 9%.

23. A note of $720, dated Jan. 13, 1846, payable in 90 days, with interest at 10%, and discounted March 3, 1846, at 9%.

24. A note of $600, dated March 2, 1884, payable in 8 mo. 7 da., with interest at 9%, and discounted July 14, 1884, at 12%.

25. A note of $450, dated Sept. 19, 1882, payable in 9 mo. 27 da., with interest at 5%, and discounted Jan. 20, 1883, at 8%.

26. A note of $5000, dated June 16, 1888, payable in 90 days, with interest at 6%, and discounted July 16, 1888, at 8%.

27. A note of $475, dated Jan. 1, 1880, payable in 4 months, with interest at 4%, and discounted Jan. 15, 1880, at 10%.

ARTICLE 197.—*Case II.*

1. The proceeds of a note, payable in 60 days, dis counted at a bank at 6%, were $494.75. Find the face of the note.

2. A note payable in 30 days was discounted in bank at 8%; the proceeds were $595.60. What was the face of the note?

3. For what sum must I make a note at 60 days, to obtain $739.50 from a bank discounting at 8%?

4. I wish to obtain $800 on a note payable in 42 days; for what sum must I give my note to a bank discounting at 4%?

5. For what sum must I give a 60-day note, to obtain $1000 from a bank discounting at 9%?

6. Sold 40 acres of land, receiving a note at 6 months, which I at once discounted in bank at 6%, receiving $2326.80; what was the price per acre?

7. I sold 20 horses, receiving a note payable in 3 months, for which I received $2338 from a bank discounting at 10%; what was the price of each horse?

8. A note dated May 3, 1885, payable in 6 months, and drawing 6% interest, was discounted in bank Sept. 27, 1885, at 9%, the proceeds being $2040.39; what was the face of the note?

ARTICLE 199.—*True Discount.*

What is the present worth and discount, at 6%, of:

1. $450.00, due in 3 yr. 4 mo.?

2. $900.00, due in 7 yr. 4 mo.?

3. $685.00, due in 6 yr. 2 mo.?

4. $810.00, due in 2 yr. 1 mo.?

5. $359.00, due in 3 yr. 3 mo. 10 da.?

6. $448.70, due in 1 yr. 1 mo. 20 da.?

7. $622.30, due in 8 yr. 10 da.?

8. $373.10, due in 5 yr. 6 mo. 15 da.?

9. $616.21, due in 7 yr. 9 mo. 13 da.?

10. $888.00, due in 8 yr. 8 mo. 8 da.?

Find the true discount, at 6%, of:

11. $961.00, due in 4 yr.

12. $427.00, due in 3 yr. 8 mo.

13. $262.80, due in 1 yr. 7 mo.

14. $490.10, due in 4 yr. 3 mo. 10 da.

15. $161.21, due in 2 yr. 6 mo. 9 da.

16. $3836.90, due in 2 yr. 1 mo. 21 da.

17. $936.43, due in 6 yr. 11 mo. 23 da.

18. $700.00, due in 9 mo. 13 da.

19. $1000.10, due in 27 da.

20. A bill of merchandise amounted to $364, at 4 months time, or 4% off for cash; if money is worth 12% per annum, how much will the buyer gain by paying cash?

21. What should be paid May 10, 1884, for a debt of $264.20, due Jan. 15, 1886, money being worth 6%?

22. A debt of $1368 is due in 2 years: how much more should be given for it, if money is worth 7%, than if money is worth 10%?

23. A balance of $514.80 is due: one third in 1 yr., one third in 2 yr., and the balance in 3 yr. What sum should pay it now, money being worth 10%?

24. What debt could be settled by paying $561.60 cash, and giving two notes, of $561.60 each, one payable in 6 mo., and the other in 1 yr., money being worth 8%?

25. A lot was bought for $1800, one third cash, one third in 1 yr., and one third in 2 yr., with interest at 6%. If money is worth 10%, what sum in cash should have been paid for the lot?

ARTICLE 201.--*Domestic Exchange.*

1. New York exchange being $\frac{1}{5}\%$ premium, what must be paid for a sight draft on that place for $4700?

2. What must be paid for a sight draft on San Francisco for $730, at $\frac{1}{2}\%$ discount?

3. Find the cost of a sight draft on Philadelphia for $4950, at $\frac{1}{20}\%$ premium.

4. Find the cost of a sight draft on Toronto for $1360, at $\frac{1}{4}\%$ discount.

5. What must be paid for a sight draft on Milwaukee for $373.84, at $\frac{1}{2}\%$ premium?

6. What will be the cost of a sight draft on Santa Fe for $2377.50, at $\frac{3}{4}\%$ discount?

7. What must be paid for a draft on New York for $1000, payable in 30 days, exchange at par, and interest 6%?

8. What must be paid for a draft on Boston for $1000, payable in 30 days, exchange being at $\frac{1}{2}\%$ discount, and interest 6%?

9. Find the cost of a 30-day draft on Savannah for $2400, exchange at $\frac{1}{8}\%$ discount, interest at 8%.

10. What cost a 60-day draft on Cleveland for $1500, exchange at $\frac{1}{5}\%$ premium, interest at 8%?

11. What was the face of a sight draft for which $796 was paid, exchange at $\frac{1}{2}\%$ discount?

12. What was the face of a 60-day draft on New York, for which $792 was paid, exchange being $\frac{1}{20}\%$ premium, and interest 6%?

13. What was the face of a 90-day draft on Mobile costing $1857.83, exchange being at $\frac{1}{4}\%$ premium, interest at 8%?

14. $1000 was paid for a sight draft on Detroit, exchange at $\frac{1}{4}\%$ discount; what was the face of the draft?

Article 202.—*Foreign Exchange.*

1. What must be paid for a bill of exchange on London for £796 5s., exchange being at $4.84?

2. What will be the cost of a bill of exchange on Edinburgh for £283 15 s., exchange being at $4.88?

3. How large a bill on Manchester can be bought for $5314.41, exchange being at $4.86?

4. How large a bill on Marseilles can be bought for $818.75, exchange being at 5 fr. 16 centimes?

5. What cost a bill on Havre for 5047 francs, exchange being at 5 fr. 15 centimes?

6. What cost a bill on Munich for 4800 reichsmarks, exchange being 96 cents for 4 reichsmarks?

7. What cost a bill on Dresden for 3742 reichsmarks, exchange being at $.98?

8. How large a bill on Stuttgart can be bought for $1000, exchange being at $.965?

INSURANCE.

Article 204.—*Fire and Marine Insurance.*

1. What must be paid for $4800 insurance on a dwelling at $\frac{7}{10}\%$?

2. A factory is valued at $18000; what must be paid for insuring $\frac{7}{9}$ of its value, at $\frac{3}{5}\%$?

3. What will be the premium for insuring $\frac{2}{3}$ of a steamer valued at $36800, at $\frac{3}{8}\%$?

4. A store is valued at $15000, and the contents at $11000; what will be the premium for insuring $\frac{3}{4}$ of the value of the store, at $\frac{2}{5}\%$, and $\frac{3}{5}$ of the value of the contents, at $\frac{1}{4}\%$?

5. Insured a mill for $\frac{3}{4}$ of its value, at $\frac{5}{8}\%$, the premium being $41.25; what was the value of the mill?

6. A merchant has goods valued at $46000, and pays $184 for insurance at $\frac{1}{2}\%$; what part of the value is insured?

7. I insured $\frac{2}{3}$ of a factory, valued at $35400, and $\frac{3}{4}$ of the stock, valued at $41200, paying $436; what was the rate of insurance?

ARTICLE 205.—*Life Insurance.*

1. What must be paid yearly for $6000 life insurance, the premium being $32.18 per $1000?

2. A man paid $382.50 for 5 years insurance on a life policy for $3000; what was the company's annual rate per $1000?

3. A father, at the age of 50, insures his life for $5000, at $47.18 per $1000 annually; his son, aged 21, insures his life for the same sum, at an annual rate of $19.89. If each lives to the age of 71, which will pay the greater sum for insurance, and how much more than the other will he pay?

4. An endowment policy for $2000 costs $107.32 per $1000 annually, for 10 years; what would be the amount of the ten payments, allowing simple interest at 6%?

TAXES.

ARTICLE 208.—*To fix the Rate of Taxation.*

1. A tax of $625000 is to be levied upon a valuation of $250000000; what will be the rate of taxation?

2. The valuation in a certain city being $165000000, and the amount of tax to be levied $3795000, what will be the rate of taxation?

3. The expense of building a school-house was estimated at $6600, to be raised by a tax of $2\frac{1}{2}$ mills on $1; what is the valuation?

4. $3471250 is to be levied upon a valuation of $571273600; what will be the rate to the hundredth of a mill?

Article 209.—*Apportionment of Taxes.*

1. $3400 is to be assessed upon a town; the valuation is $1269531.25, and 100 persons pay $1.50 each for poll tax; find the rate of levy, and construct a table to $9000.

With the above levy, find the tax to be paid by the following persons:

2. William Smith, property $7500, 2 polls.

3. G. W. Wright, property $5610, 1 poll.

4. Ruth Williams, property $6495.

5. Seth Cooper, property $1698, 1 poll.

6. William Simpson, property $1627, 2 polls.

7. Enoch Ayres, property $1240, 3 polls.

8. Matthew Wilson, property $990, 1 poll.

9. The tax to be raised in a city is $4117136; the taxable property is valued at $162580364; find the rate of levy to one thousandth of a mill, and construct a tax table to $90000.

With the above table, find the amount of tax to be paid by:

10. Eli Wiggins, property $874.

11. Marion Thompson, property $194560.

12. Timothy Stewart, property $1418720.

13. Silas Burns, property $84.

14. John Shaw, property $848.

15. Jonas Newcome, property $8484.

16. Emmanuel Goldsmith, property $84848.

ARTICLE 211.—*Internal Revenue.*

1. The tax on proof spirits is 70 cents a gallon; what would be the tax on a barrel of 48 gallons?

2. What would be the tax on a barrel of alcohol containing 52 gallons, 50% above proof?

3. What would be the postage on a book weighing 1 lb. $7\frac{1}{4}$ oz., at the rate of 1 cent for each 2 ounces or fraction thereof?

4. What would be the postage on a letter weighing 1 lb. $7\frac{1}{4}$ oz., at the rate of 2 cents for every ounce or fraction thereof?

5. What would be the postage on a package weighing 1 lb. $7\frac{1}{4}$ oz., at the rate of 1 cent for each ounce, or fraction thereof?

6. What would be the postage on 15 letters, each weighing $\frac{1}{4}$ oz.?

7. What would be the postage on 15 packages, each weighing $\frac{1}{4}$ oz.?

8. What would be the postage on 15 books, sent separately, each weighing $\frac{1}{4}$ oz.?

9. What would be the postage on 2 dozen books, each weighing 2 lb.?

10. The tax on pencils is $3 per 1000; what must be paid for 216 boxes, containing 50 each?

11. The tax on small ornaments is 50 cents per 1000; what will be the tax on 100 bundles, containing 200 small ornaments each?

12. What will be the tax on 3 T. 13 cwt. of sugar, at 8 cents a pound?

13. A firm paid $30 postage on 2-oz. letters; how many were sent?

14. Paid $30 postage on 8-oz. books; how many were sent?

ARTICLE 212.—*Duties or Customs.*

1. What is the duty on 5 T. 3 cwt. of flour sulphur, at $20 per ton?

2. What is the duty on 23040 steel pens, at 12 ct. a gross?

3. Find the duty on 1000000 lb. of iron ore, at 75 ct. per ton.

4. Find the duty on 72000 shingles, at 35 ct. per 1000.

5. A cask of borax weighs 572 lb.; allowing 6% for tare, what will be the duty at 5 ct. per lb.?

6. Imported an invoice of silk, costing $3739.30; what was the duty at 50%?

7. Imported 450 boxes raisins: gross weight of each, 25 lb., tare 8%; find the duty at 2 ct. per lb.

8. What will be the duty on 2 dozen repeating rifles, costing in England £5 5 s. each, the duty being 25%, and the pound quoted at $4.88?

9. Find the duty on 46 T. Bessemer steel, at 45%; cost per ton, £6 10 s., and the pound being $4.84.

10. Imported 10 cases woolen cloths, weighing 272 lb. each; tare, 5%; cost, 90 ct. per lb. What is the duty, at 35 ct. per lb. and 40% ad valorem?

11. Find the duty on 72 crates of queensware costing £73 6 s. 8 d. per crate, commission $3\frac{1}{3}$%, duty 55%, the pound = $4.86.

12. Imported 100 cases German toys, costing 180 marks per case, commission $3\frac{1}{3}$%; find the duty at 35%, the mark being 23.6 ct.

13. Bought 100 dozen umbrellas at £3 6 s. per dozen; what was the duty at 50%, £1 = $4.868?

14. Bought 18 bales Turkey sponge, weighing 130 lb. each, at 5 s. 4 d. a lb.; find the duty at 20%, £1 = $4.86.

RATIO.

Article 214.

What is the ratio of:

1. 140 to 7?
2. $37\frac{1}{2}$ to $3\frac{3}{4}$?
3. 56 to $2\frac{1}{3}$?
4. 100 to 17?
5. 112 to $17\frac{1}{2}$?
6. 18 to 171?
7. $18\frac{3}{4}$ to $7\frac{1}{2}$?
8. $40\frac{4}{5}$ to $25\frac{1}{2}$?
9. $7\frac{3}{7}$ to 26?
10. 1000 to $35\frac{5}{7}$?
11. $88\frac{1}{2}$ to $19\frac{2}{3}$?
12. 87 to $23\frac{1}{5}$?
13. $41\frac{2}{3}$ to $6\frac{3}{4}$?
14. $7\frac{7}{9}$ to 175?
15. $\frac{8}{9}$ to 18?
16. $\frac{4}{7}$ to 100?
17. 4.2 to .07?
18. $13\frac{3}{11}$ to 4.5?
19. 9 A. to 18 sq. rd.?
20. 7 mi. 10 rd. to 30 rd.?
21. 1 bu. 1 pk. 1 qt. to 1 qt. 1 pt.?
22. 5 lb. 4 oz. to 7 cwt.?
23. 3 weeks to 9 hr.?
24. 4 sq. mi. to 13 A.?

Article 215.

Find the antecedent in the following:

1. Consequent, 35; ratio, 20.
2. Consequent, 280; ratio, 100.
3. Consequent, $17\frac{1}{2}$; ratio, 19.
4. Consequent, $\frac{8}{9}$; ratio, $\frac{2}{7}$.
5. Consequent, $8\frac{2}{5}$; ratio, $6\frac{1}{4}$.
6. Consequent, $3\frac{4}{5}$; ratio, 4.6.
7. Consequent, 4.3; ratio, $6\frac{1}{2}$.
8. Consequent, 15 sq. mi.; ratio, .008.
9. Consequent, 2 ft. 9 in.; ratio, $4\frac{2}{3}$.
10. Consequent, 3 wk. 3 da. 12 hr.; ratio, $1\frac{4}{7}$.

Article 216.

Find the consequent in the following:

1. Antecedent, 137.2; ratio, 7.
2. Antecedent, 3.4; ratio, .08.
3. Antecedent, $4\frac{1}{2}$; ratio, $6\frac{3}{4}$.
4. Antecedent, $\frac{2}{5}$; ratio, $\frac{8}{15}$.
5. Antecedent, 4 bu. 1 qt.; ratio, 6.
6. Antecedent, 13 gal. 3 qt.; ratio, .05.
7. Antecedent, 14 hr. 40 min.; ratio, 30.
8. Antecedent, 13.2 liters; ratio, .08.

Article 217.

Find the value of the following compound ratios:

1. $\left\{\begin{array}{l} 14 : 8. \\ 18 : 7. \end{array}\right.$

2. $\left\{\begin{array}{l} 14 : 4. \\ 16 : 6. \\ 18 : 8. \end{array}\right.$

3. $\left\{\begin{array}{l} \text{16 bu. : 28 bu.} \\ \text{175 A. : 180 A.} \end{array}\right.$

4. $\left\{\begin{array}{l} \text{27 da. : 22 da.} \\ \text{77 horses : 63 horses.} \end{array}\right.$

5. $\left\{\begin{array}{l} 1.2 : .3. \\ 3\frac{1}{3} : \frac{2}{3}. \end{array}\right.$

6. $\left\{\begin{array}{l} \text{1 wk. : 8 hr.} \\ \text{16 men : 2 men.} \end{array}\right.$

7. $\left\{\begin{array}{l} 6.4 : 8. \\ 4.5 : 9. \\ 396 : 7.2. \end{array}\right.$

8. $\left\{\begin{array}{l} \text{6 men : 2 men.} \\ \text{8 da. : 16 da.} \\ \text{12 yd. : 2 yd.} \end{array}\right.$

Article 219.—*Reduction of Ratios.*

Reduce the following ratios to their lowest terms:

1. 80 : 64.
2. 259 : 111.
3. 77 : 33.
4. 999 : 99.
5. 9999 : 4545.
6. 648 : 486.
7. 388 : 1261.
8. 329 : 517.
9. 48 da. : 36 da.
10. 9 wk. : 2 da. 1 hr.
11. 22 gal.: 1 gal.: 1 qt.: 1 pt.
12. 8 oz. : 3 lb. Av.

ARTICLE 220.—*Clearing Ratios of Fractions.*

Clear the following ratios of fractions:

1. $7\frac{7}{8} : 4\frac{4}{5}$.

2. $16\frac{3}{4} : 2\frac{1}{3}$.

3. $6\frac{3}{4} : 2\frac{3}{5}$.

4. $4\frac{4}{9} : 3\frac{2}{7}$.

Express the following ratios in their simplest forms:

5. $5\frac{5}{9} : 7\frac{1}{2}$.

6. $9\frac{1}{3} : 8\frac{3}{4}$.

7. $16\frac{8}{9} : 6\frac{1}{3}$.

8. $11\frac{1}{5} : 9\frac{1}{3}$.

PROPORTION.

ARTICLE 223.—*To find Missing Terms.*

1. 9 : 12 : : 51 : what?

2. 12 : 16 : : what : 28?

3. 38 : what : : 57 : 12?

4. 36 : what : : 27 : 72?

5. $27\frac{1}{2} : 37\frac{1}{2}$: : what : $18\frac{3}{4}$?

6. 8 : 9 : : 73 : what?

7. 8 : 9 : : what : 73?

8. 8 : what : : 9 : 73?

9. What : 8 : : 9 : 73?

10. 5 qt. : 2 pk. 2 qt. : : 24 : what?

11. $\left.\begin{matrix} 7 : \text{what} \\ 8 : 3\frac{1}{2} \end{matrix}\right\} : : 26 : 45\frac{1}{2}$?

12. $\left.\begin{matrix} 11\frac{1}{2} : 7\frac{2}{3} \\ 16\frac{2}{3} : \text{what} \end{matrix}\right\} : : 50 : 8$?

13. 5 gal. : 2 gal. 1 pt. : : $\left\{\begin{matrix} 8 : 6 \\ 18 : \text{what?} \end{matrix}\right.$

14. $\left.\begin{matrix} 3.4 : 5.1 \\ 8\frac{2}{5} : 4.9 \end{matrix}\right\}$: : what : 3 cwt. 1 lb.?

ARTICLE 224.—*Simple Proportion.*

1. If 17 A. cost $205, what will 85 A. cost?

2. If 46 bu. of wheat cost $37.20, what will 115 bu. cost?

3. If $1000 will buy 160 hogs, what will 1000 hogs cost?

4. What cost 210 brooms, at $2.60 per doz.?

5. Seventy horses cost $11000; at that rate, how many can be bought for $16500?

6. If a lot 46 feet front is worth $975, what would a lot 207 feet front be worth?

7. If 49 yd. of silk cost $50.40, what will 126 yd. cost?

8. If 27 gal. of milk cost $31.50, what will 84 gal. cost?

9. If a telegram of 40 words costs $1.70, what should be paid for a telegram of 76 words for the same distance?

10. If 15 dozen brooms cost $41.40, what will 800 brooms cost?

11. If $47 will buy 1750 lb. of iron, what will 2450 lb. cost?

12. If a car travels 506 mi. in 44 hr., how long would it require to go 1587 mi.?

13. A man has corn to feed 54 horses 38 weeks; how long would it last 57 horses?

14. A laborer works for $1.25 a day, and is paid in potatoes at 55 ct. a bu.; how many bushels will he receive for 50 days work?

15. Ten pipes fill a reservoir in 64 hr.; if 2 pipes were closed, how long would it take the others to fill it?

16. A man walks $\frac{4}{5}$ mi. in $\frac{4}{11}$ hr.; how far can he walk in $\frac{16}{33}$ da.?

17. If a gallon of vinegar costs as much as 1 gal. 2 qt. of milk, how much vinegar should be given for 1 gal. of milk?

18. A watch loses 1 min. 24 sec. in a week; how much will it lose in 4 da. 12 hr.?

19. If 2 T. 5 cwt. of hay cost $25.20, how much can be bought for $84?

20. A crew of 96 men have provisions for 72 days; how many men must desert, that the remainder may have enough for 108 days?

21. A man borrows 256 bu. of oats, worth 35 ct. a bu.; how much should he return, the price having fallen 3 ct. a bu.?

22. How many bu. of oats, at 53 ct., should be given for 940 bu. 3 pk. of wheat, at 71 ct.?

23. When flour is $10 a bl. the 10 ct. loaf weighs 1 lb. 12 oz.; what should it weigh when flour is $8 a bl.?

24. A man makes 5800 steps, of 33 in. each; if his son's steps are 4 in. shorter, how many steps must he make in walking the distance with his father?

25. If a locomotive burns 200 bu. 1 pk. of coal in running $44\frac{1}{2}$ mi., how far can it run with 227 bu. 1 pk.?

26. If a man can cut 12 C. of wood in 55 hr., how much can he cut in 22 days, working 10 hr. a day?

27. If 580 sheep can graze on 72 A. 80 sq. rd. of pasture, how much will be required for 850 sheep?

28. If a yard-stick casts a shadow 4 ft. long, when held upright, how high is the tree whose shadow is 220 ft. long?

29. Bought 120 chairs, at 70 ct. apiece; had the cost been 10 ct. more apiece, how many could I have bought?

30. Had the cost been 10 ct. less apiece, how many could I have bought?

31. Had I bought 30 more for the same money, what would each have cost?

32. Had I bought 20 less for the same money, what would each have cost?

33. If a man earns $402 in $\frac{5}{8}$ of a year, how much can he earn in $\frac{5}{6}$ of a year?

34. What cost $37\frac{1}{2}$ yd. of cloth, if $\frac{3}{4}$ yd. is worth $\$\frac{4}{5}$?

35. How long should I lend a man $880, to compensate for a loan of $660 for 60 days?

36. If .68 yd. of cloth is worth $1.16, find the value of .85 yd.

37. If the composition for a book of 336 pages cost $450.52, what will be the cost of composition for a similar book of 504 pages?

38. If a hog weighing 325 lb. is worth $23.40, what should be given for one weighing 425 lb.?

39. How many men can do in $5\frac{1}{4}$ days as much work as 364 men can do in $8\frac{1}{4}$ da.?

40. What sum will pay freight on 6 T. 15 cwt., as far as 3 cwt. 25 lb. can be carried for $1.04?

41. A man was charged $132 for silk, but discovered that it had been measured with a measure $34\frac{1}{2}$ inches long, instead of 1 yd.; what was the true bill?

42. Eight cu. ft. of water weigh 5 cwt.; what will be the capacity of a vessel containing 4 T. 7 cwt. 50 lb. of water?

43. A grocer's weights are deficient at the rate of 1 oz. in 2 lb.; what is the true weight of a parcel sold for 240 lb.?

44. At 10 ct. a lb. (false), what will he charge for sugar, the true weight of which is 155 lb.?

45. If $\frac{5}{6}$ ℥ make 160 pills, how many can be made from 3 ℥ 2 ℈?

46. A town of 4750 inhabitants increased in population 950 in one year; at the same rate, what will be the increase the next year?

47. If I sell my horses at a gain of 36%, I clear $4560; what will be my profit if I sell at 63% gain?

48. If muslin $27\frac{1}{2}$ in. wide is worth 11 ct. a yd., how much should be paid per yd. for muslin 4 ft. $2\frac{1}{2}$ in. wide?

49. If a school with 750 pupils sends 80 to the high school, how many should a school of 1800 pupils send?

50. The fore wheel of a wagon is 17 ft. 6 in. in circumference; and the hind wheel, 20 ft. 5 in.; how many revolutions will the fore wheel make while the hind wheel makes 756?

51. How many revolutions will the hind wheel make while the fore wheel makes 756?

52. A mining company employed 580 miners, the weekly pay-roll of wages being $630.75; what would be the weekly wages after 40 men were discharged?

53. A man measuring a road gave the length at 840 yards, the true length being 825 yards; how much too short was his yard-stick?

54. A clock loses 1 min. 12 sec. in 48 hr.; how much will it lose in 6 da. 8 hr.?

55. A steamer goes 13 mi. 240 rd. per hour; a sailing vessel, $7\frac{1}{3}$ mi. per hour; how long will the latter be on a voyage which the steamer could perform in 73 hr. 12 min.?

56. If a county, having 350000 inhabitants, is entitled to 8 representatives, how many should be sent by a county whose population is 787500?

57. A man, whose farm is valued at $7930, is taxed $14.78 for a bridge; what will be levied upon his neighbor, whose farm is valued at $8947?

58. With a certain machine a power of 90 pounds can move a weight of 3 T. 6 cwt.; what weight can be moved by a power of 3 cwt. applied to the machine?

59. My gain on $4760 sales was $116.38; at the same rate, what will be my gain on $15928 sales?

ARTICLE 225.—*Compound Proportion.*

1. If 5 men in 6 da. earn $49.50, how much can 8 men earn in 9 da.?

2. If 6 men in 8 da. earn $78, how many men can be hired for 4 da. for $117?

3. If 8 men in 12 da. earn $120, how long can 14 men be hired for $210?

4. Twelve lots, each 15 rd. long and 12 rd. wide, cost $2400; at the same rate, what would be the price of 18 lots, each 12 rd. long and 10 rd. wide?

5. How many lots, 15 rd. by 7 rd., could be bought for $2800?

6. If lots are 9 rd. wide, how long should they be so that 22 lots should be worth $3960?

7. How wide must the lots be, so that 15, each 15 rd. long, may be worth $2700?

8. Interest for 6 mo. 10 da., at 6%, was $72.20; what would it have been for 3 mo. 24 da., at 8%?

9. A man bought 18 cows with his commission on $21600 sales, at $2\frac{1}{2}$%; how many could he buy with the commission on $44000 sales at $1\frac{1}{2}$%?

10. If 20 bu. of potatoes can be raised on a lot 20 yd. long and 20 yd. wide, how many bushels can be raised on another lot 10 rd. long and 10 rd. wide?

11. If a railroad carries 4500 pounds 1800 miles for $27, how far can 3000 pounds be carried for $11?

12. If 4000 books, of 384 pages each, require 200 reams of paper, how many similar books, of 324 pages each, can be printed from 216 reams of paper?

13. If 9 dogs catch 9 rabbits in 9 min., how many rabbits will 12 dogs catch in 12 min.?

14. If 10 cats catch 10 rats in 10 min., how many cats must be employed to catch 18 rats in 18 min.?

15. If a merchant's profits are $7380 for 9 mo., when he is clearing 8% a year, what will be his gain for 7 mo., when he is clearing 10% a year?

16. If the 10 ct. loaf weigh 2 lb. 3 oz., when flour is $9.75 per barrel, what should the 8 ct. loaf weigh, when flour is $6.50 per barrel?

17. If carpets cost $810 for a house of 12 rooms, each 15 by 18 feet, what will the same kind of carpet cost for a house of 10 rooms, each 12 by 15 feet?

18. What is the ratio of the glazing of two houses: the first contains 15 rooms, with four windows each; each window has 2 sashes; each sash, 6 panes, 11 by 16 in.; the second house has 11 rooms; each room, 3 windows; each window, 2 sashes; each sash, 2 panes, 15 by 32 in.?

19. A farmer sold his potatoes for $147.84; the next year he planted a strip which was longer in the ratio of 5 to 4, but narrower in the ratio of 3 to 4; crops were more abundant in the ratio of 10 to 9, and prices were lower in the ratio of 7 to 8; what should he receive for his crop the second year?

20. A road 300 rd. long and 40 ft. wide, was dug 2 ft. 6 in. deep by 40 men in 5 days, of 10 hr. each; how many men must be employed to make a road 5 mi. long, 2 rd. wide, dug 3 ft. deep, in 16 days, of 11 hr. each?

21. If the freight of 20 hogsheads of sugar, each weighing 13 cwt. 20 lb., is $44.88 for 65 miles, what should be the freight on 250 barrels of sugar, each weighing 2 cwt. 8 lb., for 66 mi.?

22. If a floor 33 ft. 9 in. by 26 ft. 8 in. cost $22.50, what will be the cost of a floor 39 ft. 6 in. by 29 ft. 4 in.?

23. How many flag-stones, each 88 in. long and 20 in. wide, will be required to replace a pavement containing 8800 bricks, each 8 in. long and 4 in. wide?

24. If 5 men can dig a cellar 48 ft. long, 20 ft. wide, and 9 ft. deep, in 8 da., of 8 hr. each, how many men must be employed to dig a cellar 60 ft. long, 27 ft. wide, and 10 ft. deep, in 10 days, of 10 hr. each?

25. If an engine, running 18 mi. 240 rd. in 40 min., can carry a train from one station to the next in 2 hr. 27 min., how long would the same distance take a freight train moving 8 mi. 240 rd. in 1 hr. 40 min.?

26. If the interest of a certain sum for 3 yr. 6 mo., at 6%, is $266.70, what will be the interest of a sum $\frac{6}{5}$ as large, for 6 yr. 3 mo., at 10%?

27. A certain excavation costs $75. What would be the cost of an excavation 20% wider, 25% deeper, and 50% longer?

ARTICLE 226.—*Partnership.*

1. Two partners put in $7500 and $4500; they lose $1500; how should this loss be apportioned?

2. A's capital was $850; B's, $750. At the end of one year they have $2000; how should it be divided?

3. A contributes $90; B, $80; C, $130; they lose $210; what is the loss of each?

4. Divide 3948 into 2 parts, which shall be to each other as 3 to 4.

5. Divide 3948 into 2 parts, which shall be to each other as $\frac{1}{3}$ to $\frac{1}{4}$.

6. Divide 3948 into 3 parts, which shall be to each other as 3, 4, and 5.

7. Divide 3948 into 3 parts, which shall be to each other as $\frac{1}{3}$, $\frac{1}{4}$, and $\frac{1}{5}$.

8. Divide 19.56 into 2 parts, which shall be to each other as 7.9 and 8.4.

9. Divide 3.925 into 2 parts, which shall be to each other as 28 and $\frac{1}{28}$.

10. A has 60 A. 120 sq. rd.; B, 81 A. They join these for a pasture, for use of which they receive $75.60; how should this be divided?

11. A father left his three sons the following sums: $750, $675, and $375; but his property amounts to only $1440; how should this be divided?

12. A society of 55 musicians charter a car for $44, to carry them to Columbus. If they receive a second society of 33 to go with them, how should the expense be divided?

13. A's lot is 80 ft. front; B's, 75 ft.; C's, 100 ft.; D's, 55 ft.; and E's, 85 ft. How much should each contribute, to raise $50, to pay for watering the street?

Article 227.—*Bankruptcy.*

1. A bankrupt owes $46000; his property sells for $20470, and the expenses are $1150; how much will he pay on the dollar?

2. A bankrupt's assets are $16800, his liabilities are $55000, and the expenses of settlement are $2500; how much will he pay on the dollar?

3. A speculator fails, owing $250000; the assignee sells his real estate for $23000, and his personal property for $18000, and charges $3500 for fees and expenses; what will a creditor receive for a claim of $940?

Article 228.—*General Average.*

1. A ship is valued at $63000; and its cargo, at $32000; what will be the general average on a loss of $1140?

2. A shipped 300 barrels of flour; B, 240; and C, 100 barrels; 160 barrels were lost in a storm. How much of this loss will fall on each?

3. Goods valued at $800 were thrown overboard from a ship valued as $10000, with a cargo valued at $15600: how much will A lose, his shipment being valued at $800?

4. A ship is valued at $40000; and the cargo, at $35600. During a storm, A's shipment, valued at $1890, is washed overboard; how much will he receive for it?

ARTICLE 229.—*Partnership with Time.*

1. A invested $400 for 4 mo.; B, $600 for 6 mo.; how should they divide the $780 gained?

2. A and B were to receive $152.10 for removing a bank of earth. A furnished 10 carts 8 days; and B, 12 carts 6 days. How much should each receive?

3. A and B each put in $1000 at the beginning of the year, but at the end of 6 mo. A took out $500; they gained $2310 during the year. How should it be divided?

4. A put in $500 for 4 mo.; B, $600 for 3 mo.; C, $250 for 4 mo.; they lose $576. What will be the loss of each?

5. A and B were in partnership 4 mo. A had $2000 in the whole time; B put in $1000 at the beginning of each month; the gain was $414. How should it be divided?

6. A pastured 30 cows 7 mo.; B, 50 cows 9 mo.; the expense was $217.80; How should it be divided?

7. A commenced business with $3000; 6 months after, B joined him with $3600; 4 years from commencement, they had gained $4305. What was the share of each?

8. A and B were partners for 10 mo. A put in $700 at first, and two months afterward $200 more; B put in $500 at first, and three months afterward $500 more. A's loss was $215; what was B's loss?

ARTICLE 230.—*Equation of Payments.*

Find the average time in the following:

1. $600, due in 3 mo.; $400, in 5 mo.; and $500, due in 2 mo.

2. $750, in 3 mo.; $750, in 5 mo.; and $750, in 7 mo.

3. $30, in 8 mo.; $20, in 4 mo.; and $40, in 10 mo.

4. $60, due now; $60, in 3 mo.; and $60, in 9 mo.

5. $700, due now; $500, in 10 da.; and $700, in 20 da.

6. $60, due in 60 da.; $90, in 90 da.; and $60, due in 120 da.

7. $200, due in 4 da.; and $5000, due in 30 da.

8. $70, due in 7 da.; $80, due in 8 da.; and $90, in 9 da.

9. Bought goods as follows: May 7, $10; May 9, $15; May 20, $34. Find the equated time.

10. Bought $420 worth of goods: 1 seventh cash, 2 sevenths in 7 mo., balance in 14 mo. Find the equated time.

11. Bought the following bills: July 17, $300; Aug. 26, $700. Find the equated time.

12. Bought: April 13, $400; May 1, $550; May 7, $350; May 14, $700. Find the equated time.

13. Bought: Aug. 7, $300; Aug. 28, $900; Sept. 7, $900; Sept. 28, $300. Find the equated time.

14. Bought: March 5, $500; April 1, $400; April 14, $200; May 1, $600. Find the equated time.

15. $700 was due Jan. 1; $900, May 1; and $400, July 1. Find the equated time.

16. Bought goods as follows: May 19, 1884, at 6 mo., $1360; June 12, 1884, at 4 mo., $2168; July 25, 1884, at 6 mo., $988; Aug. 3, 1884, at 4 mo., $1650. Find the equated time.

ARTICLE 232.—*Average.*

Find the average of the following:

1. 15 lb. of sugar, at 9 ct. a lb.; and 10 lb., at 14 ct. a lb.

2. 10 oz. of gold, at $\$18\frac{1}{2}$ an oz.; and 20 oz. of silver, at 95 ct. an oz.

3. 15 lb. of honey, at $.40 a lb.; and 10 lb. of sugar, at 5 ct. a lb.

4. 30 gal. of syrup, at $2.22 a gal., diluted with 7 gal. of water.

5. 7 gal. of citrus juice, at $2.40 a gal.; 2 qt. of corn syrup at 15 ct. a qt.; and 2 gal. of water.

6. A man walked 2 mi. in 20 min. 35 sec., and then $4\frac{1}{2}$ mi. in 40 min. 30 sec.; find the average time for 1 mile.

7. The barometer, at 5 observations, stood 29.81 in., 29.87 in., 29.83 in., 29.91 in., and 29.93 in.; what was the average height?

8. In a regiment, 230 men averaged 5 ft. 4 in.; 280 averaged 5 ft. 8 in.; and 205 averaged 5 ft. 9 in. What was the average height?

9. A steamer went 13 mi. 160 rd. per hour, for 7 hr.; and then 12 mi. 30 rd. per hour, for 11 hr. What was the average speed?

10. 13 members of a council were present at 11 meetings, 2 at 12, 2 at 14, and 3 at 15; what was the average number of meetings attended by each of the 20 members?

11. What was the average number of members present at each of the 15 meetings?

12. In a dwelling, 3 floors are each 15 by 17 ft.; 3 are 14 by 18 ft.; and 3 are 19 by 24 ft. What is the average surface?

INVOLUTION.

Article 234.

Find the following:

1. Second power of 81.
2. Third power of 32.
3. Fourth power of 25.
4. Fifth power of 3.1.
5. Second power of 69.3.
6. Third power of 5.5.
7. Fourth power of $6\frac{1}{2}$.
8. Third power of $16\frac{1}{10}$.
9. Second power of $99\frac{1}{9}$.
10. Sixth power of $1\frac{1}{4}$.

Find the square of:

11. 309.
12. 54.03.
13. $60\frac{3}{5}$.
14. $\frac{10}{21}$.
15. $1\frac{10}{21}$.
16. $15\frac{1}{9}$.
17. $30\frac{1}{4}$.
18. $6\frac{1}{40}$.
19. $44\frac{1}{44}$.

Find the cube of:

20. 36.
21. 125.
22. 105.
23. $13\frac{1}{3}$.
24. 19.1.
25. 347.
26. $\frac{17}{35}$.
27. 10.4.
28. $10\frac{1}{4}$.

Find the fourth power of:

29. 91.
30. 6.2.
31. $10\frac{1}{2}$.
32. $33\frac{1}{3}$.
33. 8.4.
34. 28.
35. $\frac{13}{14}$.
36. $15\frac{1}{3}$.
37. $3\frac{3}{7}$.

Find the fifth power of:

38. 11.1.
39. $27\frac{3}{4}$.
40. 105.

Reduce the following:

41. 22^3.
42. 16.5^2.
43. $(17\frac{1}{3})^4$.
44. 19.1^3.
45. 11^4.
46. $(1\frac{1}{2})$

EVOLUTION.

Article 238.—*Square Root.*

Find the square root of:

1. 144.	**10.** 1.21.	**19.** $50\frac{1}{196}$.
2. 1444.	**11.** 15.21.	**20.** $\frac{3025}{3969}$.
3. 7744.	**12.** 10609.	**21.** $12\frac{1}{2}$.
4. 625.	**13.** 9409.	**22.** 1000.
5. 5625.	**14.** 576.	**23.** $5\frac{1}{5}$.
6. 15625.	**15.** 5476.	**24.** 16.1.
7. 30625.	**16.** $96\frac{1}{25}$.	**25.** 257.
8. 50625.	**17.** $215\frac{1}{9}$.	**26.** 25.7.
9. 180625.	**18.** $1235\frac{1}{49}$.	**27.** 12.09.

Article 239.—*Square Root by Factoring.*

Find, by factoring, the square root of:

1. 1225.	**4.** 11025.	**7.** 50×450.
2. 2304.	**5.** 5184.	**8.** 125×1125.
3. 4096.	**6.** 18225.	**9.** 125.44.

Article 240.—*Applications of Square Root.*

1. The base of a right-angled triangle is 60; perpendicular, 45; find the hypotenuse.

2. The hypotenuse is 41 ft.; the base, 40 ft.; find the perpendicular.

3. A ladder 53 ft. long reaches a window 45 ft. from the ground; how far is the foot of the ladder from the bottom of the wall?

4. A well is 63 ft. deep and 16 ft. wide; what is the length of the longest pole that can be placed entirely within the well?

5. A mast, 77 ft. high, stands in the middle of ship 72 ft. wide; how long is the rope ladder from the ship's side to the mast-head?

6. A tree, 72 ft. high, is broken 20 ft. from the ground; how far from the foot will the top reach?

7. A pole, 45 ft. high, stands in the center of a circular ring 56 ft. in diameter; what is the length of the rope from the top of the pole to the edge of the ring?

8. A rope, 73 ft. long, reaches from the edge of a ring to the top of a center pole 55 ft. high; how wide is the ring?

9. Base and perpendicular each 60 ft.; how long is the hypotenuse?

10. If the hands of a clock were 3 in. and 4 in. long, how far apart would the points be at 3 o'clock?

11. A boy is due south from his home 144 mi.; he travels due west 165 mi.; how far is he then from home?

12. A stream is 120 feet wide; how long must a bridge be, if it rises in the center 11 feet above its height at the end piers?

13. Hypotenuse, 80 ft.; base and perpendicular equal; find them.

14. A is 60 mi. north of B, and 70 mi. west of C; how far apart are B and C?

15. If Cleveland is 225 mi. further north than Cincinnati, and 120 mi. further east, how far apart are the two cities?

Article 241.

1. A square farm contains 360 A.; how long is it?

2. A field is 12 rd. square; what is the side of another square field containing 1 sq. rd. more than twice as much as the first?

3. A farmer has a field 87 rd. square, which he exchanged even with his neighbor for two square fields, one 63 rd. long; how long was the other?

4. How much more fence will be required for a field 80 rd. long and 20 rd. wide, than for a square field of equal area?

5. Find the side of a square field equal to 4 fields 5 rd., 12 rd., 84 rd., and 3612 rd. square.

6. There are 3 square fields: the first is 120 rd. sq.; the second contains $3\frac{1}{16}$; and the third, $5\frac{1}{16}$ as much land as the first. What is the difference in the length of the two latter fields?

ARTICLE 244.—*Cube Root.*

Find the cube root of:

1. 13824.
2. 79507.
3. 250047.
4. 405224.
5. 314432.
6. 59319.
7. 8615125.
8. 135005697.
9. 746142643.
10. 620650.477.
11. 282.300416.
12. .030664297.
13. 3.
14. 300.
15. .009663597.
16. .000002146689.
17. $\frac{64}{226981}$.
18. .4.
19. .04.
20. .004.
21. $592\frac{88}{125}$.
22. $\frac{5}{8}$.

ARTICLE 245.

1. What is the side of a cubical box which contains 7 cu. ft. 71 cu. in.?

2. What is the side of a cubical tank which contains 2744 cu. ft.?

3. How many cubical blocks, 3 in. long, can be cut from a cubical block 15 in. long?

4. How many cubical blocks, $\frac{1}{3}$ in. long, can be cut from a cubical block 15 in. long?

5. What is the side of a cube which weighs $12\frac{1}{2}\%$ as much as a cube 11 in. in diameter?

6. What is the side of a cube which contains 2 cu. ft.?

MENSURATION.

ARTICLE 247.—*Areas of Parallelograms.*

Find the surface of:

1. A pavement, 20 yd. long and 6 ft. 9 in. wide.

2. A meadow, $\frac{3}{4}$ mi. long and 40 rd. wide.

3. A floor, 18 ft. 9 in. long and 13 ft. 4 in. wide.

4. A canal, 45 mi. long and 30 ft. 3 in. wide.

5. A park, 990 ft. by 440 ft.

6. A pasture, 20 ch. by 16 ch.

7. A wall, 8 ft. high and 30 yd. long.

8. A canvas, 5.4 m. by 7.5 m.

9. A roof, each side being 16 ft. 6 in. by 40 ft.

10. A street, 2 mi. 240 rd. long and 66 ft. wide.

11. How many bricks, 4 in. by 8 in., will be required for a pavement 40 ft. by 8 ft.?

12. How many acres in a field 120 rd. square?

13. How many yards of carpet, $\frac{3}{4}$ yd. wide, will be required for a floor 15 by 18 ft.?

14. A floor, 16 ft. long, requires 24 sq. yd. of carpet; how wide is the floor?

15. A man has a lot 54 yd. long and 24 yd. wide, which he exchanged for a square lot of equal surface; how much more fence would the first lot require than the last?

Article 248.—*Area of Trapezoid.*

1. A sky-light is 20 ft. long, and the two ends are 17 ft. and 10 ft. wide; what is the surface?

2. Find the surface of a field in the form of a trapezoid, the parallel sides being 73 rd. and 35 rd., and lying 32 rd. apart.

3. A lot is bounded by four streets: two of these are parallel, and measure 70 ft. and 90 ft. along the lot, and are 135 ft. apart; what is the surface of the lot?

Article 249.—*Area of Triangles.*

Find the area of:

1. A triangle, 40 ft. long and 20 ft. high.

2. A triangle, 96 yd. long and 55 ft. high.

3. A triangle, 10 ft. 8 in. long and 6 ft. 9 in. high.

Find the area of a right-angled triangle:

4. The base, 80 ft.; perpendicular, 60 ft.

5. The base, 60 ft.; perpendicular, 80 ft.

6. The base, 88 rd.; perpendicular, 25 rd.

Find the area of the following triangles:

7. The sides are 51 yd., 68 yd., and 85 yd.

8. The sides are 51 yd., 52 yd., and 53 yd.

9. The sides are 52 rd., 56 rd., and 60 rd.

Article 250.—*Area of Trapezia.*

1. Find the area of a trapezium, one diagonal being 120 rd., and the perpendiculars to the diagonal from the opposite angles being 45 rd. and 55 rd.

2. Diagonal measures 70 ft., and the two perpendiculars on the diagonal, 30 ft. and 40 ft.; find the area of the trapezium.

3. A man has a four-sided lot: the line between two opposite corners is 132 ft. long, and the other corners are 88 ft. and 110 ft. perpendicularly distant from that line; find the area.

4. Diagonal, 100 rd.; perpendiculars on it from opposite corners, 50 rd. and 70 rd.; find the value of the trapezium, at $960 per acre.

Article 251.—*Diameter and Circumference of a Circle.*

1. Diameter, 20 ft.; find the circumference.

2. Circumference, 20 ft.; find the diameter.

3. Radius, 26 ft.; find the circumference.

4. The diameter of a circular plat is 90 feet; what is the length of the fence around it?

5. What is the thickness of a tree, if it measures 4 ft. 8 in. around?

6. What is the distance across a circular field, if it is 170 rd. around it?

7. What is the distance around a circular field, if it is 170 rd. across it?

8. What length of tyre would be required for the wheels of a wagon, the front ones being 5 ft. 4 in. in diameter, and the hind ones 5 ft. 11 in. in diameter?

Article 252.—*Area of a Circle.*

Find the area of:

1. A circle whose radius is 25 ft.

2. A circle whose diameter is 20 ft. 10 in.

3. A circle whose diameter is $3\frac{1}{2}$ in.

4. A man lays out a lawn with a rope 60 ft. long, fastened to a stake at the center; how much land in the lawn?

5. What is the diameter of a circle that is equal to a square whose side is 30 ft.?

6. What is the side of a square that is equal to a circle whose diameter is 30 ft.?

7. A lot, 120 feet in diameter, has a gravel walk 20 feet wide just within its circumference; what is the surface of the grass plat inside the gravel walk?

8. A lot, 18 rd. in diameter, has around its center a grass plat 12 rd. in diameter; what is the area of the paved ring covering the rest of the lot?

Mensuration of Solids.

Article 254.—*Surface of Prism or Cylinder.*

1. Find the surface of a right prism 16 ft. high, standing on a triangular base whose sides are 6 ft., 8 ft., and 10 ft.

2. Find the surface of a rectangular prism 4 ft. high, standing on a base 2 ft. square.

3. Find the surface of a rectangular prism 2 ft. high, standing on a base 4 ft. square.

4. Find the entire surface of a cylinder 10 ft. high and 15 in. in diameter.

5. Find the convex surface of a cylinder 13 in. high, with a radius of 2 in.

6. Find the entire surface of a cylinder 13 ft. 2 in. high, and 6 ft. 6.54 in. in circumference.

Article 255.—*Volume of Prism or Cylinder.*

1. How many cu. in. in a prism 10 in. high, on a base 2 in. square?

2. How many cu. in. in a prism 2 in. high, on a base 10 in. square?

3. Find the volume of a flag-stone 10 ft. long, 3 ft. 9 in. wide, and 8 in. thick.

4. A sill is 40 ft. long and 9 in. wide; how thick must it be to contain 25 cu. ft.?

5. Find the volume of a cylinder 20 in. high, whose circumference is 39.27 in.

6. A cylinder 10 in. in diameter contains 1963½ cu. in.; what is its height?

Article 256.—*Surface of Pyramid or Cone.*

1. Find the convex surface of a right pyramid, the base being 18 in. square, and the slant height 4 ft.

2. Find the convex surface of a cone, the radius of the base being 6 in., and the slant height 8 in.

3. Find the entire surface of a cone, the diameter of the base being 20 in., and the slant height 40 in.

4. Find the entire surface of a cone, the diameter of the base being 40 in., and the slant height 20 in.

Article 257.—*Volume of Pyramid or Cone.*

1. Find the volume of a pyramid 48 ft. high, on a base 18 in. square.

2. The height of a pyramid is 8 ft., and the base is a triangle whose sides are 6, 8, and 10 in.; find the volume.

3. Find the volume of a cone whose altitude is 20 ft., and the diameter of the base 4 ft.

4. Find the volume of a cone, the altitude being 12 ft., and the radius of the base being 3 ft. 4 in.

5. The altitude of a cone is 2 ft., and the circumference of the base is 2 ft.; find the volume.

Article 258.—*Surface of a Sphere.*

Find the surface of:

1. A sphere whose diameter is 22 in.

2. A sphere whose radius is 4 ft.

3. A planet whose diameter is 2465 mi., supposing it to be a sphere.

4. If a base ball is $2\frac{7}{8}$ in. in diameter, how much leather will be required to cover 1600 balls, adding 10% for waste?

Article 259.—*Volume of a Sphere.*

Find the volume of:

1. A sphere 8 ft. 2 in. in diameter.

2. A globe whose radius is 20 in.

3. A planet whose diameter is 2240 miles, supposing it to be a sphere.

4. Find the weight of 500 cannon-balls, each 2 ft. in diameter, a cubic foot of iron weighing 430 lb.

Article 260.—*Applications of Mensuration.*

1. What will it cost to sod a yard 40 ft. by 32 ft., at 11 ct. a sq. yd.?

2. A room is 18 ft. long, 15 ft. wide, and 10 ft. high: what will the plastering cost, at 5 ct. a sq. yd., deducting 1 opening, 6 ft. square; 2 openings, 3 ft. 6 in. by 8 ft.; and 3 openings, 4 ft. by 7 ft. 6 in.?

3. What will it cost to paint both sides of a fence 78 ft. long and 5 ft. 6 in. high, at 14 ct. a sq. yd.?

4. A fish pond, 80 ft. in diameter, is surrounded by a tight fence 5 ft. $10\frac{1}{2}$ in. high; what will it cost to paint that fence, at 15 ct. a sq. yd.?

5. A museum room is 70 ft. long, 40 ft. wide, and 22 ft. high; what will it cost to paint the walls and ceiling at 29 ct. a sq. yd., deducting 1 sky-light, 14 ft. sq.; 4 doors, 5 ft. 3 in. by 10 ft.; and 12 windows, 6 by 9 ft.?

6. What will it cost to plaster a concert hall 100 ft. long, 70 ft. wide, and 26 ft. high, at $22\frac{1}{2}$ ct. a sq. yd.; deducting 8 openings, 8 by 12 ft., and 3 openings, 7 by 14 ft.?

ARTICLE 261.—*Board Measure.*

1. How many feet in an inch board 20 ft. long and 9 in. wide?

2. How many feet in a 3 in. plank 16 ft. long and 14 in. wide?

3. How many feet in a sill 30 ft. long, 10 in. wide, and 5 in. deep?

4. One sixth of the thickness being lost in sawing, how many feet of 2 in. plank can be made from a stick 2 ft. square and 20 ft. long?

5. One third of the thickness being lost in sawing, how many feet of $\frac{1}{2}$ in. boards can be made from a stick 2 ft. square and 14 ft. long. (All boards less than 1 in. thick are counted and measured as if 1 in. in thickness.)

6. How many feet in a plank 2 in. thick, which is 18 ft. long, 16 in. wide at one end, and 10 in. wide at the other end?

ARTICLE 262.—*Masons' and Bricklayers' Work.*

1. How many perches in a pile of stone 450 ft. long, 440 ft. wide, and 4 ft. high?

2. A cellar is 9 ft. deep, 39 ft. long, and 24 ft. wide inside: if the walls are 18 in. thick, how many perches of stone will they require?

3. A cellar is 10 ft. deep, 48 ft. long, and 19 ft. wide, measuring the outside; the walls are 2 ft. thick; what will the stone cost, at \$4.12½ a perch?

4. A pile of stone is in the form of a cone, 45 ft. in diameter at the bottom, and 17 ft. high; what is it worth, at \$1.75 a perch?

5. How many bricks in a wall 160 ft. long, 7 ft. high, and 2 ft. thick, allowing 20 bricks to 1 cu. ft.?

6. The bricks in a wall are 9 in. by 4 in., and 2½ in. thick; what will they cost, at \$7.50 per 1000, the wall being 72 ft. long, 12 ft. 6 in. high, and 2 ft. 6 in. thick?

Article 263.—*Measurement by Bushels or Gallons.*

1. How many bushels in a bin 16 ft. long, 10 ft. 6 in. high, and 4 ft. 4 in. wide?

2. How many bushels in a crib 15 ft. square and 8 ft. high?

3. A pit is 10 ft. square and 28 in. deep; how many bushels of potatoes will it hold?

4. How many bushels of lime can be made in a kiln in the form of a cone, 14 ft. high, the diameter of the base being 11 ft. 8 in.?

5. How many bushels of barley can be put in a cylindrical tub 16 ft. in diameter and 4 ft. deep?

6. How many gallons are equal in volume to 55 bu.?

7. How many bushels are equal in volume to 1536 gal.?

8. How many gallons in a tank 7 ft. in diameter and 11 ft. deep?

9. How many barrels (31½ gal. each) in a reservoir 63 ft. square and 5 ft. 6 in. deep?

10. A cistern is made 8 ft. 4 in. in diameter and 11 ft. deep; what will it cost, at 80 ct. a barrel?

PROGRESSIONS.

Article 265.—*Arithmetical Progression. Case I.*

1. The first term is 770; the common difference, 10; what would be the 20th term of an increasing series?

2. The first term is 770; the common difference, 10; what would be the 20th term of a decreasing series?

3. A new house rents for $900 per year; if the rent is reduced $30 each year, what will be the rent the 15th year?

4. The houses on an avenue are numbered regularly, beginning with 720; what will be the number of the 63d house?

5. If lots, 20 ft. wide, are numbered in regular order along a line, how far will the 36th lot be from the starting point?

6. What is the 100th term of a decreasing series, the 1st term being .004, and the common difference .000004?

Article 266.—*Case II.*

1. The extremes are 7 and 70; the number of terms, 10; find the common difference.

2. The 1st term is 18; the 8th term, 900; find the common difference.

3. The extremes are 1 and 1000; the number of terms, 28; find the common difference.

4. If boys are paid according to their ages, and a boy 13 years old earns $3.70 a week, while a boy 19 years old earns $7.30 a week, how much is the increase for each year?

5. The 1st term is 721; the 12th term, 127; find the common difference.

Article 267.—*Case III.*

1. The extremes are 4 and 80; the number of terms 20; find the sum of the series.

2. A man earned $370 the first year, and his salary was regularly increased, so that in the 9th year he received $1130; what were his total earnings in 9 yr.?

3. The extremes are 6 and 100, and the number of terms 10; find the sum of the series.

4. Extremes, 10 and 100; number of terms, 6; what is the sum of the series?

5. The 1st term is 450; common difference, 7; what is the sum of 10 terms of an increasing series?

6. The 1st term is 450; common difference, 7; what is the sum of 10 terms of a decreasing series?

7. The 15th term of an increasing series is 972; the common difference, 9; what is the sum of the 15 terms?

8. The 1st term is 11; the 8th term, 67; what is the sum of the series, there being 12 terms?

Article 269.—*Geometrical Progression. Case I.*

1. The 1st term of an increasing geometric series is 5; the ratio, 3; what is the fourth term?

2. The 1st term of an increasing geometric series is 3; the ratio, 5; find the fourth term.

3. The 1st term of a decreasing geometric series is 6; the ratio, 2; find the fifth term.

4. The 1st term of a decreasing geometric series is 2; the ratio, 6; what is the fifth term?

5. What is the 8th term of an increasing geometric series, the first term being 40, and the ratio 3?

ARTICLE 270.—*Case II.*

1. Find the sum of 10 terms of the series whose first term is 6, and ratio 2, the series being increasing.

2. Find the sum of 8 terms of the geometric series 3, 6, etc.

3. Find the sum of 8 terms of the geometric series 6, 2, etc.

4. Find the sum of the infinite decreasing series, of which the first term is $\frac{3}{4}$, and ratio $\frac{4}{3}$.

5. Find the sum of the infinite geometric series 3, 2, etc.

6. Find the sum of the infinite geometric series, whose first term is .148, and ratio 1000.

MISCELLANEOUS EXAMPLES.

1. Reduce $\frac{245632}{399152}$ to its lowest terms.

2. What is $27\frac{1}{2}\%$ of $\frac{8}{9}$?

3. What is the value of the ratio, $2\frac{1}{2}$ pk. : 4 bu.?

4. What is the interest of $745.20 for 2 yr. 7 mo. 6 da., at 5%?

5. What cost 6 bu. 6 qt. of cherries, at 60 ct. a peck?

6. What is the equated time of the following: $750, in 34 da.; $800, in 40 da.; and $950 in 50 da.?

7. An agent sent the owner $804.20 for rent of house 28 months, retaining 5% commission and $47 expenses; what was the monthly rent?

8. How much would be received for 24 bu. 3 pk. of peaches, packed in baskets containing 2 pk. 6 qt. each, and sold at $1.70 per basket?

9. What will be the proceeds of a note of $475, dated May 29, 1860, at 90 da., and discounted in bank July 1, at $4\frac{1}{2}\%$?

10. What will be the cost of a pile of wood 8.5 m. long, 6.8 m. wide, and 3.2 m. high, at 19 fr. per stere?

11. What cost 420 boards 16 ft. long, 9 in. wide, and 1 in. thick, at $3\frac{1}{2}$ ct. per ft.?

12. If $5\frac{1}{2}$ yd. cost $\$42\frac{1}{3}$, what will $8\frac{1}{4}$ yd. cost?

13. What cost 7707 lb. of wheat, at $1.20 per bu.?

14. Find the convex surface of a cone whose slant height is 16 ft., and base 12 in. in diameter.

15. What is the present worth of a debt of $320, due in 7 yr., money being worth 4%?

16. A has 275 bu. wheat; B, 405 bu. corn; C, 205 bu. oats; what would be the contents of the largest basket with which each one could exactly measure his grain?

17. A cistern is 4 ft. in diameter, and 3 ft. deep; what will it cost to line it with sheet lead weighing 5 lb. to the square foot, and costing 13 ct. per lb.?

18. What would be the amount of $333.33, at interest 3 yr. 3 mo. 3 da., at $3\frac{1}{3}$%?

19. What cost 7381 lb. of hay, at $17.50 per ton?

20. I invested $16170 in bonds, at 5% premium, and sold at 8% premium; find my gain.

21. In 14 meters, how many yards?

22. What principal, in 2 yr. 8 mo., at $7\frac{1}{2}$%, will earn $69.68 interest?

23. At 7 ct. a yd., what will a strip of canvas cost, extending along the four fences of a lot 42 rd. square?

24. Invested $23100 in bonds, at 5% premium, and sold at 5% advance; find my gain.

25. A invested $5400 for 7 mo.; B, $5600 for 9 mo.; they gained $546. Divide it.

26. Find the cost of a lot 100 rd. sq., at $100 per A.

27. Reduce $\frac{4}{15}, \frac{4\frac{1}{2}}{6}, \frac{3\frac{1}{3}}{5}$ to fractions having the least common denominator.

28. A debt of $420 will be due in 5 yr.; what should be the discount for cash, if money is worth 4%?

29. The first term of an increasing arithmetical progression is 735; the common difference, $4\frac{1}{2}$; find the 119th term.

30. Find the value of a cubical pile of wood 14 ft. long, at $2.40 a cord.

31. A vat is 11 ft. long, 7 ft. wide, and 9 in. deep; what is its capacity in gallons?

32. In $2\frac{1}{2}$ Ha. how many acres?

33. A man bought stock at 22% discount, and sold it at 4% premium; what % did he gain?

34. If 8 drivers receive $16.20 for 9 trips, of 1 hr. 30 min. each, how much should 12 drivers receive for 10 trips, of 2 hr. each?

35. 18 is what % of $33\frac{1}{3}$?

36. Reduce 11111111 sq. in. to A.

37. What is the square root of 5313025?

38. A fly-wheel is 10 ft. in diameter; what distance does a point in the circumference move in 16 revolutions?

39. After 22% of my flock died, I had 273 remaining; how many died?

40. How many bushels in a box 3 ft. long, 28 in. wide, and 16 in. deep?

41. How many minutes in the first four months of the year 1888?

42. Find the area of a triangle whose base is 4 rd., and height 4 yd.

43. What cost 1040 pwt. of silver, worth $91\frac{3}{5}$ ct. per oz.?

44. If a sidewalk, 1 mi. 120 ft. long, cost $487.60, what will one 90 rd. long cost?

45. A note for $940, dated Jan. 23, payable in 3 months, was discounted in bank March 20, at 5%; what was the discount?

46. What cost 56 three-inch planks, 30 ft. long and 12 in. wide, at 2 ct. per foot?

47. What is the least quantity of iron that would make an exact number of 25 lb. balls, or 30 lb. plates, or 35 lb. bars, without remainder in either case?

48. What debt, due in 6 years, is now worth $375, money being worth 5%?

49. What % would be lost by buying an article 20% above its value, and selling it 10% below its value?

50. In 50 kilograms how many pounds?

51. What would be the compound interest of $300 for 4 yr., at 6%?

52. How many bushels of cranberries can be bought for $39.90, at 10 ct. 5 m. a pt.?

53. A foundry building and patterns are valued at $18000; what would be the premium for insuring $\frac{3}{4}$ of this value, at $1\frac{1}{2}$%?

54. Find the side of a cubical box that will hold as much as another box 80 in. long, 75 in. wide, and 1 yd. high (inside measures).

55. What cost 49.3 meters of broadcloth, at 17 francs per meter?

56. A steamer is worth $105000, and a man sells $\frac{3}{4}$ of his interest for $14700; what part of the ship did he own?

57. A man gained 5% the first year, and 8% the second year, at the end of which he was worth $15876; what capital had he at first?

58. How many hours per day must 42 men work, for 8 da., to do as much as 56 men can do in 6 da., of 9 hr. each?

59. A debt having run 4 yr. 6 mo., at 8%, the interest was $44.10; what was the amount?

60. What cost 7000 qt. bags of salt, at 36 ct. a bu.?

61. At $16\frac{2}{3}$ ct. per doz., how many lemons can I buy for $50?

62. How many bushels will a bin hold, if it costs $189 more to fill it with wheat, at $1.05 a bu., than with corn, at 60 ct. a bu.?

63. What is the equated time of the following purchases: June 25, $470; July 3, $720; Aug. 1, $860?

64. Find the entire surface of a cone, the slant height being 20 in., and the diameter of the base 10 in.

65. Reduce $\frac{17}{18}$, $\frac{14}{15}$, $\frac{2\frac{1}{4}}{3\frac{1}{8}}$, $\frac{7}{10}$ to least common denominator.

66. A bottle of milk contains 1 pt. 3 gi.; how many dozen bottles can be filled from a tierce containing 42 gal. of milk?

67. A note is given May 15, 1885, for $500, with interest at 6%, payable annually; no interest having been paid, what is due May 15, 1890?

68. If I sell $\frac{8}{9}$ of an article for what $\frac{9}{10}$ of it cost, what % do I gain or lose?

69. A square field containing $2\frac{1}{2}$ A. is enclosed by a close fence 6 ft. high; what did the fence cost, at 2 ct. per sq. ft.?

70. In 40 yd., how many meters?

71. What is the fifth term of the increasing geometrical progression, whose first term is 7, and ratio 3?

72. Add all the odd numbers below 25, and find the square root of the sum.

73. What cost 7 T. 14 cwt. 67 lb. of Muscovado sugar, at $4\frac{3}{4}$ ct. per lb.?

74. An agent kept $560 commission on sales, and sent his principal $15440; what was his rate % commission?

75. Find the weight of 8 doz. boxes of fruit, each weighing 15.4 Kg.

76. What must I mark cloth that cost $8 a yard, so that I can deduct 20% and still gain 20%?

77. What cost a sight draft on New Orleans for $2370, at $\frac{1}{10}$% discount?

78. I bought vinegar at $1.25 per gal.; $33\frac{1}{3}$% leaked out; at what rate per gal. must I sell the remainder to gain $33\frac{1}{3}$%?

79. What cost 10000 feet of canvas cloth, at $18\frac{2}{5}$ ct. per yd.?

80. A contributed $7500; B, $5700; they gain $3872; how should they divide it?

81. A sum of money was borrowed May 22, 1884, at 4%, and $661.38 was paid in full Jan. 5, 1890; how much of this was interest?

82. Reduce $\frac{1554}{4107}$ to its lowest terms.

83. What will be the cost of a sight draft on Philadelphia for $1700, at $\frac{1}{8}$% premium?

84. How many times will a wagon wheel, 18 ft. 4 in. in circumference, revolve in going 4 miles?

85. How much will the ground cost on which a man can raise 728 bu. of potatoes, if each bu. requires $1\frac{1}{2}$ sq. rd., and land costs $7.50 per A.?

86. Invested $7840 in bonds, at 2% discount, and sold at 4% advance; find my gain.

87. How many perches in a wall 55 yd. long, 15 ft. high, and 3 ft. 3 in. thick?

88. What is the largest measure that could be used to measure out 81 gal., 120 gal., and 150 gal.?

89. A horse is fastened by a rope, 60 ft. long, to a stake in the center of a field; over what space can he graze?

90. The first term of a decreasing arithmetical progression is 873; the common difference, $2\frac{1}{3}$; find the 200th term.

91. How many cords in a pile of wood 56 ft. 3 in. long, 53 ft. 4 in. wide, and 5 ft. 4 in. high?

92. Find the hypotenuse of a right-angled triangle, the other sides being 90 and 56.

93. What is the solidity of a globe whose diameter is 12 in.?

94. What will it cost to plaster a wall for blackboard use, it being 11 ft. 3 in. by 5 ft. 4 in., the price being 50 ct. per sq. yd.?

95. What is $\frac{5}{6}\%$ of $\frac{5}{6}$?

96. If 27 oxen require 33 A. 120 sq. rd. of pasture, how much will 13 oxen require?

97. At $1\frac{3}{8}\%$ premium, what must be paid for insuring $\frac{2}{3}$ of the value of a house worth $7200?

98. Bought stock at 12% discount, and sold at 9% advance; what % did I gain?

99. At $1.94 a cu. ft., what must be paid for a granite block 28 in. long, 27 in. wide, and 32 in. high?

100. An agent bought cotton for a manufacturer, charging $\frac{1}{2}\%$ commission; the total bill was $17487; what was the agent's commission?

101. Find the value of the stamps required for 75 boxes of pencils, containing 100 each, the taxes being $3 per thousand.

102. Reduce .50625 to a common fraction.

103. What sum at interest 3 yr. 6 mo. 20 da., at $6\frac{1}{4}\%$, will amount to $532.40?

104. What cost 41 gal. 1 gi. of vanilla, at $5 per gal.?

105. Invested $7840 in bonds, at 2% discount, and sold them at 4% decline; find my loss.

106. What will it cost to plaster a room 18 ft. long, 15 ft. wide, and 12 ft. high, at 18 ct. per sq. yd., deducting 2 openings, each 4 ft. by 8 ft.; and 2 others, each $3\frac{1}{2}$ ft. by $8\frac{1}{2}$ ft.?

107. What will be the cost of a sight draft on Chicago for $847.30, at $\frac{1}{4}\%$ premium?

108. What would be the largest baskets in which either 350 bu. 1 pk. of peaches, or 250 bu. 2 pk. of plums could be packed without leaving any remainder in either case?

109. Find the convex surface of a cylinder 20 in. in diameter and 40 in. long.

110. In 50 gallons how many liters?

111. In what time time will any principal double itself at $3\frac{1}{5}\%$?

112. Find the surface of a sphere, the diameter being 14 in.

113. What cost 125 T. 7 cwt. 9 lb. of coal, at $4.50 per T.?

114. What is the diameter of a circle containing 3 A.?

115. A man realizes $1800 per annum on $24000; what is his rate of gain?

116. How many medals, each weighing 3.3 Dg., can be made from 2442 Kg. of silver?

117. What is the difference between the square of 625 and the square root of 625?

118. How many acres in a square field enclosed with 6 miles of fence?

119. What cost 1000000 in. of twine, at 4 m. per rd.?

120. A note dated Aug. 21, at 90 da., was discounted in bank Oct. 29, at 7%, and $2612.75 given for it; find the face of the note.

121. A co-operative company has 15000 shares, of $50 each; A holds 73 shares; what will be his assessment for a loss of $7920 by fire?

122. Received $51.51 interest on a loan of $367.20, at 5%; how long had it been loaned?

123. Reduce $\frac{18225}{50625}$ to its lowest terms.

124. If a stream flows 3 mi. 20 rd. in 1 hr. 4 min., how far will it flow in 3 hr. 44 min.?

125. How many perches in a breakwater 800 yd. long, 11 yd. high, and 5 yd. thick?

126. What must be paid for a fence around a lot 60 rd. square, the fence being made of four horizontal strips, each 9 in. wide, and costing $1\frac{1}{4}$ ct. per sq. ft.?

127. What is the ratio of 7.36 to $7\frac{2}{3}$?

128. $5\frac{3}{5} + 4\frac{5}{6} + 7\frac{7}{8} + 3\frac{5}{12} = ?$

129. Imported 50 casks of cologne, 45 gal. each, invoiced at 10 fr. per gal. ($1 = 5.18 fr.) Find the duty, at $2 per gal. and 50% ad valorem.

130. What must be paid for 5 sills, each 40 ft. long, 8 in. wide, and 9 in. high, at 60 ct. a cu. ft.?

131. What will it cost to fresco the ceiling of a room 36 ft. long and 22 ft. 3 in. wide, at 50 ct. per sq. yd.?

132. $6\frac{1}{4}$ is what % of 1000?

133. Find the volume of a sphere whose diameter is 44 in.

134. What is the compound interest of $500, for 4 yr., at 8%?

135. What is the least number of books that would make an exact number of either scores or gross?

136. If a man walks $4\frac{1}{2}$ miles in 1 hr., how far can he walk in 5120 sec.?

137. A debt, due in 5 years, was discounted at 7%, $420 being taken off; what was the face of the note?

138. How much grain must I take to mill, to have 154 bushels after the miller has taken out his toll of 4 qt. to the bu.?

139. Find the base of a right-angled triangle, the hypotenuse being 117, and the perpendicular 45.

140. A bill of exchange on London for £86 8 s., cost $420.12; what was the rate of exchange?

141. A man sold 520 sheep, and had 35% of the flock remaining; how many had he at first?

142. If 4 men, in 6 da., dig a cellar 45 ft. long, 16 ft. wide, and 9 ft. deep, how many men will be required to dig a cellar 75 ft. long, 18 ft. wide, and 12 ft. deep, in 3 days?

143. Reduce 50000 minutes to weeks.

144. A's money is 65% more than B's, and together they have $54325; how much has each?

145. \$552.96 was loaned July 21, 1810, at $4\frac{1}{6}\%$, and \$666.56 was paid on settlement; find the date of settlement.

146. What is the diameter of a circle containing 785 A. 64 sq. rd.?

147. How deep must a box be made, to hold 90 bu., if it is 7 ft. long and 6 ft. wide?

148. If 35 castings weigh 48 T. 4 cwt. 25 lb., what is the weight of each?

149. Consequent, $22\frac{3}{4}$; ratio, $1\frac{6}{7}$; find antecedent.

150. 24% of my land is in corn, leaving 266 A. otherwise planted; how much is cultivated?

151. What cost an abutment 66 ft. long, $22\frac{1}{2}$ ft. high, and 4 ft. thick, at \$2.25 a perch?

152. Money loaned at $4\frac{1}{2}\%$, and \$709.20 paid, of which \$69.20 was interest; how long was it loaned?

153. What cost 475 gal. 3 qt. 1 pt. of molasses, at 18 ct. a qt.?

154. If 800 men, in 30 da., can build a pier 240 ft. long, 8 ft. thick, and 12 ft. high, how long must 240 men be employed to build a pier 360 ft. long, 10 ft. thick, and 8 ft. high?

155. What would be the equated time of paying the following bills: May 5, \$230, at 6 mo.; June 1, \$250, at 4 mo.; July 5, \$320, at 5 mo.; Aug. 1, \$420, at 3 mo.

156. Bought lemons 5% below quotations, sold them at 10% above quotations, and gained \$21 on 40 boxes; what was the price per box?

157. A has 350 eggs; B, 525; C, 280; they have boxes made, in which each can exactly pack his eggs; if the boxes are the largest possible, how many eggs will each hold?

158. What cost a farm 180 meters square, at 7000 fr. per Ha.?

159. What cost a sight draft on Charleston for $950, at $\frac{1}{2}$% discount?

160. What cost 4 cwt. 59 lb. 7 oz. of beef, at 13 ct. a lb.?

161. Find the solidity of a sphere whose radius is 11 in.

162. The time past noon is $\frac{1}{15}$ of the time to midnight; what is the time?

163. A man had 450 A. of land, and sold 162 A.; what % of his farm has he still?

164. What will it cost to pave a circular court 80 ft. in diameter, at 55 ct. a sq. yd.?

165. The last term of a decreasing arithmetical progression of 19 terms is 999; common difference, 7; find the sum of the terms.

166. Reduce $\frac{19}{32}$ bu. to integers.

167. A debt was paid 8 yr. before due, and $420 deducted, at 7% discount; how much was the debt?

168. What cost 4355 gal. 1 pt. 2 gi. of ink, at 70 ct. per gal.?

169. A note dated May 19, at 90 da., was discounted June 15, at 4%, and $2.31 deducted; what was the face of the note?

170. I invested $7840 in bonds, at 2% discount, and sold them at 4% premium; find my gain.

171. At 16 fr. per meter, how many kilometers of cloth can be bought for 100000 fr.?

172. Divide $\frac{4}{15}$ of $\frac{3\frac{3}{7}}{2\frac{2}{3}}$ by $\frac{3}{10}$ of $\frac{2\frac{2}{3}}{1\frac{2}{5}}$.

173. What date 4 mo. 20 da. after Dec. 11, 1885?

174. If a man can walk 3 mi. 240 rd. in 1 hr. 12 min., how far can he walk in 2 hr. 48 min.?

175. A note is given June 10, 1870, for $480, with interest at 5%, payable semi-annually; interest having been paid for two years, what is due Aug. 25, 1876?

176. An agent bought wool at 37 ct. per lb.; commission, $\frac{3}{4}\%$; expenses, \$97.20; the total cost to the principal, \$8000.03; how many pounds were bought?

177. $3\frac{3}{5} + 13\frac{3}{4} + 23\frac{5}{6} - 33\frac{2}{3} = ?$

178. At what rate must \$450 be loaned for 2 yr. 2 mo. 20 da., to amount to \$540?

179. How many panes of glass, 10 in. by 16 in., are in a half-box containing 50 sq. ft.?

180. The base and perpendicular of a right-angled triangle are each 58; find the hypotenuse.

181. A man lost 14% of his weight by sickness, and then weighed 129 lb.; how much had he lost?

182. A rectangle 15 ft. wide contains 10 sq. rd.; how long is it?

183. The longitude of one place is 20° 10′ E.; of another, 70° 20′ W. When it is 1 o'clock P. M. at the former place, what is the time at the latter?

184. The stamps on letters are 2 cents for every half-ounce or fraction thereof; what will stamps cost for 730 letters, each weighing $1\frac{1}{5}$ oz.?

185. A box is 8 dm. high and 62.5 cm. wide; how long must it be to contain 1 m^3?

186. A invests \$5000 Jan. 1, and draws out \$1000 May 1; B invests \$4000 Jan. 1, and puts in \$1000 more May 1; July 1, they dissolve, having gained \$1350; how should the gain be divided?

187. What cost 4 T. 9 cwt. of cheese, at 12 ct. 4 m. per lb.?

188. A mill is valued at \$28000; the stock, \$36000; what would be the cost of insuring $\frac{3}{5}$ of the value of the mill at $1\frac{1}{2}\%$, and $\frac{3}{4}$ of the value of the stock at $1\frac{1}{4}\%$?

189. A note \$4800, dated June 23, 1846, payable in 90 da., was discounted at 6%, and \$23.20 was taken off; when was it discounted?

190. What cost a 30-day draft on New York for $2517, exchange being $\frac{1}{8}\%$ premium?

191. A note given June 7, 1888, for $600, with 9% interest, was endorsed as follows: Dec. 5, 1888, $25; July 20, 1889, $95.45; May 7, 1890, $20; June 20, 1890, $139.60. What was due May 7, 1892?

192. What will it cost to paper the walls of a room 20 ft. long, 14 ft. wide, and 12 ft. high, at 22 ct. per sq. yd., no allowance being made for openings?

193. How long will it take a man to walk 990000 in., if he can walk a mile in 16 min.?

194. What sum at compound interest for 2 yr., at 6%, will amount to $842.70?

195. What cost 450 boards, 12 in. long, 3 in. wide, and $\frac{1}{2}$ in. thick, at 4 ct. per ft.? (Count all boards thinner than 1 in. the same as if 1 in. thick.)

196. 28% of the pupils enrolled in a school withdrew, and 1224 remained; how many withdrew?

197. A note of $5040, dated May 23, 1856, payable in 60 da., was discounted at 5%, the proceeds being $5013.40; when was it discounted?

198. Reduce $\dfrac{17\frac{1}{7}}{250}$ to a decimal.

199. The antecedent is 10 hr. 40 min.; the ratio, $5\frac{1}{3}$; find the consequent.

200. A lot is 80 rd. sq., and worth $560; what would it be worth, if a strip 4 rd. wide is taken off all around the outside?

201. What cost a 60-day draft on San Francisco for $3913.25; exchange, $\frac{1}{2}\%$ premium, reckoning money at 6%?

202. A coin is 2 centimeters in diameter; how far would 800 such coins extend if laid in a straight line?

203. $500 was borrowed Jan. 1, at 6%, and $100 was paid on the first day of each of the next four months. What was due July 1?

204. What must be paid for insuring a hotel building and furniture: the house, valued at $130000; and furniture, at $74000; both insured at $\frac{3}{5}$% on three fourths of the valuation?

205. A ship's chronometer is set to Greenwich time; in what longitude will the ship be when the chronometer is 9 hr. 10 min. fast?

206. A sum at interest for 3 yr. 5 mo. 18 da., amounted to $95.80, of which $20.80 was interest; find the rate %.

207. What would be the equated time of the following purchases: July 1, $140; July 8, $150; July 15, $160; July 22, $170; July 29, $180; and Aug. 5, $190?

208. How many octavo books, of 240 pages each, can be printed on 100 reams of paper?

209. If a dairy furnishes 2631 gal. 1 qt. of milk in 3 wk. 4 da., how much would that be for 4 wk. 3 da.?

210. Bought 60 $100 bonds at 5% discount, and sold at 5% profit; find my gain.

211. 5 C. 23 cu. ft. is what fraction of 34 cu. yd.?

212. A field is 40 rd. square; what is the distance between opposite corners?

213. A put into the firm $7500, for 11 mo.; B, $6600 for 10 mo.; on closing business, they had $12615; how much would each lose?

214. A pillar, 8 ft. 3 in square, cost $519.75, at $3.15 a perch; how high was it?

215. The assessment for paving a street being $2.0592 per foot, what must A pay, whose lot extends along that street 3 rd. 5 ft. 8.03 in.?

216. A debt of $900 is due in 2 yr. 6 mon.; the discount for paying now is $150; what rate % is that?

217. Find the surface of a sphere whose radius is 13 inches.

218. Reduce $\frac{51821}{80087}$ to its lowest terms.

219. Find the solidity of a prism 20 ft. high, standing on a base 4 ft. 6 in. square.

220. Bought stock at 6% discount, and sold it at 5% gain; at what rate did I sell it?

221. What date is 3 mo. 22 da. before June 22, 1873?

222. What sum, at compound interest for 3 years, at 5%, will amount to $926.10?

223. A field 60 rd. long contains 15 A.; what would the fence cost, at 30 ct. a rod?

224. How many coins, weighing 5 g. each, can be made from 1 quintal of bronze?

225. $31.50 was deducted from a note having 3 yr. 9 mo. to run, leaving the present worth $140; what was the rate %?

226. How much would be realized from a lot 10 rd. long and 7 rd. wide, sold for graves, the graves being 7 ft. long and 2 ft. 6 in. wide, and costing $4.50?

227. What cost a bill of exchange on London for £138 15 s., exchange at $4.84?

228. Find the total surface of a cylinder 30 in. in diameter and 50 in. long.

229. A bankrupt owes A $500, and B $360, and pays A $77 more than B; how much does he pay each?

230. A horse is fastened to a fence by a rope 90 ft. long; over what space can he graze?

231. Reduce .065625 to a common fraction.

232. The list price is 96 ct. per gross, with 20, 25, and $37\frac{1}{2}$% off; what is the cost per gross?

233. A fruit seller found that whether he counted his pine-apples by 4's, 5's, 6's, or 8's, there was no remainder; what was the least number he could have had?

234. $480 was loaned for 5 yr. 15 da., and $108.90 was received for interest; what was the rate %?

235. What sum would be received for 2 ℥ 2 ℈ of medicine, made in 5 gr. pills, sold 20 in a box, at 25 ct. per box?

236. An agent affects an exchange of a house, at $4600, for a farm, the owner of the house receiving $1100 difference; what is the agent's commission on the two pieces of property, at $\frac{3}{4}$%?

237. A lot lies between two parallel roads $\frac{1}{2}$ mi. apart; it is 90 rd. on one road and 75 rd. on the other; what is the lot worth, at $80 an acre?

238. 44% of the workmen were discharged, and 98 remain; how many were employed at first?

239. What is the square root of 40?

240. The hypotenuse is 74 ft., and the base and perpendicular are equal; how long is the base?

241. How many lots, 50 meters long and 10 meters wide, can be made from 50 Ha. of land?

242. A crib is 18 ft. long and 4 ft. high; how wide must it be to contain 540 bu.?

243. Bought 125 bonds ($100 each) at $2\frac{1}{2}$% discount, and sold them at $6\frac{1}{4}$% premium; what was the gain?

244. A man bought 40 sheep the first year, and each succeeding year 3 more than the year before; how many did he buy in 6 years?

245. A note of $5760, dated Oct. 19, payable in 60 da., was discounted Nov. 10, and $29.52 deducted; find the rate.

246. A note is given Aug. 13, 1890, for $730, with interest at 9%, payable annually; no interest having been paid after the first year, what was due Dec. 6, 1893?

247. Reduce $\frac{397}{560}$ to a decimal.

248. The list price is $1.50 per gross, with 20 and 25 off; what is the cost per gross?

249. A draft on Dublin for £7 3 s. 4 d. cost $34.83; what was the rate of exchange?

250. Find the diameter of a sphere whose solidity is 7238.2464 cu. in.

251. A put in $850; B, $680; A's gain is $150 more than B's; what did each gain?

252. $560 was loaned Feb. 18, 1889, at 9%, and amounted to $770; when was it paid?

253. A man sent an agent 4010 barrels of pork to sell, and invest proceeds in wheat, commission $\frac{1}{4}$% in each case; pork sold at $8.80 per bbl., and wheat cost $1.33 per bu.; how many bu. were bought?

254. One city is in E. longitude 40° 17′; another, in W. longitude 30°, 13′; if a man travels from the first to the second, should his watch gain or lose time, and how much?

255. Bought bonds at 2% discount, and sold at $1\frac{1}{2}$% premium, and gained $94.50; what was the par value?

256. 150 castings weigh 17 T. 11 cwt.; find the weight of each.

257. The tax levy is 7.38 m. on the dollar; what tax must be paid on $107524?

258. What is the cube root of the square of 4096?

259. What is the area of a square field, in which a circular track containing 1256.64 A. can be made?

260. What debt, due in 3 mo., together with $800, due in 9 mo., could be paid in 7 mo. without loss to either?

261. A man insures his life for $16000 in favor of his wife; premium, $29.47 per $1000; if he dies during the seventh year thereafter, how much will his widow receive in excess of the amount paid out?

262. A put in $7000 for 6 mo.; B put in $5000, and received $\frac{5}{11}$ of the profit; how long was his money invested?

263. What is the cube of .043?

264. Divide $\frac{5}{16}$ of $\frac{4\frac{2}{3}}{7\frac{1}{5}}$ by $\frac{7}{8}$ of $\frac{6\frac{1}{4}}{10\frac{4}{5}}$.

265. A note is given Aug. 18, 1884, for $840, with 8% interest, endorsed as follows: May 9, 1885, $30.50; Dec. 15, 1885, $238.54; June 3, 1887, $137.44. What was due Oct. 20, 1888?

266. A cistern is 20 ft. in diameter and 14 ft. deep; how many barrels (31½ gal.) will it hold?

267. Find the diameter of a sphere whose surface is 7854 sq. in.

268. The first and fourth terms of a proportion are 38 and 152, and the second and third terms are equal to each other; find them.

269. A note is given Oct. 31, 1883, payable in 4 mo.; when is it legally due?

270. The sides of a triangle are 102, 104, and 106 ft.; find the area.

271. 31 gal. 2 qt. is what decimal part of 65 gal. 2 qt. 1 pt.?

272. What principal, loaned Nov. 18, 1880, at 4½%, will gain $37.52 interest on settlement Aug. 28, 1888?

273. Find the volume of a column 30 ft. high, standing on a triangular base, whose sides are 3, 4, and 5 ft.

274. $13\frac{3}{4} - 4\frac{7}{9} + 15\frac{5}{8} - 7\frac{5}{6} = ?$

275. What will be the cost of a wall 440 ft. long, 30 ft. high, and 3 ft. thick, at $3.30 per perch, if a wall 450 ft. long, 33 ft. high, and 4 ft. thick, cost $9000, at $3.75 per perch?

276. At what rate % of discount will a debt of $413, due in 4 yr. 6 mo., be now worth $350?

277. A field is 40 rd. by 100 rd.; what would be the area of a square field that could be enclosed with the same length of fence?

278. Bought stock at 16% discount, and sold at 9% discount; what % did I gain?

279. The two parallel ends of a lot measure 15 rd. and 15 yd., and are 500 ft. apart; find the area.

280. If 48 pencils cost $1, how many can be sold for $1 at a gain of 20%?

281. What cost a draft on Bordeaux for 4827.3 fr., exchange at 5.18 fr.?

282. Find a number whose square is contained 162 times in 20000.

283. The slant height of a conical hill is 440 ft., and the circumference of its base $\frac{1}{2}$ mi.; how much land on its sides?

284. Reduce $\frac{8\frac{8}{9}}{10}$, $\frac{7}{5\frac{1}{4}}$, $\frac{9\frac{1}{3}}{14}$ and $\frac{7}{12}$ to the least common denominator.

285. Find the volume of a cylindrical log, 15 in. in diameter and 40 ft. long.

286. If each of the four sides of a square field were 20% longer, how much greater would be the surface of the field?

287. What is the square of that number of which 16 is the cube root?

288. A and B were in partnership; A's capital was $8400, and he received $720 out of $1500 profit; what was B's capital?

289. If a field of 15 A. 100 sq. rd. requires 18 bu. 3 pk. of seed, how much seed would be needed for 18 A. 120 sq. rd.?

290. What sum must I pay for a house, so that after spending $50 for repairs I can gain 5% by selling for $4830?

291. What is the value of the compound ratio: $2\frac{1}{2}$ bu.: 3 pk. 15 men : 25 men. 27 da. : 6 da.

292. What date is 5 mo. 27 da. before May 27, 1885?

293. How large a draft on London can be bought for $5000, exchange at $4.87?

294. A note was dated Feb. 13, 1866, and had accumulated $21.84 on settlement, Sept. 19, 1867; what was the amount then due?

295. A could plow a field in 7 da., working 8 hr. per da.; B, in 14 da., working 6 hr. per da.; how long would it require both, working 9 hr. per da.?

296. $5000 was borrowed July 1, at 5%; paid July 28, $1000; Sept. 10, $800; Oct. 9, $850. What was due Nov. 6?

297. A tank is 21 in. sq.; how deep must it be to contain 21 gal.?

298. After losing $2600, A and B dissolve partnership, A receiving $25200; B, $11200; how much had each at first?

299. Bought bonds at 4% premium, and sold at a decline of $1\frac{1}{2}$%; what % did I lose?

300. A put in $7000 for 6 mo.; B put in $5000, and received $\frac{5}{11}$ of the profit; how long was B's money invested?

301. A ring, 100 ft. in diameter, was made in a square field 100 ft. long; how much land was left in the four corners?

302. A man has goods costing him $11200, and gained 5% by selling them through an agent, whose commission was 2%; what did the agent receive as commission?

303. If 10 horses can haul 50000 lb. 2 mi. in 4 hr., how many horses will be required to haul 70000 lb. 5 mi. in 5 hr.?

304. A debt was contracted Jan. 19, 1888, with 9% interest; debt, $375. On settlement, $141 interest was paid; find the date of settlement.

305. What is the side of a square which is equal to a right-angled triangle whose base is 30 ft. and hypotenuse 78 ft.?

306. Reduce $\frac{59085}{133926}$ to its lowest terms.

307. What is the cube of that number of which 53 is the square root?

308. A malt tub is 18 ft. in diameter and 6 ft. deep; how many gallons will it contain?

309. A note at 60 days was discounted July 13, at 8%, and $18.36 was deducted for bank discount, and $2411.64 paid the holder; what was the date of the note?

310. A pile of stone is 22 ft. long and 18 ft. wide; how high must it be to contain 96 perches?

311. Take the cubes of all the even numbers under 20; add them, and extract the square root of half the sum.

312. The tax levy being 23.64 m. on the dollar, what tax must a man pay, whose property is assessed at $43246?

313. $512 was loaned at $7\frac{1}{2}$%, and $228.80 interest was due April 7, 1886; when was the money loaned?

314. The fence was removed from a square field containing 40 A.; what would be the area of a field 20 rd. wide, which the same fence would exactly inclose?

315. A debt of $732 is now worth $600, reckoning money at 8%; how long before it is due?

316. If 15 men earn $427.50 in 19 da., of 10 hr. each, how many days, of 8 hr. each, must 38 men be employed to earn $592.80?

317. The list price is 40 ct., with $\frac{1}{3}$ and 10 off; what is the cost?

318. An agent bought, for a capitalist, ground 400 ft. along a street, charging 2% commission, and drawing on his principal for $18360 in full; what was the price per front foot?

319. A bin is 6 ft. wide and 4 ft. 8 in. high; how long must it be to contain 240 bu.?

320. A note of $600, with interest at 6%, was dated Nov. 13, 1870, and endorsed as follows: July 10, 1871, $100; May 7, 1872, $100; April 4, 1873, $100. What was due May 1, 1874?

321. I sold two farms, at $1920 each; on the first I gained 20%, and on the second lost 20%; what % did I gain or lose on the two?

322. A man saved $124 the first year, and each succeeding year $11 more than the year before; how much did he save in 20 yr.?

323. $323\frac{5}{8} - 138\frac{3}{5} + 217\frac{2}{3} - 401\frac{5}{6} = ?$

324. What % does a dealer gain who buys 450 bu. apples, at 60 ct. a bu., and sells them at 24 ct. a pk., if $\frac{1}{4}$ are lost by spoiling?

325. The list price was 72 ct. per gross, with 20, 25, and $16\frac{2}{3}$ off; find the cost per gross.

326. I paid $75.60 for insuring $\frac{2}{3}$ of the value of my factory, at $\frac{7}{8}$%; what was the factory worth?

327. A square field contains 160 A.; what would be the area of a circular field with the same length of fences?

328. When it is 6 hr. 3 min. A. M. at a place in 100° E. long., what is the time at a place in 40° W. long.?

329. Find the radius of a sphere whose surface is 380.1336 sq. in.

330. Find the cube root of the sum of the cubes of 27, 36, and 45.

331. At $1\frac{1}{2}$ ct. a sq. ft., what will lumber cost for a platform 200 ft. long, 70 ft. wide at one end, and tapering to 40 ft. at the other end?

332. Money loaned Dec. 24, 1882, at $3\frac{1}{2}$%, amounted to $600.99, June 6, 1887; how much of this was interest?

333. An arithmetical progression has 10 terms; the third term is 29, and the seventh 73; find the sum of the terms.

334. The sides of a triangle are $25\frac{1}{2}$, 26, and $26\frac{1}{2}$ in.; what is the surface?

335. A log is 20 in. in diameter; how long must it be to contain 1 C. of wood?

336. A man marks his goods at 20% above cost; in selling at wholesale he takes off 10 and 5%; what is his gain %, at wholesale?

337. If a man walks 6 kilometers in an hour, how far is that in 15 sec.?

338. By selling at 64 ct. a yd., twice as much is gained as by selling at 57 ct.; what % would be gained, at 70 ct. a yd.?

339. How large a draft on Berlin can be bought for $500, when exchange is $.965 for 4 reichsmarks?

340. A note, due June 6, 1879, was discounted at 4%, the discount being $69.60, and the present worth $480; when was it discounted?

341. What number, added 3 times to $287\frac{5}{12}$, will make the sum $352\frac{1}{4}$?

342. $700 was borrowed May 19, at 7%. There were paid: June 2, $75; June 20, $100; July 15, $90; Aug. 7, $120; what was due Sept. 7?

343. 500 bolts, each containing 8 meters of ribbon, cost 560 fr.; how much would 375 dm. cost at the same rate?

344. A note of $1600, dated Sept. 17, 1888, at 50 da., was discounted in bank Sept. 25, 1888, and $15 deducted; what rate % was that?

345. Bought bonds at 4% discount, and sold at a profit of $12\frac{1}{2}$%; at what premium were they sold?

346. What % is gained by selling $\frac{5}{9}$ of any purchase for what $\frac{4}{5}$ of it cost?

347. Divide 31 lb. 1 oz. 10 pwt. by 120.

348. A note is given Dec. 12, 1879, for $1000, with interest at 6%, endorsed as follows: June 19, 1881, $41.17; Dec. 6, 1881, $177.83; Aug. 21, 1882, $138.25; May 12, 1883, $30.17. What was due Oct. 15, 1884?

349. Bought goods at 20 and 10 off, and sold them at 10 and 10 off; what % did I gain?

350. If a field 50 rd. long and 30 rd. wide produces 27 bu. of wheat, what will a field 75 rd. long and 60 rd. wide produce in another year when crops are greater in the proportion of 7 : 6?

351. Reduce $\frac{6\frac{2}{5}}{6\frac{6}{7}}$, $\frac{3\frac{3}{5}}{3\frac{3}{11}}$, $\frac{7}{8}$, and $\frac{9}{14}$ to the least common denominator.

352. In 10 T. how many metric tons?

353. Goods were sold at $\frac{1}{4}$ and 10 off; the cost was 30 ct. per gross; what was the list price per gross?

354. What sum, at compound interest for 2 yr. 6 mo., at 10%, will amount to $431.97?

355. A bill of exchange on Bordeaux for 8600 fr. cost $1694.20; what was the rate of exchange?

356. Two men exchanged 60-day notes, and immediately discounted them in bank; the first, at 6%, receiving $2572.70; the second, at 5%; what did he receive?

357. What is the difference between annual and compound interest of $10000 for 3 yr., at 10%?

358. A pole 40 ft. high stands in the center of a circular pond, whose area is 314.16 sq. yd.; what is the length of a line from the top of the pole to the edge of the pond?

359. The discount, at 6%, on a debt due in 3 yr., is $20.16; what would be the discount on it 16 mo. before due, at 9%?

360. The square of a certain number is 2209; what is the fourth power of the same number?

361. Bought at 40 and 5 off, and sold at 40 off the same list; what % did I gain?

362. Reduce $\frac{13\frac{1}{8}}{25\frac{1}{5}}$ to a decimal.

363. Find the surface of a sphere whose solidity is 11494.0672 cu. in.

364. Three men bought a horse for $150, and sold him for $210, by which A gained $30, and B $18; what had each paid for the horse?

365. What is the difference between simple and annual interest of $100, due in 10 yr., with 10%?

366. Complete the proportion of which the first, third, and fourth terms are $5\frac{5}{7}$, $16\frac{2}{3}$, and $8\frac{3}{4}$.

367. How many ft., board measure, in a plank 20 ft. long, 3 in. thick, 18 in. wide at one end and 16 in. wide at the other end?

368. What is the equated time of paying the following bills: Aug. 5, $290, at 3 mo.; Sept. 7, $410, at 30 da.; Sept. 29, $500 cash; Oct. 4, $600, at 60 da.?

369. A cubical block contains 3 cu. ft. 648 cu. in.; what will it cost to gild 5 sides, at 84 ct. a sq. ft.?

370. A prism stands on a triangular base, whose sides are 9, 12, and 15 ft. long; how high must it be to contain 80 cu. yd.?

371. How many ars in a lot 450 m. long and 49 dm. wide?

372. A man made a 60-day note, which he discounted in bank at 8%, and received $19261.51; it being due, for what sum must he give a 90-day note to redeem it, bank now discounting at 9%?

373. A debt of $660, with 5% interest, amounted to $807.40, May 20, 1873; when was the debt contracted?

374. Goods were listed at 40 ct. per gross, and sold at $\frac{1}{4}$, 20 and 5% off; what did 150 gross cost?

375. A man took out a life insurance policy for $6000, the rate being $32.65; how much will he pay in premiums in 30 years, if he lives that time?

376. What will be the length of a cubical box containing 512 liters?

377. If 6 men, in 5 mo., have $450 by saving 30% of their wages, how much will 9 men save in 4 mo., if wages have been raised 20%, and they save 40% of their wages?

378. A railroad, with 280000 $100 shares, wishes to make an extension costing $198000; what will be assessed on a man holding 1197 shares?

379. Find the volume of a cone, the altitude being 40 in., and the diameter of the base 18 in.

380. A debt of $806 was paid July 25, 1886, less $156, deducted for discount, at 5% ; when was the debt due?

381. Reduce .013824 to a common fraction.

382. A note was given Dec. 10, 1885, for $700, with interest at 8%, payable semi-annually, and interest was paid for 18 months: what was due May 2, 1892?

383. A horse is fastened by a rope, 120 ft. long, to a post in the corner of a square field; over what space can he graze?

384. At 4½ ct. per ft., how many boards 16 ft. long, 5 in. wide, and 1½ in. thick, can be bought for $17.10?

385. The longitude of Cincinnati is 84° 20′ W.; at what place on the earth's surface is it 1 hr. 4 min. P. M., when it is half past 6, A. M., at Cincinnati?

386. A note is given May 1, 1880, for $720, with 5% interest, and endorsed as follows: May 1, 1881, $30; Nov. 1, 1881, $20; July 1, 1882, $148. On settlement, $640 was due; what was the date of settlement?

387. Bought bonds at 4% premium, and sold at a loss of 12½% ; at what discount did I sell?

388. A dealer imported 24 cases German toys, at 250 marks per case, commission 2% ; find duty at 35%, exchange being 95 ct. 2 m. for 4 marks.

389. In a four-sided lot the line between two opposite corners measures 66 yd., and the other two corners are distant from that line 50 yd. and 60 yd. ; what is the area of the lot?

390. How much iodine, at 1.3 fr. per Hg., can be bought for 2210 fr.?

391. A ladder 65 ft. long rests against a house, with its foot 16 ft. from the house: if the foot is drawn out 17 ft. further from the house, how far will the top of the ladder slide down the wall?

392. A debt, contracted June 30, 1882, amounted, when paid, to $467.50, of which $55 was interest, at 6% ; when was the debt paid?

393. Goods were bought at $\frac{1}{3}$, 20, and 10 off, and sold at $\frac{1}{4}$, 15 and 5 off; what % was gained?

394. A put in $9000 for 6 mo.; B, $10000 for 5 mo.; at settlement, A had $9270 ; how much had B?

395. What is the sixth term of the geometrical progression 9, 12, 16, etc.?

396. What cost 55 metric tons of sal soda, at .15 fr. per kilogram?

397. A man has a note dated Aug. 25, at 90 da., which he wishes to have discounted Oct. 10, and finds that he will receive $9.40 more if discounted at 5% than if discounted at 6% ; what was the face of the note?

398. A merchant, in selling at wholesale, takes off 5% from his retail prices, and gains 14% ; what is his retail profit?

399. What sum at 6%, payable annually, would amount to $935.20 in 5 years, if no interest is paid before that time?

400. Find the volume of a sphere whose surface is 31416 sq. mi.

401. Two men were employed 3 days to lay a stable floor, 70 ft. long, 30 ft. wide, and 3 in. thick; wages, $2.25 per day; lumber, $23 per thousand ft.; what was the total cost?

402. If a man can fence a lot 100 rd. in diameter in 4 days, how long will he be employed to fence a lot 200 rd. in diameter?

403. If a man can plant a lot 100 rd. in diameter in 4 days, how long will he require to plant a lot 200 rd. in diameter?

ANSWERS.

Article 19.—**1.** 2019. **2.** 3625. **3.** 3289. **4.** 3479. **5.** 3213. **6.** 4117. **7.** 29595. **8.** 31980. **9.** 33960. **10.** 39372. **11.** 47467. **12.** 408028. **13.** 292002. **14.** 489641. **15.** 500081. **16.** 485558. **17.** 4009575. **18.** 4066552. **19.** 4125789. **20.** 4246920. **21.** 4929077. **22.** 4571993. **23.** 4627806. **24.** 3894072. **25.** 59682383. **26.** 63954128. **27.** 76129904. **28.** 59356529. **29.** 44609196. **30.** 33485205. **31.** 22253849. **32.** 39479884. **33.** 33537. **34.** 367958. **35.** 318042. **36.** 258677. **37.** 277670. **38.** 304267. **39.** 343207. **40.** 345280. **41.** 237957. **42.** 341390. **43.** 1045358. **44.** 3840490. **45.** 2077898. **46.** 64138. **47.** 44467. **48.** 72527. **49.** 27803. **50.** 27810. **51.** 334834. **52.** 2126906. **53.** $50421. **54.** 13602. **55.** 1325 pounds. **56.** 108410. **57.** 1642. **58.** 80 feet. **59.** 745. **60.** 4790 pounds. **61.** 2847 bu. **62.** $10215. **63.** 1492. **64.** 60698 ft. **65.** 1797. **66.** 1314 ct. **67.** 399 ct. **68.** $34961. **69.** 1926. **70.** 1185 tons. **71.** 584870. **72.** 2000 miles. **73.** 594. **74.** 2690 pounds. **75.** $907. **76.** 1300 acres. **77.** $422. **78.** $9404. **79.** 540.

Article 26.—**1.** 1734. **2.** 46913. **3.** 29293. **4.** 80808. **5.** 2982314. **6.** 22222212. **7.** 33333323. **8.** 34202862. **9.** 26411091. **10.** 171089. **11.** 55000085. **12.** 199998989. **13.** 367889276. **14.** 900090828. **15.** 10921812. **16.** 87242906. **17.** 8999082. **18.** 3067534217. **19.** 89640055. **20.** 800028087. **21.** 80727. **22.** 2939607. **23.** 2286722. **24.** 15928384. **25.** 228170591. **26.** 10052418. **27.** 289226824. **28.** 1010094950.

29. 864197532. **30.** 3760326. **31.** 58990502765. **32.** 25630264. **33.** 194398963. **34.** 7855426. **35.** 191833945. **36.** 28775. **37.** 4567813. **38.** 4994505. **39.** 6276511. **40.** 87845. **41.** 31199027. **42.** 1160889. **43.** 7914100. **44.** 439999099616. **45.** 32731990913. **46.** $3032. **47.** $2469. **48.** $747. **49.** 273 acres. **50.** 67 years. **51.** 1789. **52.** $1445. **53.** $26716. **54.** $37028. **55.** 2361 feet. **56.** 2964. **57.** $1557. **58.** $8750. **59.** 179. **60.** 51 years. **61.** $9242. **62.** 668. **63.** 816. **64.** 9811. **65.** 37196748. **66.** 1738. **67.** 675. **68.** 582. **69.** 1625. **70.** 1830. **71.** 5839. **72.** 897. **73.** 1405. **74.** $523. **75.** 447 acres. **76.** 1003. **77.** 9566. **78.** 49018. **79.** $1687. **80.** 4200 pounds. **81.** $20218. **82.** $21950. **83.** $2414. **84.** $3200. **85.** $20879. **86.** $16590.

Article 31.—**1.** 1630. **2.** 4404. **3.** 3213. **4.** 3088. **5.** 3582. **6.** 2712. **7.** 45424. **8.** 68376. **9.** 38390. **10.** 80874. **11.** 40922. **12.** 55736. **13.** 2350257. **14.** 4239396. **15.** 4617896. **16.** 2868922. **17.** 2346330. **18.** 3661820. **19.** 6251157. **20.** 5647474. **21.** 6391920. **22.** 4082406. **23.** 2373460. **24.** 5570264. **25.** 3741367872. **26.** 2016536123. **27.** 6020532702. **28.** 7716935028. **29.** 9336976580. **30.** 6766294344. **31.** 4120819551. **32.** 5367983103. **33.** 7838070273. **34.** 6601. **35.** 10846. **36.** 9384. **37.** 15810. **38.** 9650. **39.** 12272. **40.** 33285. **41.** 21132. **42.** 35446. **43.** 262668. **44.** 182031. **45.** 278855. **46.** 181482. **47.** 528126. **48.** 352674. **49.** 543567. **50.** 224284. **51.** 76242. **52.** 31602. **53.** 291984. **54.** 243004. **55.** 445842. **56.** 766476. **57.** 223244. **58.** 665042. **59.** 374808. **60.** 892248. **61.** 3093120. **62.** 3589662. **63.** 3446546. **64.** 3856152. **65.** 3228646. **66.** 5769525. **67.** 18076200. **68.** 3378012. **69.** 1943212675. **70.** 3399899130. **71.** 3544904538. **72.** 41343239335. **73.** 7853233038. **74.** 27708855662. **75.** 9279625278. **76.** $6975. **77.** $6975. **78.** 16464 yd. **79.** 1215136 ct. **80.** 247101 lb. **81.** 241920 ems. **82.** 655960 lb. **83.** $98945. **84.** 214727 links. **85.** 120955 lb. **86.** 5695 men. **87.** $46494. **88.** 112683264 gal. **89.** 95091975 mi. **90.** 92512 lb. **91.** $404499. **92.** 45824 trees. **93.** 2108295 yd. **94.** 133152 lb. **95.** 7218882 vols. **96.** 205592 men.

Article 32.—**1.** 2985192. **2.** 8035104. **3.** 26710607. **4.** 194553198. **5.** 64065096. **6.** 18757728. **7.** 170321895. **8.** 604085568. **9.** 230351550. **10.** 26907755. **11.** 19039104. **12.** 72785952. **13.** 30948864. **14.** 52287552. **15.** 24088504. **16.** 73180665. **17.** 33273456. **18.** 70882476. **19.** 43096405. **20.** 52202416.

Article 33.—**1.** 28734000. **2.** 4986500. **3.** 6200945000. **4.** 3845030000. **5.** 46835700. **6.** 40050008000. **7.** 4007089300000. **8.** 37088900000. **9.** 268938450000. **10.** 3477926700. **11.** 4859602300000. **12.** 76540063000.

Article 34.—**1.** 26550. **2.** 3454360. **3.** 438570000. **4.** 1578960000. **5.** 3745950000. **6.** 38467552000. **7.** 3581783200000. **8.** 256576320000. **9.** 254356320. **10.** 23387136000. **11.** 56762721600000. **12.** 127264680000. **13.** 26980167900000. **14.** 4141190060. **15.** 551374704000. **16.** 70740913000. **17.** 13815594000000. **18.** 32213776000000. **19.** 131065010400. **20.** 128610595000.

Article 41.—**1.** 15226312. **2.** 8643753. **3.** 1428570380. **4.** 161401387. **5.** 49114887. **6.** 246913077. **7.** 164608718. **8.** 12345679. **9.** 37037037. **10.** 7008946. **11.** 10580037. **12.** 19146923. **13.** 90455625. **14.** 97393690. **15.** 1410934745. **16.** 69360054. **17.** 2000558288. **18.** 505279134. **19.** 86420132. **20.** 94909300. **21.** 4365777. **22.** 146090535. **23.** 98229774. **24.** 15432016. **25.** 70072815. **26.** 793651200. **27.** 68685608. **28.** 102863457. **29.** 333667334. **30.** 58007569. **31.** 934598. **32.** 920072. **33.** 8896037. **34.** 3208901. **35.** 7583366. **36.** 11201960. **37.** 7855064. **38.** 2600209. **39.** 5900470. **40.** $742. **41.** 1274. **42.** 415. **43.** 1204205. **44.** $162. **45.** 570 hr. **46.** 504. **47.** 575. **48.** 72. **49.** 349 lb. **50.** 429 miles. **51.** 128 weeks. **52.** 694. **53.** $2402. **54.** 2499. **55.** 273. **56.** 1296. **57.** $1028480. **58.** 15702. **59.** 2668.

Article 42.—**1.** 2738. **2.** 4386. **3.** 4623. **4.** 5387. **5.** 9876. **6.** 3875. **7.** 4639. **8.** 9375. **9.** 3896. **10.** 7199. **11.** 50731. **12.** 79308. **13.** 40065. **14.** 40508. **15.** 89490. **16.** 30972. **17.** 92312. **18.** 69234. **19.** 37401. **20.** 38495. **21.** 70193. **22.** 2038904. **23.** 50783. **24.** $30700\frac{11}{611}$. **25.** 68040. **26.** 38905. **27.** $133136\frac{32}{338}$. **28.** 19909. **29.** 40893. **30.** 60907. **31.** 38729. **32.** 70625. **33.** 4075008. **34.** $121440187\frac{7882}{8251}$. **35.** $67872653\frac{2232}{3456}$. **36.** $75690587\frac{1171}{4567}$. **37.** $80448947\frac{1934}{5678}$. **38.** 395. **39.** 156. **40.** 501. **41.** $305. **42.** 65. **43.** 285 days. **44.** 49 miles. **45.** 154 years. **46.** 78 miles. **47.** 3003. **48.** 1674 bu. **49.** 9208 lb. **50.** 7934. **51.** 1925. **52.** 107 min. **53.** 189 yd.

Article 43.—**1.** $188\frac{12}{24}$. **2.** 12649. **3.** $11641\frac{6}{32}$. **4.** $60813\frac{10}{45}$. **5.** $98508\frac{8}{48}$. **6.** 20864. **7.** $496796\frac{9}{27}$. **8.** $133643\frac{11}{28}$. **9.** 1514097. **10.** 1894074. **11.** $264550\frac{11}{42}$. **12.** $56811\frac{42}{63}$.

Article 44.—**1.** $47389\frac{256}{1000}$. **2.** $3678540\frac{1}{100}$. **3.** $2700000\frac{8746}{10000}$. **4.** $12345678\frac{92}{100}$. **5.** $3704605\frac{504}{1000}$. **6.** $98979\frac{69594}{100000}$. **7.** $1300270\frac{5}{100}$. **8.** $123843\frac{658}{1000}$. **9.** $44872\frac{362592}{1000000}$. **10.** $500070\frac{40}{10000}$. **11.** $3726483952\frac{7}{10}$. **12.** 430000. **13.** $12345654\frac{321}{1000}$. **14.** $754000\frac{400}{10000000000}$. **15.** $4763859\frac{2143}{10000}$.

Article 45.—**1.** $11823\frac{36}{40}$. **2.** $889842\frac{133}{140}$. **3.** $7098\frac{5324}{8000}$. **4.** $1809855\frac{882}{1900}$. **5.** $560300\frac{58}{470}$. **6.** $182344\frac{2062}{4050}$. **7.** $365137\frac{7713}{8800}$. **8.** $101604\frac{2967}{3400}$. **9.** $7153\frac{101384}{107000}$. **10.** 1282840750. **11.** $1415\frac{19500}{706700}$. **12.** $4092783\frac{49000}{97000}$. **13.** $18614\frac{1067467}{3050600}$. **14.** $10990\frac{19899}{90990}$.

Article 49.—**1.** $3296. **2.** 146640 ct. **3.** $13950. **4.** 359 A. **5.** 108419. **6.** 35 cows. **7.** 145 mules. **8.** 3088. **9.** 336735 ct. **10.** $1672. **11.** $308. **12.** $35. **13.** 2184. **14.** 51 men. **15.** 15 pounds. **16.** $7600. **17.** $16988. **18.** $10360. **19.** 69. **20.** 169. **21.** 3820 ct. **22.** 72. **23.** $10388. **24.** 448. **25.** $3736. **26.** $6240. **27.** $17001. **28.** 33462 lb. **29.** 948. **30.** $1855. **31.** 230. **32.** 244477. **33.** 97 horses. **34.** 385.

35. 82 hogs. **36.** 276676. **37.** $16. **38.** 800 times. **39.** $70. **40.** 1229 yd. **41.** 107677 yd. **42.** 2106320 lb. **43.** $1068. **44.** 15625 yd. **45.** $4140. **46.** 268850 lb. **47.** 12250 bu. **48.** 362. **49.** 262 A. **50.** 350 A. **51.** $2214. **52.** 35100 ct. **53.** 216.

Article 53.—1. $13.93. **2.** $87.493. **3.** $29.08. **4.** $157.50. **5.** $9.099. **6.** $12.002. **7.** $500.10. **8.** $200.003. **9.** $99.90. **10.** $90.99.

Article 55.—1. 9300 ct. **2.** $8. **3.** 460 m. **4.** 18 ct. 7 m. **5.** 760 ct. **6.** 45000 m. **7.** $3.009. **8.** 8917 ct. **9.** 70000 ct. **10.** 10000000 m. **11.** 4044 m. **12.** 46702 ct. **13.** 46700 ct. **14.** 83009 m. **15.** $123.

Article 56.—1. $227.75. **2.** $206. **3.** $1544. **4.** $2028.66. **5.** $63.95. **6.** $2646.95. **7.** $3857.85.

Article 57.—1. $33.34. **2.** $50.33. **3.** $23.91. **4.** $224.20. **5.** $89.10. **6.** $62.37. **7.** $309.91. **8.** $15138.60. **9.** $6317.82. **10.** $520.32. **11.** $370.40. **12.** $170.87.

Article 58.—1. $199.032. **2.** $354.06. **3.** $3675. **4.** $520.52. **5.** $547.20. **6.** $10803.20. **7.** $22224. **8.** $24.804. **9.** $121.176. **10.** $261090. **11.** $38082.80. **12.** $330.75. **13.** $10693.20. **14.** $3005.60. **15.** $393.228. **16.** $742.26. **17.** $114.72. **18.** $115.72. **19.** $877.50. **20.** $900. **21.** $3388.56. **22.** $27. **23.** $128.25. **24.** $99. **25.** $1263.50. **26.** $640. **27.** $13525.92. **28.** $783. **29.** $563.28. **30.** $384. **31.** $1275. **32.** $398.40. **33.** $3738.24. **34.** $6494.40. **35.** $13125. **36.** $7140.

Article 59.—1. 150. **2.** 525. **3.** 625. **4.** 740. **5.** 438. **6.** 735. **7.** 4760. **8.** 7090. **9.** 182 yards. **10.** 160 sheep. **11.** 6460 needles. **12.** 796 acres. **13.** 200. **14.** 152. **15.** 2500. **16.** $24.87. **17.** $13.572. **18.** $40.795. **19.** $48.448.

20. $15.56. **21.** $5.72. **22.** $3.056. **23.** $7.009. **24.** $113.89. **25.** $2.80. **26.** $48.04. **27.** 22 ct. 5 m. **28.** 62 ct. 5 m. **29.** $.055. **30.** $.075. **31.** $10104.20. **32.** $1.15. **33.** 3 ct. 5 m. **34.** $9. **35.** 48 pounds.

Article 60.—**1.** $4000. **2.** $100.95. **3.** 18 ct. **4.** 45 bu. **5.** $24.50. **6.** $62.58. **7.** $96.32. **8.** $81.40. **9.** $5.948. **10.** $37.98. **11.** $1072.95. **12.** $71.50. **13.** $2673.40. **14.** $500.50. **15.** $9.25. **16.** 400. **17.** 216. **18.** 80000. **19.** 36000. **20.** 166. **21.** $1071.72. **22.** $462.25. **23.** 349 days. **24.** $203. **25.** 2 ct. **26.** 79400 lb. **27.** $654.02. **28.** $59. **29.** 48 gallons. **30.** 70 miles. **31.** 3758. **32.** $2.35. **33.** $288.40. **34.** $67.54. **35.** $16.14. **36.** $99.73.

Article 63.—**1.** 309 pt. **2.** 581 pt. **3.** 1201 pt. **4.** 2310 pt. **5.** 2864 qt. **6.** 74 bu. 3 pk. 2 qt. 1 pt. **7.** 180 bu. 6 qt. **8.** 6399 pt. **9.** 37313 pt. **10.** 1929 bu. **11.** 78928 pt. **12.** 1639424 pt. **13.** 400 bu. 1 pk. **14.** 1543 pk. 1 qt. **15.** 224000000 qt.

Article 64.—**1.** 310 pt. **2.** 32 gal. 1 gi. **3.** 701072 pt. **4.** 2996 gi. **5.** 2983 gal. 1 qt. 1 pt. **6.** 276544 gi. **7.** 3194 gi. **8.** 466 qt. 1 pt. **9.** 2365 gi. **10.** 143 gal. **11.** 115500 cubic in. **12.** 226 gal.

Article 65.—**1.** 6000 lb. **2.** 11300 lb. **3.** 18150 lb. **4.** 15999 lb. **5.** 26013 lb. **6.** 155200 oz. **7.** 96325 oz. **8.** 6 T. 9 cwt. 45 lb. **9.** 49 T. 4 cwt. **10.** 438 T. 5 cwt. 43 lb. **11.** 1239744000 oz. **12.** 5 T. 5 lb. **13.** 143771 lb. **14.** 355 T. 17 cwt. 71 lb. **15.** 1250 T. **16.** 6 T. **17.** 281 T. 5 cwt. **18.** 34 T. 11 cwt. 20 lb. **19.** 499 T. 19 cwt. 99 lb. 15 oz. **20.** 9 T. 19 cwt. 92 lb.

Article 66.—**1.** 1797 in. **2.** 1915 in. **3.** 13320 rd. **4.** 2796 in. **5.** 1584960 rd. **6.** 157 yd. 2 ft. 2 in. **7.** 119 mi. 177 rd. **8.** 17939 in. **9.** 1168 mi. 85 rd. **10.** 1100 yd. 1 in. **11.** 12672320 rd. **12.** 123 mi. 241 rd.

Article 67.—1. 1220 sq.rd. **2.** 355200 sq.rd. **3.** 1948659 sq.rd. **4.** 24598 sq. in. **5.** 3993690 sq. rd. **6.** 128403 sq. in. **7.** 5120000000000 sq. rd. **8.** 771604 sq. yd. 8 sq. ft. 64 sq. in.

Articles 68 and 69.—1. 30 sq. yd. **2.** 66 sq. yd. **3.** 142 sq. yd. 2 sq. ft. **4.** 40 sq. yd. **5.** 80 sq. yd. **6.** 27 A. **7.** 38 A. **8.** 62 A. 80 sq. rd. **9.** $85.80. **10.** $12. **11.** $674.50. **12.** $38.40. **13.** 120 rd. **14.** 20 mi. **15.** 780 bu. **16.** 9 yd. **17.** 9 yd.

Article 70.—1. 74 cu. yd. 18 cu. ft. **2.** 140268 cu. in. **3.** 16 cu. yd. **4.** 77 C. **5.** 2625943 cu. in. **6.** 240 cu. yd. **7.** 30 C. **8.** 5120 cu. yd. **9.** $6600. **10.** $375. **11.** 10368. **12.** $570.

Article 71.—1. 268200 sec. **2.** 110880 min. **3.** 2084583 sec. **4.** 5475600 sec. **5.** 3715243 sec. 6. 1 wk. 2 da. **7.** 31 da. 17 hr. 18 min. **8.** 7560000000 sec. **9.** 7 wk. 1 da. **10.** 525600 min. **11.** 132480 min. **12.** 2419200 sec. **13.** 158112000 sec. **14.** 26280 hr. **15.** 63244800 times. **16.** 200000 min.

Article 73.—1. 103104 gr. **2.** 103698 gr. **3.** 143999 gr. **4.** 15 lb. 1 oz. 19 pwt. 4 gr. **5.** 211 lb. 1 oz. **6.** 7506000 pwt. **7.** 2 lb. 7 oz. 5 pwt. **8.** 24964 gr. **9.** 57840 gr. **10.** 21814 gr. **11.** 2603 ℈. **12.** 84007 gr. **13.** 7 ℔ 11 ℥ 1 ʒ 17 gr. **14.** 36 ℔ 2 ℥ 6 ʒ. **15.** 42 ℔ 10 ℥ 3 ʒ. **16.** 896 f. ℥. **17.** 24000 ♏. **18.** 72707 f. ʒ. **19.** 648 lines. **20.** 15 hands. **21.** 51 mi. **22.** 4 yd. **23.** 5 ft. 8 in. **24.** 80 spans. **25.** 117 hands. **26.** 40 fathoms. **27.** 4 fathoms 1 foot. **28.** 100 rd. **29.** 135457″. **30.** 68419″. **31.** 10° 31′ 4″. **32.** 1620000″. **33.** 360. **34.** 2160. **35.** 8640. **36.** 25 dozens. **37.** 50 gross. **38.** $72. **39.** $70.56. **40.** $192. **41.** $17.28. **42.** $10.40. **43.** $30.24. **44.** $2.52. **45.** $90.72. **46.** $17.28. **47.** 5760 sheets. **48.** 3840 leaves. **49.** 34560 pages. **50.** 125 reams.

Article 74.—1. 1788 in. **2.** 40392 gr. **3.** 134 sq. yd. 6 sq. ft. **4.** 3° 28′ 20″. **5.** 10 cu. yd. 21 cu. ft. 1152 cu. in. **6.** 17740 gr. **7.** 1 wk. 2 da. 23 hr. 59 min. 50 sec. **8.** 52 bu. 1 pt. **9.** 2016 dozens. **10.** 15300 lb. **11.** 103 yd. 2 ft. 2 in. **12.** 3317760 cu. in. **13.** 709 gal. 3 qt. **14.** 5184 barrels. **15.** 750 gross. **16.** 110592 qt. **17.** 165 lb. 7 oz. 10 pwt. **18.** 448224 oz. **19.** 23552 f. ʒ. **20.** 33 wk. 12 hr. **21.** 949 gal. 3 qt. 1 pt. **22.** 4 sq. mi. 162 A. 150 sq. rd. **23.** 76800 rd. **24.** 631 pt. **25.** 11491220 sec. **26.** 99510 rd. **27.** 1 T. 11 cwt. **28.** 1 wk. 4 da. 13 hr. 46 min. 40 sec. **29.** 81 C. **30.** 30816000 gr. **31.** 385 bu. 3 pk. 1 qt. **32.** 6832800 min. **33.** 599616 cu. in. **34.** 78039 lb. **35.** 49928 gr. **36.** 59940 sq. in. **37.** 1234 gal. 2 qt. **38.** 277 yd. 2 ft. 4 in. **39.** 20 bu. 2 qt. **40.** 5740 gr. **41.** 512005 sq. rd. **42.** 768 cu. yd. **43.** 199680 leaves. **44.** 13° 13′. **45.** 125000 gal. **46.** 7 ℥ 2 ʒ 1 ℈. **47.** 99 bu. 3 pk. 7 qt. 1 pt. **48.** 11520 sheets. **49.** 612 sq. yd. 4 sq. ft. 135 sq. in. **50.** 31 T. 5 cwt. **51.** 2855 in. **52.** 4204096 cu. in. **53.** 6 sq. mi. 560 A. **54.** 8816 pt. **55.** 3510055 sec. **56.** 4290 rd. **57.** 320000 lb. **58.** 961600 oz. **59.** 4 cu. yd. 18 cu. ft. **60.** 865 gal. **61.** 864 scores. **62.** 14 T. 5 cwt. 49 lb. 5 oz. **63.** 156 bu. 1 pk. **64.** 50423″. **65.** 1180 gal. **66.** 771 sq. yd. 5 sq. ft. 64 sq. in. **67.** 187 yd. **68.** 11 f. ℥. **69.** 36161 pt. **70.** 5 wk. 5 da. **71.** 300 reams. **72.** 9 T. **73.** 62020 sq. rd. **74.** 16320 rd. **75.** 18 C. 70 cu. ft. **76.** \$25.20. **77.** \$24.96. **78.** 2 cwt. 50 lb. **79.** 120 gal. **80.** \$36.27. **81.** 120. **82.** 368 dozen. **83.** \$75. **84.** \$16. **85.** \$136.80. **86.** 1496. **87.** 800. **88.** 1 min. 45 sec. **89.** 768. **90.** 1° 20′. **91.** \$61.25. **92.** 5400 lb. **93.** 7 lb. 6 oz. **94.** 2250 C. **95.** 56 doz. **96.** 60. **97.** 640. **98.** \$3.92. **99.** 4096 bu. **100.** 200 sq. yd. **101.** 5600. **102.** \$760. **103.** 400 doz. **104.** 2 da. 32 min. **105.** 4 hr. **106.** 6 bu. 1 pk. **107.** 125 reams. **108.** 2000 gal. **109.** \$9360. **110.** \$54.72. **111.** \$354. **112.** \$18. **113.** \$.035. **114.** \$121.50. **115.** 6 da. 16 hr. **116.** \$112.50. **117.** 160 T. **118.** \$144. **119.** 3 da. 4 hr. **120.** \$162. **121.** 133 cu. ft. 1176 cu. in. **122.** \$3.60. **123.** \$11650.80. **124.** \$247.50. **125.** 2592 score. **126.** 3 bu. 3 pk. 6 qt. **127.** \$224. **128.** 376. **129.** 282. **130.** \$460.80. **131.** \$8640. **132.** 75 doz. **133.** 331 gal. **134.** \$66. **135.** 16 da. **136.** 320 wk. **137.** 147 barrels. **138.** 1040 bags. **139.** 81 da. **140.** \$171.18. **141.** \$.075. **142.** \$76.80. **143.** 45 gal. **144.** 13824. 145. \$2.40. **146.** 72 sheets.

Article 75.—**1.** 60 bu. **2.** 900 bu. **3.** 192 gal. 2 qt. **4.** 31 T. 16 cwt. 11 lb. **5.** 151 gal. 1 pt. **6.** 4 T. 10 cwt. **7.** 177 gal. 3 qt. **8.** 79 yd. **9.** 57 yd. 1 ft. 3 in. **10.** 500 A. 38 sq. rd. **11.** 127 sq. yd. 3 sq. ft. 43 sq. in. **12.** 34 sq. mi. 330 A. **13.** 152 cu. yd. 6 cu. ft. **14.** 377 C. 7 cu. ft. 1130 cu. in. **15.** 57 da. 9 hr. 26 min. **16.** 5 wk. 6 hr. 32 min. **17.** 42 lb. 11 oz. **18.** 3 ℥ 5 ʒ. **19.** 2 ℔ 8 ℥. **20.** 23 score and 3. **21.** 119° 50′. **22.** 61° 1′ 1″. **23.** 35 Cong. 15 f. ℥. **24.** 1 O. 4 f. ℥. **25.** 361 gal. 3 qt. **26.** 253 C. 88 cu. ft. **27.** 258 dozen. **28.** 4 T. 18 cwt. **29.** 102 A. **30.** 149 da. 14 hr. **31.** 100 mi. 160 rd. **32.** 24 da. 23 hr. 36 min. 2 sec.

Article 76.—**1.** 19 bu. 3 pk. 5 qt. **2.** 19 bu. 1 pk. 6 qt. **3.** 50 gal. 1 pt. 2 gi. **4.** 149 gal. 1 qt. 1 pt. **5.** 1 T. 15 cwt. 18 lb. **6.** 9 cwt. 89 lb. 6 oz. **7.** 23 mi. 250 rd. **8.** 7 yd. 11 in. **9.** 62 yd. 2 ft. 10 in. **10.** 4 sq. mi. 370 A. **11.** 17 sq. yd. 5 sq. ft. 99 sq. in. **12.** 199 sq. mi. 639 A. 110 sq. rd. **13.** 27 cu. yd. 17 cu. ft. 1628 cu. in. **14.** 62 C. 127 cu. ft. 1706 cu. in. **15.** 2 hr. 46 min. 2 sec. **16.** 4 wk. 1 da. 23 hr. 57 min. 56 sec. **17.** 5 lb. 7 oz. 7 pwt. **18.** 2 ℔ 9 ℥ 4 ʒ 2 ℈. **19.** 4° 48′ 40″. **20.** 6 reams 16 quires. **21.** 1 gross 8 dozen. **22.** 6 f. ℥ 2 f. ʒ. **23.** 14 bu. 6 qt. **24.** 176 bu. 2 pk. **25.** 1 wk. 1 da. 7 hr. **26.** 316 gal. 3 qt. **27.** 83 A. 40 sq. rd. **28.** 3 cwt. 58 lb. **29.** 18 C. 113 cu. ft. **30.** 2 T. 18 cwt. 10 lb. **31.** 8° 23′ 40″. **32.** 4 ℥ 3 ʒ 10 gr. **33.** 276 T. 19 cwt. 70 lb. **34.** 96 hr. 18 min. **35.** 21 C. 32 cu. ft. **36.** 13 bu. 3 pk. **37.** 13 da. 11 hr. 3 min.

Article 77.—**1.** 1 yr. 7 mo. 18 da. **2.** 84 yr. 2 mo. 19 da. **3.** 67 yr. 9 mo. 22 da. **4.** 155 yr. 6 mo. 13 da. **5.** 1 yr. 10 mo. 14 da. **6.** 6 yr. 8 mo. 24 da. **7.** 46 yr. 4 mo. 6 da. **8.** 85 yr. 11 mo. 23 da.

Article 78.—**1.** 119 da. **2.** 64 da. **3.** 146 da. **4.** 277 da. **5.** 203 da. **6.** 195 da. **7.** 361 da. **8.** 162 da.

Article 79.—**1.** 29 bu. 1 pk. 4 qt. **2.** 63 gal. 3 qt. **3.** 1 T. 12 cwt. 75 lb. **4.** 64 yd. 1 ft. 5 in. **5.** 23 sq. yd. **6.** 2 cu. yd. 20 cu. ft. 88 cu. in. **7.** 6 lb. 8 oz. 18 pwt. **8.** 2 ℔ 5 ℥. **9.** 227

gal. 1 qt. **10.** 78° 12′. **11.** 20 reams 10 quires. **12.** 276 mi. 230 rd. **13.** 55 da. 7 hr. 35 min. 24 sec. **14.** 43 T. 15 cwt. 34 lb. **15.** 138 bu. 4 qt. **16.** 1073 yd. 1 ft. **17.** 37 bu. 2 pk. **18.** 24 da. 10 hr. 20 min. **19.** 1 hr. 54 min. 40 sec. **20.** 274 T. 15 cwt. 40 lb. **21.** 489 sq. yd. 120 sq. in. **22.** 41 bu.

Article 80.—**1.** 3 bu. 2 pk. 3 qt. **2.** 3 cwt. 72 lb. 9 oz. **3.** 3 yd. 2 ft. 4 in. **4.** 7 sq. ft. 88 sq. in. **5.** 3 hr. 30 min. 40 sec. **6.** 3 pwt. 14 gr. **7.** 1 ʒ 2 ℈ 10 gr. **8.** 7 gal. 2 qt. 1 gi. **9.** 7 yd. 8 in. **10.** 1 sq. yd. 2 sq. ft. 24 sq. in. **11.** 2 da. 7 hr. 20 min. **12.** 1 cu. yd. 864 cu. in. **13.** 23 bu. 3 pk. 1 qt. **14.** 5 gal. 1 qt. 1 pt. 3 gi. **15.** 98 lb. 5 oz. **16.** 5 cu. yd. 15 cu. ft. **17.** 16 da. 7 hr. 34 min. **18.** 32′ 26″. **19.** 249 bu. 1 pk. 4 qt. **20.** 7 mi. 206 rd. **21.** 3 T. 9 cwt. 40 lb. **22.** 1 bu. 2 pk. 7 qt.

Articles 81 and 82.—**1.** 2 hr. 40 min. **2.** 2 hr. 13 min. 20 sec. **3.** 2 hr. 25 min. 8 sec. **4.** 4 hr. 39 min. 24 sec. **5.** 6 hr. 40 min. 40 sec. **6.** 3 hr. 16 min. 54 sec. **7.** 4 hr. 24 min. 3 sec. **8.** 4 hr. 41 min. 9 sec. **9.** 6 hr. 36 min. 36 sec. **10.** 7 hr. 27 min. 26 sec. **11.** 3 hr. 55 min. 53 sec. **12.** 6 hr. 31 min. 32 sec. **13.** 169° 18′ 15″. **14.** 104° 49′ 15″. **15.** 152° 32′ 30″. **16.** 109° 21′ 45″. **17.** 228° 37′ 15″. **18.** 71° 17′ 30″. **19.** 82° 21′ 15″. **20.** 11° 56′ 45″. **21.** 1 hr. 56 min. slow. **22.** 3 hr. 8 min. fast. **23.** Shortened 3 min. **24.** 5 hr. 32 min. **25.** 10 hr. 36 min. A.M. **26.** 2 hr. 32 min. A.M. **27.** 6 hr. 20 min. P.M. **28.** 10 hr. 16 min. A.M. **29.** 6 P.M. previous day. **30.** 5 hr. 39 min.

Article 87.—**1.** 3, 17. **2.** 2, 2, 13. **3** 2, 31. **4.** 3, 3, 7. **5.** 2, 2, 2, 3, 3. **6.** 3, 5, 5. **7.** 2, 2, 19. **8.** 2, 2, 2, 3, 5 **9.** 2, 2, 3, 11. **10.** 2, 2, 2, 3, 7. **11.** 2, 2, 7, 7. **12.** 2, 3, 3, 11. **13.** 2, 2, 3, 17. **14.** 3, 3, 23. **15.** 2, 2, 3, 3, 7. **16.** 3, 11, 17. **17.** 2, 3, 3, 7, 7. **18.** 2, 2, 3, 3, 23. **19.** 2, 11, 11, 11. **20.** 3, 3, 7, 7, 7. **21.** 2, 2, 3, 3, 11, 11.

Article 88.—**1.** 2, 2, 5. **2.** 2, 3, 5. **3.** 2, 2, 2, 5. **4.** 3, 3, 5. **5.** 2, 3, 7. **6.** 2, 2, 3, 3, 3. **7.** 2, 3, 3, 3. **8.** 2, 11. **9.** 3, 7. **10.** 5, 7. **11.** 3, 11. **12.** 2, 2, 3. **13.** 13. **14.** 2, 2, 3. **15.** 2, 2, 2. **16.** 3, 5. **17.** 2, 2, 2, 3. **18.** 13. **19.** 2, 7. **20.** 11. **21.** 7. **22.** 2, 3.

Article 89.—**1.** 12. **2.** 10. **3.** 9. **4.** 7. **5.** 4. **6.** 78. **7.** 49. **8.** 11. **9.** 9. **10.** 82. **11.** 49. **12.** 21. **13.** 144. **14.** 144. **15.** 37. **16.** 27. **17.** 14. **18.** 20. **19.** 36. **20.** 27. **21.** 7. **22.** 17. **23.** 9. **24.** 15. **25.** 3. **26.** 9. **27.** 2.

Article 90.—**1.** 240. **2.** 720. **3.** 240. **4.** 400. **5.** 3024. **6.** 840. **7.** 1980. **8.** 4620. **9.** 7920. **10.** 720. **11.** 720. **12.** 360. **13.** 3024. **14.** 14762. **15.** 4199. **16.** 4225. **17.** 5145. **18.** 2250. **19.** 600. **20.** 1848. **21.** 25025. **22.** 2288. **23.** 144. **24.** 2880. **25.** 702. **26.** 2304. **27.** 3960. **28.** 16200. **29.** 30870. **30.** 8610.

Article 91.—**1.** 9 times. **2.** 3. **3.** 24 times. **4.** 6 times. **5.** 15. **6.** 54. **7.** 24. **8.** 32. **9.** 24. **10.** 16. **11.** 36. **12.** 102. **13.** 360. **14.** 120. **15.** 18 (hundred).

Article 103.—**1.** $\frac{98}{7}$. **2.** $\frac{253}{11}$. **3.** $\frac{161}{23}$. **4.** $\frac{1134}{18}$. **5.** $\frac{810}{9}$. **6.** $\frac{992}{32}$. **7.** $\frac{168}{56}$. **8.** $\frac{208}{8}$. **9.** $\frac{2835}{9}$. **10.** $\frac{2400}{12}$. **11.** $\frac{666}{18}$. **12.** $\frac{1360}{40}$. **13.** $\frac{280}{20}$. **14.** $\frac{351}{13}$. **15.** $\frac{496}{16}$. **16.** $\frac{1474}{22}$. **17.** $\frac{1710}{90}$. **18.** $\frac{2349}{29}$.

Article 104.—**1.** $\frac{127}{8}$. **2.** $\frac{138}{7}$. **3.** $\frac{892}{9}$. **4.** $\frac{731}{10}$. **5.** $\frac{548}{15}$. **6.** $\frac{767}{18}$. **7.** $\frac{1234}{7}$. **8.** $\frac{362}{19}$. **9.** $\frac{521}{18}$. **10.** $\frac{995}{22}$. **11.** $\frac{5337}{73}$. **12.** $\frac{2903}{100}$. **13.** $\frac{3000}{11}$. **14.** $\frac{10696}{27}$. **15.** $\frac{7871}{14}$. **16.** $\frac{10001}{100}$. **17.** $\frac{10923}{16}$. **18.** $\frac{5303}{41}$. **19.** $\frac{3223}{111}$. **20.** $\frac{400}{19}$. **21.** $\frac{7300}{99}$.

Article 105.—**1.** $76\frac{1}{6}$. **2.** 46. **3.** 177. **4.** $123\frac{9}{10}$. **5.** $362\frac{4}{13}$. **6.** $174\frac{7}{15}$. **7.** $243\frac{1}{19}$. **8.** $145\frac{3}{17}$. **9.** $163\frac{4}{23}$. **10.** $33\frac{13}{22}$. **11.** $403\frac{5}{14}$. **12.** $152\frac{21}{26}$. **13.** 230. **14.** $141\frac{25}{33}$. **15.** 39. **16.** $98\frac{76}{100}$. **17.** 81. **18.** $82\frac{4}{15}$. **19.** 218. **20.** $536\frac{17}{23}$. **21.** $48\frac{22}{97}$.

Article 106.—**1.** $\frac{12}{33}$. **2.** $\frac{25}{60}$ **3.** $\frac{15}{40}$. **4.** $\frac{28}{35}$. **5.** $\frac{85}{100}$. **6.** $\frac{112}{126}$. **7.** $\frac{80}{105}$. **8.** $\frac{144}{156}$. **9.** $\frac{153}{171}$. **10.** $\frac{238}{280}$. **11.** $\frac{210}{345}$. **12.** $\frac{204}{336}$. **13.** $\frac{240}{464}$. **14.** $\frac{221}{416}$. **15.** $\frac{972}{1368}$. **16.** $\frac{7128}{7744}$. **17.** $\frac{4161}{4560}$. **18.** $\frac{221}{3604}$. **19.** $\frac{203}{1911}$. **20.** $\frac{6086}{6698}$.

Article 107.—**1.** $\frac{6}{7}$. **2.** $\frac{2}{3}$. **3.** $\frac{27}{47}$. **4.** $\frac{81}{143}$. **5.** $\frac{11}{27}$. **6.** $\frac{37}{90}$. **7.** $\frac{11}{12}$. **8.** $\frac{16}{21}$. **9.** $\frac{25}{47}$. **10.** $\frac{2}{7}$. **11.** $\frac{41}{43}$. **12.** $\frac{37}{50}$. **13.** $\frac{96}{121}$. **14.** $\frac{35}{44}$. **15.** $\frac{9}{17}$. **16.** $\frac{4}{5}$. **17.** $\frac{7}{11}$. **18.** $\frac{2}{3}$. **19.** $\frac{13}{27}$. **20.** $\frac{25}{64}$. **21.** $\frac{4001}{5001}$.

Article 108.—**1.** $\frac{40}{60}, \frac{15}{60}, \frac{36}{60}$. **2.** $\frac{72}{90}, \frac{75}{90}, \frac{80}{90}$. **3.** $\frac{21}{56}, \frac{42}{56}, \frac{24}{56}$. **4.** $\frac{40}{90}, \frac{63}{90}, \frac{48}{90}$. **5.** $\frac{24}{60}, \frac{18}{60}, \frac{16}{60}, \frac{27}{60}$. **6.** $\frac{42}{48}, \frac{28}{48}, \frac{21}{48}, \frac{14}{48}$. **7.** $\frac{108}{120}, \frac{70}{120}, \frac{54}{120}, \frac{35}{120}$. **8.** $\frac{32}{120}, \frac{25}{120}, \frac{28}{120}, \frac{27}{120}$. **9.** $\frac{156}{240}, \frac{78}{240}, \frac{52}{240}, \frac{39}{240}$. **10.** $\frac{1287}{2002}, \frac{819}{2002}, \frac{693}{2002}$. **11.** $\frac{56}{72}, \frac{60}{72}, \frac{54}{72}, \frac{27}{72}, \frac{30}{72}$. **12.** $\frac{12}{100}, \frac{35}{100}, \frac{90}{100}, \frac{22}{100}$. **13.** $\frac{27}{36}, \frac{6}{36}, \frac{28}{36}, \frac{33}{36}, \frac{12}{36}$. **14.** $\frac{528}{1056}, \frac{88}{1056}, \frac{48}{1056}, \frac{33}{1056}$. **15.** $\frac{36}{120}, \frac{66}{120}, \frac{50}{120}, \frac{105}{120}$. **16.** $\frac{12}{144}, \frac{64}{144}, \frac{45}{144}, \frac{104}{144}$. **17.** $\frac{24}{90}, \frac{25}{90}, \frac{63}{90}, \frac{15}{90}$. **18.** $\frac{192}{720}, \frac{200}{720}, \frac{504}{720}, \frac{45}{720}$. **19.** $\frac{378}{1008}, \frac{280}{1008}, \frac{324}{1008}, \frac{147}{1008}$. **20.** $\frac{22}{30}, \frac{21}{30}, \frac{20}{30}, \frac{25}{30}$. **21.** $\frac{1540}{6930}, \frac{2079}{6930}, \frac{1980}{6930}, \frac{1890}{6930}$. **22.** $\frac{90}{144}, \frac{112}{144}, \frac{63}{144}, \frac{56}{144}$. **23.** $\frac{24}{132}, \frac{8}{132}, \frac{18}{132}, \frac{9}{132}$. **24.** $\frac{20}{12}, \frac{21}{12}, \frac{22}{12}, \frac{19}{12}$. **25.** $\frac{168}{60}, \frac{28}{60}, \frac{198}{60}, \frac{33}{60}$. **26.** $\frac{132}{144}, \frac{135}{144}, \frac{136}{144}, \frac{138}{144}$. **27.** $\frac{360}{630}, \frac{315}{630}, \frac{280}{630}, \frac{252}{630}$. **28.** $\frac{117}{144}, \frac{288}{144}, \frac{78}{144}, \frac{52}{144}, \frac{39}{144}$. **29.** $\frac{1071}{1260}, \frac{1080}{1260}, \frac{810}{1260}, \frac{1190}{1260}, \frac{1155}{1260}$. **30.** $\frac{32}{72}, \frac{27}{72}, \frac{420}{72}, \frac{126}{72}, \frac{642}{72}$.

Article 110.—**1.** $2\frac{2}{3}$. **2.** $2\frac{2}{3}$. **3.** $2\frac{5}{12}$. **4.** $2\frac{1}{2}$. **5.** $1\frac{1}{24}$. **6.** $\frac{4}{7}$. **7.** $2\frac{13}{20}$. **8.** $1\frac{29}{72}$. **9.** $\frac{11}{12}$. **10.** $1\frac{15}{16}$. **11.** $2\frac{7}{24}$. **12.** $2\frac{1}{2}$. **13.** $1\frac{17}{80}$. **14.** $2\frac{2}{45}$.

Article 111.—**1.** $1\frac{9}{16}$. **2.** $2\frac{5}{56}$. **3.** $2\frac{5}{8}$. **4.** $2\frac{8}{15}$. **5.** $6\frac{13}{56}$. **6.** $1\frac{1121}{1716}$. **7.** $1.\frac{107}{216}$. **8.** $2\frac{391}{420}$. **9.** $2\frac{101}{120}$. **10.** $23\frac{19}{24}$. **11.** $29\frac{71}{120}$. **12.** $98\frac{7}{12}$. **13.** $154\frac{5}{8}$. **14.** $555\frac{7}{8}$. **15.** $1498\frac{19}{24}$. **16.** $2\frac{4}{5}$. **17.** $2\frac{1}{40}$. **18.** $5\frac{23}{24}$. **19.** $14\frac{1}{24}$. **20.** $12\frac{35}{36}$. **21.** $13\frac{5}{12}$. **22.** $2\frac{19}{60}$. **23.** $7\frac{19}{24}$. **24.** $36\frac{1}{8}$. **25.** 55. **26.** $7\frac{1}{18}$. **27.** $2\frac{25}{56}$. **28.** $948\frac{11}{504}$. **29.** $174\frac{71}{120}$. **30.** $35\frac{43}{60}$.

Article 113.—**1.** $13\frac{5}{8}$. **2.** $24\frac{3}{10}$. **3.** $8\frac{4}{9}$. **4.** $9\frac{2}{5}$. **5.** $72\frac{1}{2}$. **6.** $11\frac{3}{5}$. **7.** $8\frac{3}{4}$. **8.** $159\frac{1}{3}$. **9.** $9\frac{11}{12}$. **10.** $19\frac{18}{25}$. **11.** $11\frac{2}{3}$. **12.** $199\frac{3}{4}$. **13.** $142\frac{19}{24}$. **14.** $74\frac{8}{9}$. **15.** $287\frac{1}{2}$ **16.** $26\frac{1}{5}$. **17.** $352\frac{2}{5}$. **18.** $368\frac{31}{49}$. **19.** $11\frac{22}{25}$. **20.** $327\frac{89}{100}$. **21.** $186\frac{18}{23}$. **22.** $53\frac{15}{16}$. **23.** $876\frac{1}{2}$. **24.** $279\frac{31}{60}$.

Article 114.—**1.** $\frac{1}{24}$. **2.** $\frac{13}{77}$. **3.** $\frac{1}{60}$. **4.** $\frac{29}{144}$. **5.** $\frac{23}{60}$. **6.** $\frac{29}{60}$. **7.** $\frac{13}{36}$. **8.** $\frac{15}{56}$. **9.** $\frac{13}{80}$. **10.** $\frac{7}{132}$. **11.** $3\frac{5}{12}$. **12.** $3\frac{17}{24}$. **13.** $1\frac{43}{252}$. **14.** $7\frac{3}{16}$. **15.** $1\frac{4}{21}$. **16.** $8\frac{191}{342}$. **17.** $5\frac{173}{220}$. **18.** $652\frac{8}{21}$. **19.** $578\frac{27}{28}$. **20.** $4\frac{211}{240}$. **21.** $21\frac{569}{600}$. **22.** $102\frac{39}{40}$. **23.** $8989\frac{7}{66}$.

Article 115.—1. $\frac{63}{80}$. **2.** $\frac{2}{9}$. **3.** $\frac{3}{10}$. **4.** $\frac{7}{18}$. **5.** $\frac{51}{250}$. **6.** $2\frac{1}{4}$. **7.** $\frac{1}{9}$. **8.** $\frac{5}{8}$. **9.** $\frac{10}{63}$. **10.** $1\frac{5}{7}$. **11.** $14\frac{6}{11}$. **12.** $8\frac{4}{7}$. **13.** $145\frac{3}{5}$. **14.** $34\frac{2}{7}$. **15.** 154. **16.** 84. **17.** $320\frac{2}{5}$. **18.** 675. **19.** $3473\frac{1}{3}$. **20.** $189\frac{1}{16}$. **21.** $2441406\frac{1}{4}$. **22.** $32\frac{14}{15}$. **23.** $306\frac{2}{3}$. **24.** 500. **25.** 1960. **26.** $26\frac{2}{3}$. **27.** $9\frac{6}{25}$. **28.** 840. **29.** $31\frac{1}{33}$. **30.** 32130. **31.** 5200. **32.** $48\frac{8}{9}$.

Article 116.—1. $63\frac{7}{11}$. **2.** $156\frac{3}{5}$. **3.** $77\frac{1}{2}$. **4.** $21\frac{7}{9}$. **5.** $\frac{72}{91}$. **6.** $18\frac{19}{30}$. **7.** $17\frac{1}{19}$. **8.** $37\frac{1}{3}$. **9.** $1\frac{67}{120}$. **10.** $662\frac{1}{2}$. **11.** $100\frac{4}{5}$. **12.** $56\frac{8}{19}$.

Article 117.—1. $\frac{27}{38}$. **2.** $\frac{17}{28}$. **3.** $1\frac{1}{9}$. **4.** $8\frac{1}{3}$. **5.** $\frac{85}{168}$. **6.** $1\frac{14}{195}$. **7.** $\frac{1}{45}$. **8.** $10\frac{26}{45}$. **9.** $10\frac{4}{15}$. **10.** $\frac{1}{675}$. **11.** $6\frac{3}{7}$. **12.** 7. **13.** $4\frac{7}{12}$. **14.** $10\frac{1}{5}$. **15.** $1\frac{7}{17}$. **16.** $2\frac{59}{128}$. **17.** $\frac{5}{78}$. **18.** $23\frac{4}{7}$. **19.** $\frac{3}{40}$. **20.** $5\frac{7}{9}$. **21.** $\frac{931}{2250}$. **22.** $2\frac{1}{2}$. **23.** $1\frac{1}{3}$. **24.** $84\frac{7}{12}$. **25.** $\frac{27}{35}$. **26.** $24\frac{14}{15}$. **27.** $5\frac{35}{57}$. **28.** $\frac{105}{116}$.

Article 118.—1. $31\frac{1}{4}$ ct. **2.** $56\frac{1}{4}$ ct. **3.** $64\frac{7}{12}$ ct. **4.** \$85. **5.** \$$11\frac{1}{5}$. **6.** \$$6\frac{9}{16}$. **7.** \$41280. **8.** \$$10\frac{4}{5}$. **9.** \$$4.84\frac{3}{8}$. **10.** 45 ct. **11.** \$1. **12.** \$177.30. **13.** $2\frac{5}{6}$. **14.** $7\frac{15}{28}$. **15.** $31\frac{17}{25}$. **16.** $89\frac{1}{10}$ mi. **17.** \$$136\frac{2}{3}$. **18.** 19 A. **19.** $9\frac{11}{16}$ C. **20.** \$16. **21.** \$125. **22.** \$$12\frac{13}{16}$. **23.** \$$1.37\frac{1}{2}$. **24.** $2\frac{32}{45}$ A.

Article 119.—1. $1\frac{1}{6}$. **2.** $\frac{6}{7}$. **3.** $1\frac{1}{2}$. **4.** $6\frac{2}{3}$. **5.** $21\frac{1}{3}$. **6.** $\frac{3}{160}$. **7.** $1\frac{1}{84}$. **8.** $5\frac{13}{36}$. **9.** $\frac{2}{5}$. **10.** $3\frac{1}{13}$. **11.** $17\frac{1}{2}$. **12.** $\frac{4}{15}$. **13.** $4\frac{2}{5}$. **14.** $4\frac{2}{7}$. **15.** $48\frac{6}{13}$. **16.** $\frac{2}{125}$. **17.** 1700. **18.** $3\frac{9}{11}$. **19.** $1\frac{47}{120}$. **20.** $5\frac{5}{7}$. **21.** $\frac{50}{63}$. **22.** 375. **23.** $9\frac{1}{5}$. **24.** $95\frac{3}{25}$. **25.** $\frac{18}{65}$. **26.** $\frac{11}{500}$. **27.** $21\frac{7}{16}$. **28.** $\frac{3}{5}$. **29.** $1127\frac{1}{4}$. **30.** $2\frac{2402}{2967}$. **31.** $1\frac{11}{24}$ ct. **32.** \$$34\frac{11}{14}$. **33.** $57\frac{11}{20}$ A. **34.** $\frac{1}{12}$ yd. **35.** $17\frac{7}{9}$ ct. **36.** $17\frac{19}{43}$ lb. **37.** $\frac{4}{15}$ lb. **38.** 45. **39.** $\frac{1}{24}$ oz. **40.** \$$3\frac{3}{16}$. **41.** $9\frac{3}{8}$ da. **42.** \$$\frac{16}{95}$. **43.** $12\frac{6}{7}$ yd. **44.** $8\frac{16}{25}$ lb. **45.** $7\frac{9}{25}$ da.

Article 120.—1. $\frac{3}{8}$. **2.** $\frac{4}{15}$. **3.** $\frac{1}{49}$. **4.** $\frac{13}{15}$. **5.** $\frac{7}{10}$. **6.** $\frac{1}{12}$. **7.** $\frac{9}{14}$. **8.** $\frac{72}{77}$. **9.** $\frac{1}{24}$. **10.** $\frac{9}{196}$. **11.** $\frac{3}{20}$. **12.** $\frac{15}{77}$. **13.** $\frac{7}{10}$. **14.** $\frac{7}{9}$. **15.** $\frac{1}{30}$. **16.** $\frac{35}{72}$.

Article 121.—**1.** $\frac{63}{80}$. **2.** $\frac{20}{21}$. **3.** $\frac{32}{45}$. **4.** $\frac{21}{880}$. **5.** $\frac{11}{53}$. **6.** $\frac{65}{132}$. **7.** $3\frac{1}{5}$. **8.** $\frac{21}{464}$. **9.** $\frac{369}{1240}$. **10.** $\frac{5}{49}$. **11.** $\frac{35}{48}$. **12.** $\frac{2}{3}$. **13.** $\frac{40}{129}$. **14.** $\frac{4}{9}$. **15.** $\frac{4}{9}$.

Article 122.—**1.** $2\frac{13}{16}$. **2.** $3\frac{1}{5}$. **3.** $4\frac{31}{56}$ lb. **4.** \$$13\frac{3}{4}$. **5.** $1\frac{3}{5}$. **6.** \$$61\frac{3}{5}$. **7.** $3\frac{3}{14}$ yd. **8.** $33\frac{2}{3}$ lb. **9.** $5\frac{1}{3}$ times. **10.** 8. **11.** $13\frac{8}{9}$ A. **12.** $\frac{27}{98}$. **13.** 40. **14.** $1\frac{61}{64}$. **15.** $\frac{1}{100}$. **16.** \$$16\frac{4}{5}$. **17.** $13\frac{1}{3}$ yd.

Article 123.—**1.** 132 yd. **2.** 4840 sq. yd. **3.** 40 yr. 80 da. **4.** \$$3.82\frac{1}{2}$. **5.** 22869 sq. ft. **6.** \$$180\frac{2}{5}$. **7.** 952 sq. rd. **8.** \$53.20. **9.** \$123.75. **10.** \$$33.47\frac{1}{2}$. **11.** 112392 hr. **12.** \$$15.31\frac{1}{4}$. **13.** \$21.25. **14.** $35\frac{11}{15}$ ct. **15.** $29\frac{1}{7}$ ct. **16.** \$$1.89\frac{5}{8}$. **17.** $32\frac{5}{8}$ ct. **18.** 10 mi. 12 rd. 2 ft. **19.** 18150 sq. yd. **20.** 2 mi. 4 rd. **21.** 18817920 sq. in. **22.** 12 rd. **23.** 9600. **24.** 77 yr. $35\frac{3}{4}$ da.

Articles 124 and 125.—**1.** $\frac{3}{4}$ qt. **2.** $\frac{28}{45}$ pt. **3.** $\frac{4}{5}$ oz. **4.** $\frac{121}{125}$ sq. yd. **5.** $\frac{2}{5}$ cu. ft. **6.** $\frac{3}{4}$ da. **7.** $\frac{17}{25}$ oz. **8.** $\frac{18}{25}$ pwt. **9.** $\frac{11}{20}$ ℈. **10.** $\frac{64}{65}$ sq. rd. **11.** $\frac{2187}{15625}$ cu. in. **12.** $\frac{24}{25}$ sec. **13.** $\frac{1}{125}$ pt. **14.** $\frac{132}{175}$ min. **15.** $\frac{384}{875}$ gi. **16.** 2 qt. 3 gi. **17.** 12 cwt. 72 lb. $11\frac{7}{11}$ oz. **18.** 302 rd. 1 yd. 8 in. **19.** 153 sq. rd. 10 sq. yd. 108 sq. in. **20.** 202 da. 22 hr. **21.** 9 oz. 6 pwt. 16 gr. **22.** 3 qt. 1 pt. $3\frac{7}{15}$ gi. **23.** 7 ℥ 1 ℈ 10 gr. **24.** 9 cwt. 37 lb. 8 oz. **25.** 2 yd. **26.** 1′ 48″. **27.** 5 A. 46 sq. rd. 8 sq. yd. 4 sq. ft. 72 sq. in. **28.** 3 rd. 1 yd. $3\frac{3}{5}$ in. **29.** 39 cu. ft. $874\frac{2}{3}$ cu. in. **30.** 3 f. ℥ 1 f. ʒ 36 ♏. **31.** 10 hr. 57 min. $46\frac{2}{3}$ sec.

Article 126.—**1.** $\frac{1}{1800}$ da. **2.** $\frac{1}{2560}$ C. **3.** $\frac{1}{1152}$ sq. yd. **4.** $\frac{1}{2250}$ cwt. **5.** $\frac{2}{19}$ gal. **6.** $\frac{1}{10}$ bu. **7.** $\frac{1}{1600}$ oz. **8.** $\frac{1}{3072}$ cu. yd. **9.** $\frac{1}{88}$ lb. **10.** $\frac{1}{240}$ mi. **11.** $\frac{3}{10240000}$ sq. mi. **12.** $\frac{1}{90}$ yr. **13.** $\frac{1}{2880}$ T. **14.** $\frac{1}{216}$ chain. **15.** $\frac{9}{112}$ gal. **16.** $\frac{1}{512}$ bu.

Article 127.—**1.** $\frac{4}{15}$. **2.** $\frac{34}{65}$. **3.** $\frac{1}{72}$. **4.** $\frac{5}{26}$. **5.** $\frac{1}{9}$. **6.** $\frac{807}{2420}$. **7.** $\frac{11}{40}$. **8.** $\frac{5}{61}$. **9.** $\frac{50}{171}$. **10.** $\frac{3}{10}$. **11.** $\frac{161}{320}$. **12.** $\frac{7}{24}$. **13.** $\frac{1}{360}$.

Article 128.—1. 1 sq. ft. 72 sq. in. **2.** 124 cu. ft. **3.** 44′ 12″. **4.** 4 oz. 12 pwt. **5.** 6 cwt. 70 lb. **6.** 1 Cong. 3 O. 5 f. ℥ 2 f. ʒ 40 ♏. **7.** 191 rd. 2 yd. 1 ft. 4 in. **8.** 3 rd. 2 yd. 2 ft. 5 in. **9.** 5 da. 17 hr. 16 min. **10.** 3 pk. 7 qt. **11.** 2 qt. 1 pt. **12.** 12 cwt. 9 lb. 4 oz. **13.** 87 rd. 3 yd. 2 ft. 6 in. **14.** 2 ʒ 1 ℈. **15.** 70 cu. ft.

Article 129.—1. $\frac{19}{30}$. **2.** 145 A. 72 sq. rd. 22 sq. yd. **3.** $5\frac{1}{4}$. **4.** $13\frac{1}{3}$. **5.** $\frac{56}{126}$. **6.** $\frac{9}{13}$. **7.** $\frac{18}{20}$. **8.** $7\frac{1}{5}$. **9.** 21. **10.** $\frac{17}{35}$. **11.** $\frac{49}{77}$. **12.** $\frac{1}{125}$. **13.** $\frac{8}{31}$ lb. **14.** $\$5\frac{5}{14}$. **15.** $131.25. **16.** $\$2\frac{7}{8}$. **17.** $\frac{4}{75}$. **18.** $26\frac{2}{3}$ T. **19.** $\$62\frac{13}{20}$. **20.** $23\frac{6}{11}$. **21.** $\frac{3}{7}$. **22.** $55. **23.** $\frac{9}{25}$. **24.** 2 cwt. 57 lb. 11 oz. **25.** $544\frac{4}{5}$. **26.** 270. **27.** 264. **28.** $\frac{60}{72}$, $\frac{64}{72}$, $\frac{42}{72}$, $\frac{45}{72}$. **29.** 18. **30.** $678. **31.** $11.75. **32.** 60. **33.** $70. **34.** $3368. **35.** $\$4\frac{1}{40}$. **36.** $396.80. **37.** $1638\frac{21}{22}$ A. **38.** $\$1415\frac{11}{26}$. **39.** $\frac{9}{50}$. **40.** 6 A. 125 sq. rd.

Article 130.—1. $112.50. **2.** $49. **3.** $77. **4.** $420.625. **5.** $180. **6.** $85.89. **7.** $605.25. **8.** $1280.50. **9.** $31.25. **10.** $1351.50. **11.** $298.50. **12.** $222. **13.** $370.50. **14.** $631. **15.** $14.375. **16.** $42.40. **17.** $47.43. **18.** $\$1.68\frac{3}{4}$. **19.** $1.50. **20.** $6.468. **21.** $13.50. **22.** $13.41. **23.** $11.85. **24.** $14.90. **25.** $30.54. **26.** $25.30. **27.** 21 bu. **28.** $42\frac{1}{2}$ yd. **29.** $6.25. **30.** $1.25. **31.** $\$12.33\frac{1}{3}$. **32.** $\$1.33\frac{1}{3}$. **33.** $83\frac{1}{3}$ A. **34.** $\$58.66\frac{2}{3}$. **35.** $8.05. **36.** $137.64.

Article 141.—1. $\frac{7}{8}$. **2.** $\frac{16}{25}$. **3.** $\frac{64}{125}$. **4.** $\frac{5}{8}$. **5.** $\frac{1}{40}$. **6.** $\frac{32}{125}$. **7.** $\frac{1}{400}$. **8.** $\frac{139}{625}$. **9.** $\frac{39}{40}$. **10.** $\frac{21}{2500}$. **11.** $\frac{3}{16}$. **12.** $\frac{15}{32}$. **13.** $4\frac{9}{200}$. **14.** $26\frac{9}{50}$. **15.** $\frac{1}{80}$. **16.** $19\frac{5}{8}$. **17.** $300\frac{1}{4}$. **18.** $46\frac{7}{8}$. **19.** $13\frac{23}{25}$. **20.** $20\frac{1}{50}$. **21.** $\frac{11}{16}$. **22.** $14\frac{3}{160}$. **23.** $9\frac{1}{125}$. **24.** $\frac{11}{32}$.

Article 142.—1. .375. **2.** .45. **3.** .3125. **4.** .44. **5.** .26. **6.** .1875. **7.** .40625. **8.** .53125. **9.** 1.3125. **10.** .01875. **11.** .00125. **12.** .068. **13.** .018. **14.** .85625. **15.** .0171875. **16.** .953125. **17.** 1.78. **18.** .56179+. **19.** .2394+. **20.** .4. **21.** .75. **22.** .9423+. **23.** .135. **24.** .0418+.

Article 143.—**1.** 153.13. **2.** 146.23. **3.** 600. **4.** .458843. **5.** 662.2829. **6.** 694.532. **7.** 989.1009. **8.** 3551.979. **9.** 192.06. **10.** 2767.9932. **11.** 1872.448. **12.** 5517.789. **13.** 599.4. **14.** 1472.827755.

Article 144.—**1.** 27.488. **2.** 9.17. **3.** 35.8761. **4.** 253.125. **5.** 256.7989. **6.** 225.612. **7.** 8.4476. **8.** 88.888. **9.** 16.92924. **10.** 18.825. **11.** 49.911. **12.** 124.1376. **13.** .576. **14.** 88.850034. **15.** 50895.3573.

Article 147.—**1.** .57227. **2.** 222.5. **3.** 740.25. **4.** .01575. **5.** 2377.05. **6.** .0006. **7.** .093. **8.** .00135. **9.** .9702. **10.** 3696.3. **11.** .0021. **12.** 2250. **13.** .031777. **14.** .02121696. **15.** 4207.5. **16.** 169.119. **17.** 294.06. **18.** .0797449. **19.** 730675.2. **20.** 729. **21.** 80000. **22.** 4503744. **23.** 310. **24.** 94.87.

Article 150.—**1.** 1.67. **2.** 7.53. **3.** 2.115. **4.** 2.5. **5.** .024. **6.** 14.95. **7.** .00345. **8.** 12.5. **9.** 400.3. **10.** 4000. **11.** .21. **12.** 41000. **13.** .96875. **14.** .000025. **15.** 4.5. **16.** .0625. **17.** 9.25. **18.** .75. **19.** 10000. **20.** .32. **21.** .06636+. **22.** .301003+. **23.** .0000066+. **24.** 98.21428+.

Article 151.—**1.** .8 pt. **2.** .2184 pt. **3.** .86 lb. **4.** .99 in. **5.** .768 sq. rd. **6.** .11664 cu. in. **7.** .972 sec. **8.** .48 cu. ft. **9.** .7452 sq. in.

Article 152.—**1.** 1 pk. 6 qt. **2.** 1 qt. 1 pt. 2 gi. **3.** 3 cwt. 12 lb. 8 oz. **4.** 50 rd. **5.** 250 A. **6.** 89 cu. ft. 1036.8 cu. in. **7.** 138 da. 19 hr. 4 min. 48 sec. **8.** 16° 55′ 12″.

Article 153.—**1.** .0055 bu. **2.** .015 gal. **3.** .0005 sq. yd. **4.** .0000125 cu. yd. **5.** .01475 bu. **6.** .0003375 da. **7.** .000256 cwt. **8.** .04875 gal. **9.** .0000015 da. **10.** .000234375 bu. **11.** .000000625 C. **12.** .00002 yr. **13.** .0000125 mi. **14.** .00024 T. **15.** .000000027+ A.

Article 154.—1. 1 hr. 12 min. **2.** $16.24. **3.** 5 A. **4.** $2.185 **5.** 118 lb. 2 oz. **6.** 42 rd. **7.** 36 C. 32 cu. ft. **8.** 128 rd. 2 yd. 1 ft. .6 in. **9.** 14 cwt. 95 lb. **10.** 32 gal. 1 qt. 1 pt. **11.** $9990. **12.** 7 qt. 1 pt. **13.** $61.32. **14.** 233 mi. 132.8 rd. **15.** 38 da. 5 hr. 48 min. **16.** .375. **17.** 1 pk. 7 qt. .4 pt. **18.** 42 sq. rd. **19.** 1 cwt. 33 lb. 12 oz. **20.** $109.20. **21.** 20 yd. 1 ft. 10.5 in. **22.** 158 lb. 8 oz. **23.** $121.80. **24.** $65.73. **25.** 81 ct. **26.** 281 da. 5 hr. 49 min. 12 sec. **27.** 9 hr. 13 min. 7.5 sec. **28.** $6. **29.** 3 mi. 40 rd. **30.** $612.50.

Article 156.—1. 394500 dm. **2.** .09364 Km. **3.** 1.23456 Mm. **4.** 98765 Dm. **5.** .000034 Mm. **6.** 74600 cm. **7.** .837 Mm. **8.** 3700 m. **9.** 46000000 dm. **10.** 5.8 Hm. **11.** 374500000 cm. **12.** .6725 Km. **13.** 8.9364 Dm. **14.** 4.56 Hm.

Article 157.—1. 37.468 Ha. **2.** 49320 ca. **3.** 3.8743 a. **4.** 3.8743 a. **5.** 4387.5 m^2. **6.** .0000457 Ha. **7.** .89734 Ha. **8.** 583900 m^2. **9.** .3843 Ha. **10.** 397000 ca.

Article 158.—1. 48 l. **2.** 39500 cl. **3.** .4937 Hl. **4.** 583900 cl. **5.** 4.57 l. **6.** 678.9 cl. **7.** 346.92 Dl. **8.** 4.2789 l. **9.** 3.2584 Hl. **10.** .047 Dl. **11.** 3800000 dl. **12.** 2.97 Dl. **13.** .04683 Hl. **14.** 3870000 dl. **15.** 49000 l. **16.** .37282 m^3. **17.** .678 m^3. **18.** 303 dl.

Article 159.—1. .065 M. T. **2.** 4893100 mg. **3.** 465.3 Dg. **4.** .6543 Q. **5.** 87000 Kg. **6.** .000937 g. **7.** 123456 dg. **8.** 8.734 Dg. **9.** 88736000 cg. **10.** .000000086 Q. **11.** .0000765 M.T. **12.** .3945 Hg. **13.** 3894000 gr. **14.** 87300000000 mg. **15.** 89.9 Mg. **16.** 4890 dg. **17.** .4 Mg. **18.** 12 Kg. **19.** 9.876541 Q. **20.** 34560 g. **21.** 4800.48 Hg. **22.** 90830000 mg.

Article 160.—1. 43 yd. 2 ft. 2.8 in. **2.** 123 A. 88 sq. rd. **3.** 8 cwt. 26 lb. 11.6 oz. **4.** 126 rd. 4 yd. 6 in. + **5.** 14 T. 6 cwt. 59.8 lb. **6.** 25 C. 110.8 cu. ft. **7.** 2 lb. 4 oz. 2 pwt. 15 gr.

8. 654 cu. yd. **9.** 747.5 sq. yd. **10.** 148 sq. rd. 8 sq. yd. **11.** 127 bu. 2 pk. 6 qt. **12.** 2.54 + m. **13.** 160.9347 + Km. **14.** 83.612 + m^2. **15.** 40.4694 + Ha. **16.** 76.4526 m^3. nearly. **17.** 12.14 + a. **18.** 16.3295 M. T. nearly. **19.** 160 Hl. **20.** 249.834 + l. **21.** 500 g. **22.** 278.7068 m^2. nearly. **23.** 20 Hl. **24.** 1 Kg.

Article 161.—**1.** $41.8874. **2.** $295.275. **3.** $68.975. **4.** $2266.89 +. **5.** 38.4 lb. **6.** $27000. **7.** $46.80. **8.** $85. **9.** $1400. **10.** $3800. **11.** $10800. **12.** $75. **13.** $14. **14.** 8 hr. 20 min.

Article 164.—**1.** 259. **2.** 156. **3.** 207. **4.** 99.2. **5.** 65. **6.** 3.3. **7.** 7.25. **8.** .21. **9.** 199. **10.** 420. **11.** 42. **12.** .5188 +. **13.** 6400. **14.** $\frac{1}{100}$. **15.** 396 bu. **16.** 5 da. 22 hr. 48 min. **17.** 48 ct. **18.** 355 A. **19.** 1 T. 11 cwt. 80 lb. **20.** 3 gal. 3 qt. 1 pt. **21.** 3 bu. 2 pk. **22.** 58 gal. **23.** $\frac{1}{400}$. **24.** $\frac{1}{15}$. **25.** $2\frac{7}{9}$. **26.** 144.0285.

Article 165.—**1.** 12. **2.** 75. **3.** 17. **4.** 75. **5.** 75. **6.** 16. **7.** 44. **8.** 200. **9.** 1000. **10.** 75. **11.** 125. **12.** .2. **13.** $22\frac{1}{2}$. **14.** $12\frac{1}{2}$. **15.** .02. **16.** $36\frac{1}{2}$. **17.** 40. **18.** 150. **19.** 150. **20.** 60.

Article 166.—**1.** 70. **2.** 225. **3.** 63000. **4.** 175. **5.** 320. **6.** $5\frac{1}{7}$. **7.** 390. **8.** 75. **9.** $2666\frac{2}{3}$. **10.** 17.5. **11.** 242. **12.** 15 bu. 2 pk. 4 qt. **13.** 3 da. 11 hr. 20 min. **14.** 18 gal. 3 qt. **15.** 82 T. **16.** 23 A. 20 sq. rd.

Article 167.—**1.** 1300. **2.** 400. **3.** 555. **4.** 1295. **5.** 150. **6.** 37.5. **7.** $\frac{3}{4}$. **8.** 20. **9.** $6\frac{2}{3}$. **10.** 42000. **11.** $55\frac{5}{9}$. **12.** 30.4.

Article 169.—**1.** $1900. **2.** 95. **3.** 16. **4.** 128. **5.** $1600. **6.** 456. **7.** 150 ft. **8.** 48 A. **9.** 600 A. **10.** 160 A. **11.** 400 A. **12.** 1728 mi. **13.** 5 ft. 6 in. **14.** 42 lb. Troy. **15.** 1 oz. 8 pwt.

16 gr. **16.** 2580 gr. **17.** 1260 oz. **18.** 550 bu. **19.** $13\frac{1}{2}$ wk. **20.** 620. **21.** 74 %. **22.** 46000 doz. **23.** 365. **24.** 15 %. **25.** $\frac{1}{2}$ %. **26.** 126 A. **27.** 105.84 A. **28.** 294 A. **29.** 1395 bu. **30.** 175 A. **31.** 637 T. 10 cwt.

Article 172.—**1.** $98.50. **2.** $2717. **3.** $1\frac{2}{3}$ %. **4.** $2\frac{2}{5}$ %. **5.** $58.50. **6.** $1068. **7.** $210.20. **8.** $1275. **9.** $20. **10.** $47045. **11.** $45. **12.** $218.875. **13.** $1\frac{1}{2}$ %. **14.** $15. **15.** $462612.50.

Article 173.—**1.** $1254. **2.** $2880. **3.** $850. **4.** $2750. **5.** $2750. **6.** $326. **7.** $300.

Article 174.—**1.** $42. **2.** $3.75. **3.** $370. **4.** $15. **5.** $294. **6.** $6\frac{4}{5}$ %. **7.** 6 %. **8.** 20 %. **9.** 25 %. **10.** $70\frac{2}{3}$ %. **11.** $77\frac{7}{9}$ %. **12.** 220 %. **13.** 20 %. **14.** 25 %. **15.** $33\frac{1}{3}$ %. **16.** $1.25. **17.** $6\frac{2}{3}$ %. **18.** 20 %. **19.** $16\frac{2}{3}$ %. **20.** $3\frac{7}{11}$ %. **21.** $1340. **22.** 10 ct. a yd. **23.** $7843.14 nearly. **24.** $8163.27. **25.** $8160. **26.** $7840. **27.** $166\frac{2}{3}$ %. **28.** $3171.875. **29.** 25 %. **30.** $66\frac{2}{3}$ %.

Article 175.—**1.** $7\frac{11}{27}$ %. **2.** $817.50. **3.** $60. **4.** 28 %. **5.** $8791.20. **6.** $250. **7.** 12 %. **8.** 40 %. **9.** $4620. **10.** 25 %. **11.** $5\frac{5}{19}$ %. **12.** 5 %. **13.** $37\frac{1}{2}$ %. **14.** $33\frac{1}{3}$ %. **15.** 25 %.

Article 177.—**1.** $\frac{1}{5}$ %. **2.** $\frac{3}{10}$ %. **3.** $117. **4.** $\frac{1}{10}$ %. **5.** $12.25. **6.** 250. **7.** $1378. **8.** $66.25.

Article 178.—**1.** $1950. **2.** $172.50. **3.** 2240. **4.** 30 %. **5.** $261. **6.** $7\frac{1}{2}$ %. **7.** $1680. **8.** 350.

Article 179.—**1.** $3555. **2.** $35770. **3.** $6210. **4.** 52. **5.** 532. **6.** $\frac{1}{4}$ %. **7.** $112.50. **8.** $98\frac{2}{51}$ ct. **9.** $41\frac{1}{4}$ %. **10.** $1431. **11.** $1439.94. **12.** 216. **13.** $1590.

Article 180.—**1.** \$468. **2.** 10 %. **3.** \$444. **4.** 70. **5.** \$294. **6.** \$300. **7.** \$100. **8.** \$91.80. **9.** 80 %. **10.** 60 %. **11.** 120 %. **12.** $4\frac{11}{16}$ %. **13.** 24 %. **14.** \$3.

Article 183.—**1.** \$45. **2.** \$45. **3.** \$7.20. **4.** \$240. **5.** \$273. **6.** 55 ct. **7.** \$608.40. **8.** \$80. **9.** \$9185.72. **10.** \$526.40. **11.** \$963.50. **12.** \$1088.91. **13.** \$70.56. **14.** \$39.60. **15.** \$270.03. **16.** \$1428.16. **17.** \$438.25. **18.** \$816.52. **19.** \$500. **20.** \$1073.40. **21.** \$180. **22.** \$12. **23.** \$18000. **24.** \$18.08. **25.** \$3.60. **26.** \$1.10. **27.** \$80.76. **28.** \$20.09. **29.** \$31.76. **30.** \$13.34. **31.** \$198.75. **32.** \$976.50. **33.** \$487. **34.** \$600.855. **35.** \$4179.15. **36.** \$380.87. **37.** \$3. **38.** \$1.65. **39.** \$1.16. **40.** 20 ct. **41.** \$1.72. **42.** \$4.41. **43.** \$4747.90. **44.** \$6.02. **45.** \$480.80. **46.** \$16265.60. **47.** \$388.275. **48.** \$475.67. **49.** \$87. **50.** \$39.75. **51.** \$73.20. **52.** \$119.20. **53.** \$83.50. **54.** \$223.425. **55.** \$150.70. **56.** \$455.41. **57.** \$512. **58.** \$879. **59.** \$846.25. **60.** \$1404.16. **61.** \$556.76. **62.** \$97.19. **63.** \$1696.27. **64.** \$5622.65. **65.** \$130.76. **66.** \$76.85. **67.** \$19.20. **68.** \$57.76. **69.** \$383.47. **70.** \$278.42. **71.** \$109.13. **72.** \$8258.90. **73.** \$696.72. **74.** \$549.28. **75.** \$630.45. **76.** \$430.42. **77.** \$507.74. **78.** \$787.35.

Article 184.—**1.** \$.062. **2.** \$.097. **3.** \$.294$\frac{1}{3}$. **4.** \$ 439$\frac{2}{3}$. **5.** \$.250$\frac{1}{3}$. **6.** \$.609$\frac{1}{3}$. **7.** \$.480$\frac{1}{3}$. **8.** \$.239$\frac{2}{3}$. **9.** \$.0225. **10.** \$.07. **11.** \$.061$\frac{1}{3}$. **12.** \$.07. **13.** \$.016. **14.** \$.023$\frac{1}{4}$. **15.** \$.042$\frac{7}{36}$. **16.** \$.020$\frac{1}{6}$. **17.** \$.02$\frac{11}{72}$. **18.** \$.002$\frac{5}{6}$. **19.** \$.14. **20.** \$.078$\frac{1}{6}$. **21.** \$.080$\frac{8}{9}$. **22.** \$.38. **23.** \$.420$\frac{5}{6}$. **24.** \$13. **25.** \$88.50. **26.** \$77.04. **27.** \$78.12. **28.** \$245. **29.** \$191.59. **30.** \$16.87. **31.** \$55.80. **32.** \$14.75. **33.** \$15.48. **34.** \$80.48. **35.** \$4844.44. **36.** \$6.38. **37.** \$.31. **38.** \$1460.70. **39.** \$756.16. **40.** \$1018.36. **41.** \$105.71. **42.** \$6712.60. **43.** \$3. **44.** \$439.80. **45.** \$86.32. **46.** \$1365. **47.** \$63.58. **48.** \$631.94. **49.** \$809.65. **50.** \$110.08.

Article 185.—**1.** 3 yr. **2.** 2 yr. 6 mo. **3.** 2 yr. 2 mo. **4.** 25 yr. **5.** 12 yr. 6 mo. **6.** 2 yr. 6 mo. **7.** 20 yr. **8.** 5 yr 8 mo. **9.** 2 mo. 20 da. **10.** 1 yr. 7 mo. 6 da. **11.** 11 yr. 1 mo.

10 da. **12.** 3 yr. 1 mo. 15 da. **13.** 3 yr. 4 mo. **14.** 12 yr. 6 mo. **15.** 3 mo. 6 da. **16.** 6 yr. 3 mo. **17.** 31 yr. 3 mo. **18.** 1 yr. 11 mo. 21 da. **19.** 1 yr. 10 mo. 6 da. **20.** 3 mo.

Article 186.—**1.** 6 %. **2.** 8 %. **3.** 6 %. **4.** 5 %. **5.** $8\frac{1}{3}$ %. **6.** 5 %. **7.** 8 %. **8.** 5 %. **9.** 8 %. **10.** 30 %. **11.** 72 %. **12.** $6\frac{2}{3}$ %. **13.** $3\frac{1}{2}$ %. **14.** 4 %. **15.** $4\frac{1}{2}$ %. **16.** 120 %. **17.** $4\frac{31}{36}$ %. **18.** $2\frac{1}{2}$ %. **19.** 3 %. **20.** $4\frac{1}{2}$ %.

Article 187.—**1.** $260. **2.** $725. **3.** $200. **4.** $24500. **5.** $17600. **6.** $90. **7.** $720. **8.** $4500. **9.** $1964.40. **10.** $424.80. **11.** $612. **12.** $360.

Article 188.—**1.** $600. **2.** $800. **3.** $180. **4.** $120. **5.** $135. **6.** $45. **7.** $410. **8.** $150. **9.** $197.50. **10.** $175. **11.** $242.50. **12.** $880.

Article 190.—**1.** $441. **2.** $693. **3.** $491.30. **4.** $629.86. **5.** $138.66. **6.** $137.92. **7.** $67.42. **8.** $563.26. **9.** $339.72. **10.** $17.20. **11.** $31.38. **12.** $1040.60. **13.** $4.86. **14.** $5.51.

Article 191.—**1.** $595.40. **2.** $596.75. **3.** $252. **4.** $1052.64. **5.** $2004. **6.** $312.75. **7.** $1834.87. **8.** $242.80.

Article 192.—**1.** $455.76. **2.** $464.40. **3.** $605. **4.** $605. **5.** $677.97. **6.** $465.93. **7.** $915.06. **8.** $623.42.

Article 193.—**1.** $218.10. **2.** $14.70. **3.** $110.50. **4.** $2.32. **5.** $3.30.

Article 196.—**1.** Sept. 6–9; $4.20, $395.80. **2.** June 16–19; $9.30, $440.70. **3.** July 17–20; $9.30, $390.70. **4.** Sept. 14–17; $6.04, $513.96. **5.** Sept. 16–19; $8.37, $531.63. **6.** April 25–28; $1.26, $78.74. **7.** April 15–18; $1.86, $178.14. **8.** Oct. 19–22;

$6.12, $473.88. **9.** Jan. 13–16; $4.92. $315.08. **10.** April 26–29; $18.54, $791.46. **11.** Aug. 28–31; 53 ct., $88.87. **12.** Feb. 18–21; 50 ct., $13.43. **13.** Dec. 5–8; $5.89, $394.10. **14.** Mar. 17–20; $20.30, $1102.03. **15.** Nov. 18–21, 1880; 92 da., $6.13, $393.87. **16.** Oct. 24–27, 1870; 83 da., $13.83, $486.17. **17.** April 19–22, 1880; 66 da., $3.30, $446.70. **18.** Jan. 12–15, 1876; 55 da., $5.50, $714.50. **19.** Aug. 19–22, 1877; 57 da., $2.28, $357.72. **20.** Aug. 17–20, 1877; 55 da., $2.20, $357.80. **21.** July 11–14, 1875; 41 da., $8.03, $775.26. **22.** April 16–19, 1884; 66 da., $6.74, $401.46. **23.** April 13–16, 1846; 44 da., $8.12, $730.48. **24.** Nov. 9–12, 1884; 121 da., $25.71, $611.79. **25.** July 16–19, 1883; 180 da., $18.75, $450. **26.** Sept. 14–17, 1888; 63 da., $71.08, $5006.42. **27.** May 1–4, 1880; 110 da., $14.71, $466.78.

Article 197.—**1.** $500. **2.** $600. **3.** $750. **4.** $804.02. **5.** $1016. **6.** $60. **7.** $120. **8.** $2000.

Article 199.—**1.** $375; $75. **2.** $625; $275. **3.** $500; $185. **4.** $720; $90. **5.** $300; $59. **6.** $420; $28.70. **7.** $420; $202.30. **8.** $280; $93.10. **9.** $420; $196.21. **10.** $583.70; $304.30. **11.** $186. **12.** $77. **13.** $22.80. **14.** $100.10. **15.** $21.21. **16.** $436.90. **17.** $276.43. **18.** $31.53. **19.** $4.48. **20.** 56 ct. **21.** $240. **22.** $60. **23.** $431. **24.** $1621.60. **25.** $1738.18.

Article 201.—**1.** $4709.40. **2.** $726.35. **3.** $4952.47. **4.** $1356.60. **5.** $375.71. **6.** $2359.67. **7.** $994.50. **8.** $989.50. **9.** $2379.40. **10.** $1482. **11.** $800. **12.** $800. **13.** $1892.21. **14.** $1002.51.

Article 202.—**1.** $3853.85. **2.** $1384.70. **3.** £1093 10 s. **4.** 4224.75 fr. **5.** $980. **6.** $1152. **7.** $916.79. **8.** 4145.08 m.

Article 204.—**1.** $33.60. **2.** $84. **3.** $92. **4.** $61.50. **5.** $8800. **6.** $\frac{4}{5}$. **7.** $\frac{4}{5}$ %.

Article 205.—**1.** \$193.08. **2.** \$25.50. **3.** Son, \$18.60. **4.** \$2854.712.

Article 208.—**1.** $2\frac{1}{2}$ mills on \$1. **2.** 23 mills on \$1. **3.** \$2640000. **4.** 6.08 mills on \$1.

Article 209.—**1.** 2.56 mills on \$1. **2.** \$22.20. **3.** \$15.86. **4.** \$16.63. **5.** \$5.85. **6.** \$7.17. **7.** \$7.67. **8.** \$4.03. **9.** 25.324 mills. **10.** \$22.13. **11.** \$4927.04. **12.** \$35927.67. **13.** \$2.13. **14.** \$21.48. **15.** \$214.85. **16.** \$2148.69.

Article 211.—**1.** \$33.60. **2.** \$54.60. **3.** 12 ct. **4.** 48 ct. **5.** 24 ct. **6.** 30 ct. **7.** 15 ct. **8.** 15 ct. **9.** \$3.84. **10.** \$32.40. **11.** \$10. **12.** \$584. **13.** 750. **14.** 750.

Article 212.—**1.** \$103. **2.** \$19.20. **3.** \$375. **4.** \$25.20. **5.** \$26.90. **6.** \$1869.65. **7.** \$207. **8.** \$153.72. **9.** \$651.22. **10.** \$1834.64. **11.** \$14583.80. **12.** \$1536.50. **13.** \$803. **14.** \$606.60.

Article 214.—**1.** 20. **2.** 10. **3.** 24. **4.** $5\frac{15}{17}$. **5.** $6\frac{2}{5}$. **6.** $\frac{2}{19}$. **7.** $2\frac{1}{2}$. **8.** $1\frac{3}{5}$. **9.** $\frac{2}{7}$. **10.** 28. **11.** $4\frac{1}{2}$. **12.** $3\frac{3}{4}$. **13.** $6\frac{14}{81}$. **14.** $\frac{2}{45}$. **15.** $\frac{4}{81}$. **16.** $\frac{1}{175}$. **17.** 60. **18.** $2\frac{94}{99}$. **19.** 80. **20.** 75. **21.** $27\frac{1}{3}$. **22.** $\frac{3}{400}$. **23.** 56. **24.** $196\frac{12}{13}$.

Article 215.—**1.** 700. **2.** 28000. **3.** $332\frac{1}{2}$. **4.** $\frac{16}{63}$. **5.** $52\frac{1}{2}$. **6.** 17.48. **7.** 27.95. **8.** 76 A. 128 sq. rd. **9.** 4 yd. 10 in. **10.** 5 wk. 3 da. 12 hr.

Article 216.—**1.** 19.6. **2.** 42.5 **3.** $\frac{2}{3}$. **4.** $\frac{3}{4}$. **5.** 2 pk. 5 qt. 1 pt. **6.** 275 gal. **7.** 29 min. 20 sec. **8.** 165 liters.

Article 217.—**1.** $4\frac{1}{2}$. **2.** 21. **3.** $\frac{5}{9}$. **4.** $1\frac{1}{2}$. **5.** 20. **6.** 168. **7.** 22. **8.** 9.

Article 219.—**1.** 5:4. **2.** 7:3. **3.** 7:3. **4.** 111:11. **5.** 11:5. **6.** 4:3. **7.** 4:13. **8.** 7:11. **9.** 4:3. **10.** 216:7. **11.** 16:1. **12.** 1:6.

Article 220.—**1.** 105:64. **2.** 201:28. **3.** 135:52. **4.** 280:207. **5.** 20:27. **6.** 16:15. **7.** 8:3. **8.** 6:5.

Article 223.—**1.** 68. **2.** 21. **3.** 8. **4.** 96. **5.** $13\frac{3}{4}$. **6.** $82\frac{1}{8}$. **7.** $64\frac{8}{9}$. **8.** $64\frac{8}{9}$. **9.** $\frac{72}{73}$. **10.** 86.4. **11.** 28. **12.** 4. **13.** $10\frac{1}{5}$. **14.** 3 cwt. 44 lb.

Article 224.—**1.** \$1025. **2.** \$93. **3.** \$6250. **4.** \$45.50. **5.** 105. **6.** \$4387.50. **7.** \$129.60. **8.** \$98. **9.** \$3.23. **10.** \$184. **11.** \$65.80. **12.** 138 hr. **13.** 36 wk. **14.** $113\frac{7}{11}$ bu. **15.** 80 hr. **16.** $25\frac{3}{5}$ mi. **17.** $2\frac{2}{3}$ qt. **18.** 54 sec. **19.** 7 T. 10 cwt. **20.** 32. **21.** 280 bu. **22.** 1260 bu. 1 pk. **23.** 2 lb. 3 oz. **24.** 6600. **25.** $50\frac{1}{2}$ mi. **26.** 48 C. **27.** 106 A. 40 sq. rd. **28.** 55 yd. **29.** 105. **30.** 140. **31.** 56 ct. **32.** 84 ct. **33.** \$536. **34.** \$40. **35.** 45 da. **36.** \$1.45. **37.** \$675.78. **38.** \$30.60. **39.** 572. **40.** \$43.20. **41.** \$126.50. **42.** 140 cu. ft. **43.** $232\frac{1}{2}$ lb. **44.** \$16. **45.** 592. **46.** 1140. **47.** \$7980. **48.** $20\frac{1}{5}$ ct. **49.** 192. **50.** 882. **51.** 648. **52.** \$587.25. **53.** $\frac{9}{14}$ in. **54.** 3 min. 48 sec. **55.** 137 hr. 15 min. **56.** 18. **57.** \$16.68. **58.** 11 T. **59.** \$389.43.

Article 225.—**1.** \$118.80. **2.** 18. **3.** 12 da. **4.** \$2400. **5.** 24 lots. **6.** 18 rd. **7.** $10\frac{4}{5}$ rd. **8.** \$57.76. **9.** 22 cows. **10.** 151 bu. 1 pk. **11.** 1100 mi. **12.** 5120 books. **13.** 16 rabbits. **14.** 10 cats. **15.** \$7175. **16.** 2 lb. 10 oz. **17.** \$450. **18.** 2:1. **19.** \$134.75. **20.** 60 men. **21.** \$89.76. **22.** \$28.97. **23.** 160. **24.** 6 men. **25.** 13 hr. 7 min. 30 sec. **26.** \$952.50. **27.** \$168.75.

Article 226.—**1.** 1st., \$937.50; 2d., \$562.50. **2.** A. \$1062.50; B. \$937.50. **3.** A. \$63; B. \$56; C. \$91. **4.** 1692 and 2256. **5.** 2256 and 1692. **6.** 987, 1316 and 1645. **7.** 1680, 1260 and 1008. **8.** 9.48 and 10.08. **9.** 3.92 and .005. **10.** A. \$32.40; B. \$43.20. **11.** \$600, \$540, \$300. **12.** First society, \$27.50; second, \$16.50. **13.** A. \$10.13; B. \$9.49; C. \$12.66; D. \$6.96; E. \$10.76.

Article 227.—**1.** 42 ct. **2.** 26 ct. **3.** $141.

Article 228.—**1.** General Average $1\frac{1}{5}$ %. **2.** A. 75 bl.; B. 60 bl.; C. 25 bl. **3.** $25. **4.** $1842.75.

Article 229.—**1.** A. $240; B. $540. **2.** A. $80.05; B. $72.05. **3.** A. $990; B. $1320. **4.** A. $240; B. $216; C. $120. **5.** A. $184; B. $230. **6.** A. $69.30; B. $148.50. **7.** A. $2100; B. $2205. **8.** $212.50.

Article 230.—**1.** 3 mo. 6 da. **2.** 5 mo. **3.** 8 mo. **4.** 4 mo. **5.** 10 da. **6.** 90 da. **7.** 29 da. **8.** 8 da. **9.** May 15. **10.** 10 mo. **11.** Aug. 14. **12.** May 3. **13.** Sept. 2. **14.** April 5. **15.** April 1. **16.** Nov. 20.

Article 232.—**1.** 11 ct. per lb. **2.** $6.80 per oz. **3.** 26 ct. per lb. **4.** $1.80 per gal. **5.** $1.80 per gal. **6.** 9 min. $23\frac{11}{13}$ sec. **7.** 29.87 in. **8.** 5 ft. 7 in. **9.** 12 mi. 205 rd. per hr. **10.** 12 meetings. **11.** 16 members. **12.** 321 sq. ft.

Article 234.—**1.** 6561. **2.** 32768. **3.** 390625. **4.** 286.29151. **5.** 4802.49. **6.** 166.375. **7.** $1785\frac{1}{16}$. **8.** 4173.281. **9.** $9823\frac{1}{81}$. **10.** $3\frac{3337}{4096}$. **11.** 95481. **12.** 2919.2409. **13.** $3672\frac{9}{25}$. **14.** $\frac{100}{441}$. **15.** $2\frac{79}{441}$. **16.** $228\frac{28}{81}$. **17.** $915\frac{1}{16}$. **18.** $36\frac{481}{1600}$. **19.** $1938\frac{1}{1936}$. **20.** 46656. **21.** 1953125. **22.** 1157625. **23.** $2370\frac{10}{27}$. **24.** 6967.871. **25.** 41781923. **26.** $\frac{4913}{42875}$. **27.** 1124.864. **28.** $1076\frac{57}{64}$. **29.** 68574961. **30.** 1477.6336. **31.** $12155\frac{1}{16}$. **32.** $1234567\frac{73}{81}$. **33.** 4978.7136. **34.** 614656. **35.** $\frac{28561}{38416}$. **36.** $55277\frac{19}{81}$. **37.** $138\frac{438}{2401}$. **38.** 16850581551. **39.** $16455646\frac{47}{1024}$. **40.** 12762815625. **41.** 10648. **42.** 272.25. **43.** $90266\frac{70}{81}$. **44.** 6967.871. **45.** 14641. **46.** $11\frac{25}{64}$.

Article 238.—**1.** 12. **2.** 38. **3.** 88. **4.** 25. **5.** 75. **6.** 125. **7.** 175. **8.** 225. **9.** 425. **10.** 1.1. **11.** 3.9. **12.** 103. **13.** 97. **14.** 24. **15.** 74. **16.** $9\frac{4}{5}$. **17.** $14\frac{2}{3}$. **18.** $35\frac{1}{7}$. **19.** $7\frac{1}{14}$. **20.** $\frac{55}{63}$. **21.** 3.53553+. **22.** 31.62277+. **23.** 2.28035+. **24.** 4.01248+. **25.** 16.0312+. **26.** 5.06951+. **27.** 3.47706+.

Article 239.—**1.** 35. **2.** 48. **3.** 64. **4.** 105. **5.** 72. **6.** 135. **7.** 150. **8.** 375. **9.** 11.2.

Article 240.—**1.** 75. **2.** 9 ft. **3.** 28 ft. **4.** 65 ft. **5.** 85 ft. **6.** 48 ft. **7.** 53 ft. **8.** 96 ft. **9.** 84.8528+ ft. **10.** 5 in. **11.** 219 mi. **12.** 122 ft. **13.** 56.5685+ ft. **14.** 92.1954+ mi. **15.** 255 mi.

Article 241.—**1.** 240 rd. **2.** 17 rd. **3.** 60 rd. **4.** 40 rd. **5.** 3613 rd. **6.** 60 rd.

Article 244.—**1.** 24. **2.** 43. **3.** 63. **4.** 74. **5.** 68. **6.** 39 **7.** 205. **8.** 513. **9.** 907. **10.** 85.3. **11.** 6.56. **12.** .313. **13.** 1.4422+. **14.** 6.6943+. **15.** .213. **16.** .0129. **17.** $\frac{4}{61}$. **18.** .7368+. **19.** .34199+. **20.** .15874+. **21.** $8\frac{2}{5}$. **22.** .85498+.

Article 245.—**1.** 1 ft. 11 in. **2.** 14 ft. **3.** 125. **4.** 91125. **5.** $5\frac{1}{2}$ in. **6.** 1 ft. 3.119+ in.

Article 247.—**1.** 45 sq. yd. **2.** 60 A. **3.** 250 sq. ft. **4.** 165 A. **5.** 10 A. **6.** 32 A. **7.** 80 sq. yd. **8.** 40.5 m^2. **9.** 146 sq. yd. 6 sq. ft. **10.** 22 A. **11.** 1440. **12.** 90 A. **13.** 40 yd. **14.** 13 ft. 6 in. **15.** 12 yd.

Article 248.—**1.** 270 sq.ft. **2.** 10 A. 128 sq. rd. **3.** 10800 sq.ft.

Article 249.—**1.** 400 sq. ft. **2.** 880 sq. yd. **3.** 4 sq. yd. **4.** 2400 sq. ft. **5.** 2400 sq. ft. **6.** 6 A. 140 sq. rd. **7.** 1734 sq. yd. **8.** 1170 sq. yd. **9.** 8 A. 64 sq. rd.

Article 250.—**1.** 37 A. 80 sq. rd. **2.** 2450 sq. ft. **3.** 48 sq. rd. **4.** $36000.

Article 251.—**1.** 62.832 ft. **2.** 6.366 + ft. **3.** 163.3632 ft. **4.** 282.744 ft. **5.** 1 ft. 5.825 + in. **6.** 54.1125 + rd. **7.** 1 mi. 214.072 rd. **8.** 70 ft. 8.232 in.

Article 252.—**1.** 1963.5 sq. ft. **2.** 340 sq. ft. 127.5 sq. in. **3.** 9.62115 sq. in. **4.** 1256.64 sq. yd. **5.** 33.85+ ft.. **6.** 26.58+ ft. **7.** 5026.56 sq. ft. **8.** 141.372 sq. rd.

Article 254.—**1.** 432 sq. ft. **2.** 40 sq. ft. **3.** 64 sq. ft. **4.** 41 sq. ft. 104.31 sq. in. **5.** 1 sq. ft. 19.3632 sq. in. **6.** 92 sq. ft. 143.07 sq. in.

Article 255.—**1.** 40 cu. in. **2.** 200 cu. in. **3.** 25 cu. ft. **4.** 10 in. **5.** 1 cu. ft. 726.375 cu. in. **6.** 2 ft. 1 in.

Article 256.—**1.** 12 sq. ft. **2.** 1 sq. ft. 6.7968 sq. in. **3.** 10 sq. ft. 130.8 sq. in. **4.** 17 sq. ft. 65.28 sq. in.

Article 257.—**1.** 36 cu. ft. **2.** 768 cu. in. **3.** 83.776 cu. ft. **4.** 139 cu. ft. 1082.88 cu. in. **5.** 366.69 + cu. in.

Article 258.—**1.** 1520.5344 sq. in. **2.** 201.0624 sq. ft. **3.** 19089068.46 sq. mi. **4.** 317 sq. ft. 54 + sq. in.

Article 259.—**1.** 285 cu. ft. 328 + cu. in. **2.** 19 cu. ft. 678.4 cu. in. **3.** 5884962406.4 cu. mi. **4.** 450 T. 5 cwt. 92 lb.

Article 260.—**1.** \$15.64. **2.** \$4.16. **3.** \$13.35. **4.** \$24.61. **5.** \$212.22. **6.** \$369.45.

Article 261.—**1.** 15 ft. **2.** 56 ft. **3.** 125 ft. **4.** 400 ft. **5.** 896 ft. **6.** 39 ft.

Article 262.—**1.** 32000. **2.** 72. **3.** \$420. **4.** \$637.24. **5.** 44800. **6.** \$324.

Article 263.—**1.** 585 bu. **2.** $1446\frac{3}{7}$ bu. **3.** 187 bu. 2 pk. **4.** 401 bu. nearly. **5.** 646.272 bu. **6.** 512 gal. **7.** 165 bu. **8.** 3166.7 + gal. **9.** 5184 bl. **10.** \$113.98.

Article 265.—**1.** 960. **2.** 580. **3.** $480. **4.** 782. **5.** 700 ft. **6.** .003604.

Article 266.—**1.** 7. **2.** 126. **3.** 37. **4.** 60 ct. **5.** 54.

Article 267.—**1.** 840. **2.** $6750. **3.** 530. **4.** 330. **5.** 4815. **6.** 4185. **7.** 13635. **8.** 660.

Article 269.—**1.** 135. **2.** 375. **3.** .375. **4.** $\frac{1}{648}$. **5.** 87480.

Article 270.—**1.** 6138. **2.** 765. **3.** $8\frac{728}{729}$. **4.** 3. **5.** 9. **6.** $\frac{4}{27}$.

Miscellaneous Examples.

1. $\frac{8}{13}$. **2.** $\frac{11}{45}$. **3.** $\frac{5}{32}$. **4.** $96.88. **5.** $14.85. **6.** 42 da. **7.** $32. **8.** $61.20. **9.** $471.44. **10.** 3514.24 fr. **11.** $176.40. **12.** $63½. **13.** $154.14. **14.** 25 sq. ft. 19.1232 sq. in. **15.** $250. **16.** 5 bu. **17.** $40.84. **18.** $369.53. **19.** $64.58. **20.** $462. **21.** 15.31 + yd. **22.** $348.40. **23.** $64.68. **24.** $1100. **25.** A. $234, B. $312. **26.** $6250. **27.** $\frac{16}{60}$, $\frac{45}{60}$, $\frac{40}{60}$. **28.** $70. **29.** 1266. **30.** $51.45. **31.** 432 gal. **32.** 6 A. 28.4 sq. rd. **33.** 33⅓ %. **34.** $36. **35.** 54 %. **36.** 1 A. 123 sq. rd. 12 sq. yd. 5 sq. ft. 107 sq. in. **37.** 2305. **38.** 502.656 ft. **39.** 77. **40.** 7½ bu. **41.** 174240 min. **42.** 44 sq. yd. **43.** $47.63. **44.** $134.09. **45.** $4.83. **46.** $100.80. **47.** 10 cwt. 50 lb. **48.** $487.50. **49.** 25 %. **50.** 110.23 lb. **51.** $78.74. **52.** 5 bu. 3 pk. 6 qt. **53.** $202.50. **54.** 5 ft. **55.** 838.1 fr. **56.** $\frac{14}{75}$. **57.** $14000. **58.** 9 hr. **59.** $166.60. **60.** $78.75. **61.** 3600. **62.** 420 bu. **63.** July 13. **64.** 392.7 sq. in. **65.** $\frac{425}{450}$, $\frac{420}{450}$, $\frac{324}{450}$, $\frac{315}{450}$. **66.** 16 doz. **67.** $668. **68.** Gain 1¼ %. **69.** $158.40. **70.** 36.576 + m. **71.** 567. **72.** 12. **73.** $734.68. **74.** 3½ %. **75.** 1478.4 Kg. **76.** $12 a yd. **77.** $2367.63. **78.** $2.50. **79.** $613.33. **80.** A. $2200, B. $1672. **81.** $121.38. **82.** $\frac{14}{37}$. **83.** $1702.12. **84.** 1152 times. **85.** $51.19. **86.** $320. **87.** 325. **88.** 3 gal. **89.** 1256.64 sq. yd. **90.** 408⅔. **91.** 125 C. **92.** 106. **93.** 904.7808 cu. in. **94.** $3.33. **95.** $\frac{1}{144}$. **96.** 16 A. 40 sq. rd.

97. $66. **98.** $10\frac{5}{22}$ %. **99.** $27.16. **100.** $87. **101.** $22.50. **102.** $\frac{81}{160}$. **103.** $435.60. **104.** $205.16. **105.** $320. **106.** $18.77. **107.** $849.42. **108.** 3 pk. **109.** 17 sq. ft. 65.28 sq. in. **110.** 189.268 + l. **111.** 31 yr. 3 mo. **112.** 615.7536 sq. in. **113.** $564.10. **114.** 24.72 + rd. **115.** $7\frac{1}{2}$ %. **116.** 74000. **117.** 390600. **118.** 1440 A. **119.** $20.20. **120.** $2625. **121.** $38.54. **122.** 2 yr. 9 mo. 20 da. **123.** $\frac{9}{25}$. **124.** 10 mi. 230 rd. **125.** 48000. **126.** $148.50. **127.** $\frac{24}{25}$. **128.** $21\frac{29}{40}$. **129.** $6672. **130.** $60. **131.** $44.50. **132.** $\frac{5}{8}$ %. **133.** 44602.3424 cu. in. **134.** $180.25. **135.** 720. **136.** 6 mi. 128 rd. **137.** $1620. **138.** 176 bu. **139.** 108. **140.** £1=$$4.86\frac{1}{4}$. **141.** 800. **142.** 20. **143.** 4 wk. 6 da. 17 hr. 20 min. **144.** A. $33825; B. $20500. **145.** June 26, 1815. **146.** 1 mi. 80 rd. **147.** 2 ft. 8 in. **148.** 1 T. 7 cwt. 55 lb. **149.** $42\frac{1}{4}$. **150.** 350 A. **151.** $540. **152.** 2 yr. 4 mo. 25 da. **153.** $342.63. **154.** 125 da. **155.** Nov. 4. **156.** $4. **157.** 35. **158.** 22680 fr. **159.** $945.25. **160.** $59.73. **161.** 5575.2928 cu. in. **162.** 12.45 P. M. **163.** 64 %. **164.** $307.18. **165.** 20178. **166.** 2 pk. 3 qt. **167** $1170. **168.** $3048.63. **169.** $315. **170.** $480. **171.** 6.25 Km. **172.** $\frac{3}{5}$. **173.** May 1, 1886. **174.** 8 mi. 240 rd. **175.** $590.40. **176.** 21200 lb. **177.** $7\frac{31}{80}$. **178.** 9 %. **179.** 45. **180.** 82.024 +. **181.** 21 lb. **182.** 11 rd. **183.** 6 hr. 58 min. A. M. **184.** $43.80. **185.** 2 m. **186.** A. $700; B. $650. **187.** $1103.60. **188.** $589.50. **189.** Aug. 26. **190.** $2506.31. **191.** $496.87. **192.** $19.95. **193.** 4 hr. 10 min. **194.** $750. **195.** $4.50. **196.** 476. **197.** June 17. **198.** .06857 +. **199.** 2 hr. **200.** $453.60. **201.** $3891.73. **202.** 16 m. **203.** $108. **204.** $918. **205.** 137° 30′ W. Long. **206.** 8 %. **207.** July 20. **208.** 3200. **209.** 3262 gal. 3 qt. **210.** $285. **211.** $\frac{13}{18}$. **212.** 56.5685 + rd. **213.** A. $825; B. $660. **214.** 60 ft. **215.** $113.60. **216.** 8 %. **217.** 2123.7216 sq. in. **218.** $\frac{11}{17}$. **219.** 405 cu. ft. **220.** $1\frac{3}{10}$ % discount. **221.** Feb. 28, 1873. **222.** $800. **223.** $60. **224.** 20000. **225.** 6 %. **226.** $4900.50. **227.** $671.55. **228.** 42 sq. ft. 78.12 sq. in. **229.** A. $275; B. $198. **230.** 1413.72 sq. yd. **231.** $\frac{21}{320}$. **232.** 36 ct. **233.** 120. **234.** $4\frac{1}{2}$ %. **235.** $2.50. **236.** $60.75. **237.** $6600. **238.** 175. **239.** 6.32455 +. **240.** 52.3259 +. **241.** 1000. **242.** 9 ft. 4 in.

243. $1093.75. **244.** 285. **245.** $4\frac{1}{2}$ %. **246.** $891.65. **247.** .708928+. **248.** 90 ct. **249.** £1 = $4.86. **250.** 2 ft. **251.** A. $750; B. $600. **252.** April 18, 1893. **253.** 26400 bu. **254.** Gain 4 hr. 42 min. **255.** $2700. **256.** 2 cwt. 34 lb. **257.** $793.53. **258.** 256. **259.** 1600 A. **260.** $400. **261.** $12699.36. **262.** 7 mo. **263.** .000079507. **264.** $\frac{2}{5}$. **265.** $666.27. **266.** 1044.48 bl. **267.** 50 in. **268.** 76. **269.** March 3, 1884. **270.** 4680 sq. ft. **271.** .48. **272.** $107.20. **273.** 180 cu. ft. **274.** $16\frac{55}{72}$. **275.** $5280. **276.** 4 %. **277.** 30 A. 100 sq. rd. **278.** $8\frac{1}{3}$ %. **279.** 1 A. 108 sq. rd. 18 sq. yd. **280.** 40. **281.** $931.91. **282.** $11\frac{1}{9}$. **283.** $13\frac{1}{3}$ A. **284.** $\frac{32}{36}$, $\frac{48}{36}$, $\frac{24}{36}$, $\frac{21}{36}$. **285.** 49.0875 cu. ft. **286.** 44 %. **287.** 16777216. **288.** $9100. **289.** 22 bu. 2 pk. **290.** $4550. **291.** 9. **292.** Nov. 30, 1884. **293.** £1026 13 s. $10\frac{1}{2}$ d. **294.** $249.34. **295.** $3\frac{11}{15}$ da. **296.** $2414.27. **297.** 11 in. **298.** A. $27000; B. $12000. **299.** $1\frac{23}{52}$ %. **300.** 7 mo. **301.** 2146 sq. ft. **302.** $240. **303.** 28. **304.** March 23, 1892. **305.** 32.863 + ft. **306.** $\frac{15}{34}$. **307.** 22164361129. **308.** 11421 + gal. **309.** June 14. **310.** 6 feet. **311.** 90. **312.** $1022.34. **313.** April 22, 1880. **314.** $17\frac{1}{2}$ A. **315.** 2 yr. 9 mo. **316.** 13 da. **317.** 24 ct. **318.** $45. **319.** 10 ft. 8 in. **320.** $398.25. **321.** Lost 4 %. **322.** $4570. **323.** $\frac{103}{120}$. **324.** 20 %. **325.** 36 ct. **326.** $12960. **327.** 203.717 + A. **328.** 8 hr. 43 min. P. M. of the previous day. **329.** $5\frac{1}{2}$ in. **330.** 54. **331.** $165. **332.** $80.99. **333.** 565. **334.** $292\frac{1}{2}$ sq. in. **335.** 58.67 ft. nearly. **336.** $2\frac{3}{5}$ %. **337.** 25 m. **338.** 40 %. **339.** 2072.54 marks. **340.** Oct. 21,1875. **341.** $21\frac{11}{18}$. **342.** $325.20. **343.** 5.25 fr. **344.** $7\frac{1}{2}$ %. **345.** 8 %. **346.** 44 %. **347.** 3 oz. 2 pwt. 6 gr. **348.** $873.03. **349.** $12\frac{1}{2}$ %. **350.** 94 bu. 2 pk. **351.** $\frac{784}{840}$, $\frac{924}{840}$, $\frac{735}{840}$, $\frac{540}{840}$. **352.** 9.0719 + M. T. **353.** $44\frac{4}{9}$ ct. **354.** $340. **355.** 1 fr. = 19 ct. 7 m. **356.** $2577.25. **357.** $10. **358.** 50 ft. **359.** $14.16. **360.** 4879681. **361.** $5\frac{5}{19}$ %. **362.** .52083 +. **363.** 2463.0144 sq. in. **364.** A. $75; B. $45; C. $30. **365.** $45. **366.** 2nd term 3. **367.** 85 ft. **368.** Oct. 28. **369.** $9.45. **370.** 40 ft. **371.** 22.05 a. **372.** $20000. **373.** Dec. 2, 1869. **374.** $34.20. **375.** $5877. **376.** 8 dm. **377.** $864. **378.** $846.45. **379.** 1.963 + cu. ft. **380.** May 13, 1891. **381.** $\frac{216}{15625}$. **382.** $1022.36. **383.** 1256.64 sq. yd. **384.** 38. **385.** E. Long. 14° 10′. **386.** Nov. 1, 1883. **387.** 9 %.

388. \$509.95. **389.** 120 sq. rd. **390.** 17 Mg. **391.** 7 ft.
392. Sept. 20, 1884. **393.** $26\frac{11}{64}$ %. **394.** \$10250. **395.** $37\frac{25}{27}$.
396. 8250 fr. **397.** \$7200. **398.** 20%. **399.** \$700.
400. 523600 cu. mi. **401.** \$158.40. **402.** 8 da. **403.** 16 da.

Who Is Joseph Ray?

Joseph Ray lived as a contemporary of Abraham Lincoln. Youth in that generation finished their schoolbooks and then read the Bible, sang from the hymnbooks of Lowell Mason, and read Roman and Greek classics in the original languages. It was not unusual for a blacksmith to carry a Greek New Testament under his cap for reading during his lunch break. The literacy rate, even on the frontier, was higher than today's rate.

Ray was Professor of Mathematics for twenty-five years at a preparatory school in Ohio. He had no use for indolence and sham. He was always delighted to join his students in sports. He knew how to use balls, marbles, and tops as concrete illustrations to help young children make the transfer from solid objects to abstract figures.

From the Presidency of Abraham Lincoln to that of Teddy Roosevelt, few Americans went to school or were taught at home without considerable exposure to either Ray's Arithmetics or McGuffey's Readers—usually both. Ray and McGuffey challenged students to excellent accomplishment. Their influence on our country has certainly eclipsed Mann's and rivaled Dewey's, yet education histories, edited by humanists, seldom mention these men.

Ray's classic Arithmetics are now brought to a new generation which is in search of excellence.

Ray's Arithmetic Series

Primary Arithmetic. Reading, writing and understanding numbers to 100; adding and subtracting with sums to 20; multiplication and division to 10s; and signs and vocabulary needed for this level of arithmetic.

Intellectual Arithmetic. Reading, writing and understanding of higher whole numbers, fractions, and mixed numbers; addition, subtraction, multiplication and division of higher numbers; computation of simple fractions; beginning ratio and percentage; and signs and vocabulary needed for all these operations.

Practical Arithmetic. Roman numbers; carrying in addition and borrowing in subtraction; measurement and compound numbers; factors; decimals and percentage; ratio and proportion; powers and roots; beginning geometry; advanced vocabulary.

Higher Arithmetic. Philosophical understandings; principles and properties of numbers; advanced study of common and decimal fractions, measurements, ratio, proportion, percentage, powers, and roots; series; business math; geometry.

Test Examples. A supply of problems for making tests to accompany study in *Practical Arithmetic* and *Higher Arithmetic*.

Key to Ray's Primary, Intellectual and Practical Arithmetics. Answers to problems in the three lower books.

Key to Ray's Higher Arithmetic. Answers to problems in the higher book.

Parent-Teacher Guide. Gives unit by unit helps for teaching; suggests grade levels for each book; provides progress chart samples for each grade and tests for each unit.

McGuffey's Reading Series

Primer. Begins with the alphabet, moves to simple one-syllable words such as *cat* and *fox*, then on to more difficult one-syllable words such as *horse* and *spring*.

Pictorial Primer. Begins with the alphabet. First lessons have simple three- and four-word sentences with no paragraphing. The lessons progress to longer sentences and ordinary paragraphing.

First Reader. Follows the Primers at second or third grade. Words usually have the main alphabetic sounds, and few have silent letters. Helps to build fluency in using the phonics principles learned at primer levels. Stories of children who want to please God and love to learn.

Second Reader. Begins with fairly easy one- and two-syllable words and progresses to more difficult words. Reading selections on a variety of topics. Can be used to about fifth grade.

Third Reader. For students who have mastered basic reading skills and are fluent in easy reading. This Reader develops more advanced vocabulary and thinking skills. Can be used for two or three years, beginning at about sixth grade.

Fourth Reader. Develops advanced comprehension, requiring students to understand a variety of viewpoints and think about abstract ideas. Readings on themes such as life values, truth, religion, and freedom. Can be used at high school level.

Progressive Speller. Can be used at all grade levels. Begins with phonics rules. Covers spelling difficulty from one-syllable words to very complex words.

Parent-Teacher Guide. Explains how to teach reading and has specific ideas for using the lessons in this series of Readers. Also gives guidelines for helping children grow in all the language arts—spelling, writing, speaking, penmanship, grammar.

Materials for Teaching Phonics and Spelling

Phonics Made Plain by Michael S. Brunner. Flashcards for teaching sounds of the letters and letter combinations which make up the code for reading and writing. Wall chart for classroom reference and teaching of the sounds. Instructions for use.

The ABC's and all Their Tricks by Margaret M. Bishop. A comprehensive book of phonics knowledge for teachers. Useful for study, reference, solving students' spelling problems, and answering any phonics question you can think of. Tells how to teach children of all ages who have difficulty with phonics.

A Measuring Scale for Ability in Spelling by Leonard P. Ayres. The classic book from 1915, describes the research which identified one thousand most commonly used words and arranged them into difficulty groups to use for testing children's spelling level and for teaching spelling. Includes complete directions for testing.

Mrs. Silver's Phonics Workbook by Claudine Silver. A lesson on each single letter and on some digraphs such as *ck*, *sh*, and *th*. Ideas enough to spend several days on each lesson and learn it well. Each sound is correlated with a Bible verse and with science, art, and other school subjects. Can be used at kindergarten or first grade level. With the McGuffey series, it should be used before the Primers. Available in both a pupil edition and a teacher edition.

Rice Christian Reader and Speller by Carolyn Rose and Karma Hudson. A drill book for helping pupils memorize the phonic sounds. Spelling rules to learn and lists of words for practicing the rules. Can be used for a range of levels from kindergarten to seventh grade. Teacher instructions included within the book.

Phonics in Song by Leon V. Metcalf. Book of catchy tunes for teaching each letter of the alphabet and the digraphs *ch*, *sh*, *th*, and *wh*. A sing-along tape is also available.

The Complete Book of

Card Games

The Complete Book of Card Games

hamlyn

An Hachette UK Company
www.hachette.co.uk

First published in Great Britain in 2001 by
Hamlyn, an imprint of Octopus Publishing Group Ltd
Endeavour House, 189 Shaftesbury Avenue
London WC2H 8JY
www.octopusbooks.co.uk
www.octopusbooksusa.com

This edition published in 2012

Distributed in the US by
Hachette Book Group USA
237 Park Avenue
New York NY 10017 USA

Distributed in Canada by
Canadian Manda Group
165 Dufferin Street
Toronto, Ontario, Canada M6K 3H6

ISBN 978-0-600-62395-3

A CIP catalogue record for this book is available from the British Library

Page make up and illustrations by Publish on Demand Ltd.
Card designs based on Waddingtons No. 1 Playing Cards.

Printed and bound in China

10 9 8 7 6 5 4 3 2

CONTENTS

INTRODUCTION

The card games selected for inclusion in this book include games which have stood the test of time and have so caught public fancy as to have earned the right to be included and others which, while they have not become so widespread, nevertheless have their followers and will repay those who make the effort to learn them.

The bulk of the descriptions were written by the late George F. Hervey, and appeared originally in a book entitled *The Hamlyn Illustrated Book of Card Games* (Hamlyn 1973). Later many were incorporated into a book which embraced other types of indoor games entitled *The Complete Book of Indoor Games* (Hamlyn 1981). They are reprinted with minor changes of style and presentation.

Mr Hervey's introduction to the former book outlined his intention and paragraphs from it which are relevant to this volume are reprinted here:

Card games do not admit of a precise arrangement. In this book they have been arranged according to the number of players who may take part at one table. As, however, most card games can be played, in one form or another, by a varying number of players, it is more correct to say that the games have been arranged according to the number of players for which they are best suited. But party games and banking games are grouped separately, and among the party games some will be found suitable for members of the younger generation. It is not an ideal arrangement, but it has the merit of convenience, and is less arbitrary than arranging the games in alphabetical order, and more practical than arranging them by their family resemblances. Most card games have a number of variations. Only the more popular ones have been given a place in this book, and, with some rare and inevitable exceptions, descriptions of them follow the description of the parent game.

The aim of the present writer is nothing higher than to explain how the various games are played; and when no authoritative organization has laid down the scoring, rules of play and appropriate penalties for breaking them, the practice that he recommends is that of the majority of experienced players. If here and there he has broken form and given a few hints on skilful play, it is not to compete with the text books, but because without them the bare bones would be unreadable. When the play of a deal is summarized, the standard practice of underlining the card that wins the trick (the player leading to the next trick) is followed.

George Hervey was one of the best writers on card games and, although he points out that his aim was 'nothing higher than to explain how the various games are played', his descriptions of sample games nevertheless convey the elements of good play.

Other games have been added to those originally described by George Hervey. Some first appeared in a book entitled *The Book of Games* (general editor Peter Arnold, Newnes Books 1985). These were written by Peter Arnold (Gin Rummy) and by Matthew Macfadyen (Skat, Canasta, Miss Milligan, Terrace and Three Blind Mice). Some descriptions were specially written for this book by Peter Arnold: Eights, *Le Truc*, Russian Bank, Calabrasella, Five Hundred, 500 Rum, Oklahoma, Schafkopf, Cinch, Quinto, Crazy Eights, Lift Smoke, Panguingue, Beleaguered Castle and Golf.

The descriptions of these games follow the principles set out by George Hervey. It is hoped that readers will try games with which they are at present unfamiliar, and that they will find them satisfying.

ALL FOURS

ALL FOURS *was mentioned in Charles Cotton's* Compleat Gamester *in 1674 as being 'much played in Kent'. It became popular in the United States, where it acquired other names such as Seven-up, High-low Jack or Old Sledge.*

NUMBER OF PLAYERS

All Fours is a game for two players, but it can be adapted for four as described later.

CARDS

The full pack of 52 cards is used, the cards ranking from Ace (high) to 2 (low).

Six cards are dealt in lots of three to both players, and the 13th card is turned up to determine the trump suit.

The deal passes in rotation.

THE PLAY

The game is won by he who first scores seven points. The points are scored thus:

High. The player who is dealt the highest trump in play scores one point.

Low. The player who is dealt the lowest trump in play scores one point.

Jack. The player who wins the Jack of trumps (if it is in play) scores one point.

Game. Each player counts the honours among the tricks he has won, and, counting the Ace as four, the King as three, the Queen as two, the Jack as one and the 10 as ten, the player with the highest total scores one point. If there is equality the non-dealer scores the point.

The points are not counted until the end of the deal, but they should be understood from the start because they illustrate the object of the game.

The non-dealer now declares whether he will stand or beg. If he says 'I stand' he accepts the turned-up card as the trump suit and play begins. If he says 'I beg' he rejects the turned-up card as the trump suit, and the dealer must either accept or refuse the proposal to make another suit trumps. To refuse he says 'Take one'. The non-dealer then scores one point for gift and play begins. To accept he says 'I run the cards'. He deals three more cards to his opponent and three to himself, and turns up the next card to determine the trump suit. If this is the same suit as the original trump suit, he runs the cards again, and continues to run them until a different trump suit is turned up. In the rare, but not impossible, event of the pack being exhausted without a different trump suit being turned up, there is a redeal by the same player. If the turned-up card is a Jack, the dealer scores one point, and if, when the cards are run, the turned-up card is again a Jack, the dealer again scores one point.

Play begins when the trump suit has been determined, and if the cards have been run, the players first discard from their hands enough cards to reduce the number held to six. The non-dealer leads to the first trick. His opponent must follow suit or trump. Unlike at most games, however, a player may trump even though he is able to follow suit, but he must not discard if he holds either a card of the suit led or a trump. If he does he has revoked and his opponent scores one point.

The winner of a trick leads to the next, and so on until all six tricks have been played. The players then turn up their tricks and score for High, Low, Jack and Game.

These four scoring features are fundamental to the game and are counted whenever it is possible to do so. If, for example, there is only one trump in play it counts two points, because it is both High and Low.

ALL FOURS FOR FOUR PLAYERS

This version is played with two players playing in partnership against the other two in partnership.

The method of play is the same as in the parent game for two players, except that only the dealer and the opponent on his left (eldest hand) look at their cards to determine the trump suit. When they have done this, but not before, the other two players look at their cards and come into the game for play.

If a player exposes a card it is liable to be called by an opponent, i.e. the player must play it at the first legitimate opportunity.

SEVEN-UP

This is a variation of the parent game that takes its name from the method of scoring.

Both players (or both sides if four are playing) begin with seven counters each. Every time that a point is scored the player (or side) that wins it puts a counter aside, and the player (or side) who first gets rid of his counters wins the game. If both go out in the same deal, the winner is he who first counts out when the points are scored for High, Low, Jack and Game.

ALL FIVES

This variation of the parent game is played for 61 points up. For convenience the score is best kept on a cribbage board.

The mechanics of the game are the same as those of the parent game, and points are pegged when the following trumps are won in a trick: Ace four points, King three points, Queen two points, Jack one point, 10 ten points and 5 five points.

After the hand has been played, the honours are counted as in the parent game, to determine the point for Game, with the addition that the player who has won the 5 of trumps scores five points for it.

BEZIQUE

BEZIQUE *was popular in France and came to England in the late 19th century, where the Prince of Wales helped popularize it before he succeeded to the throne. Americans generally prefer the development from it called Pinocle.*

NUMBER OF PLAYERS

Bezique is for two players, but can be adapted for three or four as described later.

CARDS

Bezique is played with two packs of cards from which the 6s, 5s, 4s, 3s and 2s have been removed, but can be played with three, four, six or eight packs as described later. The cards rank in the order: Ace, 10, King, Queen, Jack, 9, 8, 7.

Eight cards are dealt to each player - three, two and three at a time. The remaining 48 (the stock) are placed face downwards on the table, and the top card exposed alongside to denote the trump suit; if it is a 7 the dealer scores 10 points.

THE PLAY

The non-dealer leads to the first trick. As in most games the winner of a trick leads to the next, but it is a feature of bezique that a player is under no obligation to follow suit to the card led. The object of the game is to score points for declaring certain cards and combinations of cards. The declarations, and the points that may be scored for them, are as follows:

Double bezique Two ♠ Q and two ♦ J (or ♣ Q and ♥ J if spades or diamonds are trumps) 500
Sequence in trumps A, 10, K, Q, J of the trump suit 250
Any 4 Aces 100
Any 4 Kings 80
Any 4 Queens 60
Any 4 Jacks 40
Bezique ♠ Q (or ♣ Q if spades or diamonds are trumps) and ♦ J (or

♥ J if spades or diamonds are trumps) 40
Royal marriage K and Q of trump suit 40
Common marriage K and Q of same plain suit 20

A player scores 10 points if he holds a 7 of the trump suit and exchanges it for the turn-up card; and 10 points are scored for playing a 7 of the trump suit.

When a player has won a trick he may declare by placing the appropriate cards face upwards on the table. He may make as many declarations as he chooses, always provided that the declarations do not involve the same cards. If the exposed cards show more than one declaration the player must announce which declaration he intends to score, and leave the other to be scored when he wins another trick. A card that has once scored cannot again be used to form part of a similar declaration. As an example, a player may expose ♠ K, ♠ Q, ♦ J score 40 for bezique and announce 'Twenty to come' meaning that the next time he wins a trick he will score 20 points for the common marriage of the ♠ K and ♠ Q. He may not expose a second ♦ J and score bezique with the ♠ Q. The cards that have been declared, and so exposed on the table, remain a part of the player's hand and he may play them to later tricks.

Tricks should be gathered and kept by the player who wins them, because at the end of a deal a player scores ten points for every Ace and every 10 that he has won. They are known as brisques.

When both players have played to a trick they replenish their hands from the stock: the winner takes the top card, the loser the next.

When the stock is exhausted the last eight tricks are played, and the game takes on a rather different character. Now, if a player has a card of the suit that has been led he must play it, and he must win a trick if he is able to. No further declarations may be made, and the aim of the player is to win brisques and the last trick, for which 10 points are scored.

The deal passes to the other player, and so alternately, until one of them has reached an agreed number of points, usually 2,000.

The score cannot be kept satisfactorily with pencil on paper. It is best to use the special bezique markers that take the form of indicators marked as clocks on thin cardboard.

The following deal, played by two experienced players, illustrates many of the finer points of good play.

South dealt, and the hands were as in the illustration opposite.

Clubs were trumps, the ♣ 10 having been turned up.

The turn-up card is important because it is a sequence card, and a high one at that since it ranks immediately below the Ace.

The main features of North's hand are that he holds two sequence cards (the ♣ Q and ♣ J), a 7 of trumps to exchange for the valuable 10, and three Queens, which put him well on the way to a declaration of four Queens.

The main features of South's hand are a bezique Queen (the ♠ Q) and three low trumps, including the 7; but,

North

South

of course, as yet South does not know that North holds both the Queens of trumps, so that a sequence for him is impossible. It is South's lead, and it is necessary for him to win a trick to exchange the ♣ 7 for the ♣ 10. An inexperienced player might be tempted to lead an indifferent card, such as the ♥ 7, hoping that North will have nothing to declare and will refuse to win the trick. This, however, is very artless play, and the better play is for South to lead his highest trump because it compels North to use a sequence card if he wants to take the trick and make a declaration. So...

Trick 1 South led the ♣ 9. North, who appreciated the importance of the turn-up card, won with the ♣ Q. This was North's best play, although it suffers from the defect that it reduces North's best chance of declaring four Queens, and it informs South that he has virtually no hope of a sequence because North would hardly play a sequence card if he lacked a duplicate. North exchanged the ♣ 7 for the turn-up card, and scored 10 points. He drew the ♣ K (giving him no fewer than four of the five sequence cards), and South the ♥ 9.

Trick 2 North led the ♦ 9, and South played the ♥ 7. North declared the royal marriage and scored 40 points, making his total 50 points. North drew the ♥ K, and South the ♥ A.

Trick 3 North led the ♥ 7, and South played the ♦ 9. North declared the common marriage in hearts and scored 20 points, making his total 70 points. North drew the ♣ A, and South the ♥ J.

Trick 4 North now held a sequence, but, in order to declare it, he had first to win a trick. A heart must be led, and he chose the Queen. Undoubtedly it was the best lead. The ♥ A is not a good lead, because, if trumped, it will cost North a brisque; and it is better for North to save for four Kings, instead of for four Queens, because not only does it gain 20 more points, but North had already played a Queen so the chance of drawing a Queen was slightly less than that of drawing a King. South played the ♥ 9. North declared his ♠ A, 10, J, and scored 250 points for the sequence, giving him a total of 320 points. South had not yet scored. North drew the ♥ 10, and South the ♦ J.

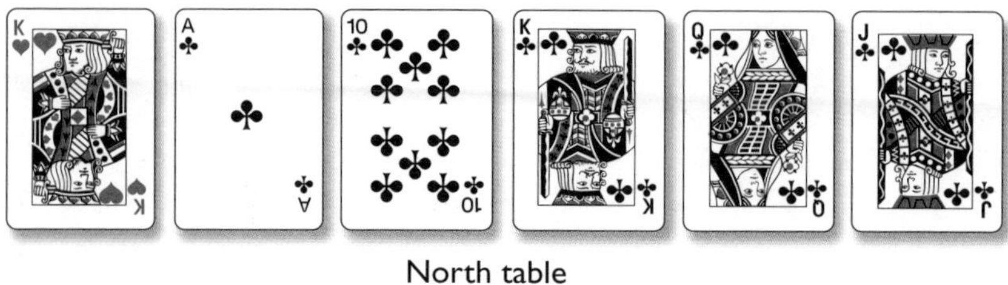

North table

North

South

At this point the hands were as in the illustration above.

Trick 5 North's trumps were no longer of vital importance to him, and could be played if desired. The two Kings were important because North had made up his mind to save for Kings, and it is an error of tactics to change one's mind during the game. The Aces and 10s were important, because they furnish brisques. So North led the ♣ J. South had a bezique in his hand, but unfortunately he could not win the trick and declare it. The best he could do was to play the ♥ J. North drew the ♦ 8, and South the ♦ Q.

Trick 6 North led the ♦ 8. South won with the ♦ 10, putting away a brisque for himself and declared bezique. South's 40 points for bezique was his first score, and he was a long way behind North's 320 points. South drew the ♥ 10, and North the ♣ A.

Trick 7 South now had the lead. He chose the ♣ 7 and scored 10 points, making his total 50. It was the best lead, because the lead of either heart would probably be trumped and a brisque lost. He had to save for four Queens, and the ♦ J was out of the question since there was always the possibility of declaring double bezique. North was more or less compelled to win with the ♣ Q. North drew the ♦ 8, and South the ♠ Q.

Trick 8 North led the ♦ 8, and South won with the ♣ 8 and declared four Queens (60 points) giving him a total of 110. North, with a total of 320 points, was still well ahead, but he noted with some concern that South would be able to declare double bezique if he was lucky enough to draw the other ♦ J. South drew the ♠ 9, and North the ♠ 8.

Trick 9 South led the ♠ 9, and North won with the ♠ 10. North drew the ♠ J, and South the ♠ 8.

Trick 10 North led the ♠ 8, and South played the other ♠ 8. North drew the ♥ 8, and South the ♥ J.

Trick 11 North led the ♥ 8, and South won with the ♥ 10. South drew the ♦ K, and North the ♥ 8.

At this point the hands were as in the illustration below.

The score was North 320 points, South 110 points.

Trick 12 South led the ♥ J, and North played the ♥ 8. It would not have been good play for North to win with the ♥ A because, though this would have given him a brisque, it is better for North to save for four Aces now that he held three. South laid down his ♦ K and scored a common marriage (20 points), giving him a total of 130 points. South drew the ♠ 7, and North the ♠ A.

Trick 13 South led the ♠ 7. North won with the ♠ J, and declared four Aces (100 points). This raised his total to 420, and he had a good lead on South, whose score was only 130 points. North drew the ♣ J, and South the ♠ 9.

The hands were now as in the illustration overleaf.

South's hand with its three bezique cards was not without possibilities.

Trick 14 North led the ♣ J, and South played the ♠ 9. North drew the ♠ J, and South the ♥9.

Trick 15 North led the ♠ J, and South played the ♥ 9. North drew the ♣ K, and South the ♦ J.

Trick 16 Now, of course, the whole game changed, because South held a double bezique, though he had to win a

North

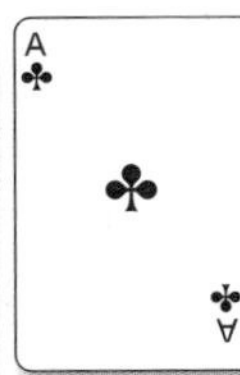

North table

South

South table

North hand

North table

South hand

South table

trick before he could declare it. If the stock is nearly exhausted it is proper for North to lead trumps in an attempt to prevent South from winning a trick. It was, however, too early in the game for these tactics, so North led the ♠ A, hoping that it would not be trumped, and South, who had no trump in his hand, discarded the married ♦ Q. North drew the ♦ 10, and South the ♣ 10, a vital card.

Trick 17 North, who by this time suspected that South held double bezique, led the ♥ A, hoping that South would still not be able to trump. This time, however, he was doomed to disappointment, because, of course, South was able to win with the ♣ 10 and declare double bezique. The score of 500 points for double bezique raised South's total to 630 and gave him a lead of 210 points because North's score was only 420 points. South drew the ♠ A, and North the ♠ K.

Trick 18 South, who had no further use for his bezique Jacks, led a ♦ J. North won with the ♦ 10 and declared four Kings (80 points), raising his score to 500 points. North drew the ♣ 9, and South the ♦ A.

Trick 19 North led the ♣ 9, and South played the ♦ J. North drew the ♣ 8, and South the ♦ A.

The hands were now as at the top of the opposite page.

Trick 20 North now suspected that South was on the point of declaring four Aces. His tactics, therefore, had to be aggressive, and, since the other ♣ 10 had been played, his trumps were all winners, and he played them to prevent South from declaring. North led the ♣ A, and South played the ♠ Q. North drew one ♦ 7 and South the other.

Trick 21 North led the ♣ A, and South played the ♦ 7. North drew the ♥ Q, and South the ♥ 10.

North hand North table

South hand

South table

Trick 22 North led the ♣ 10, and South played the ♠ Q. North declared the common marriage in hearts (20 points) raising his total to 520 points. North drew the ♠ K, and South the ♠ 7.

Trick 23 North led the ♣ K, and South played the ♠ 7. North drew the ♦ K, and South the ♥ 10.

Trick 24 (last trick) North led the ♣ K, and South played the ♦ Q. North scored 10 points for the last trick, bringing his total to 530 points. South's score was 630 points, and from the time that he had declared double bezique North had little chance to overtake him. He did well, however, to prevent South from declaring four Aces and so adding another 100 points to his score. North drew the ♥ K, and South picked up the ♣ 7 exposed on the table.

After picking up their cards from the table, the hands of the two players were as below.

North South

The play to the last eight tricks was:

North	South
♥ K	♥ A
♦ 7	♦ A
♦ K	♦ A
♠ K	♠ A
♥ Q	♥ 10
♠ K	♠ 10
♣ 8	♦ K
♥ K	♣ 7

South was lucky to win all his brisques, giving him a score of 100 points; North won six brisques for a total of 60 points. The final score, therefore, was South 730 points, North 590 points.

Altogether a fine deal, and one worth studying, because it illustrates the importance of playing for double bezique. For the first half of the deal North was well ahead, but after South had won the highest prize that the game has to offer, it was practically impossible for North to win the deal, and all his efforts had to be directed towards preventing South from gaining an even bigger lead. North played well to reduce South's lead of 210 points (gained at the 17th trick) to 140.

RUBICON BEZIQUE

This version of the game has the advantage over the parent game that, as long ago as 1887, a committee of the Portland Club drew up a code of laws under which it should be played.

It is very similar to the parent game, and, like it, is a game for two players, but four packs of cards, not two, are used, and there are some differences in the preliminaries, the scoring and the routine of the game.

In the preliminaries, nine cards (not eight) are dealt to each player, either singly or in threes, and there is no turn-up of the top card of the stock, so that the peculiar value of the 7 of trumps is lost.

The scoring is the same as in the parent game, with the following additions:

Carte blanche a hand without a court card 50

Both players are entitled to score it. Before a player can score, however, he must show his hand to his opponent. Thereafter, each time that he draws a card from the stock he may show it to his opponent and score 50 points if it is not a court card.

Ordinary sequence A, 10, K, Q, J of any suit other than the trump suit 150
Triple bezique Three ♠ Q and three ♦ J (or ♣ Q and ♥ J if either spades or diamonds are trumps) 1,500
Quadruple bezique Four ♠ Q and four ♦ J (or ♣ Q and ♥ J if either spades or diamonds are trumps) 4,500
Last trick 50

The routine differs from that of the parent game in the following essentials:

A game is complete in one deal.

Trumps are determined by the first marriage or sequence declared by either player.

The tricks are left exposed on the table until such time as a brisque is played. After this the tricks are gathered and turned as usual.

If a card is played from a declared combination, subsequently the combination may be filled by adding an appropriate card and the declaration scored again.

If a player has declared two marriages in the same suit, he may rearrange the Kings and Queens on the table and declare two more.

Brisques are disregarded for scoring except to break a tie or to save a player from being rubiconed.

If a player fails to score 1,000 points he is rubiconed. His score is added to (not subtracted from) that of his opponent, who adds a further 1,300 points for the game. Further, if a player fails to score 100 points, the winner adds an extra 100 points to his score.

BEZIQUE FOR THREE PLAYERS

This is played with three packs of cards, and the players all compete against each other. The play is the same as in the parent game with the addition of a score of 1,500 points for triple bezique.

BEZIQUE FOR FOUR PLAYERS

This is played with six packs of cards, or 192 cards in all. Two play in partnership against the other two.

The dealer places 24 cards face downwards in a pile on the table, and on this he places a marker so that the players will be warned when the stock is nearing exhaustion. He deals nine cards to each of the four players and places the remainder of the pack (132 cards in all) face downwards on top of the marker.

In general, the play follows that described under rubicon bezique but there are some differences in the scoring and in declaring.

Carte blanche	100
Double carte blanche Both partners being dealt hands without a court card	50
Quintuple bezique Five ♠ Q and ♦ J (or ♣ Q and ♥ J if either spades or diamonds are trumps)	13,500
Sextuple bezique is so unlikely that no score has been allotted to it. Should it occur, the correct score is	40,500
Any 4 Aces	1,000
Any 4 Tens	900
Any 4 Kings	800
Any 4 Queens	600
Any 4 Jacks	400

The game bonus is 1,000 points, the rubicon 2,500 points and brisques are disregarded.

In all other essentials the scoring is the same as in rubicon bezique. The partnership principle, however, introduces two new features in the methods of declaring combinations. First, after winning a trick, a player may either declare or leave it to his partner to do so. Secondly, a player may declare a combination either with his own cards (including those on the table already declared by him) or with one or more of his own cards and one or more of his partner's declared cards. Indeed, since a player holds only nine cards, quintuple bezique (and sextuple bezique if it occurs) can only be declared with the help of a partner.

The player on the left of the dealer leads to the first trick.

Beyond these additions, the play follows that of rubicon bezique.

SIX-PACK BEZIQUE

This version, sometimes, but rarely, known as Chinese bezique, is a game for two players, and generally considered the most popular variation of the family. Sir Winston Churchill was a keen player and an able exponent of the game.

Six packs are shuffled together and both players lift a part of the pack and show the bottom cards to determine choice of seat and deal. The one who shows the higher card has the choice, and would be advised to pass the deal to his opponent because there is a slight disadvantage in dealing. If equal value cards are shown the players cut again.

The dealer takes a number of cards at random off the top of the pack, and the non-dealer estimates how many have been taken. If his estimate proves correct he scores 150 points. The dealer deals 12 cards, one by one, to his opponent and himself, and scores 250 points if he has taken exactly 24 cards from the top of the pack.

There is no turn-up to determine the trump suit. It is determined, as in rubicon bezique, by the first declared marriage or sequence by either player.

The declarations are scored for as follows:

Sequence in trumps	250
Sequence in plain suit	150
Royal marriage	40
Common marriage	20
Bezique	40
Double bezique	500
Triple bezique	1,500
Quadruple bezique	4,500

If spades are trumps bezique is ♠ Q and ♦ J; if diamonds are trumps ♦ Q and ♠ J; if hearts are trumps ♥ Q and ♣ J; and if clubs are trumps ♣ Q and ♥ J.

Four aces in trumps	1,000
4 10s in trumps	900
4 Kings in trumps	800
4 Queens in trumps	600
4 Jacks in trumps	400
Any 4 Aces	100
Any 4 Kings	80
Any 4 Queens	60
Any 4 Jacks	40
Carte blanche	250

The non-dealer leads to the first trick. It is not compulsory to follow suit, and the card that is led holds the trick unless a higher card of the same suit is played or a trump is played to the lead of a plain suit. As points are not scored for brisques, nor for winning tricks, the tricks are not gathered and turned but left face upwards on the table in a pile. The winner of a trick may score for a declaration. He takes the top card of the stock (the loser takes the next card of the stock) and leads to the next trick.

A declaration is made by placing the appropriate cards face upwards on the table. They are left there and are available for play as though in the hand of the player. Declarations are scored when made, and the same card may be counted in a declaration more than once.

No declaration may be made after the last two cards of the stock have been drawn. The players then pick up any cards they have on the table and play off the last 12 tricks. As in the parent game, a player must now follow suit to the card led, and must win a trick if he is able to.

Every deal constitutes a game, and the player with the higher score wins. He adds 1,000 points to his score, and rubicons his opponent if he has failed to score 3,000 points.

EIGHT-PACK BEZIQUE

This game is identical to Six-Pack Bezique except for the increased number of cards and the following differences in the routine and scoring between the two variations:

1. Each player is dealt 15 cards.
2. The scores for beziques are:

Bezique	50
Double bezique	500
Triple bezique	1,500
Quadruple bezique	4,500
Quintuple bezique	9,000

3. In the trump suit the scores are:

5 Aces	2,000
5 Tens	1,800
5 Kings	1,600
5 Queens	1,200
5 Jacks	800

4. A player who fails to score 5,000 points is rubiconed.

CALIFORNIA JACK

CALIFORNIA JACK *is a game arising from All Fours, but it uses the full pack rather than only the cards that are dealt, and is more complex and skilful. It is thought by most to be better than the original game.*

NUMBER OF PLAYERS

California Jack can only be played satisfactorily by two players.

A good California Jack hand. There are two good cards for trick-winning and three for losing.

CARDS

California Jack is played with the full pack of 52 cards, the Ace ranking high, the 2 low.

The non-dealer cuts the pack and exposes the bottom card to decide the trump suit. The dealer deals six cards, one at a time, to each player, and places the remainder of the pack face upwards on the table, taking the precaution to square it up so that only the top card can be seen.

THE PLAY

The non-dealer leads to the first trick. The winner of a trick takes the top card of the stock, the loser the next card. A player must follow suit if he can, and he loses one point if he revokes.

When the stock is exhausted and the last six cards have been played, the tricks won by each player are examined, and one point is scored for winning High (Ace of trumps), Low (2 of trumps), Jack (Jack of trumps) and Game (majority of points, counting each Ace won as four points, each King as three points, each Queen as two points, each Jack as one point and each 10 as ten points).

The game is won by the player who first scores ten points.

The player should aim to keep both winning and losing cards in his hand because if the exposed card of the stock is valuable he will wish to win it, but if it is not, he will wish to lose the trick on the chance of the next card of the stock being a more valuable one. The 10s, of course, are the cards to go for.

SHASTA SAM

This is a variation of the game in which the stock is placed face downwards on the table instead of face upwards. It is a less skilful game as, of course, the winner of a trick does not know what card he will draw.

CASINO

CASINO *is a game of Italian origin, sometimes spelt as Cassino, but this is believed to be an early printing error which was perpetuated. The game possibly takes its name from the casino – where gambling takes place.*

NUMBER OF PLAYERS

Although Casino is essentially a game for two, it may be played by three or four. The only difference is that if three players take part they all play against each other, and if four take part two play in partnership against the other two.

CARDS

The full pack of 52 cards is used.

The numeral cards count at their pip values. The Ace counts as 1, and the court cards are used only for pairing: they have no pip value.

The dealer deals two cards face downwards to his opponent, then two face upwards to the table, and then two face downwards to himself. This is repeated, so that both players end with four cards each, and there are four exposed cards (the layout) on the table. The remaining 40 cards (the stock) are placed face downwards on the table.

The object of the game is to take in cards which score as follows:

♦ 10 (great casino)	2
♠ 2 (little casino)	1
Majority of cards (27 or more)	3
Majority of spades (7 or more)	1
Aces	1
All cards in layout (the sweep)	1

THE PLAY

Each player in turn, beginning with the non-dealer, plays a card until both players have exhausted their four cards. When this occurs, the same dealer deals four more cards to his opponent and four to himself but none to the layout. Play continues in this way until the stock has been exhausted. In all, therefore, there are six deals to complete the game, and before making the final deal the dealer must announce it. If he does not, his opponent has a right to cancel the deal.

When a player plays a card from his hand he has the choice of several plays.

He may *Pair*. If, for example, there are one or more 5s in the layout, he may play a 5 from his hand and take it up as a trick with all the other 5s in the layout. A court card, however, may be paired with only one card of the same rank at a time.

He may *Combine*. It is an extension of pairing that allows a player to pick up cards from the layout of the total pip value of a card in his hand. Thus a player playing a 9 may take up a 7 and a 2, or a 6 and a 3 from the layout, or all four cards if they are in the layout.

He may *Build*. He may play a card to a card in the layout to make up a total that he is in a position to take with another card in his hand. If, for example, a player holds a 9 and a 2, and there is a 7 in the layout, he may build the 2 on the 7, so that the next time he plays (provided his opponent has not forestalled him) he may play the 9 and take all three cards as a trick. The build may be continued by either player up to a maximum of five cards, but a

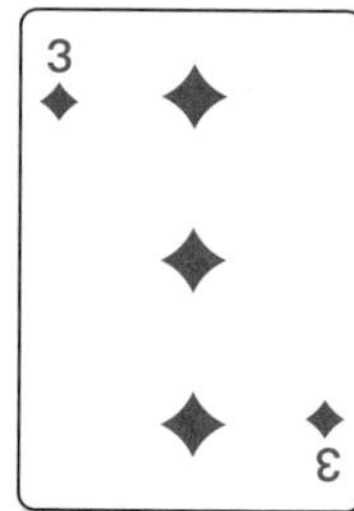

Layout

Hand

build can be taken only as a unit. The player who has built must take up the combination when next it is his turn to play, unless he prefers to win something else, or he decides to make another build.

He may *Call*. It is an extension of building that allows a player to earmark one or more combinations for subsequent capture. Suppose, for example, a player holds in his hand two 8s and that there is a 5 and a 3 in the layout (see illustration). He could, of course, combine one of his 8s with the 5 and 3 in the layout, but this would only give him three cards in the trick. The better play, therefore, is for him to play one of his 8s to the layout and announce 'Eight'. Then, when next it is his turn to play, provided his opponent has not forestalled him, he may play his other 8 and pick up all four cards in the trick.

When a player cannot pair, combine, build or call, he must play one of his cards to the layout. It is known as trailing. It is advisable to play a low card, but not an Ace, little casino or a spade.

When the last eight cards have been played any left in the layout are the property of the winner of the final trick, but it does not count as a sweep.

This ends the game, except for the formality of the players examining their tricks and counting their scores.

There is no penalty for making a build incorrectly, or for capturing cards to which a player is not entitled, because his opponent has the opportunity to see the error and demand that it is corrected. If, however, a player makes a build when he has no card in his hand to capture it or trails when he has a build in the layout, he automatically forfeits the game. If a card is faced in the pack, or if the dealer when dealing exposes a card, other than when dealing cards to the layout, the exposed card is played to the layout and the dealer plays the hand with fewer than four cards.

Casino is sometimes considered a game for children. It is, however, very far from being so. Among card players it is widely spoken of as one of the best of all two-handed games and it is often played for high stakes. To be successful a player needs an elephantine memory, and the capacity to deduce from the card played by an opponent what cards he is most likely to be holding in his hand.

ROYAL CASINO

This is an improvement on the parent game because the court cards play a more important part. The Aces count 1 or 14 (at the option of the player), the Kings 13, the Queens 12 and the Jacks 11, and they may be used for combining and building. Thus an 8 and a 4 may be taken with a Queen, a 6, a 4 and a 3 with a King, and so on.

Twenty-one points constitute the game.

DRAW CASINO

In this version of the game, after the first round of a deal, the 40 undealt cards are placed face downwards on the table to form a stock. Then each player, after playing, draws a card from the stock to bring the number of cards in his hand up to four. When the stock is exhausted the hands are played out and the count made as in the parent game.

SPADE CASINO

This version may be played either as royal casino or as the parent game, with the addition that the ♠ A, ♠ J and ♠ 2 count two points each, and all the other spades one point each.

Game is 61 points, and it is convenient and customary to keep the score on a cribbage board.

COLONEL

COLONEL *is a version of Coon Can (**see page 165**), adapted for fewer players and with fewer cards.*

NUMBER OF PLAYERS

Colonel is for two players only.

CARDS

The full standard pack of 52 cards is used, cards ranking from Ace (high) to 2 (low).

The players cut for deal, and the higher deals. Each player is dealt ten cards, one at a time. The rest of the pack is placed face downwards on the table, between the players, and the top card (known as the optional card) is turned face upwards and placed alongside the stock.

THE PLAY

The object of the game is to make sequences of the same suit, or threes or fours of a kind, and declare them by placing them face upwards on the table. The hand ends when one of the players has declared all his cards. A sequence must be of at least three cards, but once it has been declared either player, in his turn, may add to it. In the same way, if three of a kind has been declared, either player in his turn may add the fourth card to it.

The non-dealer plays first. He takes into his hand either the optional card or

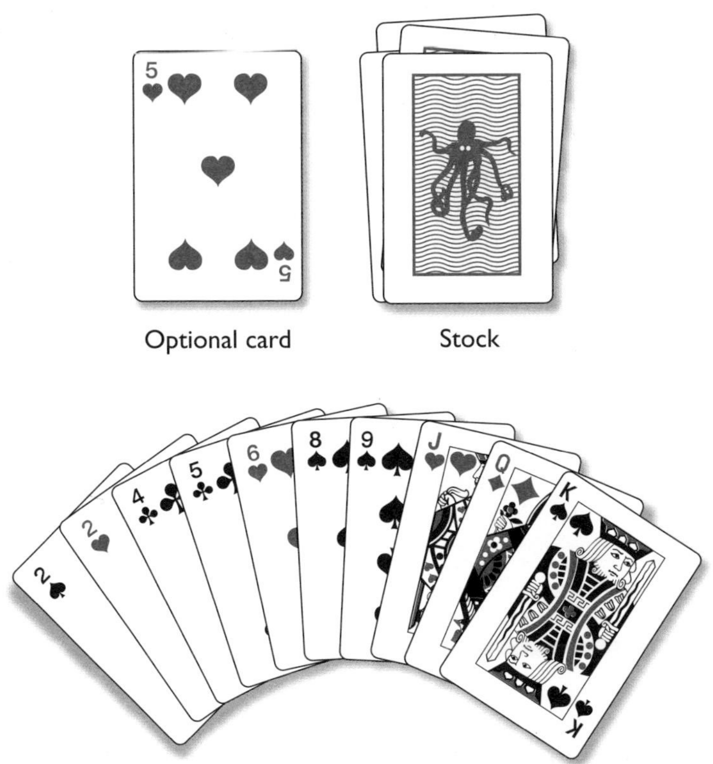

It would be good play to take the ♥ 5 as it gives chances of a set of 5s or a sequence in hearts. The ♠ K might be discarded.

the top card of the stock. He declares any sequences, or threes or fours of a kind that he holds, and discards a card from his hand. The discard is placed on top of the optional card, or in its place if the optional card has been taken up. The dealer plays next. He has the choice of taking the card that the non-dealer has discarded or the top card of the stock.

It will be seen, therefore, that the routine of the play is very simple. Each player in turn takes into his hand either the top card of the stock or the card his opponent has discarded, he then declares any sequences, threes or fours that he holds, or adds to those already declared either by himself or his opponent, and then discards a card from his hand. In a sequence the Ace is high. A player is not under compulsion to declare: indeed it is good play to refuse to declare for as long as possible in an attempt to declare one's hand all at once. This way one's opponent has less chance to declare all his cards, but it is to be borne in mind that a player who fails to declare when he can runs the risk that his opponent will go out before him.

When a player has declared all his cards, his opponent loses points for every card remaining in his hand, the Ace, King, Queen and Jack counting as 10 points each, the remaining cards their pip values.

If the stock is exhausted before either player has declared all his cards, both players show the cards remaining in their hands and the player with the lower total wins the hand. He adds to the score the total of his opponent's hand less that of his own.

A refinement of the game is that before the stock is exhausted either player may challenge. If the challenge is rejected by the opponent, the hand continues to be played out. If, however, the challenge is accepted, both players expose their hands and the player with the lower total wins. He adds to his score the total of his opponent's hand without deducting his own. If the right cards to make sequences and threes of a kind are not coming to a player, it is good play for him to fill his hand with low cards and then challenge.

COMET

COMET *was probably invented around 1759 (when Halley's Comet reappeared and caused great excitement).*

NUMBER OF PLAYERS

Comet is for two players, but a variation called Commit (no doubt a mistake by an early printer, but nevertheless useful) can be played by up to five players, and is described later.

CARDS

Two 52-card packs, with the same design on their backs, are used alternately. The packs must be prepared by rejecting all the Aces, putting all the red cards into one pack and all the black cards into another, and interchanging a red and a black 9.

Eighteen cards are dealt to each player, one at a time, and the remaining 12 cards are put aside; they play no part in the game.

THE PLAY

The non-dealer begins the game by playing one of his cards, face upwards, to the centre of the table. The players then, alternately, build up on it by rank only. Suits are disregarded. Any number of cards, provided they are of the proper rank, may be played in one turn. The four 8s, for example, may be built on a 7, the four Jacks on a 10, and so on. When a player is unable to build it is a stop, and his opponent begins a new sequence by playing any card he chooses. Obviously a King is always a stop.

The 9 of the opposite colour is called the comet. It may represent any card that the holder chooses, but may be played only in turn. It is a stop, and the player who plays it begins a new sequence.

The player who is first to get rid of all the cards in his hand is the winner. He scores the total of pips left in his opponent's hand, the court cards counting as 10 each. If both players are stopped and both are left with cards in their hands, both hands are counted. The lower hand wins and scores the value of his opponent's hand less the value of his own. If a player wins the hand while the comet is in the hand of his opponent he scores double. If a player wins by playing the comet, he doubles his score, and if he wins the hand by playing the comet as a 9 he quadruples his score.

COMMIT

This is a variation of the parent game that is suitable for more than two players. It is played with the standard pack of 52 cards from which the ♦ 8 has been removed, and as many other 8s and 7s as may be necessary for all of the players to be dealt an equal number of cards.

The players place an equal number of units into a pool.

The player on the left of the dealer begins by playing any card to the centre of the table. The others play cards on it as able, and not necessarily in rotation. The cards played must follow in sequence. Only the ♠ 6 may be played on the ♠ 5, the ♣ 8 on the ♣ 7, and so on.

The ♦9 is the comet and may be played either when all the players are stopped or when the holder of it has played regularly and is unable to continue the sequence. After it has been played, any player in rotation may either continue by playing the ♦ 10 on it, or the card next above that for which the comet has been substituted.

The player who plays the comet receives two units from each of the other players, and any player who plays a King receives one unit from each of the other players. The player who is first to get rid of his cards wins the pool, and receives two units from a player who has been left with the comet in his hand, and one unit for each King.

CRIBBAGE

CRIBBAGE *is believed to have been developed out of the older card game of Noddy by Sir John Suckling in the reign of Charles I. In the manner of scoring it is unique, and the play calls for no effort of memory. Good judgement and concentration are the chief qualities that lead to success.*

NUMBER OF PLAYERS

Originally cribbage was a two-handed game as described first, but variations for three and four players are now played and are described later.

The two-handed game is the most popular, and of it there are three variations: five-, six- and seven-card.

CARDS

The full pack of 52 cards is used, and they rank from King (high) to Ace (low). The King, Queen and Jack count as ten each, and the other cards their pip values.

Five-card Cribbage for two players, which is the original game, is generally considered the most scientific of the variations.

The players cut for deal; the lower deals first. Five cards are dealt to each player, and the non-dealer pegs three holes (Three for Last) as compensation against the advantage of the first deal of a game.

A cribbage or noddy board.

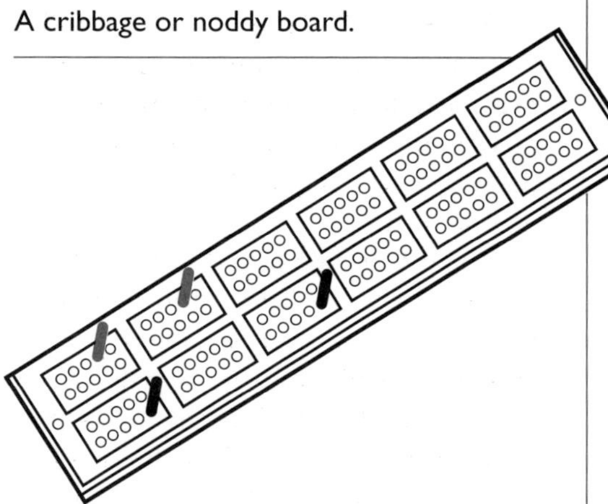

THE PLAY

Points won are marked with a peg on what is known as a cribbage or noddy board (see illustration). It is oblong in shape, has a double row of holes, 30 in each row, and is divided, for convenience in scoring, into groups of five holes. The board is placed between the two players; both start from the same end of the board and peg their scores first along the outer row of holes and then along the inner row – once round the board at the five-card game, twice round at the six-card game and three times round at the seven-card game. In each case the game ends when one player reaches the hole from which he started. Thus, at five-card cribbage the game is 61 holes, at six-card 121 holes, and at seven-card 181 holes.

The players look at their cards, and then place two of them face downwards on the right of the dealer. These four cards are known as the crib or box. The non-dealer then cuts the pack, and the dealer turns up the top card of the cut and places it on top of the pack. The card is known as the start, and if it is a Jack the dealer pegs two holes (Two for his Heels).

Scores are made partly in play and partly by the scoring values of the cards in hand. The latter, however, are not pegged until the play ends.

During the play of the hand, scores are made as follows:

If a player plays a card of the same rank as the previous one played, he pegs two for a pair, but court cards pair only rank with rank – that is to say King with King, Queen with Queen and Jack with Jack.

If a player plays a third card of the same rank as a pair he pegs 6 for pair-royal.

If a player plays a fourth card of the same rank as a pair-royal he pegs 12 for a double pair-royal.

A sequence (or run) is pegged at one for each card with a minimum of three cards and a maximum of seven. The cards need not be of the same suit, nor need they be played in sequential order, but, as the Ace is low, A, K, Q is not a sequence, and a sequence is destroyed by a pair or an intervening card. If the dealer plays a 7 and the non-dealer a 5, the dealer may now play a 6 and peg three, and the non-dealer may continue either with a 4 or an 8 and peg four.

If a player plays a card which, with those already played, adds up to 15 he pegs two, and, again, if they total 31 he pegs two.

West

East

Out of this an important point arises. If, when the player whose turn it is to play cannot do so without exceeding 31, he says 'Go'. His opponent then plays a card or cards up to the limit. If the cards that he plays bring the total up to exactly 31 he pegs two; if not he pegs one (One for Last).

This ends the play, and the players, beginning with the non-dealer, count their scores by combining their own cards with the start. The dealer then exposes the crib (it is his exclusive property) and any values that he finds in it (making full use of the start) he pegs to his score. Should either player hold

the Jack of the same suit as the start he pegs one (One for his Nob). If a player holds in his hand three cards all of the same suit he pegs three for a flush, and four if the start is of the same suit. In the crib, however, nothing is scored for a flush unless, with the start, it is a flush of five; if it is the dealer pegs five.

Two other features of the scoring call for special mention. First, a player must count his hand aloud, and if he overlooks any score, either in play or otherwise, his opponent may call 'Muggins', point out the omission, and peg the score for himself. Secondly, if a player reaches the game hole before his opponent has gone halfway round the board a lurch is scored, that is to say the winner scores two games instead of only one.

Points are scored during the play by a player adding the value of the card played by the opponent to a card played from his own hand. Thus if a 10 or court card is led, and a player plays a 5, he scores 15 and pegs two holes (*fifteen-two* as it is called for short). If a 6 is led, and he plays another 6, he scores for a pair and pegs two. Again, if a 4 is led and he plays a 6 and the opponent plays a 5: he pegs three for a sequence and two for 15. And so on.

The general principles may be illustrated in the elementary deal.

East is the dealer.

West (see illustration on page 31) holds a sequence of four. As a result the ♣ K will go to the crib, and for his other card he must choose between the ♣ 6 and the ♥ 9. There is not much in it, but as the ♣ 6 is of the same suit as the King, there is a slight advantage in discarding the ♥ 9, because the ♣ 6 (along with the King) might help to give East a flush in his crib.

East has an easy choice of discards. Indeed, it is obvious that he will discard the ♣ A and ♦ 3.

West cuts the cards, and East turns up the ♠ K.

The position is now as in the illustration opposite.

West leads the ♦ 7 and says 'Seven'. It is his best lead because if East plays an 8 and pegs two for 15, West can play the ♣ 6 and peg three for sequence. He will not, of course, play the ♠ 8, because if East holds another 8 he will play it and not only peg for a pair-royal but for 31 as well.

In the event, East cannot play an 8 and score for 15. His best play, therefore, is the ♣ 10, announcing 'Seventeen'. This makes it impossible for a 15 to be scored against him.

West has no better play than the ♠ 8, announcing 'Twenty-five', because the closer the total to 31 the better the chance that East will be unable to play.

East plays the ♠ 5, announcing 'Thirty'.

West says 'Go' and as East has not got an Ace he pegs One for Last.

The hands are now counted.

West is not helped by the start. All he can score is two for 15 and three for sequence. This with his Three for Last (as non-dealer) gives him eight.

East pegs six for 15 (two 10s and the ♠ K in the start, each combined with the ♠ 5) and two for the pair of 10s. In the crib he finds an Ace, a King, a 9 and a 3. With the start this gives him two for the pair of Kings. He therefore pegs 10 holes, making 11 in all as he has already pegged One for Last.

SIX- AND SEVEN-CARD CRIBBAGE

The six- and seven-card variations of cribbage differ very little from the five-card game. There is, in fact, no difference in the play nor in the crib, and very little in the mechanics of the game. The only differences of importance, apart from the number of cards, are that the non-dealer does not receive Three for Last, that the cards are played out to the end (the player failing to score for go leading again, thus giving his opponent the chance of making a pair or 15) and that in the six-card variation the play is twice round the board (121 holes) and in the seven-card three times round (181 holes).

The general principles explained for the parent game hold good at the six-card variation. It is to be noted, however, that in the six-card variation the number of cards in hand and in the crib are the same, from which it follows that it is not so important for the non-dealer to make an effort of trying to baulk the crib by his discard. The two objectives – preserving any values in hand and baulking the opponent's crib – are in this case on the same level, and either objective may be preferred, as the nature of the hand dictates.

THREE-HANDED CRIBBAGE

With three players, five cards are dealt to each player, and an extra one to the crib, to which each player contributes one card only. There is no Three for Last. The start is cut for in the usual way. The player on the left of the dealer plays first, and has first Show. He deals the succeeding hand. The score may be pegged on a triangular board open in the centre, or on the standard board with a pivoted arm that permits a third player to peg. The game is once round the board.

FOUR-HANDED CRIBBAGE

With four players, two play as partners against the other two, the partners sitting facing each other. Each player is dealt five cards and discards one to the crib, which is the property of the dealer. The player on the left of the dealer plays first. The others follow in clockwise rotation. Consultation between partners is not allowed, nor may they prompt each other, but a player may help his partner in the count of the hand or crib. The cards are played out to the end, as in the six and seven-card variations. Game is usually twice round the board (121 holes).

ECARTÉ

ECARTÉ *is a gambling game, once one of the most popular in France. It requires a knowledge of probabilities only, and to a player with a complete knowledge of these it is a mechanical game.*

NUMBER OF PLAYERS

Ecarté is suitable for two players only.

CARDS

Ecarté is played with a 32-card pack; that is to say with a pack from which the 2s, 3s, 4s, 5s and 6s have been removed. The cards rank in the order: King (high), Queen, Jack, Ace, 10, 9, 8, 7 (low).

The two players are dealt five cards each, either in sets of three and two, or two and three, and the rest of the pack is placed face downwards on the table, between them. To determine the trump suit the top card of the pack is turned face upwards.

THE PLAY

After looking at his cards, the non-dealer either plays or proposes. If he proposes, the dealer has the choice of either accepting or playing, and if he accepts both players may exchange any or all their cards for others from the pack. By agreement the exchange of cards may continue until the pack is exhausted.

The non-dealer has first lead. The object of the game is to win three tricks, called the Trick. The winner scores one point for this, and if he wins all five tricks (the Vole) he scores two points. The game is won by the player who first wins five points, and it is customary to count a treble if a player wins the game and his opponent has failed to score; a double if his opponent has scored only one or two points, and a single if his opponent has scored three or four points.

So far, then, Ecarté appears to be childishly simple. The game, however, lends itself to a number of refinements that raise it to the level of an adult game. If the non-dealer does not propose, but plays, and fails to make the trick, the dealer scores two points instead of only one. In the same way, if the dealer refuses a proposal, and plays, and fails to make the trick, the non-dealer scores two points. The value of the vole (two points) is not affected by playing without proposing.

Another important feature of the game is that if the dealer turns up a King as trumps, or if a player is dealt the King of the trump suit, he scores one point. The point can be scored by the non-dealer only if he declares the King before he makes the opening lead, and by the dealer only if he declares it before he plays to the first trick. A player is under no compulsion to declare the King, and, indeed, sometimes it is better to sacrifice the point than to disclose to the opponent that this important card is held against him.

With the score at West three points, East four points, West deals and the ♠ 8 is turned up. The hands are as below.

East decides to play and must win the game if he handles his cards correctly. In the event he loses the game by incautious play. He leads ♣ K on which West plays ♣ 7. West does not declare the ♠ K because East has played without proposing and, therefore, will lose two points if he fails to win the Trick. On the other hand, if he wins the Trick, declaring the King will be of no help to West.

East is lulled into a false sense of security, and unaware that the ♠ K is against him he assumes that it is safe to lead ♠ Q. West wins with ♠ K, leads ♦ Q to force East to win with ♠ J, and comes to the last two tricks, and wins the game, with ♠ A and ♥ A.

There are a number of stock hands, holding which a player should play and not propose, and equally refuse the opponent's proposal. The more important of them are listed below. In all cases spades are trumps:

Any three trumps supported by two inferior cards in outside suits – ♠ J, 10, 7; ♥ 8; ♦ 10.
Any two trumps supported by three cards in one outside suit – ♠ 10, 8; ♥ J, 8, 7.
Any two trumps supported by the King and a low card in an outside suit, and one indifferent card in another suit – ♠ A, 8; ♥ K, 7; ♦ 9.
Any one trump supported by four cards headed by the King (or Queen) in an outside suit – ♠ J; ♥ K, 9, 8, 7 (or Q, J, 8, 7).

West

East

West

East

Any one trump supported by three cards headed by a court card in an outside suit, and any high court card in another suit – ♠ 10; ♥ J, 10, 7; ♦ Q.

Any hand that contains three Queens (or better) and even though it may lack a trump card – ♥ Q, 7; ♦ Q, 7; ♣ K.

Any hand that contains four high cards (King, Queen, Jack) and even though it may lack a trump card – ♥ K ♦ Q J; ♣ Q, 7.

These stock hands are based on the law of probability, supported by the experience of the best players, who set great store on them. So far as the dealer is concerned, they are the minimum types of hands for him to play on. In a number of cases he may do better if he follows his luck, or decides to play on what is called a hunch, but the non-dealer should never propose when holding a hand similar to one of the above types. The reason is that he has the opening lead, and, at Ecarté, the opening lead is of vital importance.

East deals and the ♠ 10 is turned up. The hands are shown above.

West plays and if he leads ♥ Q he wins the Trick no matter how East plays.

If, however, West had dealt, East would be on lead and if he led the ♦ K he would win the Trick no matter how West played. In fact, West would be hard put to save the Vole, and, indeed, would do so only if he retained the ♣ J and not the ♥ Q. An experienced player would, of course, retain the ♣ J (although the ♥ Q is a higher card) because he holds three hearts and only one club, and since there are only eight cards in a suit it is about seven to five on that East's last card is a club and not a heart.

The deal is of some interest because it illustrates the danger of leading the Queen of trumps, unless the King has been turned up as trumps. It will be seen that if West decides to lead the ♠ Q, East wins with the ♠ K, runs his diamonds (scoring the Trick) and West will save the Vole only if he retains the ♣ J. On the other hand, it is to be noted that the lead of the singleton King of trumps is nearly always a good lead, and rarely damages the leader's hand.

As a general rule it is best for a player to play when he cannot see his way to discarding more than two cards; but if a player's hand guarantees him the Trick, or virtually so, he should propose or accept, because if the proposal is refused he is on easy street (since the Trick is more or less in his pocket) and if the proposal is accepted he has the opportunity to convert his hand into one on which he may win the Vole.

EIGHTS

EIGHTS *is a game of the Stops family and is regarded as one with better opportunities for skill than other members of the family. It probably originated in the USA, where it is also called Swedish Rummy, although there is no connection with games of the Rummy family. The game is also called Switch (usually with Jacks rather than 8s being the most significant cards).*

NUMBER OF PLAYERS

The game is best for two players, although three can play, and four can play in two partnerships, as explained later.

CARDS

The full pack of 52 cards is used.

Each player draws a card; lower deals (Ace high). Thereafter the deal alternates with each hand. The dealer shuffles, the non-dealer cuts, and the dealer gives seven cards, one at a time, to each player. The remainder of the pack is placed face down to form the stock, and the top card then turned face up beside the stock to become the starter.

THE PLAY

The non-dealer plays first. He must begin a talon pile by laying onto the starter a card from his hand of either the same suit or the same rank as the starter. If he is unable to, he must draw cards one at a time from the top of the stock until he can.

When a player has laid a card, his opponent takes his turn and play continues alternately. If the stock becomes exhausted, a player unable to make a turn passes.

The game gets its name from the fact that all 8s are wild. An 8 may be played at any time, whether or not the player holding it could play another card. The player laying an 8 can specify which suit it represents (but not which rank). He can thereby change the suit or stipulate that the previous suit continues.

A player may choose to draw from the stock even if able to play, but he must eventually lay a card if able - he cannot pass while holding a card which can be played.

The winner is the first to get rid of all his cards. If the stock is exhausted and neither player can play, the game ends in a block, but is still valid for scoring.

A player is debited for the cards in his hand when his opponent goes out, on the following scale: an 8 counts 50 points, a King, Queen or Jack counts ten points, and all other cards count their pip value (Ace counts one point). If the game ends in a block, each player is debited for the cards in his hand. When a player's debit score reaches 100, his opponent wins the game, and wins by 100 points plus the difference between the two totals. Settlement is made on the basis of an agreed amount per ten points, the difference being rounded up to the nearest ten.

Good play comes from keeping count of the number of cards played in each suit, in deciding when to change the suit, and in particular in the use of the 8s. It is best to keep an 8 for emergencies, and it might sometimes be worth drawing from stock rather than playing an 8. A player with the last 8 who knows a suit is exhausted might deliberately call for that suit to cause a block, if he is confident that his opponent holds cards counting more than he does himself.

EIGHTS FOR THREE PLAYERS

This version is played cut-throat style, i.e. each player for himself. After deciding dealer, the deal passes to the left. Each player is dealt five cards (not six as with two players) one at a time, and the player to the dealer's left plays first. Play continues in turn to the left. When one player's debit score reaches 100, each player's score is rounded up to the nearest ten, and the players settle with each other according to the difference between them at a rate agreed beforehand. There is no bonus for winning the game.

EIGHTS FOR FOUR PLAYERS

This version is played in partnerships of two, each player sitting opposite his partner. Each is dealt five cards. For a partnership to win a hand, both partners must get rid of their cards. The side which fails to go out is debited with the cards held in the hands of the players on that side (there might be one hand or two to count). When one partnership is debited with 100, the winning partnership score the difference in the two totals (rounded up to the nearest ten) plus 100 for game. Each winning partner collects from his opponent on his right settlement at an agreed rate per ten points based on the winning margin (i.e. if the margin is 130, each loser pays to his right-hand opponent 13 units).

GERMAN WHIST

GERMAN WHIST *was invented for two players who like Whist and cannot find another pair. It is a simple game but to play it well requires a good memory.*

NUMBER OF PLAYERS

German Whist is essentially a game for only two players.

CARDS

The full pack of 52 cards is used. Cards rank from Ace (high) to 2 (low).

Each player is dealt 13 cards. The remaining 26 cards are placed face downwards between the players and the top card is turned face upwards to denote the trump suit.

THE PLAY

The non-dealer leads to the first trick. Thereafter the player who wins a trick leads to the next, and so on. A player must follow suit if he can. If he cannot, he may either trump or discard. The winner of a trick takes into his hand the exposed card from the top of the stock; the loser takes the next card from the stock (he does not show it to his opponent) and turns up the next card of the stock.

When the stock is exhausted, the players play out the remaining 13 cards, and at this stage of the game the player with a good memory will know exactly which cards his opponent holds.

The game is complete in one deal, and the player who wins the majority of tricks receives an agreed number of points per trick for all in excess of those won by his opponent. If both players win 13 tricks, there is, of course, no score.

Although German whist is a simple game it offers good memory training for those who aspire to succeed at more advanced games, and, at the same time, gives exercise in the technique of card play.

If a player holds a strong trump suit he should lead his trumps early in the game so as to command the game in the later stages of the play, and if the exposed card is a trump it is always good play to make an effort to win it.

On the other hand, it is not always

Stock

West

good play to win a trick. Much depends on the value of the exposed card. For example, suppose the ♦ 9 is exposed. West leads the ♦ 7 and East holds ♦ Q, 6, 3. East should play ♦ 3, and allow West to win the trick. It is not worth while wasting the ♦ Q which should be kept in hand for better things later in the game. However, if the ♦ J is the exposed card, East should win the trick with the ♦ Q, because now he is exchanging the ♦ Q for an equivalent card and adding a trick to his total.

It is advisable to hold command of as many suits as possible, because it enables one to take a trick whenever the exposed card is worth winning, without losing control of the suit.

West holds the hand in the illustration. Spades are trumps, and the exposed card is ♣ K.

The ♣ K is worth winning, but leading the ♣ A is not the best play. West will win the trick, but the value of his hand will remain unchanged. West should prefer to lead the ♦ K, because if it wins the trick his hand will be that much better, and if East is able to win the trick with the ♦ A, West's ♦ Q has been promoted to top diamond.

GIN RUMMY

THE INVENTION OF *Gin Rummy has been credited to E. T. Baker in a New York club in 1909. It is a variant of the parent game Rummy, which is frequently shortened to Rum, and acquired its name Gin by extension of the alcoholic drink theme. It became very popular due to the publicity it received when taken up by film stars in Hollywood in the 1940s.*

NUMBER OF PLAYERS

Gin Rummy is a game for two players only. There are forms of Rummy for more players – see under Rummy on page 184.

CARDS

The full pack of 52 cards is used, cards ranking from King (high) to Ace (low).

Dealer is determined by the players each drawing a card from the pack: higher has choice of dealing first or not. If cards of equal rank are drawn, the suit determines precedence in the order: spades (high), hearts, diamonds, clubs. After the first deal, the winner of each hand deals the next.

The dealer deals ten cards to each player, one at a time, beginning with his opponent. The remainder of the pack is placed face down between the players to form the stock. The top card of the stock is placed face up beside the stock and becomes the upcard, at the same time beginning a discard pile.

THE PLAY

The object of the play is to form the hand into sets of three or more cards. A set may be of two kinds: three or four cards of the same rank, or three or more cards in sequence in the same suit (Ace being in sequence with 2, 3, not King, Queen).

The non-dealer may take the first upcard into his hand or refuse it. If he refuses, the dealer has the option of taking it or refusing it. If the dealer also refuses it, the non-dealer draws the top card from the stock and takes it into his hand, discarding a card (the new upcard) face up on the discard pile. The discarded card may, in fact, be the card picked up, and the player may merely look at it and discard it immediately. Thereafter each player in turn draws a card, either the upcard or the top card of the stock, and discards, so that the number of cards in each player's hand remains at ten.

Cards which are not included in a set are 'unmatched' cards. After drawing (and only then), a player may 'knock', i.e. terminate the hand, whenever the pip value of the unmatched cards in his hand total ten or less. For this purpose, court cards (King, Queen, Jack) count as ten points each, the Ace counts as one, and the other cards as their face value.

Knocking involves laying down the hand, arranged in sets, with unmatched cards separate, making the usual discard. The count of unmatched cards represent points against the player. If all ten cards are in sets, the player is said to 'go gin', and the count against him is nought.

If the player drawing the fiftieth card discards without knocking (i.e. there are only two cards left in the stock) the hand is abandoned and there is no score for that deal.

When a player knocks, there is one further stage before the calculation of

Knocker (left) goes out with a count of three. His opponent lays off with ♥ J, 10 and has a count of 11.

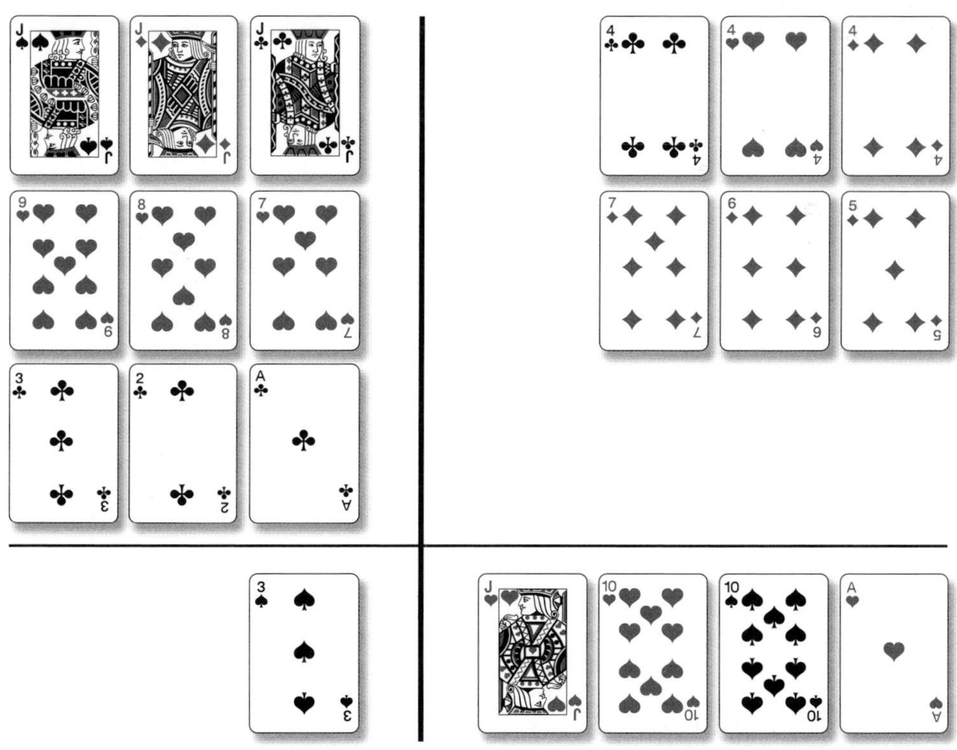

the score, and that is the 'laying off'. The opponent of the knocker lays down his cards in sets, and, unless the knocker has gone gin, may lay off any of his unmatched cards on the sets of the knocker, thereby reducing the count against him.

The illustration on page 43 shows a completed deal in which the opponent of the knocker can lay two unmatched cards on the knocker's sets.

SCORING

If the knocker has the lower of the two counts in unmatched cards, he scores the difference in the counts (in the illustration the knocker scores eight points). It is possible that the player who did not knock has the lower count. In this case he 'undercuts' the knocker and scores the difference in the count plus a bonus of 20 points. Should the count be equal, the opponent of the knocker still undercuts him, scoring the bonus 20 points, but nothing for difference in point count. The illustration below shows a completed deal, in which the knocker is undercut.

It must be remembered that cards cannot be laid off on a knocker who goes gin. Going gin therefore guards against being undercut.

A player who goes gin scores a bonus of 25 on top of the point count.

The first player to score 100 points wins the game, but scoring does not end there. The winner of the game adds 100

Knocker (left) is undercut when opponent lays off with ♥ A, ♥ 6 and ♥ 7 on his sequence.

Me	Thee
18	27
22	29
58	61
70	+60
75	121
92	
101	
+100	
+140	
341	

A completed score card.

points bonus to his score. Each player then adds 20 points to his score for each of his 'boxes' - each deal he won. The winner wins by the difference in the two scores. This difference is doubled if the lower did not score a point. This is called a 'shutout' or 'schneider'. The score of a completed game is illustrated above.

There is a more complex scoring system, which was used in the days of popularity in Hollywood and which is known as Hollywood scoring.

The scores are recorded on a sheet of ruled paper (see overleaf). The first time a player wins a deal he enters the points in the first column only. The second time he enters the points in the second column and also adds them to the score in the first column. The third time he enters the points in the third column and adds them to the score in the first two columns. Thereafter points won are added to the scores in all three columns. The illustration below represents a game in progress, showing some scores entered.

When the score of a player in a column reaches 100 or more, the column is closed. The player winning it scores a bonus of 100 points, and each player scores 20 points for each box won, as in the orthodox scoring. The winner wins by the difference in the scores, and if the loser fails to score in a column the difference is doubled. A player who is shut out in the first column must clearly make his first entry in the second column. A game ends when all three columns are won.

STRATEGY

Players must use judgement in deciding how long to hold high cards presenting a good chance of a set. For three or four draws it might pay to hold them, as high cards are likely to be discarded by the opponent. Many gin hands are won after only five or six draws, however, with six or seven cards in sets, and three or four unmatched. At this stage, therefore, a player should consider discarding these high cards in favour of lower ones.

Low cards, if drawn, ought to be retained, as clearly they reduce the loss if your opponent wins, and they enable a player to knock as soon as he holds two or three sets.

	Me	Thee	Me	Thee	Me	Thee
Box 1	25	17	2	3	12	
Box 2	27	20	14		18	
Box 3	39		20			
Box 4	45					
Box 5						
Box 6						
Box 7						

Hollywood scoring, with a game in progress.

A player in a position to knock will have to weigh the chances of being undercut. In the first four turns, a player might feel safe in knocking as soon as he can. From about the eighth turn, however, he might decide to knock only with a count of, say, five or lower. In deciding whether to knock he will consider the upcards which both players have taken and try to calculate how many sets his opponent has and what he might be able to lay off.

With an opportunity to knock with a low count it is usually a mistake to wait for gin. If your opponent goes gin first it is a costly error.

HONEYMOON BRIDGE

HONEYMOON BRIDGE *is a game invented for Bridge fanatics who find themselves as a pair rather than a foursome.*

NUMBER OF PLAYERS

As with all honeymoons, two is the only suitable number.

CARDS

The full pack of 52 cards is used, cards ranking from Ace (high) to 2 (low).

Thirteen cards are dealt to each player and the remaining 26 are placed face down between them, to form the stock.

THE PLAY

The non-dealer leads to the first trick. Thereafter the player who wins a trick leads to the next. A player must follow suit if he can. The winner of a trick takes the top card of the stock, the loser takes the next card. The first 13 tricks are played without a trump suit, and do not count in the final score.

When the stock is exhausted, the two players bid as in Bridge (see page 104) the dealer first; bidding continues until one player passes a bid, double or redouble. The player who does not make the final bid leads to the first trick, and the play continues as in the parent game. The players score as in Bridge.

If a player revokes during the play of the first 13 tricks, or if he draws a card out of turn, or sees more than one card when drawing from the stock, his opponent, when it is his turn to draw from the stock, may look at the two top cards and take either. Other irregularities are governed by the laws of Bridge.

HONEYMOON BRIDGE WITH A WIDOW

In this version of the game, the players sit in adjacent seats and the cards are dealt into four hands (as in the standard game) of 12 cards each. The remaining four cards (the widow) are placed face downwards in the centre of the table.

The players bid as in the standard game (the dealer bids first) and when a bid has been passed, doubled or redoubled, the player who has won the declaration takes up the widow hand and, without showing it to his opponent, takes one card into his own hand, one into his dummy, and gives the other two cards to his opponent to take one into his hand and the other into his dummy.

The player who has won the declaration may demand the opening lead to be made either by his opponent or by his opponent's dummy.

SEMI-EXPOSED HONEYMOON BRIDGE

The players in this version sit in adjacent seats and the cards are dealt as in the standard game, except that the first six cards to the dummies are dealt face downwards in a row, the remaining cards, six face upwards on top of them and one face upwards by itself.

The dealer bids first, and the bidding ends when a bid has been passed, doubled or redoubled. The hand on the left of the player who has won the declaration leads to the first trick. The play and scoring are as in the parent game, except that a player may play from his dummy only a face-upwards card. When a face-upwards card has been played, the card under it is turned face upwards, and is available for play.

JO-JOTTE

ALTHOUGH *Jo-jotte was invented by Ely Culbertson in 1937 it is not altogether a modern game, but a variation of the old French game of Belotte, in itself very similar to Klaberjass (see page 52) and its several variations.*

NUMBER OF PLAYERS

Jo-jotte is a game for two players.

CARDS

Jo-jotte is played with the short pack,

namely a pack from which all cards below the rank of 7 have been removed.

The rank of the cards varies. If there is a trump suit, the cards of the suit rank in the order: Jack, 9, Ace, 10, King, Queen, 8, 7. In plain suits, or if the hand is played in no trumps, the order is: Ace, 10, King, Queen, Jack, 9, 8, 7.

Each player is dealt six cards (either singly, or in twos or threes) and the 13th card of the pack is placed face upwards on the table. This is known as the turned card.

BIDDING

There are two rounds of bidding. The non-dealer bids first. He may either accept the suit of the turned card as trumps, or pass. If he passes, the dealer has the same option. If both players pass, the non-dealer may name any suit, other than that of the turned card, as trumps, or he may declare no-trumps or he may pass. If he passes for the second time, the dealer has the same option. If both players pass twice the hand is abandoned and the deal passes, but if either player names a suit as trumps, his opponent may overbid it by declaring no-trumps, but not by naming another suit as trumps. Either player may double his opponent's declaration, and any double may be redoubled.

THE PLAY

When the declaration has been determined (doubled, redoubled or passed) the dealer deals three more cards to his opponent and to himself, and he places the bottom card of the pack face upwards on top of the undealt cards of the pack. It has no significance in play but is solely informatory and, therefore, is known as the information card.

The player who has made the final declaration is known as the declarer: his opponent as the defender.

At this stage of the game the defender may announce that instead of defending against the declarer's contract he will himself become declarer at a nullo contract; a contract, that is, to lose every trick. The declarer may now declare a slam, a contract to win every trick either in the suit originally named by him (he cannot change the suit) or in no-trumps.

The defender then announces his melds, if he holds any. A meld is four of a kind (except 9s, 8s and 7s at no trumps, and 8s and 7s in a suit declaration). A meld carries a score of 100 points and is scored (as at Bridge, see page 104) above the line. Only the player with the highest-ranking meld may score for it, and he may score for a second meld if he holds one.

Next, beginning with the defender, the players score for sequences, and for this purpose the cards take their normal rank of Ace (high), King, Queen, Jack, 10, 9, 8, 7. For a sequence of five cards the holder scores 50 points above the line, for a sequence of four 40 points, and for a sequence of three 20 points. If two sequences are of equal length, that headed by the highest card takes precedence. If both sequences are equal, a sequence in the trump suit wins over one in a plain suit; if both sequences are

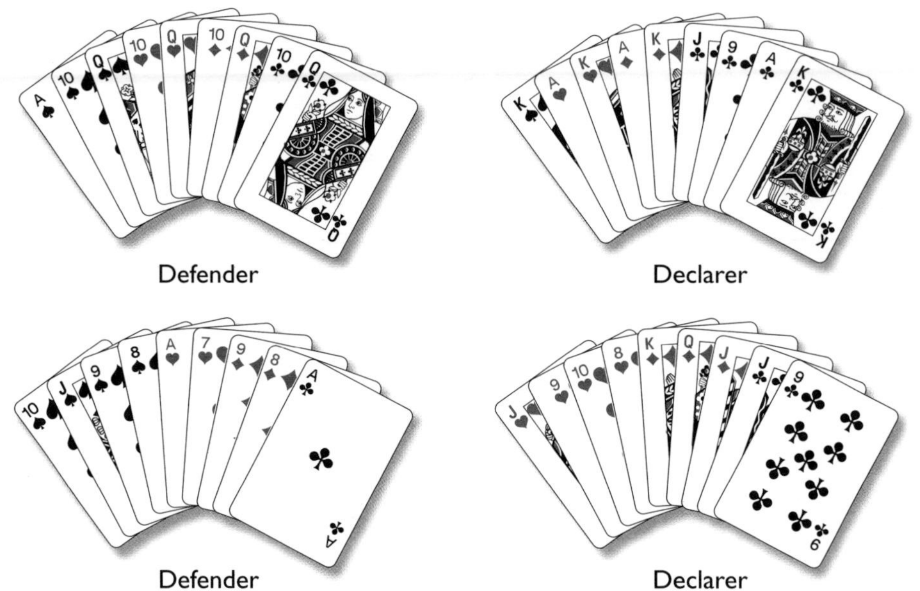

in plain suits neither is scored for. Only the player with the higher-ranking sequence may score for it, and he may score for any other sequences that he may hold.

In the top illustration above, clubs are trumps. Defender scores 200 points above the line for his melds of 10s and Queens, and the declarer cannot score for his meld of Kings because in the trump suit the 10 is higher than the King.

In the lower of the illustrations above, hearts are trumps. Neither player has a meld. Defender declares his four-card sequence in spades but he cannot score for it because the declarer has an equal sequence in the trump suit (hearts). The declarer, therefore, scores 40 points above the line for his four-card sequence in hearts and a further 20 points for his three-card sequence in diamonds.

Finally, it is to be noted that if the declarer elects to play the hand in the same suit as the turned card, either player if he holds the 7 of the suit may exchange it for the turned card.

The player who leads to a trick may lead any card that he chooses. The second player is limited in his play; for he must obey the three rules that follow:

He must follow suit if he can.

If a trump has been led he must not only follow suit if he can, but win the trick by playing a higher trump if he holds one.

If a plain suit has been led and he is unable to follow suit, he must win the trick by trumping if he can.

Second player may discard a worthless card only when he is unable to obey one or other of these three rules.

Winning a trick has no value in itself. What counts is winning tricks with certain cards in them; these are scored as follows:

Jack of trumps	20
9 of trumps	15
Any Ace or 10	10
Any King or Queen	5
Last trick (except at nullo)	10

The example that follows is a simple one to illustrate the mechanics of the game (see hands illustrated below).

Hearts are trumps. The turned card is ♠ K: the information card ♦ Q.

Defender leads ♣ A, and the play is:

Defender	*Declarer*
♣ A	♣ Q
♣ 10	♥ 10
♦ 8	♦ A
♦ J	♦ 7
♣ 8	♥ 8
♥ 9	♦ 9
♠ 10	♠ 9
♠ Q	♥ A
♥ 7	♥ J

Declarer scores for taking:

Jack of trumps (♥)	20
♥ A	10
♠ A	10
♥ 10	10
♣ 10	10
♠ Q	5
Last trick	10
	75 points

Defender scores for taking:

9 of trumps (♥)	15
♣ A	10
♠ 10	10
♣ Q	5
	40

In addition to the above, if a player holds the King and Queen of the trump suit (if there is one) he may score 20 points provided he announces 'Jo' when he plays the King and later 'Jotte' when he plays the Queen. He cannot score for the combination if he plays the Queen before the King.

Game is won by the player who first scores 80 points below the line, which may be made in one hand or in a series of part-scores, and the player who wins the rubber (best out of three games) scores a bonus of 300 points.

The declarer of a nullo contract scores a bonus of 200 points if he loses every trick; if he takes a trick, however, his opponent scores 200

Defender

Declarer

points for the first and 100 for every subsequent trick.

The declarer of a slam scores a bonus of 500 points if he wins every trick; and if a player wins every trick but has not bid slam he scores a bonus of 100 points.

Scoring below the line, towards game, is calculated as follows:

1. If the declarer's total score, including melds, sequences, trick scores and bonuses is greater than the defender's total score, he scores his trick score below the line, and the defender scores his trick score above the line.
2. If the defender's total score is greater than the declarer's, the two trick scores are added together and scored by the defender below the line.
3. If the contract is doubled or redoubled, the player with the higher total scores both his and his opponent's trick score, doubled or quadrupled, below the line.
4. If there is a tie in total points, the trick scores of both players are put in prison and awarded to the player who obtains the higher total in the following deal.

KLABERJASS

KLABERJASS *is probably better in the United States than in Britain, because, under the names of Clabber, Clobber, Clubby, Klab and Klob, it occurs in Damon Runyon's amusing stories, and in 1937 a variation of the game, under the name Jo-jotte (see page 48) was publicized by Ely Culbertson. Despite the similarity of names it is not identical with the Hungarian game of* Kalabriás, *which is a game for three or four players. There may have been a common ancestor, or possibly the game was taken to the New World by Central European immigrants and there adapted as a two-handed game with Klaberjass as a bowdlerized version of* Kalabriás.

NUMBER OF PLAYERS

Klaberjass is primarily a game for two players, but can be played by four, in two partnerships, as described later.

CARDS

The game is played with a pack from which the 6s, 5s, 4s, 3s and 2s have been removed. In the trump suit the cards rank in the order Jack, 9, Ace, 10, King, Queen, 8, 7; and in the other three suits Ace, 10, King, Queen, Jack, 9, 8, 7.

Six cards are dealt to both players, in two lots of three cards each. The next card of the pack is turned face upwards on the table (it is known as the turn-up card) and the rest of the pack is placed face downwards so as partly to cover it.

BIDDING

The non-dealer bids first. He may take-it (i.e. accept the turn-up card as the trump suit); pass (i.e. refuse to accept the turn-up card as the trump suit); or schmeiss (i.e. offer to play with the turn-up card as the trump suit or throw in the hand, as his opponent prefers). If the opponent says 'Yes' to a schmeiss there is a fresh deal; if he says 'No' the hand is played with the turn-up card as the trump suit.

If the non-dealer has passed, the dealer may either take-it, pass or schmeiss.

If both players pass there is a second round of bidding. Now the non-dealer may name any one of the other three suits as trumps, or he may schmeiss (i.e. offer to name one of the other three suits as trumps or throw in the hand, as his opponent prefers), or he may pass. If he passes, the dealer may name one of the other three suits as trumps, or throw in the hand.

When a player accepts or names a trump suit, the bidding ends, and the player who has accepted or named a suit as trumps is called the maker.

There are never more than two rounds of bidding, and, when the trump suit has been settled, the dealer deals three more cards, one at a time, to the two players. He then turns up the bottom card of the pack and places it on top of the pack. It takes no part in the play, and is put where it is only to be seen.

If either player has been dealt the 7 of the trump suit, he may exchange it for the turn-up card.

THE PLAY

Only sequences are melded, and for melding the cards rank in the order from Ace (high) to 7 (low). A three-card sequence counts 20 points, a four-card or longer one 50 points.

The non-dealer begins by announcing the value of his best sequence. If his best sequence is of three cards he says 'Twenty'; if of four or more cards he says 'Fifty'. If the dealer has a better sequence he says 'No good'; if he lacks a better sequence he says 'Good'; if he has an equal sequence he asks 'How high?' The non-dealer then announces the top card of his sequence. The dealer then says whether it is good, no good, or if he has a sequence headed by an equal card. In this last event neither player scores unless one of the sequences is in the trump suit, which wins over a sequence in a plain suit.

The non-dealer leads to the first trick; thereafter the winner of a trick leads to the next. A player must follow suit if he can, and if he cannot he must play a trump if he holds one. If a trump is led, the second player must win the trick if he can.

After the first trick has been played, the player with the highest meld shows it and scores for all sequences in his hand. His opponent cannot score for any sequences that he may hold.

A player who holds the King and Queen of the trump suit may score 20 points so long as he announces 'Bella' immediately after he has played the second of them to a trick. If a player holds the Jack of the trump suit, as well as the King and Queen, he may score for the sequence as well as for bella.

When all the cards have been played, each player examines his tricks and scores points for winning in his tricks:

Jasz (Jack of trumps)	20
Menel (9 of trumps)	14
Any Ace	11
Any 10	10
Any King	4
Any Queen	3
Any Jack (except Jasz)	2
Last trick	10

If the maker's total, including melds and cards won, is higher than the opponent's, each scores all the points he has won. If the totals of the two players are equal, the opponent scores the points he has won, the maker nothing. If the opponent's total is higher than the maker's, the two totals are added together and the opponent scores them.

The player who first reaches 500 points wins the game.

KLABERJASS FOR FOUR PLAYERS

This game is played in partnership, two playing against two. Eight cards are dealt to each player, and the dealer turns up his last card for trumps.

Each player in turn, beginning with the player on the left of the dealer, may either take-it or pass. There is no schmeiss. If all four players pass, there is a second round of bidding during which each player in turn has a right to name the trump suit. If all four players pass the second round of bidding there is a fresh deal.

The player who names the trump suit becomes the maker, and his side must score more than the opposing side.

The player on the left of the dealer leads to the first trick.

LE TRUC

LE TRUC *is an old French gambling game which is very simple to play. Since bluff plays a considerable part, it is best when played for stakes (a bluff is easier to attempt if financial penalties would not accompany its failure), but some play the game happily for points.*

NUMBER OF PLAYERS

The basic game is for two players, but four may play in partnerships of two, as described later.

CARDS

A short pack of 32 cards is used. Removed from the standard pack are the 8s, 5s, 4s, 3s and 2s. The cards rank in the order 7, 6, Ace, King, Queen, Jack, 10, 9. The suits are immaterial.

Players cut for deal, and lower deals (cards ranking for this purpose normally, i.e. Ace high and 6 low). The deal thereafter alternates with each hand.

The dealer shuffles and non-dealer cuts, and dealer deals three cards to each player, one at a time.

THE PLAY

The non-dealer looks at his hand and may say 'I play', in which case play begins, or he may ask for a new deal. If the latter, the dealer has two options. He may accept, in which case both hands are laid aside unexposed, and the dealer deals two fresh hands, or he may refuse, in which case both players play with the cards they have. The non-dealer may ask for new cards once only.

The object in each deal is to win two of the three tricks. There are no trumps and no obligation to follow suit, suits being immaterial. Each player can play whichever card he likes on each trick. The non-dealer leads to the first trick, thereafter the winner of a trick leads to the next. A trick is won by the higher card in it irrespective of suit. Should both players play a card of equal rank, the trick is spoiled and is claimed by the first player to win a trick. Thus if the first trick is spoiled it is claimed by the player to win the second (if that is spoiled too, both are claimed by the player to win the third). If the second trick is spoiled, it is claimed by the player who won the first trick. It is possible that all three tricks are spoiled, in which case that deal is declared a draw and the deal passes to the next player. If a trick is spoiled, the leader to it leads to the next.

Each deal is worth one point, should neither player double, and a game consists of 12 points.

However, it is the doubling which gives the game its appeal, and introduces the opportunity to bluff. At any time a player about to play his card (whether it is first, second or third and whether he is leading or following) may offer to double the value of the hand. If his opponent accepts, the play continues at double value. But a player offered a double may decline it, in which case he concedes the hand at its current value. A hand may be doubled to be worth two points, then four, then eight, but no more. The reason is that a player cannot double the value of the hand beyond a point where, if he won, the value would take his score past the game-winning 12 points. In this case, he can, however, increase the stake to however many points he needs to win the game by saying: 'My remainder'. For example, if his score is seven, and the value of the game is four, he cannot double the stake again because this would take him past 12, but he can win the necessary five points for game by saying: 'My remainder'. However, this call carries a risk, because if the 'remainder' call is accepted, the points at stake become the opponent's remainder as well, irrespective of how many points he had before the hand was dealt, so the winner of the hand automatically wins the game.

The normal way for a player to double is to state the new value of the game, thus: 'Two if I play?' and 'Four if I play?' and so on. His opponent either says 'Yes' or throws in his cards to concede at the former value.

Each game is a separate entity and is settled as such.

Good play arises first of all for the non-dealer in whether or not to call for new cards. While he might invariably do so with poor cards, he might occasionally do so with good cards, to lure the dealer into a trap. Good play for the dealer begins with making the best decisions on accepting or refusing such calls.

The remaining skill comes in the order of playing the cards in the hand and in the doubling.

Imagine two hands are dealt as in the illustration below. The non-dealer decides to play. If he leads his ♣ 7, the dealer might spoil the first trick, and when the non-dealer follows with ♥ 6 he might spoil the second, too, but the non-dealer will win the hand with his ♥ A.

On the other hand, when the non-dealer leads his ♣ 7, the dealer's best play is to play ♥ J, deliberately losing. He will now win the hand because, whichever of his two cards the non-dealer plays next, the dealer will beat it and win the last trick.

The non-dealer, despite having the better hand, is similarly doomed if he leads ♥ A first. The dealer will win it with ♦ 6 and then double because he cannot lose. He plays his ♦ 7 next, and if the second trick is spoiled, which is the worst that can happen, the dealer will take the trick on the strength of having won the first, and thus will win the hand. Would the non-dealer have accepted the double? Well, he could lose only if the dealer held a 7 as well as the 6 already played … or an improbable three 6s.

Non-dealer

Dealer

Although the dealer, by best play, will win the hand if the non-dealer leads ♣ 7 or ♥ A, the non-dealer can be sure of winning by leading ♥ 6. If the dealer this time throws away ♥ J, the non-dealer is certain to win with his ♣ 7 on the second trick. If the dealer spoils the first trick, he can do no better than spoil the second when the non-dealer leads ♣ 7, so the non-dealer wins on the third trick. The dealer's best hope is to win the first trick with his ♦ 7, but whatever he leads to the second trick the non-dealer will beat and still win the last trick.

While it is generally regarded as vital to win the first trick, in order to guard against spoiled tricks, this example hand shows that this is not always so, and that there is plenty of scope for skill. And as well as the playing of the cards, both sides in this hand could have had decisions to make on whether to double or to accept a double on every card played.

LE TRUC FOR FOUR PLAYERS

This version is played in partnerships of two, each player sitting opposite his partner. Cards are cut to determine partners, the two highest playing against the two lowest, the lowest dealing. The deal passes to the left, as does the turn to play to a trick. One player from each side, the dealer and the player to his left (eldest) are the captains for the hand. Only eldest may call for a new deal, and only the dealer may refuse or accept. Neither may be helped by their partners to reach these decisions. If the dealer accepts a new deal, only he and eldest are dealt new hands - the other players keep theirs. Eldest leads to the first trick.

A spoiled trick is one in which equally high cards are played by both partnerships. If the high cards come from the same partnership the trick is not spoiled but won by that partnership. If three cards of equal rank are highest, the trick remains spoiled, i.e. it is not won by the side which contributed two of the cards.

As before, a spoiled trick is won by the side which first wins a trick, a player winning a trick leads to the next, and a leader to a spoiled trick leads to the next. Where one side contributes equal cards to win a trick, the player who played the first of the two cards leads to the next.

Only the captain of a side may double or remainder, and he must do so before his side plays its first card to a trick. Only the captain of the opposing side may accept the double or concede the hand.

When playing for stakes, it is best if partners are scrupulous about not passing information to each other in any way, but for light-hearted friendly games some schools allow the captain to ask his partner to lead high or low and in very light-hearted games the partner can give his captain information about his holding by various gestures (e.g. a wink for holding a 7, etc.).

PINOCLE

PINOCLE *is frequently spelt Pinochle, but the Oxford Dictionary does not sanction the 'h'. It was derived from the old French game of Bezique, and was popular in Europe as a two-handed game. It has become extremely popular in the USA, where it is played by three or more players. The original form is described here and the version for more players is to be found in the later section of this book where card games for four are described.*

NUMBER OF PLAYERS

Pinocle is for two players (but see above).

CARDS

Pinocle is played with a pack of 48 cards, consisting of two Aces, 10s, Kings, Queens, Jacks, 9s (in this order) from each of the four suits.

Twelve cards are dealt to each player, either three or four cards at a time, and the next card is turned face upwards to indicate the trump suit. The rest of the pack is placed face downwards on the table to half cover the exposed card.

THE PLAY

The object is to win tricks including cards which carry a scoring value when won in a trick, and to meld certain card combinations that carry a scoring value.

When taken in a trick each Ace scores 11 points, each 10 scores ten, each King four, each Queen three, and each Jack two . The player who wins the last trick scores 10 points.

The values of the melds are:

Class A	
A, 10, K, Q, J of trumps	150
K, Q of trumps (royal marriage)	40
K, Q of a plain suit (common marriage)	20
Class B	
Pinocle (♠ Q and ♦ J)	40
Dis (9 of the trump suit)	10
Class C	
1 Ace of each suit	100
1 King of each suit	80
1 Queen of each suit	60
1 Jack of each suit	40

The non-dealer leads to the first trick. Thereafter the winner of a trick leads to the next. It is not necessary for a player to follow suit to a led card. The winner of a trick replenishes his hand by taking the top card of the stock; the loser of the trick takes the next.

After a player has won a trick and before drawing from the stock, he may meld any of the above combinations. To meld he places the cards face upwards on the table in front of him, where they remain until he decides to play them to a trick, or until the stock is exhausted. Melding is subject to the three rules that follow:

1. Only one meld may be made at a turn.
2. For each meld, at least one card must be taken from the hand and placed on the table.
3. A card already melded may be melded again so long as it is in a different class, or in a higher-scoring meld of the same class. That is to say, if hearts are trumps a player may meld ♥ K, Q and score for the royal marriage, and later he may add ♥ A, 10, J and score for the sequence. He cannot first declare ♥ A, 10, K, Q, J and score for sequence and later declare the royal marriage.

If the dealer turns up a dis as the trump card he scores 10 points. Thereafter a player holding a dis may count it merely by showing it when winning a trick. He may count the dis and make another meld at the same time. After winning a trick, the holder of a dis may exchange it for the trump card.

The player who wins the twelfth trick may meld if he is able to. He then draws the last face-downwards card of the stock and must show it to his opponent. The loser of the trick takes the card exposed on the table.

The last 12 tricks are now played off. During this period of play a player must follow suit if he can to the card led; if he cannot he must trump the trick if he holds a trump. If a trump is led the second player must win the trick if he can.

Melds are scored when they are declared. The score for cards won in tricks are added after the hand has been played out; a total of seven, eight, or nine points is counted as ten.

Every deal may constitute a game, or the players may prefer that the winner will be he who first reaches an agreed figure.

At pinocle skill and experience count for much. An ability to remember which cards have been played contributes much towards success. When it comes to playing off the last 12 cards, the experienced player will never be in any doubt about which cards his opponent holds. Thus, when playing to the last trick before the stock is exhausted, a player should be able to weigh up the merits of winning the trick and melding, preventing his opponent from melding, or losing the trick and so obtaining the exposed trump card to add to his trump length in the final play off.

PIQUET

PIQUET *is probably the best known of all card games for two players; there is no doubt that it is more skilful and interesting than any other.*

NUMBER OF PLAYERS

Although Piquet has been adapted for three or four players, these variations are not described, as it is essentially a game for two.

CARDS

Piquet is played with the 32-card pack, i.e. the standard pack from which the 6s, 5s, 4s, 3s and 2s are removed. Cards rank from Ace (high) to 7 (low).

Players cut for deal, and the higher has the right of first deal; he would be advised to take it because there is some advantage to be gained from it.

Twelve cards are dealt to each player in either twos or threes, and the remaining eight cards (talon) are placed face downwards on the table between the players. The non-dealer may now exchange any five of his cards with the five top cards of the talon. He need not exchange as many as five cards, but he must exchange at least one, and, if he has not exchanged five cards, he may look at those that he was entitled to draw. The dealer may exchange cards up to the number that remain in the talon. He, too, must exchange at least one card. If he does not exchange all the cards, he may look at those that he was entitled to, but he must show them to his opponent if he does. The players place their discards face downwards on the table in front of them. The discards of the players should not be mixed together as, during the play of the hand, the players are entitled to look at their own discards, but not their opponent's.

The score is made up in three ways: the count of the hand; the count during the play of the cards; the extraordinary scores.

The hand is always counted in the following way:

The point, which is the number of cards held in the longest suit. The player who holds the longest suit wins the point, and scores one point for each card that he holds in it. If the number of cards in the suits held by the players is the same, the player with the highest count (Aces 11,

Kings, Queens and Jacks 10 each, and other cards at their pip values) wins the point. If the count is equal neither player scores.

Sequences, which must not be of less than three cards of the same suit, are won by the player who holds the most cards in one sequence. As between sequences of equal length, the highest wins. For a sequence of three (tierce) three points are scored; for a sequence of four (quart) four points are scored. For a sequence of five (quint) 15 points are scored; for a sequence of six (sixième) 16 points; for a sequence of seven (septième) and for a sequence of eight (huitième) 18 points.

Quatorzes and trios are any four or three cards of the same rank higher than the 9. The player who holds the superior quatorze or trio wins. Thus, a player who holds a trio of Aces will win even though his opponent may hold trios of Kings and Queens. In the same way, a player who holds trios of Aces, Kings, Queens and Jacks will score nothing if his opponent holds a quatorze of 10s. Quatorzes are scored at 14 points each; trios at three points each.

The count of the hand must be declared in the order: point, sequence, quatorze and trio, and, on demand, a player must show any combinations of cards for which he has scored. In practice, however, this is rarely necessary, because the opponent is usually able to infer from his own cards what cards are held against him by his opponent.

When counting the hand a player is not compelled to declare all that he holds. It is in order, and sometimes the very best play, to mislead one's opponent by declaring less than one holds in order to conceal one's strength. The practice is known as sinking. The player who holds a quatorze of Aces may declare only a trio. The opponent may inquire which Ace is not being reckoned, and the player may name any Ace he chooses, because the explicit reply: 'I do not count the Ace of Clubs' is not a guarantee that the player does not hold this card.

THE PLAY

After the non-dealer has counted his hand he leads a card. The dealer then counts his hand and plays a card to the non-dealer's lead. Two cards constitute a trick, and it is compulsory for the second player to follow suit to the led card if he can do so. If not he may play any card he chooses, because there is no trump suit. The player who leads to a trick scores one point, and if his opponent wins it he scores one point for doing so (except in the case of the last trick, when he scores two points) and leads to the next trick, scoring one point for the lead. After all 12 tricks have been played, the player who has won most tricks scores 10 points for having done so (Ten for the Cards, as it is called). There is no score to either player if they win six tricks each.

There are four extraordinary scores:

Carte blanche. If a player is dealt a hand that contains no court card he may claim carte blanche and score 10 points. It takes precedence over any other scoring combination, but the player must announce his carte blanche as soon as he picks up the cards dealt to him, and he must show his hand, though he need not do so until after his opponent has discarded.

Pique. If a player scores in hand and plays 30 points, before his opponent scores anything, he wins a pique and scores 30 points for it. Only the non-dealer can win a pique, because he scores one point for the first lead before the dealer counts his hand; this, of course, automatically rules out the dealer from scoring for a pique.

Repique. If a player scores in hand alone a total of 30 points, before his opponent scores anything, he wins a repique and scores 60 points for it. Either player may score for a repique, because points in hand are counted in priority to those won in play.

Capot. If a player wins all 12 tricks he wins a capot and scores 40 points, not 10, for the cards. The capot, however, is not counted towards a pique because the points are not scored until the hand has been played.

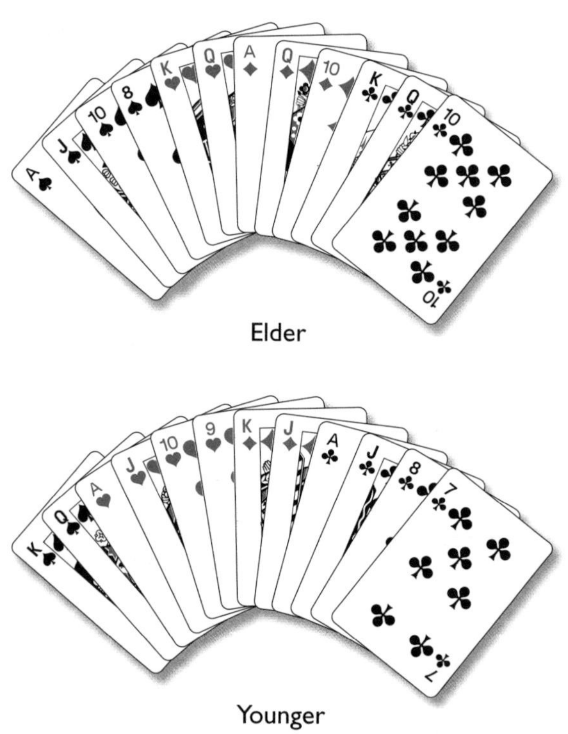

Elder

Younger

The players deal alternately, and a *partie* (game) consists of six deals (three deals each). At the end of the *partie* the player with the higher score deducts from his score that of his opponent, and adds 100 points to the result. If, however, one player fails to score 100 points, he is rubiconed, and the player with the higher score adds the two scores together, and a further 100 points. If the score after six deals is equal, each player has one more deal, and if the score still remains equal the *partie* is a draw.

Most card games are played in silence. Piquet is a continuous dialogue. When a player counts his hand he declares his point, sequences, quatorzes and trios, and his opponent confirms whether they are 'Good', 'Not good' or 'Equal', and, if equal, the player announces the pip total which his opponent declares 'Good', 'Not good' or 'Equal'. Then, during the play of the hand, the two players announce their scores as each trick is played.

At piquet it is customary to call the non-dealer the elder (hand) and the dealer the younger (hand). The deal opposite (after both players have discarded) illustrates the method of scoring and is not to be accepted as an example of good play.

Elder: 'Point of four'.
Younger: 'Making?'.
Elder: 'Thirty-nine'.
Younger: 'Not good'.
Elder: 'Queens and Tens – six'. (He counts his score for his trios without waiting for younger to confirm that the count is good. He knows that his trio of Queens is good because, from his own cards, he can see that younger cannot hold a quatorze or a better trio than one of Jacks. His announcement 'Queens and Tens' means that he holds three Queens and three 10s. If he held four Queens and three 10s he would announce 'Fourteen Queens and three Tens'.)

Elder, who has no more to count, leads the ♠ A: 'Seven'.

Younger now counts his hand.

Younger: 'Point of four – forty'. (Elder has a right to ask in which suit the point is. In this case, however, he has no need because he knows from his own cards that it can only be in hearts.) 'and tierce to the Jack – seven'. (Here, again, elder has no need to ask because, from his own cards, he knows that the tierce must be in hearts.)

Younger plays the ♠ Q on elder's ♠ A, and repeats his score – 'Seven'.

The rest of the play is:

Elder		*Younger*	
♠ J	'Eight'	♠ K	'Eight'
♥ Q	'Eight'	♥ A	'Nine'
♥ K	'Nine'	♥ J	'Ten'
♠ 10	'Ten'	♣ 7	'Ten'
♠ 8	'Eleven'	♣ 8	'Ten'
♣ K	'Twelve'	♣ A	'Eleven'
♦ 10	'Twelve'	♥ 10	'Twelve'
♦ Q	'Twelve'	♥ 9	'Thirteen'
♣ Q	'Thirteen'	♣ J	'Fourteen'
♦ A	'Fourteen'	♦ J	'Fourteen'
♣ 10	'Fifteen'	♦ K	'Fourteen'

Elder, winning the trick: 'Sixteen, and the cards twenty-six'. This ends

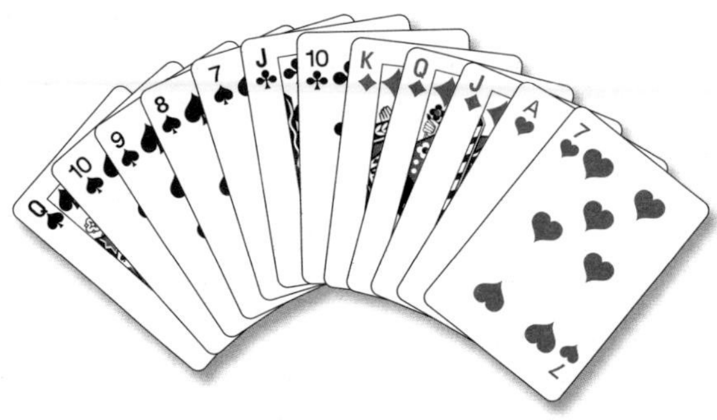

the deal with the score at elder 26, younger 14.

A player's first consideration must be the point. The importance of scoring for the point cannot be overestimated, because not only does it add to a player's score, but it protects him against a pique or repique, and, of course, scoring for point diminishes the opponent's score to the same extent. Normally, therefore, a player should retain his longest suit intact and discard from shorter suits. This, however, does not always hold good, particularly if the longest suit consists mainly of low cards, and the shorter suits of high ones. The inexperienced player who is dealt the hand above will be tempted to retain the spades, and discard from the other suits, with a view to scoring for point and sequence. The experienced player will know that the better course is to discard all five spades, because the ♠ J is the only card that will raise the suit from a quart to a sixième, and the odds are about three to one against drawing it. It is likely that retaining the spades will win the point, but almost certainly it will result in the loss of the cards. This will make a big difference to the score, and the cards must always be considered together with the point. If the non-dealer holds a long suit headed by top cards, usually it guarantees the point and the cards. The suit, therefore, must be preserved at all costs, but this is of much less importance for the dealer because he may never obtain the lead.

A good general rule emerges. The discards of the non-dealer should be made towards obtaining an attacking hand; that of the dealer towards obtaining a defensive hand, that is to say a hand in which there is some strength in as many suits as possible.

Subject to these considerations, it is best to discard from as few suits as possible, and, once a player has made up his mind to discard from a suit, he should discard the whole of it, unless it is necessary to retain the suit guarded. Sequence cards should be retained in preference to non-sequence cards, and, of course, cards that help to make up trios and quatorzes should never be discarded if it can be avoided.

Playing to the score is very important, particularly in the last deal of a *partie*. As an example: if a player is well ahead, and sees the opportunity to gain a rubicon, he should discard cautiously and play so as to prevent his opponent from saving the rubicon by scoring 100 points. On the other hand, if a player is in danger of being rubiconed, he should be prepared to take some risks, since only a big score will save him. It must be remembered, however, that if a player is rubiconed his score is added to that of his opponent, so if there is no chance of saving the rubicon he should play to keep his score down. To this end he should declare only equities or those scores that will save pique and repique, and he should aim to divide the cards.

AUCTION PIQUET

This version originated in Oxford, and was developed by some British prisoners of war during the First World War.

The bidding takes place before the discard. It is opened by the non-dealer. He may pass, and if he does and the dealer does also, there is a redeal by the same player. The lowest bid that may be made is one of seven. It is an undertaking to win, or lose, seven of the 12 possible tricks. There is no penalty for a bid out of turn or for an underbid, because these irregularities merely give information to the opponent.

The most interesting feature of the game is the minus bid. It is an undertaking to lose the stated number of tricks. It ranks neither above nor below a normal (plus) bid. In a minus deal the player scores everything good in his opponent's hand. A player may double a bid made by his opponent, and the player who has been doubled may redouble or shift to a higher bid.

After bidding, the players discard. The routine is the same as in the parent game except that there is no compulsion for the players to discard at least one card.

The declarations follow, and the players may declare the point, sequences, trios and quatorzes in any order they choose. Sinking is allowed in plus deals but not in minus ones.

The scoring is as follows:

The value of point, sequences, trios, quatorzes, cards and capot, are the same as in the parent game.

In plus deals pique (30 points) is obtained on the score of 29 and repique (60 points) on the score of 30. In minus deals both pique and repique are obtained on the score of 21.

The *partie* (six deals) is worth 150 points, and rubicon is under 150 points. In the event of a tie a seventh deal is played and the *partie* ends if it is tied.

A player scores 10 points for every trick won in a plus deal (or lost in a minus deal) above (or below) the declared contract.

If a player fails to make his contract the opponent scores 10 points for every trick by which he is short.

Overtricks and undertricks are effected by doubling and redoubling, but scores in hand and play are not.

Although a player scores one point for winning a trick he does not score for leading a losing card, nor an additional one point for winning the last trick.

RUSSIAN BANK

RUSSIAN BANK *is similar to some patience games, in that cards are built on foundations, but it is a competitive game. It is also called Crapette and Stop!*

NUMBER OF PLAYERS

Russian Bank is for two players.

CARDS

Two full packs of 52 cards with different backs (for ease of sorting into two packs afterwards) are used. The cards rank from King (high) to Ace (low).

Each player draws a card from one of the packs. The player with the lower card plays first. Each player has one complete pack, and each player shuffles his opponent's pack and places it face down before his opponent. Players sit opposite each other.

The first player deals 11 cards face down to a pile to his right, turning the 12th card face up and placing it on top of the pile. This is his depot. He deals the next four cards face up in a column to his left so that the column runs from his left hand to his opponent's right hand. This is his file. He places the rest of his cards face down to his left. This is his stock.

THE PLAY

The object is to pack onto the cards in the files in descending sequences of alternate colours. Cards should be packed outwards from the centre. Any Aces are played to a foundation column to the right of the file. The Aces in the foundation column are built up to King, as cards become available, in suit sequence. The cards initially available are the cards in the file and the card face up on the depot. One card in the file can be packed on another, and when a card in the file is packed upon, it is still available, and can be packed onto another card in the file provided all the cards packed on it are transferred with it. Players of the patience game Demon (or Canfield) will recognize the principles.

When the first player has completed his layout as described, he first moves any Ace from the file to its foundation

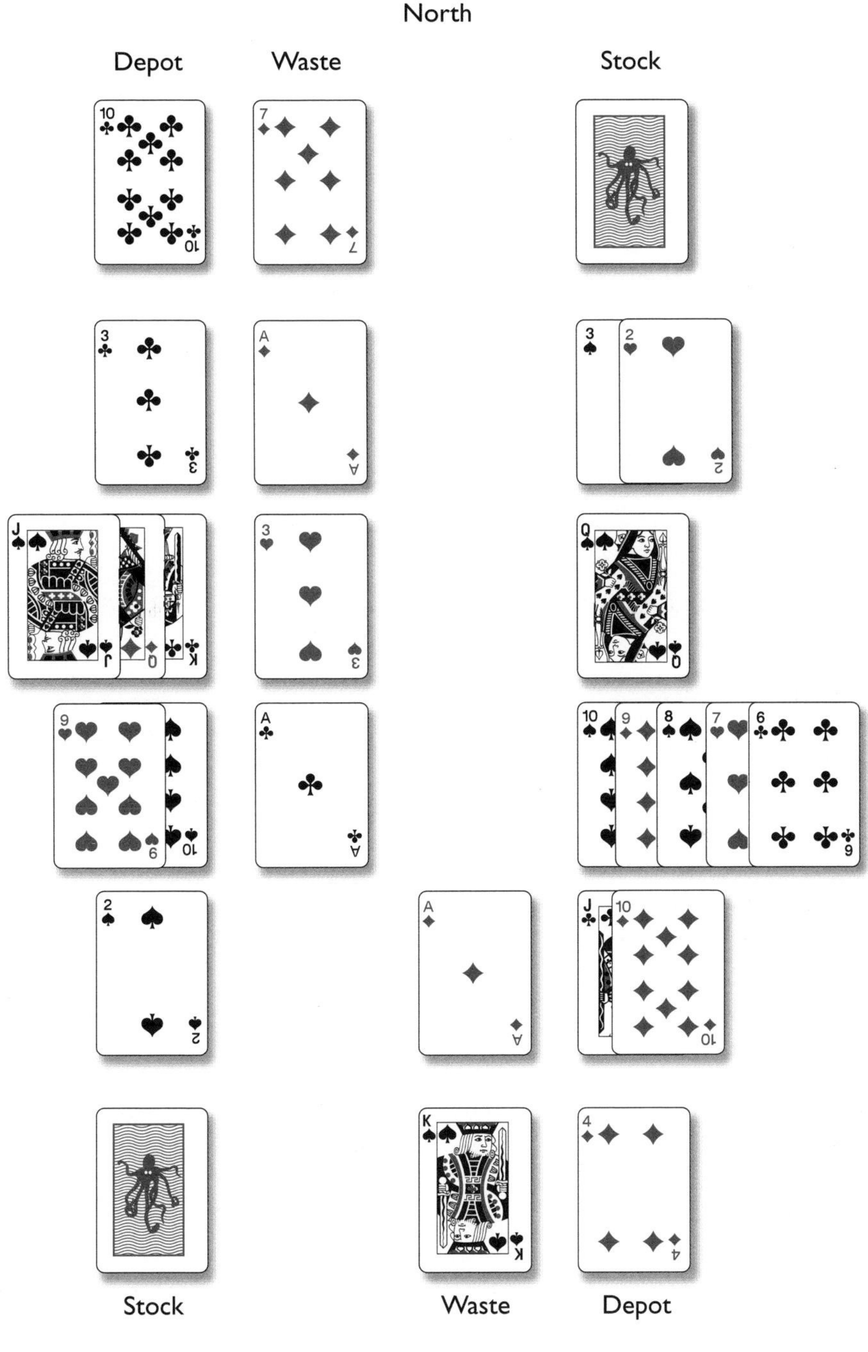

Russian Bank – a game in progress.

space. The space created in the file is filled by the top card of the depot, and the next card in the depot is turned face up. He then makes any further plays available, filling spaces created from the depot each time, until no further plays are possible. He then turns over the first card of his stock. If he can build it onto a foundation or pack it onto a file he does so and turns the next card and so on. When he finally turns a card which cannot be played to a foundation or file, he plays it to a waste heap to his right, next to his depot. He then turns the next card from the stock face up to the waste heap ready for play on his next turn, and his current turn ends.

The second player then deals a depot, a file and a stock in the same way, so that his cards interlock with the first to form a complete tableau (the illustration on page 67 shows a game in progress). The second player makes his moves as the first, but he has the advantage of also being able to build to his opponent's foundations, and pack onto his opponent's files. He can also play from his own depot and file onto his opponent's waste heap in either ascending or descending sequence, irrespective of suit or colour. However, he cannot pack onto his opponent's waste heap from his own waste heap or stock. Each player from now on has these options on his turn. Cards available for play are those exposed at the top of a file, depot or waste heap. A turn ends when a player cannot play a card from stock except onto his waste heap.

When a player's stock is exhausted, he turns over his waste heap (without shuffling) to form a new stock. When his depot is exhausted, he fills spaces in his file from his stock.

Plays must always be made in the following order:

A space in a file must be filled before any other play is made.
A player must play from his depot before he plays from his file or waste heap.
When a card is played from the depot, the next card must be turned face up before the next play is made.
A player must play to a foundation if possible, before playing to a file. A player must play to a file if possible, before playing to a waste heap.

A player who sees his opponent violate any of these rules or make any other mistake may cry 'Stop!' before his opponent has made a further play, and thus bring his turn to an end. He then points out the mistake, retracts the wrong play and makes the play his opponent failed to. He then takes over the turn himself.

The winner is the first player to get rid of all the cards in his stock and waste heap.

TABLANETTE

TABLANETTE *is a game that is easy to learn and worth learning because it is remarkably fascinating to play.*

NUMBER OF PLAYERS

Tablanette is for two players but can be played by three, as described later.

CARDS

The full pack of 52 cards is used. Cards have their pip values, except that Ace can count as 11 or 1 at the discretion of the holder. King counts as 14 and Queen as 13. The Jack has no value, but plays a special part in the game, as will be seen.

Tablanette cards in hand (below) and on table (above).

Six cards are dealt face downwards to the two players, and four cards face upwards to the table between them. The rest of the pack is temporarily set aside. If any Jacks are dealt to the table they are removed, placed at the bottom of the pack, and the spaces filled with cards from the top of the pack.

THE PLAY

The non-dealer plays first. If he plays a card of the same rank as any of the four cards on the table, he takes the card; or, if there are any two or three cards on the table whose values if added together equal that of the card played, he takes these cards.

If the cards on the table and the player's hand are as shown on page 69 he will play the ♥ K and take the ♠ K from the table. If he holds the cards in the hand above he will play the ♥ A and take the ♥ 2 and ♣ 9 from the table on page 69, because together they total 11, the value of an Ace.

The cards played and those taken from the table are kept in a pile, face downwards, on the table by the player who took them.

If at any time a player is able to take all the cards on the table (there may be

only one, or there may be more than four) he announces 'Tablanette' and scores the total value of all the cards taken plus the value of the card he has played. If, for example, the cards on the table are as illustrated in the lower illustration on page 70, and a player holds any of the other three Kings, he will be able to announce 'Tablanette', because his King will take the ♠ K and the other three cards whose values total 14. The score for this will be 42 points (i.e. 14 x 3).

The special function of the Jack is that playing it allows the player to take all the cards on the table, but it does not allow him to score for a tablanette. Obviously, therefore, a Jack is an excellent card to hold, because playing it compels the opponent to play a lone card to the table and when there is only one card on the table the player whose turn it is to play is in a good position to score a tablanette.

The players play in rotation until they have exhausted their six cards. The dealer then deals another six cards to each, and so on until the pack is exhausted.

When the last batch of six cards has been played, any cards left on the table are taken by the player who last took a card from the table.

The players examine the cards they have taken, and score one point for the ♣ 2 and for every Ace, King, Queen, Jack and 10 (except the ♦ 10 which scores two points). Finally, if a player has taken 27 or more cards he scores three points.

The deal passes in rotation, and the game is won by the player who first scores a total of 251 points.

There is more skill in the game than may be apparent at first sight. If, for example, there is only an 8 on the table and the player holds the cards shown above, his best play is the ♥ 4, because no one card has a value of 12 and the opponent, therefore, cannot score a tablanette.

As at all card games it is very important to keep in mind the cards that have been played. The opponent has scored a tablanette and the player holds:

He has to play a card to the table, and the natural tendency is to play the ♥ 3, because this will give the opponent a minimum score if he can again announce 'Tablanette'. But if no 3s have been played, but a 10 has, then it is better to play one of the 10s, because the chances are against the opponent holding the remaining 10, and there is a possibility that he holds one of the remaining three 3s.

TABLANETTE FOR THREE PLAYERS

Should three wish to play, the game is played in the same way as the parent game, except that the players are dealt four cards (instead of six) at a time.

GAMES FOR THREE PLAYERS

BLACK MARIA

BLACK MARIA, *sometimes known as Black Lady and sometimes as Slippery Anne, is very similar to Hearts and its several variations (see page 140).*

NUMBER OF PLAYERS

Black Maria is best played by three players, but can be played by four or five as described later.

CARDS

The full pack is used minus the ♣ 2, making a pack of 51 cards. Cards rank from Ace (high) to 2 (low).

Seventeen cards are dealt to each player. The deal passes in rotation clockwise. After a player has looked at his cards, he passes three of them to his right-hand opponent and receives three from his left-hand opponent, which he must not look at before he has passed his three on.

THE PLAY

When the exchanges of cards have been made, the player on the left of the dealer leads to the first trick. Thereafter, the player who wins a trick leads to the next. A player must follow suit to the led card provided he can do so. Otherwise he may discard any card he chooses. There is no trump suit.

The object of the game is to avoid winning a trick which contains a penalty card. These cards, and the penalties that go with them, are:

All hearts	1
♠ A	7
♠ K	10
♠ Q (Black Maria)	13

The game introduces two features: the discard and the play of the cards.

The inexperienced player, if he is dealt a high spade, will assume that he cannot do better than pass it on to his right-hand opponent. It is, however, not always the best play. Provided a number of low spades are held in support of the high ones, it is very often better to retain the high cards with a view to controlling the suit during the play of the hand. Indeed, a player who has been dealt any spades or hearts lower than the Queen would be well advised to keep them in order to protect himself against any top cards in the suits that may be passed on to him. The main principle of discarding should be to try

and set up either a void suit – in order to get rid of penalty cards by discarding them during the play – or at obtaining long suits, provided low cards in them are held. A player who has been dealt the hand illustrated at the top of page 73 cannot do better than pass on the three diamonds. The spades must be kept to protect against receiving a high card in the suit, the hearts are adequately protected, and there is nothing to fear in clubs.

An ability to count the cards is the first essential to success. Towards the end of a deal an experienced player will know pretty well which cards are still left to be played, and he will be able to make a shrewd guess who holds them. It is in the end-play, therefore, that opportunity comes for skilful play.

A three-card ending is illustrated at the bottom of page 73. After 14 tricks the players should know which cards remaining cards are in play.

West is on lead and leads the ♠ 6, North plays the ♠ 2 and East, perforce, wins with the ♠ K. Now, if East returns the ♦ 5, West must win with the ♦ 7 and North saddles him with the ♠ Q (Black Maria). If, however, East returns the ♣ 3, North will have to win with the ♣ 6 on which West will have played the ♠ A.

East's play will be directed by the score, and whether it is more advantageous to him to saddle West or North with all 20 points. The strategy is quite ethical so long as East puts his own interest first and is not moved by malice aforethought.

FOUR-HANDED BLACK MARIA

With four players the game is played in the same way as the parent game, except that no card is removed from the pack, and every player, therefore, receives 13 cards. The players may play all against all, or two in partnership against the other two.

FIVE-HANDED BLACK MARIA

Five players can play in the same way as in the parent game, but the ♦ 2 as well as the ♣ 2 is removed from the pack. Each player, therefore, is dealt ten cards.

CALABRASELLA

CALABRASELLA *is played with what is now usually called the Spanish pack of 40 cards, but which was also the Italian pack, and the game might have come originally from the province of Calabria, in the extreme south of Italy. It is a game usually played for stakes.*

NUMBER OF PLAYERS

Calabrasella is for three players, although four often play in rotation, the dealer giving no cards to himself, and sitting out the hand.

CARDS

The Spanish pack of 40 cards is used, made from the standard pack by discarding the 10s, 9s and 8s. The remaining cards rank in the order 3, 2, Ace, King, Queen, Jack, 7, 6, 5, 4. In the game the Ace is worth three points, the 3, 2, King, Queen, Jack one point each.

Players draw for deal, the lowest dealing first. The deal thereafter passes in rotation to the left. Dealer deals 12 cards to each hand in twos. The four cards remaining are set aside face down to form a widow.

THE PLAY

The object is to make tricks containing cards of a counting value (see above). Players study their hands, and the player to the left of the dealer announces either 'I play' or 'I pass'. Should he pass, the next player has the same option, and if he passes, the dealer. Should all pass, the hand is abandoned, but if any player announces 'I play', the play begins.

The player electing to play is called the Player. He first specifies by suit any 3 not held in his hand. If either of the other players hold that 3 he must pass it to the Player, who may exchange for it any card he wishes from his own hand, not showing it to the third player. If the Player holds all four 3s, he may specify any 2, and so on. If the card he specifies is in the widow, no exchange takes place.

The Player next discards face down any number of cards from his hand from one to four (he must discard at least one). The widow is then exposed, and the Player selects from it sufficient cards to restore his hand to 12 cards. The remainder, plus the Player's discards, are set aside, and are later claimed by the winner of the last trick.

The game now becomes a trick-taking game, with the other two combining in a temporary partnership against the Player. He to the left of the Player makes the opening lead, and may lead any card he likes. The others follow in a clockwise direction, and are obliged to follow suit to the card led if they are able; if unable to they may discard. There are no trumps. The winner of a trick leads to the next.

The winner of the last trick takes the four cards not used in the trick-taking phase, and is also awarded a bonus of three points. As there are eight points in each suit, the total points available in each deal are 35.

The side which wins the majority of the points (18 or more) collects from the other side the difference in the two totals. If the Player scores 20 points and his opponents 15, the Player receives five units from both opponents. If the opponents had scored the 20 points, each would receive five units from the Player. The amount to be paid per point must obviously be agreed beforehand.

The game can be played for recreation only by keeping a running profit and loss score with pencil and paper.

Calabrasella offers opportunities for skill. Much depends on the decision whether or not to play. Of prime importance are stoppers in all suits. Should one of the opponents be able to run off a long suit, the other will be able to discard high-scoring cards (Aces) on it. Should the Player win all the cards in one suit, he might score only eight points from the tricks, whereas an opponent with the same cards will get scoring discards from his partner. The Player can gain the advantage of calling in a 3, but should not rely on much from the widow. In order to keep guards in each suit, he might not be able to discard more than two cards. It is important for him to remember which cards he discards, since only the Player knows which cards are not in play, and thus which suits are short. The disadvantage of playing against two players is a big one, and the commonest mistake is to play with too weak a hand.

CUT-THROAT BRIDGE

MANY SUGGESTIONS *have been made to make Bridge (see page 104) suitable for three players. The most satisfactory is Towie (see page 100) but what has become known as Cut-throat Bridge is the original and the simplest of the three-handed variations.*

NUMBER OF PLAYERS

This game is specifically designed for three players unable to find a fourth for Bridge.

CARDS

The full pack of 52 cards is used.

The players take seats at random and after drawing for deal, shuffling and cutting in the usual way, the dealer deals 13 cards each to the three players and to a fourth hand that is temporarily set aside.

THE PLAY

The auction, beginning with the dealer, is conducted as in the parent game, and when a player's bid, double or redouble has been passed by the other two players, the player on his left leads to the first trick. The player who has obtained the final contract then sorts the fourth hand, spreads it in front of him on the table, and plays it as his dummy, against the other two players in partnership with each other.

The play and scoring are the same as in the parent game, except that if a player loses his contract both his opponents score the penalty points. The winner of a rubber receives a bonus of 700 points if neither opponent has won a game, but 500 points if either has.

Very clearly the game is a gamble, because the players must bid in the hope of finding the cards they need in the dummy hand.

A variation designed to make the game less speculative is for every player to be dealt 17 cards and the 52nd card face downwards to the dummy. After looking at their cards, and before bidding them, every player contributes four of them, face downwards, to the dummy. This way every player knows four out of the 13 cards that he is bidding for.

In another variation, instead of bidding for the dummy, an agreed number of deals (that must be divisible by three) is played, and, in turn, every player plays the dummy against the other two playing in partnership.

In this variation rubbers are not played, but the player who bids and makes game scores a bonus of 300 points. There is no vulnerability.

FIVE HUNDRED

FIVE HUNDRED *is a trick-taking game invented early in the 20th century, which was very popular for a long time in the USA.*

NUMBER OF PLAYERS

The game is designed for three players, but may be played by two to five, as described later.

CARDS

The usual short pack of 32 is required, plus the Joker, making a pack of 33. From a standard pack the 6s, 5s, 4s, 3s and 2s are removed.

The game is played with a trump suit, and the cards in the trump suit rank as follows: Joker, Jack (called right bower), Jack of the same colour as the trump suit (called left bower), Ace, King, Queen, 10, 9, 8, 7.

The cards in the plain suits rank normally: Ace, King, Queen, Jack, 10, 9, 8, 7, except that the suit of the same colour as the trump suit will not contain a Jack. Therefore the suits have an unequal number of cards: the trump suit has ten cards, the suit of the same colour has seven cards and the other two suits have eight cards.

In addition, the suits are ranked: hearts (high), diamonds, clubs, spades.

Players draw for deal, the lowest dealing. For this purpose the cards rank in their usual order, but Ace counts low, and Joker lowest of all. The dealer shuffles, the player on his right cuts, and the dealer deals three cards to each hand, beginning on his left, then three to the centre to form a widow, then four to each hand, then three to each hand. Each player therefore has ten cards, with the extra three being in a widow.

THE PLAY

The players examine their cards and bidding begins. A bid is an offer by a player to make a stated number of tricks with a specified trump suit or without a trump suit (a bid in 'no trumps'). Each bid must be higher than the previous bid. The values of the bids are as follows:

	Six	*Seven*	*Eight*	*Nine*	*Ten*
Spades	40	140	240	340	440
Clubs	60	160	260	360	460
Diamonds	80	180	280	380	480
Hearts	100	200	300	400	500
No trumps	120	220	320	420	520

Eldest begins and may bid or pass, and bidding continues until two players in succession pass, whereupon the last bid made constitutes the contract. (In some schools the bidding is not continuous, and each player is allowed one bid only, while in other schools the bidding is progressive but a player who passes cannot re-enter the bidding.)

Should none of the players bid, the deal is abandoned, and passes to the next player.

Once a player has won the contract, he picks up the widow, and discards three cards face down to keep his hand to ten cards.

The ten tricks are now played out, with the player with the contract leading to the first trick. The winner of a trick leads to the next. The normal rules of trick-taking apply: each player must follow suit to the lead, and if unable to follow suit he may trump or discard. A trick is won by the highest trump played, or if there is none by the highest card in the suit led.

In a no-trump contract, the Joker remains a trump – the only one. It can be played only if its holder cannot follow suit. If the Joker is led in a no-trump contract, its player specifies the suit it represents, and the other players must play cards of that suit if they are able to. The Joker always wins the trick.

The object, so far as the declarer is concerned, is to make at least as many tricks as he contracted to do. His opponents score individually for the tricks they make, so they are playing for themselves, but they should also play in partnership, because defeating the contract will cost the declarer more than the points they can make individually for themselves.

If the declarer makes his contract, he scores its value as set out in the table above. There is no bonus for overtricks, with one possible exception, which is that a player who takes all ten tricks scores a minimum of 250 points. So if a player's contract is worth less than 250 (i.e. eight spades or less), he will earn a bonus by taking all ten tricks.

If the declarer fails to make his contract, he loses the value of his bid. A player can thus have a minus score, which is recorded with a circle round it, and the player is said to be 'in the hole'.

Each of the two players opposing the declarer scores separately for the tricks they make – ten points per trick, and there is no bonus for defeating the declarer. Game is to 500 points (hence the name). It is rare for a player to win without making at least one contract, so, as stated earlier, the ten points per trick are of less significance than the making or defeating of contracts.

Should the declarer and an opponent pass 500 on the same deal, the declarer is the winner. Should the two opponents pass 500, the one who took the trick to take his score to 500 first is the winner.

It is customary to set a limit to the 'hole', say 500. Should a player reach 500 in the hole, the opponent who is leading at the end of the deal is the winner. This is to prevent a player in the hole bidding recklessly and preventing his opponents from making a contract, and in effect spoiling the game.

To outline the mechanics of the game, suppose hands are held as in the illustration. Player A has bid seven diamonds, and has been lucky enough to find ♣ A in the widow. He decides to lead trumps immediately, hoping to lose one only, to ♥ J (left bower), which will ensure his contract. Play proceeds as follows overleaf:

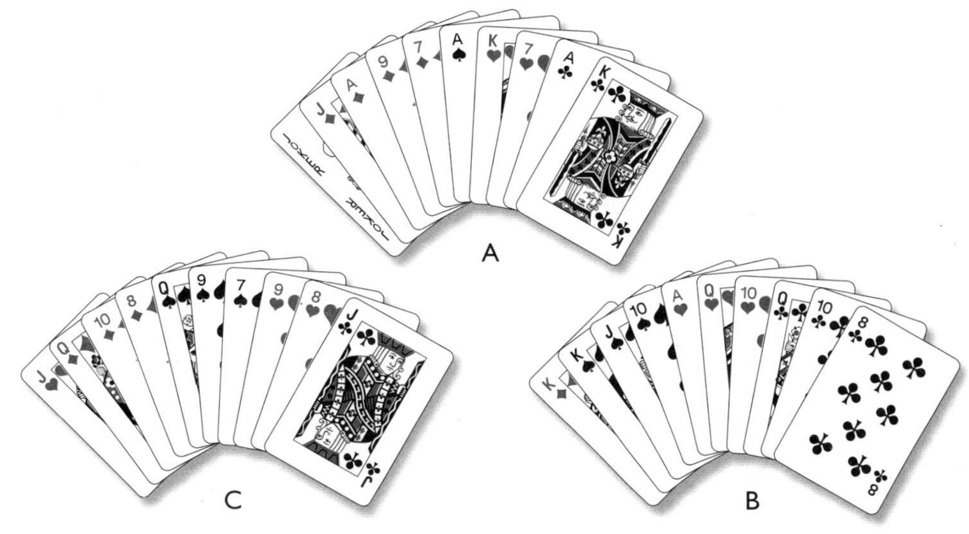

	Player A	*Player B*	*Player C*
1	Joker	♦ K	♦ 8
2	♦ J	♣ 8	♦ 10
3	♣ A	♣ 10	♣ J
4	♣ K	♣ Q	♦ Q
5	♥ K	♥ A	♥ 8
6	♥ 7	♥ Q	♥ 9
7	♦ 7	♥ 10	♠ 7
8	♦ A	♠ 10	♥ J
9	♠ A	♠ J	♠ 9
10	♦ 9	♠ K	♠ Q

From trick 2, when ♦ J (right bower) failed to drop ♥ J, Player A knew that his best chances were that Player C held the ♥ A, which would give him a chance of making ♥ K, or that Player C could be forced to lead his remaining trumps (in which case Player A would lose only one trump) or that the defenders would make a mistake with their discards. As it happened, the defenders played well, and Player A was forced to lose both hearts and two trumps.

Player A therefore failed to make his contract of seven diamonds, and scored 180 points in the hole. Players B and C each made two tricks, so each scored 20 points.

Strategy in playing the cards is similar to most trick-taking games. The main skill in Five Hundred lies in the bidding. As the trump suit consists of ten cards, one player must hold at least four, so four trumps is the minimum requirement for a bid, and even then they must be good ones and supported by side Aces. Unless six or more trumps are held in the deal, the chances are slightly in favour of at least one more being in the widow, but this should not be relied upon. As a rough guide, a player might count any of the top four trumps (Joker, right and left bower, Ace) as one point each, all trumps held in excess of three as one point each, all master cards in side suits as one point each, and a guarded King in a side suit as half a point, and bid accordingly. In the example above, Player A held three points in top trumps, two more with the ♦ 9, 7, one more with ♠ A, and two half-points with guarded Kings, the ♥ K and ♣ K (he found ♣ A in the widow). He therefore had seven points and bid seven diamonds. The ♣ A would usually have made his contract a good one, but as it happened the outstanding trumps were badly split for him, and the ♥ A was badly placed.

A variation often played is to allow an extra bid, called nullo. This is a contract to win no tricks at all. There are no trumps. The value of the bid is 250, placing it between eight spades and eight clubs. A player holding the Joker can play it only when void of the suit led. If the Joker is led, its player specifies the suit it represents. The Joker always wins the trick in which it is played. When the declarer makes nullo, he scores 250 and his opponents score nothing. When he fails he is debited 250, and his opponents score ten points each for each trick he makes.

FIVE HUNDRED FOR TWO PLAYERS

The cards are dealt as for the three-handed game described, the third hand being put to one side and taking no part. With ten cards being dead, the game is much more one of chance than the three-handed version.

FIVE HUNDRED FOR FOUR PLAYERS

With four players the pack must be enlarged to allow each player to have ten cards. The 6s, 5s, and two red 4s are added to the 33-card pack. Play is in partnerships, partners sitting opposite each other. Bidding proceeds as before, and the player making the highest bid leads to the first trick. Each side keeps its tricks separately, and scoring is as before.

FIVE HUNDRED FOR FIVE PLAYERS

The full pack is used, plus the Joker, so that each player receives ten cards and there are three in the widow as before. Each player plays for himself, but the player who wins the contract calls upon one of the others to be his temporary partner, and the two play that hand against the other three. In some schools the declarer names the player he wants as his partner, who will possibly be a player who has bid, and who therefore is known to have a good hand. More usually, the declarer calls upon the holder of a specific card to be his partner. This will usually be the highest missing trump, but it might be an Ace in a side suit. The holder of the card does not announce it, so until he plays the card only he knows that he is partnering the declarer. With neither method does the partner of the declarer change his seat.

Each partner trying to make a contract scores the relevant points if successful and is debited with them if unsuccessful. The opponents each score ten points for each trick taken.

500 RUM

THE GAME *of 500 Rum is much more closely allied to the Rummy family than to Five Hundred.*

NUMBER OF PLAYERS

The game is best for three, which is the version described here, but it can be played by any number from two to eight, as described later.

CARDS

The full standard pack of 52 cards is used (with five or more players two packs are used). Cards rank in the order: King, Queen, Jack, 10, 9, 8, 7, 6, 5, 4, 3, 2, Ace. Cards also have values for scoring points as follows: King, Queen, Jack are each worth ten points, Aces are worth 15 points each if melded as Aces, but one point if used in a sequence of Ace, 2, 3. All other cards score according to their pip value.

Each player draws a card to decide dealer; lowest deals. The dealer shuffles the pack, which is cut by the player to his right, and deals seven cards, one at a time, to each player, beginning with eldest. The remaining cards are placed face down to form the stock, and the top card is turned face up and placed beside the stock to begin the discard pile.

THE PLAY

The object of the game is to form sets of three or four cards of the same rank, or sequences of three or more cards of the same suit. Sequences stop at Ace at one end and King at the other: Ace, King, Queen is not a sequence.

Beginning with eldest, each player may take either a card or cards from the discard pile, or the top card of the stock. After drawing, the player may meld as many cards as he likes by placing sets and/or sequences on the table in front of him, and he then discards one card to the discard pile and the turn passes. Should a player draw from the discard pile, he must meld, and he must use the card taken from the discard pile in his meld. In other words a card cannot be taken from the discard pile unless it is used immediately in a meld.

This game differs from most other variations of Rummy in that all the cards in the discard pile are available, therefore the discard pile is not strictly a pile but a collection of cards spread out so that all their indices can be seen (see illustration opposite). When a player takes a card from the discard pile, he must also take all the cards above it. After melding with the card taken, he leaves on the table for one round any other cards taken from the discard pile which he has not melded, so that all other players may memorize them. On his next turn he takes them into his hand.

A player may on his turn add cards to any meld on the table, whether it is his meld or an opponent's. These cards are not actually attached to the melds, if they be opponents' melds, but kept on the table before the player, who will score for them later. It may happen that a card thus placed on the table would fit onto two existing melds, in which case the player must state which meld he is fitting his card or cards to. This is important because other players may subsequently add to the melds further.

Play continues until one player gets rid of all the cards in his hand or until the stock is exhausted. When the last card is drawn from stock, and the drawer has discarded, play may continue if the next player can draw from the discard pile and meld, and again if the next player can, and so on until one player passes.

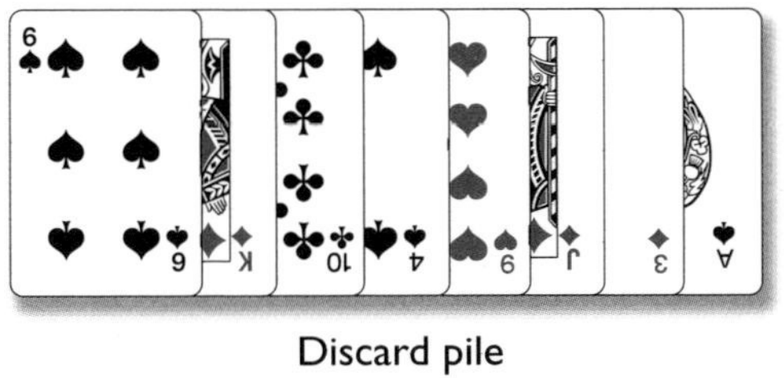
Discard pile

Stock

Hand

The player holding this hand will be advised to pick up ♦ 3. He can immediately meld ♦ 2, 3, 4; ♠ 4, 5, 6; ♦ K, ♥ K, ♠ K. He must leave ♦ J, ♥ 9 and ♣ 10 on the table before him for one round, and should discard ♠ Q.

At the end of the game, each player adds up the values of all the cards he has melded, and from the total he deducts the values of all the cards left in his hand, if any (an Ace in hand counts 15). Once a player has gone out, no further melds can be made by the other players, and any sets or sequences held, or cards which might be added to melds, are debited. A player may thus end with a minus score on the hand.

A running total is kept of each player's score, and the first to reach 500 is the winner.

500 RUM FOR TWO PLAYERS

When played by two players, each receives 13 cards. Otherwise the game is played as above.

500 RUM FOR FOUR PLAYERS

The game may be played by four players as cut-throat, each playing against each, or it may be played in two partnerships, partners sitting opposite each other. The play is as above, but partners try to co-operate with each other. Scores are kept for each side.

500 RUM FOR FIVE TO EIGHT PLAYERS

Two packs shuffled together must be used. Otherwise the game is played as above, each player playing for himself.

KNAVES

KNAVES *is so called because the four Knaves (or Jacks) are penalty cards and the object of the players is to avoid winning tricks that contain them.*

NUMBER OF PLAYERS

Knaves is a game for three players.

CARDS

The full pack of 52 cards is used, cards ranking from Ace (high) to 2 (low).

Seventeen cards are dealt to each player and the last card is turned face up on the table to denote the trump suit. It takes no other part in the game.

THE PLAY

The player on the left of the dealer leads to the first trick; thereafter the player who wins a trick leads to the next. A player must follow suit, if he can, to the card led. If he cannot he may either trump or discard a card of a plain suit.

The player who wins a trick scores one point for it, but four points are deducted from a player's score if he wins the Knave of hearts, three points if he wins the Knave of diamonds, two points if he wins the Knave of clubs, and one point if he wins the Knave of spades. The aggregate score for each deal, therefore, is seven points (i.e. 17 points for tricks minus 10 points for Knaves) unless one of the Knaves is the card turned up to denote the trump suit. Game is won by the first player to score 20 points.

The players play all against all, but skilful play introduces temporary partnerships that add much to the interest of the game. If, for example, one player is in the lead and the other two are trailing behind, they will combine with the aim of preventing the leading player from winning still more, even if they cannot reduce his score by forcing him to win tricks that contain Knaves. In the same way, if two players have an advanced score, and the third is down the course, the two who are ahead will so play that such points as they cannot themselves win will go to the player with the low score rather than to the one with the high score.

The game, therefore, gives ample scope for clever play. Until the last

Knave has been played, a player has to strike a balance between the incentive to take a trick, and so score a point, and the fear of being saddled with a Knave, resulting in a loss.

There is much more in the game than appears on the surface. Consider the hands in the illustration.

No score to anyone.

East deals and the ♣ 7 is turned up.

With his preponderance of trumps North appears to be in a position to score well. In reality, however, his hand is far from being a good one, because, although the trumps give him the advantage of winning tricks, this advantage is more than offset by the fact that he is in the dangerous position of being forced to take Knaves. Indeed, North is very likely to come out with a poor score; against good play by West he will be hard put to avoid taking the Knaves of both hearts and diamonds – for a loss of seven points – and, in any case, he can hardly avoid taking one of them.

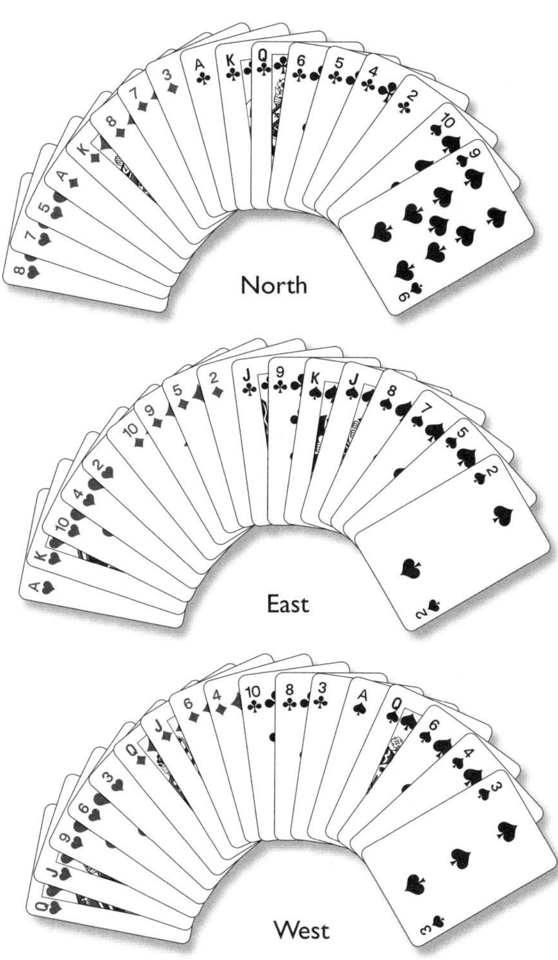

OKLAHOMA

OKLAHOMA *is a game of the Rummy family, not unlike Canasta. It is less complex than Canasta but satisfying to those who like to make lots of melds and hold plenty of cards in their hands.*

NUMBER OF PLAYERS

Oklahoma is best for three players, as described here, but can be played by two, four or five players without any alteration to the rules.

CARDS

Two standard packs are joined together and a Joker added, making a pack of 105 cards in all. The cards rank from Ace (high) to 2 (low), but all eight 2s and the Joker are wild cards, representing any cards that the player holding them wishes. Ace in a sequence can be either high (as in Ace, King, Queen) or low (Ace, 2, 3) but cannot be used 'round the corner (King, Ace, 2). The cards have special values in scoring, as detailed later.

Players draw to decide dealer, the lowest card drawn denoting the dealer (the Joker counts low). Thereafter the winner of a hand deals the next.

The dealer deals 13 cards to each player, one at a time. The remaining cards are placed face down in the centre to form the stock. The top card is turned over and placed face up beside the stock to begin a discard pile.

THE PLAY

The object is to form sequences or sets as described.

The player to the dealer's left may take the upcard into his hand or refuse it. If he refuses it the second player has the option and if he refuses it the dealer has the option. The card can be taken only by a player who can meld with it immediately, i.e. he can use it to complete a set of three or more cards of the same rank, or a sequence of three or more cards of the same suit, which he lays down on the table in front of him. A player who takes the card and melds completes his turn by discarding another card face up in its place, the turn passing to the next player clockwise. Play then proceeds normally as described below.

Should the turn pass round the table and back to eldest hand again, eldest takes the top card from stock into his hand. He may now meld or not, but completes his turn by discarding a card onto the discard pile. From now on play proceeds with each player having the option of taking the top card of the discard pile into his hand, or the top card of the stock.

There are two obligations for a player taking the top card of the discard pile. He must immediately meld with it, either by using it to form a new meld or by adding it to a meld he already has on the table. Players may at any time on their turn add cards to their own melds (but not to their opponents'). Having melded with the top card, the player is obliged to take the rest of the discard pile into his hand. He may then make as many melds with these cards as he pleases. His turn does not end until he discards, which he does by beginning a fresh discard pile.

A melded sequence can be as long as 14 cards (a complete suit with an Ace at each end), but a set of cards of the same rank cannot be of more than four cards, whether or not it includes wild cards.

When a wild card is used in a sequence, its user must announce the card that it represents, and it cannot be changed. Thus a player using a 2 to form a meld of, say, ♥ 9, ♥ 8, ♣ 2, specifying the ♣ 2 as being the ♥ 7, cannot later add the ♥ 7 to the meld and use the ♣ 2 as the ♥ 6 or ♥ 10. However, the Joker has a special property. If a player uses a Joker in a meld, and later acquires the card that the Joker represents, he can, on his turn, replace the Joker with the card and take the Joker into his hand for use a second time. A player can take the discard pile if it is headed by the card his Joker represents, by taking the card to replace his Joker.

When discarding, a player is not allowed to discard the ♠ Q, unless it is the only card left in his hand.

The deal ends either when one player goes out (i.e. melds all his cards and discards) or when the stock is exhausted. A player taking the last card of the stock is allowed to meld, if able, and discard, whereupon the deal ends, and no further melds are allowed.

A player cannot go out without discarding. It follows that a player with two cards only in his hand cannot go out by drawing a card from stock to form a set or sequence with them, because this would leave him with no card to discard, so his only chance is to acquire cards to add to his existing melds. When a player goes out, his opponents cannot add cards from their hands to their melds.

At the end of the deal, each player scores for the cards in his melds, with the cards still held in his hand debited against him. Cards have values as follows:

Joker: melded 100; in hand -200.
♠ Q: melded 50; in hand -100.
Ace: melded 20; in hand -20.
K, Q, J, 10, 9, 8 (excluding ♠ Q): melded 10; in hand -20.
7, 6, 5, 4, 3: melded 5; in hand -5.
2: melded, the value of the card it represents (except if it represents ♠ Q, when it is worth 10); unmelded -20.

A player who goes out is given a bonus score of 100 points, but not if he goes out on his first turn. A player who goes out (except on his first turn) who has not previously melded is said to go out 'concealed', and gets an additional bonus of 250, which, however, does not count towards his running game score. The game score is 1,000 points, the game ending with the deal on which a player passes that score. If two or three pass 1,000 on the same deal, the highest score wins. The winner receives a bonus of 200 for game (if two or three are equal the bonus is shared) and settlement is made on the basis of differences.

OMBRE

OMBRE *is a Spanish game of considerable antiquity. It was introduced into England by Catherine of Braganza, who married Charles II in 1662, and it immediately became very popular. Nowadays it is rarely played in Great Britain, but it is popular in Denmark (which saw the publication of a book about it in 1965) and it is played in Spain under the name of Tresillo and in Latin America as Rocamber. It deserves to be more popular.*

NUMBER OF PLAYERS

Ombre is a game only for three players.

CARDS

The game is played with a pack of 40 cards, i.e. the standard pack from which the 10s, 9s and 8s have been removed. It is not a difficult game to play, but it is first necessary to master the rather involved and unusual order of the cards.

In plain suits the cards in the red suits rank in the order: King, Queen, Jack, Ace, 2, 3, 4, 5, 6, 7; those in the black suits rank in the normal order: Ace, King, Queen, Jack, 7, 6, 5, 4, 3, 2. In trump suits if a red suit is trumps the order of the cards is: ♠ A (Spadille), 7 (Manille), ♣ A (Basto), A (Punto), K, Q, J, 2, 3, 4, 5, 6; if a black suit is trumps the order of the cards is: ♠ A (Spadille), 2 (Manille), ♣ A (Basto), K, Q, J, 7, 6, 5, 4, 3.

The three top trumps, Spadille, Manille and Basto, are collectively known as Matadores. The holder of one need not follow suit with it to a trump lead, but he must play one if a higher Matador is led and his hand contains no other trump card.

To determine the dealer, a card is dealt face upwards to each player in turn, and he who is first to receive a black Ace is dealer. It is here to be noted that, as in all games of Spanish origin, in dealing and play the game progresses anti-clockwise.

Nine cards are dealt to each player in threes. The remaining 13 cards are placed face down in the centre of the table.

THE PLAY

Each deal is complete in itself. One player (ombre) plays against the other two playing in partnership. The player on the right of the dealer has first option of being ombre. It carries two privileges: he names the trump suit, he may discard from his hand as many cards as he chooses and draw fresh cards from the stock. If the player on the right of the dealer wishes to become ombre he says 'I play'. His right-hand neighbour may then announce that he wishes to become ombre, and, by so doing, he tacitly agrees that he will play without exchanging any of his cards. The first player may then reconsider the position, and is entitled to remain ombre if he is willing to play without exchanging any of his cards. If the second player passes, the third player (the dealer) may announce that he wishes to play without discarding. Again, the first player has a right to reconsider and may remain ombre without discarding.

If all players pass, i.e. if none wishes to play ombre, the deal is abandoned.

If the first player is allowed to play ombre unopposed, he discards as many cards as he chooses from his hand, and draws cards from the stock to replace them. The second player does the same, and then the dealer. If any cards are left in the stock after the three players have made their exchanges, the dealer is entitled to look at them. If he does he must show them to the other two players: if he does not, the other two may not.

Ombre now names the trump suit and leads a card. The game proceeds, anti-clockwise, every player following suit, if he can, to the led card, or trumping or discarding if he cannot. The winner of a trick leads to the next, until all nine tricks have been played.

At the beginning of a deal each player puts an agreed sum in a pool. Now:

Sacardo. If ombre wins more tricks than either of his opponents individually, he takes all that is in the pool.

Codille. If one of the opponents wins more tricks than ombre, ombre pays him a sum equal to the amount in the pool, and the amount in the pool is carried forward to the next deal.

Puesta. If ombre and one, or both, of his opponents win the same number of tricks, ombre doubles the amount in the pool and it is carried forward to the next deal.

After every deal the dealer for the next is determined by dealing the cards, face upwards, until one player receives a black Ace.

The deal that follows is a simple one to illustrate the mechanics of the game:

West	*North*	*East*
♥K, 7	♥none	♥4, 5, 6
♦6	♦7	♦2, 3, 4, 5
♠7,5	♠J, 6, 4, 3, 2	♠Q
♣Ma, Ba, K, 5	♣Q, J, 6	♣7

North deals.

West says: 'I play'. East and North pass.

West discards ♥ 7, ♦ 6, ♠ 7, ♠ 5. He draws ♥ 3, ♦ Q, ♦ A, ♣ 4.

East discards ♥ 4, ♥ 5, ♥ 6. His hand is of no value and he hopes to end with a void suit. He draws ♥ Q, ♥ A, Spa.

North discards ♦ 7, ♠ J, ♠ 6, ♠ 4, ♠ 3, ♠ 2. He draws ♥ J, ♥ 2, ♦ K, ♦ J, ♠ K, ♣ 3.

The hands are now:

West	*North*	*East*
♥ K, 3	♥ J, 2	♥ Q, A
♦ Q, A	♦ K, J	♦ 2, 3, 4, 5
♠ none	♠ K	♠ Q
♣ Ma, Ba, K, 5, 4	♣ Q, J, 6, 3	♣ Spa, 7

West names clubs as the trump suit.

His hand is none too good, but the lead of a trump is called for. He, therefore, leads ♣ K, and East wins with Spadille, because West would hardly have led the King of trumps if he did not hold Manille, and probably Basto as well. East has no better return than ♣ 7, on which North plays ♣ J. West allows it to win, by playing ♣ 4, because he is aware that North holds the more dangerous hand, and that sooner or later a trick in trumps must be lost to him. North must keep his top diamonds and ♠ K, and he cannot safely lead a heart. He, therefore, leads a club. West wins with Basto, draws North's last trump with Manille, and continues with ♣ 5. It puts North on the spot. If he discards ♦ J, West will lead the suit and later win ♥ K and a diamond; if North discards ♥ 2 or ♠ K, West will win ♥ K, and continue with ♥ 3, so that he will either win ♦ Q, or North and East will divide their tricks three-two. Either way it is sacardo, and West scoops the pool.

SCHAFKOPF

SCHAFKOPF *is an old game which lent some of its principles to the highly organized game of Skat. Schafkopf is less complex and is enjoyed widely without having had codified rules.*

NUMBER OF PLAYERS

Schafkopf is for three players.

CARDS

A short pack of 32 is used, i.e. a standard pack from which are removed the 6s, 5s, 4s, 3s and 2s.

There is a trump suit which consists of all the Queens, all the Jacks and all the diamonds. The trump suit, consisting of 14 cards, ranks as follows: ♣ Q, ♠ Q, ♥ Q, ♦ Q, ♣ J, ♠ J, ♥ J, ♦ J, ♦ A, ♦ 10, ♦ K, ♦ 9, ♦ 8, ♦ 7.

In the plain suits the cards rank as follows: Ace, 10, King, 9, 8, 7.

The high cards have point values as follows:

Ace	11
10	10
King	4
Queen	3
Jack	2

One player shuffles the pack and deals the cards face up to each player clockwise, and the first to receive a Jack is the first dealer. The deal subsequently rotates to the left.

The dealer shuffles, the player to his right cuts, and the dealer deals first three cards to each player clockwise, then two to the centre to form a skat or widow, then the remainder to the players in lots of four and three.

THE PLAY

The player to the dealer's left is called Forehand, and the player to the dealer's right is called Middlehand. The object is to win in tricks cards of scoring values as detailed above.

The player who picks up the skat becomes the Player, and plays the hand in opposition to the other two players – the Middlehand and the Forehand.

Forehand has the first option, and may pick up the skat or pass. If he passes, Middlehand has the next option, and if he passes the dealer has the option. If all three pass the hand is played as Least, to be described later.

When a player picks up the skat, he discards two cards face down, and a trick-taking phase begins. Forehand leads to the first trick, thereafter the winner of a trick leads to the next. Players are required to follow suit to the card led, and if they are unable to, they can trump or discard. The trick is won by the highest trump it contains, or if it contains none, by the highest card in the suit led. The Player adds any points among his discards to his own total.

The Player scores points as follows: if his tricks plus his discards contain cards worth 61 to 90 points, two game points; 91 or more, four game points (known as Schneider). If he wins all the tricks, he scores six game points (known as Schwartz).

For failing to score 61 points, the Player is debited as follows: if his tricks and discards contain 31 to 60 points, he is debited two game points; 30 or fewer, he is debited four game points. If he loses all the tricks, he is debited six game points.

Game is to ten points.

When all three players pass, Least is played. The uninspected skat is set aside, the cards it contains to be added later to those of the player who takes the last trick. Forehand makes the opening lead as usual, but this time the object is to win as few as possible cards of point value. Each player plays for himself, there being no Player.

If one player takes no tricks, he scores four game points. If one player takes all the tricks, he is debited four game points. If each player takes a trick, then the player with the fewest points among his cards scores two game points. If two tie for fewest, the one who collected his last trick earliest wins the two game points. If all three tie with 40 points each among their cards, the dealer wins the two game points.

It should be remembered that of the 30 cards in play, 14, or nearly half of them, are trumps, so the requirement to pick up the skat amounts to something like seven trumps, including four Queens and Jacks. Remember the odds are very much against a plain suit going round twice, as there are only six cards in each plain suit, and it is actually slight odds against all six being in play. So Ace, 10 in a side suit is likely to make two tricks only if all trumps are drawn first. The Player should consider that high-scoring cards like 10s and Aces might be best left in the skat, where the Player will score for them without risking having them taken in play by the opponents.

SKAT

ORIGINATING *in the south Leipzig in eastern Germany in the early part of the 19th century, Skat has become a popular pub game over most of German-speaking central Europe. Played at the highest level Skat is one of the most skilful of all card games, and it is particularly recommended for people who enjoy Hearts but find that game too straightforward.*

NUMBER OF PLAYERS

Skat is a game for three players.

CARDS

The pack is of 32 cards (as used for Piquet, Euchre, etc.), and consists of four suits: clubs, spades, hearts and diamonds, each suit containing Ace, King, Queen, Jack, 10, 9, 8, 7.

The four Jacks are always part of the trump suit in Skat, and they always rank in the order: clubs, spades, hearts, diamonds (clubs are high). The 10 ranks between Ace and King.

The order of the trump suit is:

♣ J; ♠ J; ♥ J; ♦ J, A, 10, K, Q, 9, 8, 7 (11 cards).

And the order of the other three suits is:

Ace, 10, King, Queen, 9, 8, 7 (seven cards).

There is also a contract, called 'Grand', in which there are, effectively, five suits. The four Jacks, which are trumps, form a small suit by themselves, and the other four suits have seven cards each.

(Note that in all contracts the Jacks are treated exactly as ordinary members of the trump suit for the purposes of play, so that, for example, if hearts are trumps and the ♦ J is led, the other players are forced to follow with hearts [or Jacks] if they have any.)

The cards have widely differing values as follows:

Ace	11
10	10
King	4
Queen	3
Jack	2
9, 8, 7	0

This makes a total of 120 points in the pack. The object of the game is to capture half these 'card points' in tricks (Declarer needs 61 points to win, the defenders need 60 to beat him).

The skat counts as part of the declarer's tricks, so that if he discards two 10s, for example, he already has 20 points – almost a third of his target.

Note that the Jacks, which are the most powerful cards for winning tricks, are not in themselves worth many points – this special feature of Skat is responsible for much of the strategic richness of the game.

To determine the dealer for the first hand, cards are dealt out one at a time by whoever happens to hold them, face up, one to each player. The first person to get a Jack is dealer. The dealer shuffles, then someone else cuts, then the dealer deals, clockwise starting with the player on his left, three cards to each player, then two to the skat, then four cards each, then another three each (the peculiar English habit of dealing cards one at a time is rare in central Europe). The deal moves round to the left on subsequent hands. The player on Dealer's left is called 'Forehand', the other player is called 'Middlehand'.

BIDDING

The bidding consists of an auction between the three players. The bids are numbers, and represent the number of points the player contracts to score if he becomes the declarer. If someone else eventually becomes the declarer then there is no obligation on the bidder. If the declarer makes a higher score than he bid then that is fine – he scores the higher number. Note that these bids are scores, not numbers of card points – the contract is always to make 61 card points (unless Schneider is announced).

The process of bidding is for one player to call numbers in ascending order while a second player says 'Yes' after each bid. Eventually one of them drops out of the auction by saying 'Pass'.

The auction begins with Middlehand bidding and Forehand saying 'Yes' (or 'Pass'), then when one of these two has passed, the dealer starts bidding and the other says 'Yes' (or passes).

One may only bid numbers which it is possible to score. The full bidding sequence starts with:

diamonds with, or without, one Jack	18
hearts with one	20
spades with one	22
null	23
clubs with one	24
diamonds with two	27
hearts with two	30
spades with two	33
null hand	35
clubs with two or diamonds with three	36
hearts with three or grand with one	40
spades with three	44
diamonds with four	45
null open	46
clubs with three	48
hearts with four	50
diamonds with five	54
spades with four	55
null hand open	59
clubs with four, hearts with five or grand with two	60
and so on up to grand hand with four with Schwartz announced	200
and theoretically club hand with Schwartz announced	204

In practice the auction never gets past 60 among skilful players.

A typical auction might go: (M Middlehand, F Forehand, D Dealer).

M: 18	F: Yes
M: 20	F: Yes
M: 22	F: Yes
M: 23	F: Yes
M: 24	F: Pass
D: 27	M: Yes
D: Pass	

The result of this auction is that Middlehand has contracted to make at least 27 points.

If all three players pass, the hand is thrown in and the deal passes on.

If the declarer overbids, either by accident or because he was hoping to play without several Jacks and finds one in the skat, then it is possible that he has absolutely no way to make his contract, even by making Schwartz. In this case he loses the next higher multiple of his base value above his bid. Suppose, for example, that a player holding:

♥ 10, K, Q, 9, 8, 7
♣ A, 10
♠ A, K

plays hearts in hand, after bidding up to 59 points. He makes 82 card points, but the ♠ J proves to be in the skat. Far from being 'without five' as he had hoped, he is only 'without one' and so scores only 30 (without one, game two, hand three). He loses 60 points for this, since that is the next multiple of 10 above his bid. It is always a bit dangerous trying to go without the Jacks because of the risk of finding one in the skat.

THE PLAY

Skat is a trick-taking game, like Bridge, Solo Whist and Hearts. Play proceeds in a series of tricks, in each of which one player leads a card, and the other two, in turn clockwise round the table, follow with one card. The player leading can choose any card he likes, but the others are forced to play cards of the suit led, unless they have no such card when they are free to choose any card. The trick is won by the highest card of the suit led, except that one suit (called the trump suit) always beats the other suits and a trick to which trumps are played is won by the highest trump irrespective of the suit led.

The winner of each trick keeps the three cards it contains face down in front of him, and leads to the next trick. The player on the dealer's left ('Forehand') leads to the first trick.

SCORING

Adding up the value of the cards captured and seeing whether the declarer has achieved 61 card points determines whether he has won or not. The amount of money he gets for doing so (or the score he gets if you are not playing for money) is determined in an unlikely sounding manner which takes a little getting used to. It is the product of two numbers which we shall call the 'base value' and the 'multiplier'.

The base value depends only on the trump suit:

Diamonds	9
Hearts	10
Spades	11
Clubs	12
Grand	20

The multiplier depends mostly on he number of top trumps the declarer holds, but various bonuses may be added:

If declarer holds the ♣ J (the top trump), the multiplier is the number of trumps he holds in sequence from the ♣ J down.

If declarer does not hold the ♣ J, the multiplier is the number of trumps he is missing, in sequence from the ♣ J down.

If declarer plays 'in hand', i.e. he does not look at the skat, but just puts the two cards in his pile of tricks, he adds one to the multiplier. If declarer makes 'schneider', i.e. he takes 90 or more card points in his tricks, he adds one to the multiplier. If declarer announces that he is going to make schneider at the beginning of the hand, then he adds another one to the multiplier in addition to the one for making schneider. It is illegal to announce schneider except when playing in hand. If declarer announces schneider and takes fewer than 90 card points, then the multipliers for schneider and schneider announced still apply, but he loses.

If declarer makes 'schwartz' (German for black – he takes all the tricks), then he gets another one added to the multiplier in addition to the one for schneider.

If declarer announces schwartz then he gets yet another one added, but, as for schneider, he may only announce schwartz when playing in hand.

One is always added to the multiplier 'for the Game'.

If declarer fails to make his contract he loses double the score he would have won, except when playing in hand.

Let us consider some examples:

The declarer plays in hearts, holding ♣ J, ♠ J, ♦ J, and he takes 76 card points. He is 'with two' Jacks (the ♥ J is missing) and claims:

'With two, game three, times 10, makes 30.'

The declarer plays a Grand holding ♥ J, ♦ J, and he makes 59 card points (not enough) and announces:

'Without two, game three, off six, times 20, loses 120.'

The declarer plays in spades, in hand, holding ♣ J, ♠ J, ♦ J; and he announces Schneider. He makes 87 card points (not enough), therefore loses:

'With three, game four, hand five, schneider six, announced seven, times 11, loses 77.

The declarer plays in clubs, in hand, holding ♣ J, ♥ J, ♦ J, and the Ace of clubs. He makes 96 card points, and the ♠ J proves to have been in the skat (lucky). He claims:

'With five, game six, hand seven, schneider eight, times 12, makes 96.'

In addition to the normal trump contracts, there is a contract called null, which is a contract to take no tricks at all. Card points do not count, and the hand stops immediately if the declarer takes a trick (he has lost).

The order of the cards is different in null. There are no trumps, and the four suits each have eight cards: Ace, King, Queen, Jack, 10, 9, 8, 7 in that order (the 10s and Jacks are back where you would expect them to be).

In null it is possible to play 'open'. The declarer exposes all his cards, and plays with them face up on the table. There are four contracts, depending on whether declarer looks at the skat:

Null	23
Null Hand	35
Null Open	46
Null Hand Open	59

As with ordinary contracts, the declarer loses double the number of points if he has looked at the skat, but just loses what he would have won if he plays in hand.

Skat scoring is designed for players who use piles of money on the table in front of them, and settle up after each hand – the rule is that the declarer is paid by (or pays if he has lost) each of the other players.

If you intend to play for honour (or if you, or the publican, do not like having money on the table) then the score can be kept on a piece of paper. After each hand add the score for that hand to the total under the declarer's initial. At the end each player pays each other the difference between their scores. (If you are not playing for money it's just the player with the biggest score who wins, which is simpler).

Requirements to bid a suit contract. The important cards are Jacks and Aces, and the average hand has 1⅓ of each of them. The advantages of getting the skat, discarding, and choosing trumps almost outweigh the disadvantage of being one player against two, and most hands with three cards which are Jacks or Aces can reasonably be bid up to the value of their lowest ranking long suit.

To bid grand. Here Jacks and Aces are especially important. Normally you need five of them (or perhaps four if you are Forehand, and have the lead). Tens to support your Aces are much better than 10s by themselves.

To bid null. You need 7s. Competent defenders will nearly always force you to take a trick if you have a three-card suit containing the Ace or King, or a four-card suit missing the 7, or a single card of a suit which is not 7, 8 or 9.

Going in hand. If you have a rock-crushing collection of Aces and Jacks you might as well go in hand to score for the extra multiplier, but there are two common reasons for not doing so:

(a) a holding which is almost sure to make game in hand can be converted, using the skat, to one which is absolutely sure to make game and almost sure to make schneider – the extra multiplier for schneider is just as good as the one for hand, and you are insured against dangers like a 5-0 trump split.

(b) many holdings which would make game in hand in a suit could be converted into a grand given one more Ace or Jack from the skat. Since grand is so much more valuable than the suit contracts it is often worth forgoing the multiplier for hand in the hope of something bigger. If there are four particular cards any one of which would let you make grand, the chance of finding one of them in the skat is about one in three.

Discarding the skat. The declarer should try to create void suits where he holds one or two cards without the Ace. One odd low card can cost 21 card points. It is much better to have two low cards in one suit than one in each of two suits. Never discard an Ace.

Counting. Counting is quite important in Skat. If you can only remember one number, then count trumps. If you can manage two, then count trumps and the number of card points the defenders have collected.

Choosing trumps. If you have two suits of equal length, then choose the weaker one as trumps, which avoids devaluing your Aces.

The following example hand (see illustration overleaf) covers a number of other aspects of skilful play – you may find it easier to follow by laying the cards on a table.

First, let's consider what the players should be prepared to bid:

Forehand: He has no chance in anything except null. His clubs and hearts are safe, but he might be forced to take a trick either in spades or diamonds (the diamonds are about as worrying as the spades – any long suit missing the 7 is a liability in null). He has a reasonable chance of improving one or both these suits if he looks at the skat, so he can bid up to 23.

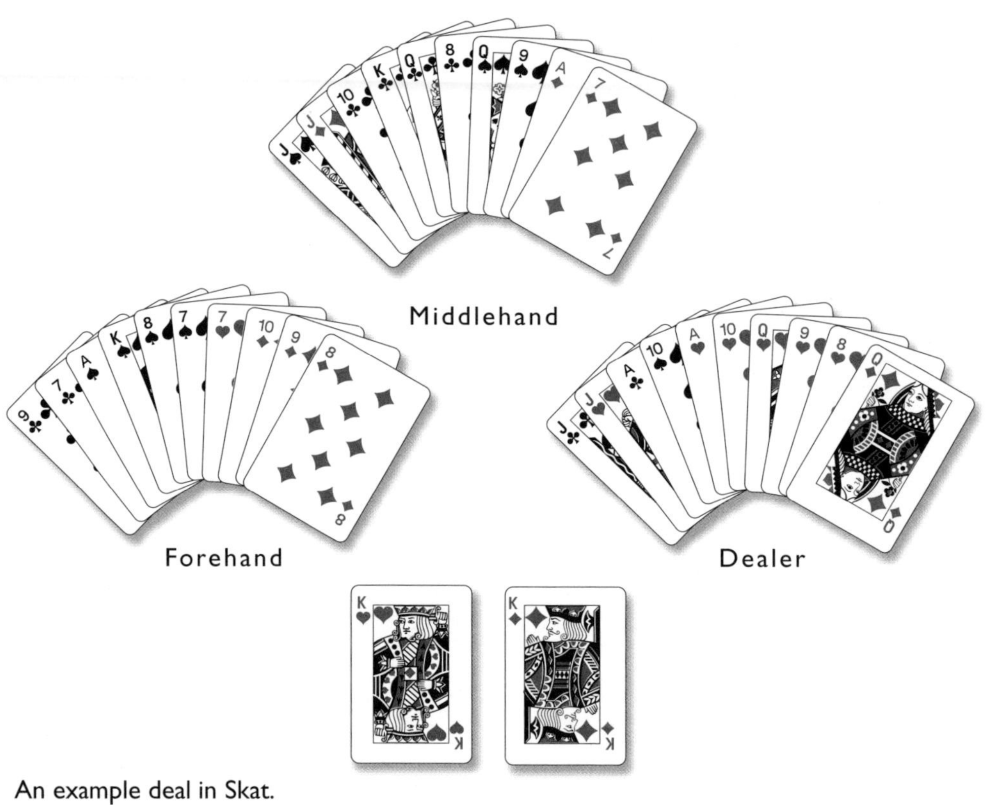

An example deal in Skat.

Middlehand: He has a reasonable hand for playing in clubs (he can even consider playing in hand) but he would feel much happier if he could see the skat, and find another club, or a Jack, or an Ace. He can bid up to 24 (clubs without one).

Dealer: He has quite a good hand. He can consider playing hearts in hand, but the ♠ 10 is a severe embarrassment – it is almost sure to be caught by the Ace. Ideally the dealer would like to look at the skat. If he finds an Ace, or possibly a Jack, he will be strong enough to play grand, and if he can discard the embarrassing ♠ 10 into his trick pile, then hearts are almost cast-iron. In a hand like this, with few losers, it is worth doing a calculation to see how many points the defenders can collect. In this case we would suppose that the defenders catch the ♠ 10 with the Ace and King, for 25 points, that they catch the ♦ Q with the Ace and 10, for a further 24 points making 49, and then we are left with the question of whether they can collect 11 points in trumps (assuming hearts are trumps, of course). There are four trumps outside the dealer's hand, and he should be prepared for them to divide three-one between the opponents. In this case the defenders can arrange for at least one trick to happen when one of them is winning a trump, while the other is out of trumps and can throw on some valuable card like the ♣ 10. This will make up the required 11 points and the dealer will lose. Of course, in practice, the defenders will rarely manage to put the maximum possible number of points on his losing cards, but the calculation shows that the dealer is not quite safe playing hearts in hand.

The bidding goes as follows:

Middlehand: 18	Forehand: Yes
M: 20	F: Yes
M: 22	F: Yes
M: 23	F: Yes
M: 24	F: Pass
Dealer: Pass	

The dealer decides to pass since his hearts hand contract is not quite safe and he has very good chances of defeating any contract Middlehand might try. This is rather cowardly – most players would bid up to 30 with the dealer's cards.

Middlehand looks at the skat, fails to find any of the key cards he was hoping for, and discards ♥ K and ♠ Q, getting 7 points home and creating a void in hearts.

Middlehand then announces his contract: 'clubs are trumps'.

The play proceeds as follows (F = Forehand, M = Middlehand, the Declarer, D = Dealer):

Trick 1: F leads the ♠ A. Normal practice is for the player in front of the declarer to play long suits, while the other defender plays short suits – the reason soon becomes apparent. M follows the ♠ 9 and D plays the ♠ 10.

Score: M 7 points, Defenders 21.

Trick 2: F leads the ♠ K. This is the position the defenders have been trying to create, with D, void of the suit led, playing after the declarer. This means that if M trumps the card led, D can overtrump, while if M throws away some odd card, D can put something valuable on (in this case, the ♥ A). M decides to trump with the ♣ Q, and D overtrumps with the ♣ A.

Score: M 7 points, Defenders 39.

Trick 3: D leads the ♥ A. He expects M to trump this card, but it is far better to force M to trump than to allow him an opportunity to get rid of an odd card. F plays the 7, and M trumps with the ♣ 10.

Score: M 28 points, Defenders 39.

Trick 4: M leads the ♦ J. It is almost always best for the declarer to get rid of trumps as soon as possible. D wins with the ♥ J, and F plays the ♣ 7.

Score: M 28 points, Defenders 43.

Trick 5: D leads the ♥ Q. He is saving the ♥ 10 for later, in case F is taking a diamond trick which he (D) will want to put a valuable card on. F plays the ♣ 9. He is not expecting to win this trick, since M will probably want to trump anyway, but the ♣ 9 is worse than useless – if his partner wins another trump trick then F wants to be free to put the ♦ 10 on, and not to be forced to follow suit with the ♣ 9 which is worth no points. M wins with the ♣ K.

Score: M 35 points, Defenders 43.

Trick 6: M leads the ♣ 8 – he makes sure that D's trump goes on a nice cheap card, and hopes that it is D, not F, who has the outstanding trump so that D will

be embarrassed by having to lead diamonds. D wins with the ♣ J, and F decides to play the ♠ 7, since he has been counting the points carefully. If he played the ♦ 10 the defenders would get to 55 points but would not have much chance of getting any more – he is hoping the ♦ 10 will take a trick.
Score: M 35 points, Defenders 45.
Trick 7: D leads the ♦ Q. This brilliant play depends on his having worked out that F and M both have three diamonds (do you see how?). F plays the 9, and M, who rather enjoys having D on lead, plays the 7.
Score: M 35 points, Defenders 48.
Trick 8: If D now plays a small heart then M will throw away his ♦ K, and win the rest of the tricks. D therefore plays his ♥ 10, to force M to trump. F plays the ♠ 8, and M trumps with the ♠ J.
Score: M 47 points, Defenders 48.
Trick 9: M plays the ♦ A, hoping that he has miscounted the points. D plays the ♥ 8, and F follows with the ♦ 8.
Score: Declarer 58 points, Defenders 48.
Trick 10: M plays his last card, the ♦ K. D plays his heart, and F wins with the ♦ 10.
Final score: M 58 points, Defenders 62. So Forehand and Dealer win 'without one, game two, off four, times 12, loses 48'.

VARIATIONS IN THE RULES

The rules of Skat described above are among those most commonly used across central Europe, but Skat is the type of pub game in which local variations are common, such as the base value for grand is often taken as 24, not 20.

TOWIE

TOWIE *was originated by J. Leonard Replogle as a variation of Bridge (see page 104).*

NUMBER OF PLAYERS

The game is played by three active players, and so is most suitable for that number, but can be played by more, as described later.

CARDS

The full pack of 52 cards is used.

Four hands of 13 cards each are dealt in the usual way; the one to the quarter opposite the dealer is the dummy hand to be bid for. After dealing, the dealer chooses (without looking at them) six cards from the dummy hand, and turns them up.

THE PLAY

The players, beginning with the dealer, bid as in the parent game, but part scores are not reckoned and if the bidding ends without a game or higher contract being reached, there is a goulash deal, with further goulashes if necessary.*

When the bidding ends the player on the left of the declarer makes the opening lead. The dummy hand becomes the property of the declarer who sorts it, exposes it on the table, and plays it against the other two players in partnership, as in the parent game.

The scoring is the same as in Bridge with the following differences:

1. In no trump contracts the trick score is 35 points a trick.
2. For winning a first game the declarer scores a bonus of 500 points and becomes vulnerable. For winning a second game – and with it the rubber – a player scores 1,000 points.
3. The declarer who makes a doubled or redoubled contract scores a bonus of 50 points if not vulnerable, and 100 points if vulnerable.
4. For undoubled overtricks the declarer scores 50 points each. If doubled or redoubed he scores for them as in the parent game.
5. The penalties for undertricks are:

Not vulnerable

Undoubled:	50	points per trick
Doubled:	100	points for the first and second tricks
	200	points for the third and fourth tricks
	400	points for the fifth and subsequent tricks

Vulnerable

Undoubled:	100	points for the first trick
	200	points for the second and subsequent tricks
Doubled:	200	points for the first trick
	400	points for the second and subsequent tricks

If the contract is redoubled the scores for doubled contracts are multiplied by two.

Large penalties are not uncommon in Towie because a player has no partner during the auction period and cannot do more than bid on the strength of his own hand, the six cards that he sees in dummy, and the seven cards that he expects to find there. Over-bidding is frequent, but risks must be taken, and the game is not for the chicken-hearted or cautious bidder. The play of the defence offers scope for skill, but, on the whole, the main object of a player must be to play the dummy, particularly when five are in the game (see overleaf).

* For a goulash deal the players sort their cards into suits (the dealer sorts the dummy hand) and the hands are placed face downwards in a pile, one on top of the other, in front of the dealer. The cards are cut without being shuffled, and the same dealer deals the cards.

The dummy hand after the face-down cards have been exposed

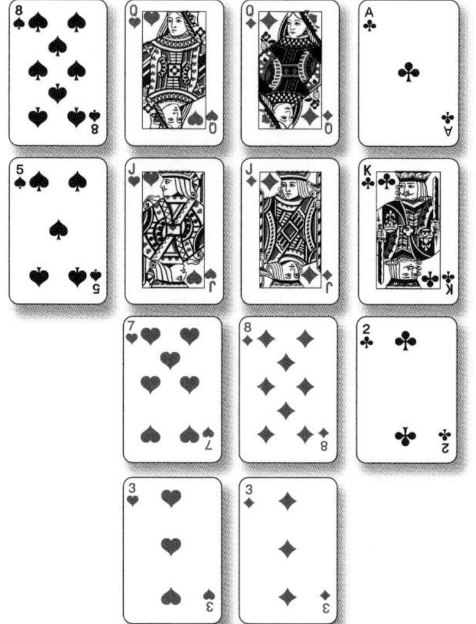

Consider the hands and dummy as dealt in the illustration below with the fully exposed dummy shown on the left.

South and East were vulnerable, and South dealt. He bid a cautious One Spade, and, after a pass by West, East bid Three No Trumps. South lacked the courage to bid Four Spades, and East, with dummy's cards opposite him, had an easy ride for his contract.

TOWIE FOR FOUR OR MORE

If there are more than three players participating in the game the inactive players are opponents of the declarer.

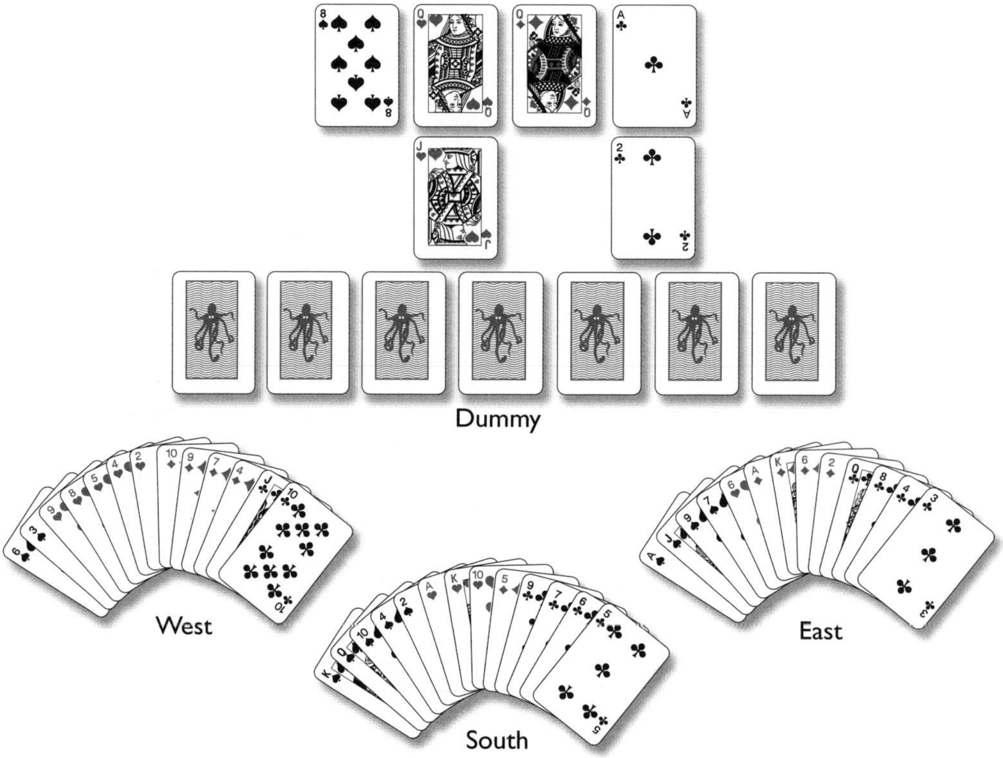

Dummy

West

East

South

They take no part in the bidding or play, but participate in the scoring, losing when the declarer makes his contract, and scoring the undertrick penalties when the declarer's contract is defeated.

At the end of a deal the declarer, whether he has won or lost his contract, retires from the table and his place is taken by one of the waiting players. The inactive players come into the game in turn, replacing the declarer of the previous deal. No vulnerable player, however, may re-enter the game if a non-vulnerable player is waiting to play.

The game ends when one player has won two deals.

GAMES FOR FOUR PLAYERS

AUCTION PITCH

AUCTION PITCH, *commonly known as Pitch and sometimes as Set Back, is a variation of All Fours (see page 9).*

NUMBER OF PLAYERS

Auction Pitch is at its best and most popular when played by four players, each playing for himself. It can, however, be played by any number from two to seven.

CARDS

The full pack of 52 is used and cards rank from Ace (high) to 2 (low).

Each player is dealt six cards in two lots of three each. No card, however, is turned up to determine the trump suit.

THE PLAY

The player on the left of the dealer bids first, and each player, in his turn, may either make a bid or pass. A bid must be for at least two points, and for more than the preceding bid, except for the dealer, who is entitled to buy the hand for the same number of points as the preceding bid. The maximum number of points in a deal is four, and a player who expects to win them bids smudge. The dealer cannot take the declaration from him.

The successful bidder is known as the maker, and he pitches (leads) to the first trick. The card that he leads determines the trump suit.

At each trick a player must follow suit to the card led, if he can, otherwise he may discard or trump. The winner of a trick leads to the next.

As in the parent game, points are scored as follows:

High. The player who holds the highest trump scores one point.

Low. The player who holds the lowest trump scores one point.

Jack. The player who wins the trick that contains the Jack of the trump suit (if it is in play) scores one point.

Game. Counting the Ace as four, the King as three, the Queen as two, the Jack as one and the 10 as ten, the player with the highest total in the tricks he has won scores one point. If there is a tie no player scores the point.

Every player records what he scores, and if the maker fails to reach his bid he is set back by the full amount of it. He records the score and if it reduces him to a minus score he encircles it and is said to be in the hole.

The game is won by the player who first reaches seven points, and if the maker and one or more of the other players reach seven points in the same deal, the maker wins. As between the other players, the points are counted in the order High, Low, Jack, Game.

A player who smudges and wins all four points automatically wins the game regardless of his score, unless he was in the hole when he smudged. In this event he scores only four points.

BRIDGE

MODERN BRIDGE, *more precisely Contract Bridge, but the 'Contract' has for long been dropped, was developed out of Auction Bridge and introduced to card players in the early 1920s. It took firm root quickly, and made rapid progress, to become the most popular game in the history of card-playing. Today it is played by millions, rich and poor, from peers to peasants, and it has attracted to itself a vast literature in most European languages.*

NUMBER OF PLAYERS

Bridge is a game for four players, two playing in partnership against the other two, players sitting opposite each other.

CARDS

The full pack of 52 cards is used. Although only one pack of cards is necessary, it is customary to use two, of different design or colour, and while one is being dealt the other is shuffled by the partner of the dealer, in readiness for the next dealer.

The cards rank in the order Ace (high) to 2 (low), and the Ace, King, Queen, Jack and 10 of a suit are known as the honour cards. The suits rank in the order spades, hearts, diamonds, clubs; the spade and heart suits are known as the major suits: the diamond and club suits as the minor suits.

To determine partners, a pack is spread on the table. The four players draw cards from it, and the two who draw the two highest cards play in partnership against the other two. If two players draw cards of equal rank, precedence is determined by the rank of the suits. The player who draws the highest card has choice of seats and cards, and deals first. Thereafter the deal passes round the table clockwise. His partner sits opposite to him; the other two partners sit one on each side of him. It is usual to denote the four players by the cardinal points of the compass.

BIDDING

During the bidding, which the two partnerships compete against each other to establish which suit shall be made trumps or whether the hand shall be played without a trump suit.

The dealer bids first, and the bidding continues round the table clockwise. When a player bids he states the number of tricks in excess of six that he undertakes to win, and in the denomination that he undertakes to play. The lowest bid, therefore, is a bid of One (a contract to win seven tricks) and the highest is a bid of Seven (a contract to win all 13 tricks). As no-trumps takes precedence over the suits, the lowest possible bid is One Club, and the ascending scale is: One Club, One Diamond, One Heart, One Spade, One No Trump, Two Clubs, Two Diamonds ... Seven Hearts, Seven Spades, Seven No Trumps. A contract of Six (to win 12 tricks) is called a small slam; a contract of Seven (to win all 13 tricks) is called a grand slam.

In turn each bid must name either a greater number of tricks than the previous one, or an equal number of tricks in a higher denomination. If a player has no wish to contract to win tricks he says 'No Bid', and if all four players do so, the hand is thrown in and the deal passes.

In his turn any player may double a bid made by an opponent. The effect of a double is to increase the score whether the contract succeeds or fails: and the partnership whose contract has been doubled may redouble thereby increasing the score, win or lose, still further. Doubling and redoubling, however, do not increase the size of a contract: e.g. a bid of Four Clubs is inferior to a bid of Four Diamonds and remains inferior to it even though it may have been doubled and redoubled.

The bidding period continues until the last and highest bid has been followed by three passes. The player who first mentioned the denomination in the final contract then becomes the declarer.

Bridge is not a difficult game unless a player makes it so by ill-advised bidding. Its most important feature is that a player scores towards game only for the tricks that he has contracted to win, and, by a logical extension, he scores the big bonuses for slams only if the necessary amount of tricks has been contracted for. It follows that it is of paramount importance for the partners to estimate the trick-taking power of their combined hands, and not only must a player estimate as accurately as possible the position of the adverse high cards and distribution (as revealed by the bids of the other players) but convey by his bidding as much information as possible to his partner. In short, bidding may be defined as a conversation between the partners, and both must speak the same language.

OPENING BIDS

Most modern players value their hands by means of the well-known Milton Work count of 4 points for an Ace, 3 for a King, 2 for a Queen, and 1 for a Jack.

Suits

The player who opens the bidding with a bid of One of a suit promises to make a further bid if his partner responds with One in a higher-ranking suit, or Two in a lower-ranking suit. For this reason a player should not open unless he can see a sound rebid in his hand over his partner's most likely response.

The strength to justify an opening bid varies, but in general it may be said that a hand totalling at least 13 points should be opened. It is clear, however, that the more points a player holds the less length does he need in the trump suit, and the fewer points in the hand the greater must be the length in the trump suit. With less than 13 points in the hand the practice is to open an 11- or 12-point hand with a reasonable five-card suit, and with only 10 points in the hand, sometimes less, a player needs a reasonable six-card suit, or two five-card suits.

Open One Heart. The hand totals only 11 points, but the heart suit is worth showing and if it is not shown at once it may be too late.

Open One Spade. The hand totals only 11 points, but is strong by reason of its distribution. With two suits of equal length it is proper to bid the higher-ranking before the lower-ranking one.

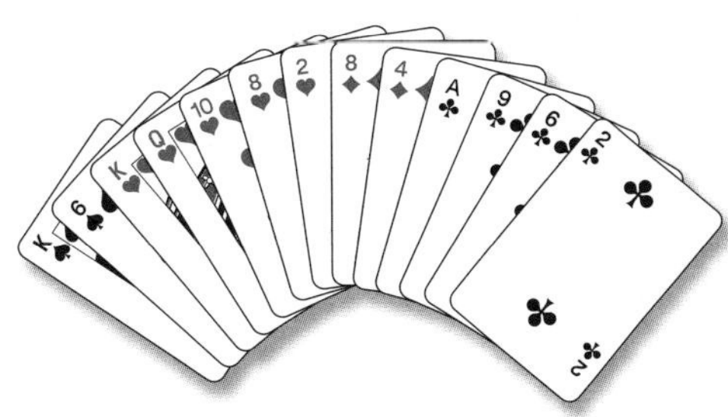

Open One Spade. The hand totals a mere 10 points, but the six-card spade suit is too good to be held back.

A pre-emptive bid is defined as an opening bid at the level of Three or higher. It is a bid of great value because either it prevents the opponents from entering the auction or compels one of them to bid at a level that is dangerously high when he has no notion of what cards his partner may be holding. Postulating that the bid of Three is weak and that an opponent holds strength in the other three suits, the most practical way of countering the pre-emptive bid is to bid Three Diamonds over Three Clubs and Three No Trumps over Three Spades, Hearts or Diamonds. Either bid invites partner to bid his best suit.

When an opponent has bid a suit at the level of One, a player should enter the auction only if he can be reasonably sure that his bid, if passed out, will not be defeated by more than two tricks if vulnerable and three if not vulnerable. This general rule, however, must be accepted with some reservation. It would, for example, not be wrong for a player who holds …

… to bid One Heart over an opponent's One Diamond. The bid might prove costly, but not very often, and it is cowardly not to contest the part-score for fear of the worst happening. A player has a right to assume that even if his partner has a blank hand and only two or three low hearts, the hand will win three tricks in hearts and one in each of the black suits.

No trumps

A bid of One No Trump is advised with a total of 16 to 18 points. The bid should never step outside the stipulated range, because your partner needs to rely on it for his response. With nine points he will jump to Three No Trumps; with seven or eight he will bid Two No Trumps and leave it to the opener to pass with a minimum, but bid Three with a maximum. A no trump range of 16 to 18 points is known as a strong no-trump. Some experienced players favour, particularly when not vulnerable, a range of 12 to 14 points. It is known as a weak no trump. Whether a strong or a weak no trump is played is a matter of personal choice, but it must be agreed between the partners before play begins, because if a weak no trump is played partner must increase his responses by four points.

In the same way, an opening bid of Two No Trumps is advised on 20 to 22 points, leaving it to partner to raise to Three if he holds five points, and to pass with less.

Opening bids of One No Trump and Two No Trumps postulate a balanced distribution of 4-3-3-3 or 4-4-3-2. A bid of Three No-Trumps is tactical. It shows a hand containing a solid minor suit, and altogether a hand that has a reasonable prospect of winning nine tricks if partner has one or two top cards in the right places.

The hand qualifies for an opening bid of Three No Trumps. There is every prospect of making the contract; if not it will not cost a lot and there is the consolation that it has probably stopped the opponents from bidding a game that would have been a greater loss.

Weak and strong bids

An opening bid of Three of a suit is a weakness bid. It is made with a hand that has little, if any, defensive strength, offers small chance of success of game, and with one long suit that, if trumps, is unlikely to be defeated by more than two tricks if vulnerable and three if not vulnerable.

This type of hand qualifies for an opening bid of Three Spades if only because, even if doubled and partner has no support, it cannot cost more than 500 points (two down). It is a reasonable loss if the opponents have a game in one of the other suits.

There is also a range of strong bids. The strongest of all is an opening bid of Two Clubs. It is strictly conventional and may be made even if the player is void in the suit. The bid guarantees either five or more high cards and distributional strength, or 23 or more points and a balanced distribution. With one exception the bid is forcing to game. Partner must respond no matter how weak his hand is, and with a weak hand he bids Two Diamonds. Any other response by him shows an Ace and a King or two King-Queen combinations or the equivalent in high cards. The exception to the bid not being forcing to game occurs when the opener has bid Two Clubs with a balanced hand and, after the negative response of Two Diamonds, has rebid Two No Trumps.

West	*East*
♠ K, J, 3	♠ Q, 6, 2
♥ A, Q, 6	♥ 9, 7, 4
♦ A, K, 4	♦ 8, 5, 3, 2
♣ A, Q, J, 2	♣ 7, 4, 3

Bidding	*Bidding*
2 ♣	2 ♦
2 No Trumps	No Bid

West, with 24 points, is too strong to open with any other bid than Two Clubs, and over East's negative response he cannot do better than rebid Two No Trumps. East with only two points in his hand does well to pass, but another point in his hand would make a big difference and with three points or more he would bid Three No Trumps.

The opening bid of Two in any other suit is forcing for one round, and shows a hand containing not fewer than eight playing tricks and at least one powerful suit.

The hand above is best opened with Two Spades. If it is opened with One Spade there is no satisfactory way of coping with a response of Two Hearts.

A strong two-suited hand also qualifies for an opening bid of Two. The higher-ranking suit is bid first.

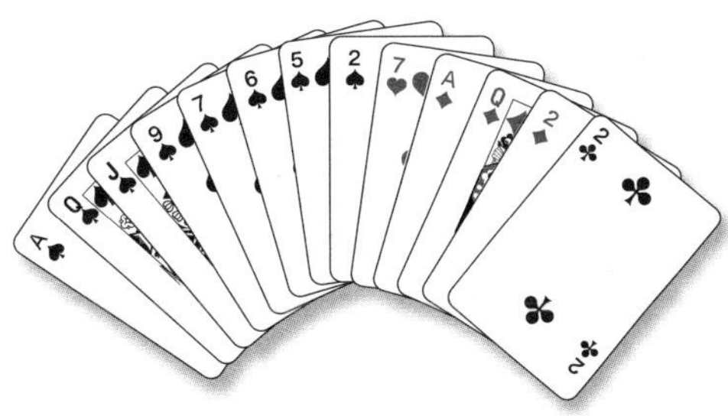

A one-suited hand may also be opened with a Two bid. This hand should be opened with a bid of Two Spades, and Three Spades should be bid over any response made by partner.

As well as an opening bid of Two Clubs there are several other bids that are forcing to game. The most frequent is a jump bid in a new suit.

West	*East*
♠ Q, 8, 4	♠ A, K, 6
♥ 9, 2	♥ A, Q, J, 10, 6, 4
♦ A, J, 3	♦ 8, 2
♣ A, K, 9, 3, 2	♣ J, 4

Bidding	*Bidding*
1 ♣	2 ♥

The situation is typical. East's bid of Two Hearts sets up a forcing situation. It is true that a bid of One Heart by East cannot be passed by West, but it is better for East to get the hand off his chest, and by bidding Two Hearts he makes certain that the bidding will not be dropped until a game level is reached.

It is much the same if the opener makes a jump in a new suit over his partner's response:

West	*East*
♠ K, J, 6	♠ A, Q, 9, 2
♥ A, K, J, 7, 4	♥ 10, 8, 3
♦ 6	♦ K, Q, 9
♣ K, Q, J, 7	♣ 10, 6, 3

Bidding	*Bidding*
1 ♥	1 ♠
3 ♣	

In this situation (or a similar one) West's bid of Three Clubs is a game force and East cannot pass it.

In many cases a forcing situation is set up by reason of the logic behind the bidding.

West	*East*
♠ A, K, 9, 6, 3	♠ Q, 7, 4, 2
♥ K, J, 9, 2	♥ Q, 10, 8, 3
♦ A, 8, 4	♦ K, 6, 2
♣ 9	♣ 5, 4

Bidding	*Bidding*
1 ♠	2♠
3 ♥	?

As West rebid at the level of Three, over East's weak response of Two Spades, and when there was no need for him to rebid, he must have a very strong hand, and East must make a further bid. He bids Four Hearts and West passes.

An inferential force is even more pronounced in a sequence such as:

West	*East*
1 ♥	1 ♠
2 No Trumps	3 ♥
?	

West must not pass because East is very clearly inviting him to choose between playing the hand in Three No Trumps or Four Hearts, whichever contract best suits him.

Bidding slams

There are 40 points in the pack and experience has taught that if the combined hands have a total of 25 points game will be made, if 33 the small slam, and if 37 the grand slam. There are, of course, exceptions, but in the long run the rule is to be relied on.

When the bidding of the partners shows that they hold between them the balance of strength, they should consider bidding a slam. As a guide it may be said that prospects of a slam are good when a player holds enough to make a positive response to a forcing bid; or when the point count of the combined hands totals at least 33; or when a player has enough for an opening bid opposite a partner who has opened with a bid of Two, or who has opened the bidding and made a jump rebid.

Before a slam can be bid with a measure of safety, it is essential for the partners to find out if they hold between them control of the vital suits. The Blackwood convention has been designed to enable the partners to learn how many Aces and Kings are held by the partnership.

When the trump suit has been agreed either directly by support or by implication, or if a forcing situation has been set up, a bid of Four No Trumps by either partner asks the other to bid Five Clubs if he lacks an Ace or holds all four, Five Diamonds if he holds one Ace, Five Hearts if he holds two and Five Spades if he holds three. If the player who has bid Four No Trumps, after his partner's response continues with a bid of Five No Trumps, he is showing that he holds all four Aces and is asking his partner to bid Six Clubs if he lacks a King, Six Diamonds if he holds one King, Six Hearts if he holds two, Six Spades if he holds three and Six No Trumps if he holds all four. Look at the hands at the foot of the page. Bidding:

West	*East*
1 ♠	2 ♥
3 No Trumps	4 ♠
4 No Trumps	5 ♥
6 ♠	No Bid

Once East has shown that he has support for spades, West, with support for hearts, visualizes a slam. His bid of Four No-Trumps asks East how many Aces he holds, and East's response of Five Hearts tells West that he holds two. It is important for West to bid the slam in spades, because if East plays in hearts and his two Aces are in hearts and clubs (as they are) the opening lead of a diamond from South may break Six Hearts out of hand. When West plays in Six Spades, the ♦ K is protected against the opening lead and 12 tricks are assured.

As West knows that there is an Ace against the hand the grand slam is out of the question and West, therefore, has no need to bid Five No Trumps to ask East how many Kings he holds.

The convention is a very useful one, but it must be used with discretion, because if partner lacks the necessary Aces the partnership may find itself carried out of its depth. As a rule, it may be said that if the final contract is to be in clubs the bid of Four No Trumps should not be made unless the bidder holds at least two Aces, and if the contract is to be in diamonds he should hold at least one Ace.

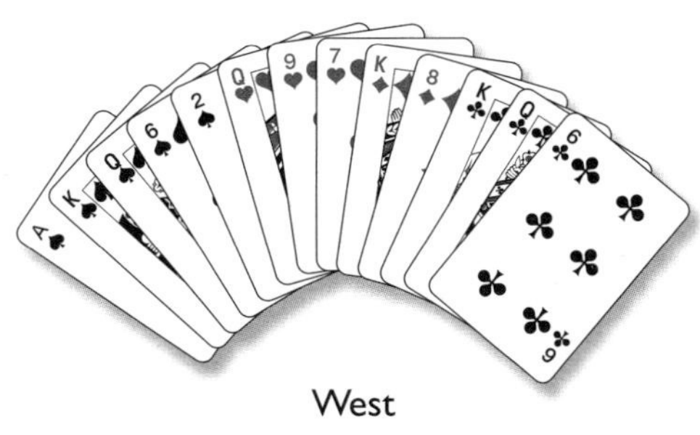

West

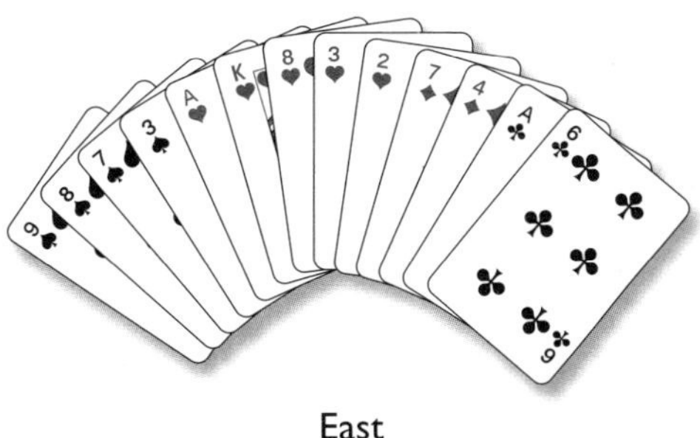

East

A limit bid is a bid that informs partner of the precise strength of the hand, and so permits him to estimate the combined strength of the partnership, and drop the bidding if he can see no future for it.

No trump bids are limit bids because they are made on an agreed number of points in the hand. A single raise of partner's suit is a limit bid that shows moderate strength and support for the suit; a double raise of partner's suit shows that the hand is too good for a mere simple raise and invites him to bid game if his hand is above average; a triple raise is distributional, it promises good support for the suit and a few scattered points, but no more because with good support for the suit coupled with high-card strength it would be more in order to make a gradual advance to a possible slam.

RESPONDING BIDS

Suits

A jump overcall shows strength, and, though it is not forcing, partner is expected to take action if he holds the values that would justify a response to a bid of One.

An overcall should be based on a five-card or longer suit, though it is reasonable to overcall with A, K, Q, x or K, Q, J, x at the level of One. It is nearly always very unwise to overcall with a broken suit.

In general, when an opponent has opened the bidding with a bid of One of a suit, it is better to counter it with a take-out double than with a weak overcall. A double in this situation shows weakness in the suit doubled and a total of about 13 or 14 points with a balanced hand and 11 or 12 with an unbalanced one. If the doubler's partner has not bid (if he has the double is for a penalty) the doubler invites partner to bid his best suit.

West	*East*
♠ K, J, 9, 6, 2	♠ 5, 3
♥ K, J, 9, 2	♥ A, Q, 8, 3
♦ 6	♦ K, 7, 2
♣ A, Q, 7	♣ 10, 8, 6, 2

If South has bid One Diamond, West should double. East bids hearts and the good fit has been found. If West bids One Spade over South's One Diamond the heart fit will never be found and a good result will be exchanged for a bad one.

If partner's best suit is the one that has been doubled, either he bids no trumps or passes for a penalty if he holds length in the suit.

A double of One No Trump is made with a balanced hand and a count of about two points more than the no-trump bidder's average. With a weak hand partner will take out into his best suit, but if the combined count totals 23 or more he will pass for a penalty.

The responses to opening Two bids (of suits other than clubs) are not so well defined and clear-cut as the responses to an opening bid of Two Clubs. In general, if partner holds a biddable suit he should bid it at the lowest level. If he lacks a biddable suit, but has a total of from 10 to 12 points, he should bid Three No Trumps. If he lacks a biddable suit and insufficient points to bid Three No Trumps, but has adequate support (i.e. x, x, x or Q, x) for partner's suit and a count of five, he should give a simple raise in partner's suit. If he lacks a biddable suit, insufficient points for Three No Trumps, and insufficient support for partner's suit, he should make the negative response of Two No Trumps.

No trumps

The partner of the player who opens the bidding with No Trumps raises on a very precise number of points. The number of points, however, may be reduced slightly if the responder holds a five-card suit. Over a bid of One No Trump, partner holds:

The hand totals eight points and nine points are normally necessary to jump to Three No Trumps. Here, however, the jump to Three No Trumps is justified on the length of the spade suit, and the good intermediate cards. It is unwise to bid spades because if it is assumed that partner holds a balanced 16-point hand he is just as likely to win nine tricks in No Trumps as the responder is to win ten in spades. If Three No Trumps cannot be made there is no reason to suppose that Four Spades can.

A jump take out into a suit is a game force. It does not, however, promise a very strong hand: rather it means that the responder, who knows the precise strength of his partner's bid, can foresee game for the partnership but cannot tell whether the combined hands will play better in No Trumps or in a suit.

West	*East*
♠ Q, J, 4, 3	♠ K, 10, 9, 7, 2
♥ A, Q, 2	♥ J, 6, 4
♦ K, 9, 3	♦ A, J, 8, 2
♣ A, 7, 6	♣ 8

Bidding	*Bidding*
1 No Trump	3 ♠
4♠	No Bid

Over West's opening bid of One No Trump (16 to 18 points) East who has 9 points has enough to jump to Three No Trumps. He prefers Three Spades, however, which West raises to game, because game in spades can hardly fail, but in No Trumps will be defeated if a club is led.

Another important feature of responding to a No Trump bid is the Stayman convention. It is a bid of Two Clubs over partner's One No Trump, or Three Clubs over his Two No Trumps, made, irrespective of the holding in the suit, to ask partner to bid his better four-card major suit, or, if he lacks one, to bid diamonds.

West	*East*
♠ K, Q, 2	♠ A, J, 4, 3
♥ A, J, 6, 2	♥ K, Q, 8, 4
♦ Q, 6, 4	♦ 3, 2
♣ A, Q, 4	♣ J, 8, 5

Bidding	*Bidding*
1 No Trump	2 ♣
2 ♥	4 ♥
No Bid	

Without the convention East, with 11 points, would have no alternative except to jump his partner's opening bid of One No Trump (16 to 18 points) to Three. The combined total of 29 points is more than adequate for the bid, but Three No Trumps may be defeated if a diamond is led and Four Hearts can hardly fail.

There is a large range of bids which show weakness and that may be recognized as such by the logic of the situation.

West	*East*
1 ♠	2 No Trumps
3 ♠	?

East's bid of Two No Trumps shows a count of from 11 to 13 points, and over it West cannot do more than repeat his suit. His hand, therefore, cannot be strong, and his bid of Three Spades no more than the cheapest way of keeping his promise to rebid, which he made when he opened with One Spade.

In the same way, if the bidding is:

West	*East*
1 No Trump	2♠
?	

West should pass. East's bid must be showing a weak hand that he considers will play better in a suit than in No Trumps, otherwise, over an opening bid of One No Trump, it would be impossible for partner ever to play in Two of a suit.

Or we may consider the following sequences:

West	*East*	*West*	*East*	*West*	*East*
1 ♥	2 ♥	1 ♥	2 ♣	1 ♣	1 ♥
3 ♣	3 ♥	2 ♥	3 ♦	1 ♠	2 ♥
		3 ♥		2 ♠	3 ♥

In all these sequences the bid of Three Hearts shows weakness. A player cannot be holding much of a hand when he cannot do better than rebid his suit at the lowest level, and it is particularly pronounced when he rebids it twice.

If we assume that South deals, a sequence of bidding to illustrate some of the points mentioned might be:

South	*West*	*North*	*East*
1 ♦	No Bid	1 ♥	1 ♠
1 No Trump	2 ♠	3 ♦	No Bid
3 No Trumps	Double	No Bid	No Bid
4 ♦	No Bid	5 ♦	Double
Redouble	No Bid	No Bid	No Bid

The final contract, therefore, is Five Diamonds, and the hand will be played by South, because he was the first on his side to mention diamonds as the trump suit.

THE PLAY

During the playing, the player who has won the contract strives to make it, playing his own hand and that of his partner exposed on the table, against the 'defenders' striving to prevent him.

The playing period begins by the player on the left of the declarer leading to the first trick. As soon as he has done so, the partner of the declarer places his cards face upwards on the table as dummy. He takes no further part in the play except that he has a right to draw his partner's attention to certain irregularities, such as asking him if he has none of a suit when he fails to follow suit, and warning him against leading out of the wrong hand. The declarer plays the dummy hand as well as his own.

The play follows the normal routine of trick-taking games: if a player is able to do so he must follow suit to the card led; otherwise he may either discard or trump. The trick is won by the player who plays the highest card of the suit led, or the highest trump. The player who wins a trick leads to the next. If a trick is won in the dummy, the next trick must be led from there.

DECLARER'S PLAY

After the opening lead has been made, and the dummy hand exposed, it is of first importance for the declarer, before he plays a card from dummy, to take stock of the position and decide upon the best way to play the cards.

In the deal below, against West's contract of Three No Trumps, North leads the ♠ Q. At first sight it may seem immaterial whether West wins the trick with the Ace in dummy or with the King in his own hand. In the event, it matters a lot in which hand he wins the trick. If West gives consideration to the position he will appreciate that he must win the first trick with the ♠ K in his hand, win the ♣ K, Q, J, reach dummy, by leading the ♠ 4 to the Ace, to win dummy's Ace and ♣ 7, and finally the two red Aces in his own hand. If West wins the first trick with dummy's ♠ A, he will lose the contract if the adverse clubs fail to divide three-two, because he has left himself with no side entry to the clubs.

When the declarer is playing a No Trump contract, usually his first aim should be to establish his longest suit. In many cases, however, it is better to develop a short and strong suit rather than a long and weak one.

In the top deal overleaf, North leads a club against West's contract of Three

West

East

No Trumps. Consideration shows that West's best play is to win with the ♣ K and play on spades to knock out the Ace. This way, West makes sure of his contract with three tricks in spades, three in hearts, one in diamonds and two in clubs. The diamond suit is longer than the spade suit, but West cannot develop East's diamonds without first losing the lead twice. By then the opponents will have set up the clubs and broken the contract; in any case, only three tricks in diamonds will be developed for eight in all, which is not enough.

In a suit contract, it is usually the right play for the declarer to draw the adverse trumps at the first opportunity. Trumps, however, should not be drawn if there is a better use for them.

In the deal illustrated below, West plays in Four Hearts, and North leads a club. West wins the first trick with the ♣ A, and if he draws the trumps at once his contract will depend on the finesse of the ♠ Q being successful. It is no more than an even chance. The contract is a certainty if West, after winning the first trick with the ♣ A, leads either the 7 or 3 of the suit. It does not matter whether North or South wins the trick, or what card is returned. Declarer wins the next trick and trumps a club in

dummy. Now the adverse trumps may be drawn, and West comes to ten tricks with one spade, five hearts, two diamonds and one club by straight leads, and the ruff (trump) of a club on the table.

A valuable weapon in the armoury of the declarer is the ability to manage a suit to make the most tricks out of it.

West	*East*
A, 9, 3, 2	K, Q, 10, 5, 4

In this position it is vital to play the King first. Then, if either North or South is void of the suit, there is a marked finessing position over the Jack, and five tricks will be made.

The unthinking player who first plays the Ace, on the assumption that it does not matter which high card he plays first because the outstanding cards will normally divide three-one or two-two, will lose a trick in the suit whenever North is void and South holds J, 8, 7, 6. It will occur about five times in every hundred.

West	*East*
A, K, 10, 5, 3	9, 7, 6

If West cannot afford to lose more than one trick in the suit, his play is to win either the Ace or King; if both opponents follow suit, he enters East's hand in a side suit, leads the 7 from the table and if South plays the 8, plays the 10 from his own hand. This protects him against losing two tricks in the suit if South started with Q, J, 8, x.

There is a percentage play or a safety play for almost every combination of a suit, and it may be found by analysing the division of the remaining cards in the suit.

West	*East*
♠ A, K, 4, 2	♠ 5, 3
♥ A, 9, 7	♥ 10, 6, 2
♦ A, 9, 4	♦ K, 8, 7
♣ K, 7, 6	♣ A, 10, 5, 4, 3

Against West's contract of Three No Trumps, North leads a spade. West can make his contract only if he wins four tricks in clubs. After winning the first trick with the ♠ K, the right play is for West to win the ♣ K. If North and South both follow suit, West continues with the ♣ 7 and plays the 4 from the dummy if North plays an honour, but the 10 if North plays a low card.

If South follows suit, there is only one more outstanding club and it will fall under East's Ace. If North shows out on the second round of clubs, then South started with Q, J, x, x of the suit and West cannot do anything about it. The directed play, however, guarantees that he will win four tricks in the suit if North originally held Q, J, x, x of the suit.

Most important of all, however, is an ability to count the cards. It is not all that difficult, and, in the main, is largely a matter of drawing deductions from the bidding and previous play of the cards, coupled with training oneself to think along the right lines.

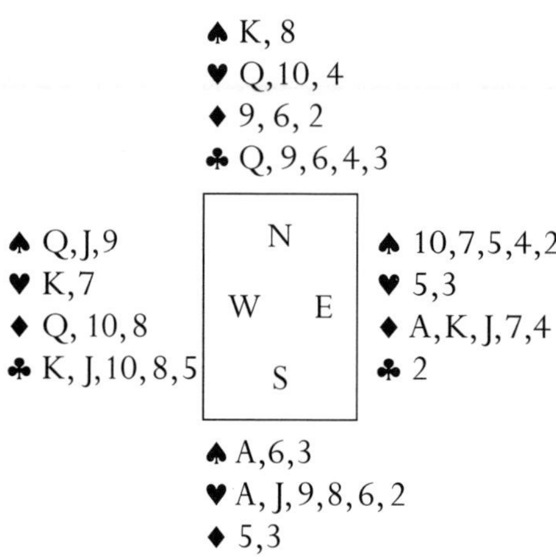

West deals at love all, and the auction is:

West	*North*	*East*	*South*
1 ♣	No Bid	1 ♦	1 ♥
2 ♦	2 ♥	2 ♠	4 ♥
No Bid	No Bid	No Bid	

West leads diamonds and East wins the first two tricks with the Ace and King of the suit. A third round of diamonds is ruffed by South with the ♥ 8.

As South has lost two tricks, it would seem that his contract is doomed, because West, by reason of his opening bid and lacking either the Ace or King of diamonds, must surely be holding the Kings of hearts and clubs.

South, however, has a partial count of the hand that will enable him to make his contract if he knows how to take advantage of it. On the assumption that West almost certainly started with three diamonds and probably five clubs, he cannot have more than five cards in spades and hearts. South, therefore, wins the ♥ A (in case the King is singleton) and when the ♥ K does not come down, he leads a spade to dummy's King, a spade from dummy to the Ace in the closed hand, and then trumps his last spade with dummy's ♥ 10. As West played the ♥ 7 under South's Ace and followed to the three rounds of spades, South may reconstruct the position as:

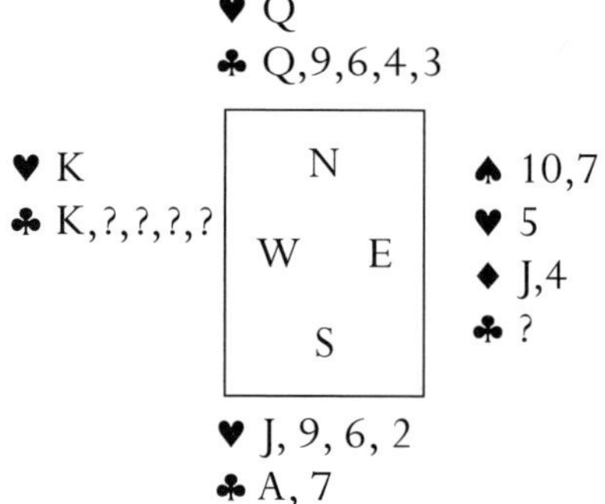

Now, by leading the ♥ Q from dummy, West is put on lead with the King, and as he must return a club, South wins two tricks in the suit.

DEFENDERS' PLAY

Leading

When the bidding period ends, and the playing period begins, the player on the left of the declarer leads to the first trick. It is only after he has led that the partner of the declarer exposes his hand on the table as dummy. It follows, therefore, that the opening lead has to be made in the dark, since the player can see only his own hand and is left to judge the best lead from it, coupled with the information that he has obtained from the bidding. The opening lead must be chosen with care. It is of great importance, because quite often the choice of a good or bad lead will decide whether or not the declarer's contract will be made.

Against a No Trump contract, if partner has bid a suit, leading it usually offers the best chance of defeating the contract, unless the player on lead holds only a singleton in the suit or he has a good suit of his own.

With two cards of partner's suit the higher should be led; with three cards the highest should be led, unless the suit is headed by the Ace, King, Queen or Jack, when the lowest should be preferred. With two honours in partner's suit the higher should be led; with a sequence (a combination of three or more cards of adjacent rank) the highest should be led. In all other cases the fourth highest should be led.

When a player leads his own suit, he should lead the fourth highest of his longest suit, unless he holds a sequence (when he should lead the highest), a long suit headed by the Ace and King and an entry in another suit (when he should lead the King), or an intermediate honour sequence, e.g. A, Q, J, x or K, J, 10, x (when the higher of the two touching honours should be led).

The reason for leading the fourth highest card of a suit is that if partner subtracts the number of the card from eleven, the remainder will be the number of higher cards held by the other three players. The Rule of Eleven.

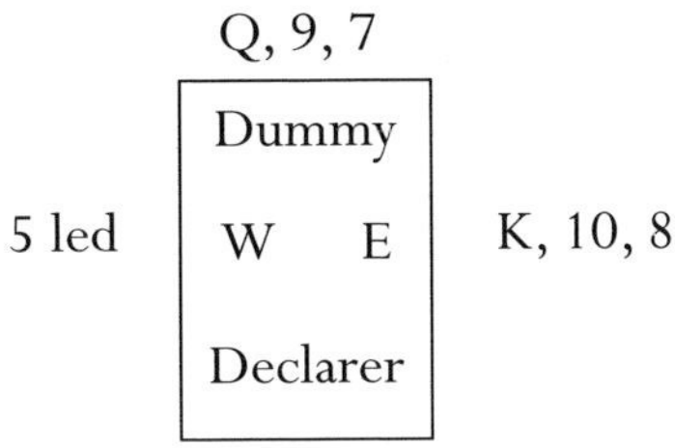

West leads the 5. As 11 - 5 = 6, and East can see six cards higher than the 5 in dummy and in his own hand, he will know that the declarer cannot hold a card higher than the 4, so that whichever card is played from dummy he can win the trick with the card just higher.

Against a suit contract it is usually best to lead partner's suit, if he has bid one. If he has not, and the player on lead has to lead from his own suit, he should give preference to leading the top card of an honour sequence. He should avoid leading a card that may cost a trick, e.g. leading the King from K, Q, x, or a card that might enable the declarer to win a trick with a card that might have been captured, e.g. leading the Ace from A, Q, x. The lead of a trump is a good lead if the bidding has suggested that the dummy will be able to trump side suits.

Play

The play of the defenders is more difficult than that of the declarer, because a defender has to combine his hand with that of the unseen one held by his partner. They have the slight advantage of a partnership language that enables them to exchange information and advice, but, for the most part, success in defence comes mainly from drawing the right deductions from the bidding, and the cards that have been played to previous tricks.

To lead the highest card of a sequence, to win with the lowest, and to follow suit as the situation dictates, is a general rule that does not need to be enlarged on. Most of the general rules for defence play, however, have been handed down from the days when whist was the fashionable game. At bridge reservations have to be made, because the bidding and the exposed dummy hand allow for modifications.

To return the suit that partner has led is not always the best play. Sometimes it is more important to take time by the forelock.

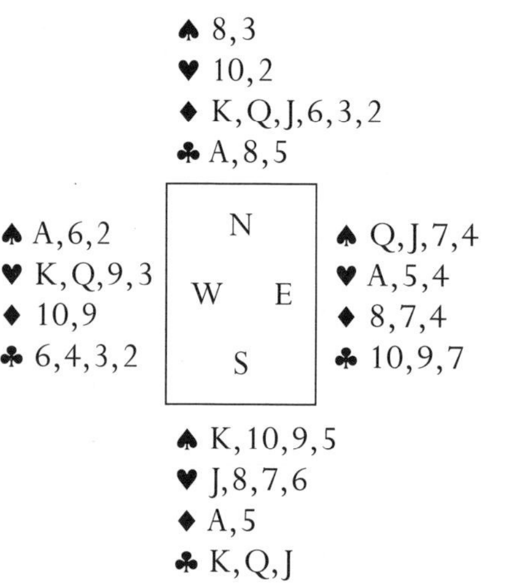

South deals and opens the auction with One No Trump (12 to 14 points) and North jumps him to Three.

West leads the ♥ 3 and East wins with the Ace. If East returns a heart, South has no difficulty in making nine tricks, because dummy's ♥ 10 protects the Jack in the closed hand and the defenders cannot win more than one trick in spades and three in hearts. With the ♥ 2 on the table, East should appreciate that his partner cannot hold more than four hearts and that they cannot be better than K, Q, 9, 3, because if they were K, Q, J, 3 he would have led the King and not the 3. As once East gives up the lead he can never regain it, he must take advantage of the time factor, the tempo, and lead the ♠ Q. The only chance of defeating the contract is to find West holding the ♠ A, and as South's bid of One No Trump postulates a maximum of 14 points, East, who holds seven points and can count 10 on the table, can count West with just enough room for the ♠ A as well as for the ♥ K, Q.

To cover an honour with an honour may be good play in many cases, but it is not when the honour has been led from a sequence.

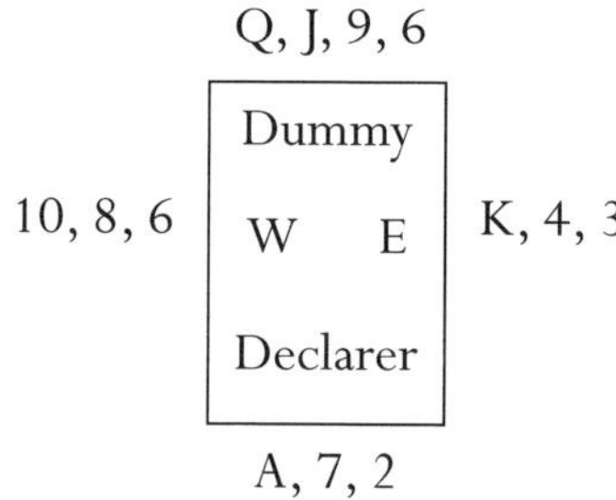

The Queen is led from dummy. If East covers with the King, the declarer will win four tricks in the suit by winning with the Ace and returning the suit to finesse against West's 10. East, therefore, should not cover. The Queen will win, but now the defenders will always win a trick in the suit because if the declarer continues with dummy's Jack, the lead is no longer from a sequence and East covers it with the King. With K, x only, East should cover the Queen, otherwise the declarer, after winning dummy's Queen may continue with a low spade (not the Jack) from the table and East's King will be wasted.

Second hand plays low; third hand plays high, is another general rule that has been handed down from the past. It is, perhaps, a rule worth remembering, because exceptions when second hand should play high are few and far between, and when third hand sees only low cards on his right, there are virtually no exceptions to his playing high.

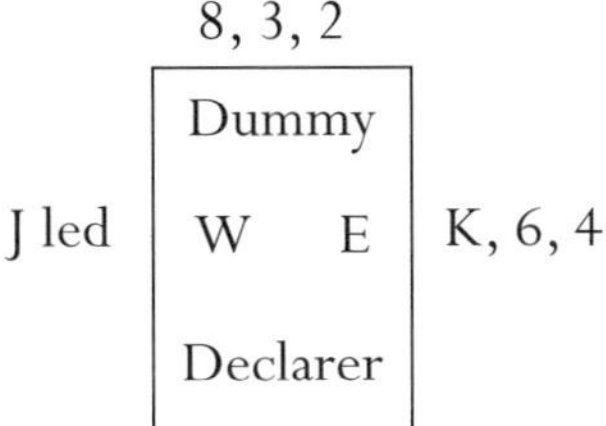

West leads the Jack. East should play the King. He knows that the declarer holds the Queen (otherwise West would have led it in preference to the Jack) and if declarer holds the Ace as well the King is doomed. East, therefore, must play on the chance that West has led from A, J, 10, x and that declarer holds Q, x, x.

A very important weapon in the armoury of the defenders is the echo or peter, sometimes called the come-on or high-low signal. Reduced to its simplest terms, when a defender plays a higher card followed by a lower one of the same suit, it is a request to partner to play the suit. In many cases a defender can afford to play the suit only once. In such a case to play a 7 or a higher card is an encouragement to partner, and to play a lower card is a discouragement to him. Against a trump contract, the high-low play in a side suit shows that a doubleton is held and that the third round can be trumped. If the play is made in the trump suit itself, it shows that three trumps are held. Against a No Trump contract, the echo shows length in the suit, usually four cards.

The defenders are frequently compelled to discard, and nearly always discarding presents them with a problem. The general rules to follow are not to retain the same suit as partner; not to discard from a suit in which you have the same length as dummy or suspect the declarer has in his hand; and never to discard so that the declarer is given information.

Counting the cards is, of course, as important to the defenders as it is to the declarer. In some ways, however, the defenders have it a bit easier. If the declarer is in a No Trump contract he will have limited his hand to an agreed number of points. It follows, therefore, that if the declarer's limit is 16 to 18 points and he has shown up with 15 points, the defenders know that he has left in his hand no more than a King or its equivalent. In much the same way, in a suit contract the declarer and his dummy will rarely hold less than eight trumps between them. It follows, therefore, that if a defender holds three trumps, he knows that his partner is probably holding not more than two.

In conclusion, it may be said that good defence consists in playing those cards that give as much information as possible to partner, and making things as easy as possible for him; by contrary, in playing those cards that give as little information as possible to the declarer and making things as difficult as possible for him. Whenever it is possible to do so, a defender should play the cards that the declarer knows are in his hand, and retain those of which he knows nothing. If all this comes as a counsel of perfection – the best Bridge players are perfectionists.

SCORING

When all 13 tricks have been played, the players record their scores, and those of their opponents, on a marker, or sheet of paper, as illustrated.

The main object is to win a rubber, which is the best out of three games. When a player makes his contract, the score for tricks won is entered below the horizontal line. All other scores are entered above this line.

A game is won when a partnership scores 100 points below the horizontal line, either in one or more deals.

A partnership that wins a game becomes vulnerable and is subject to higher bonuses if it makes its contract, and increased penalties if it fails. Vulnerability does not affect the points for winning the tricks contracted for.

If a partnership scores less than game in one deal, it is said to have a part-score

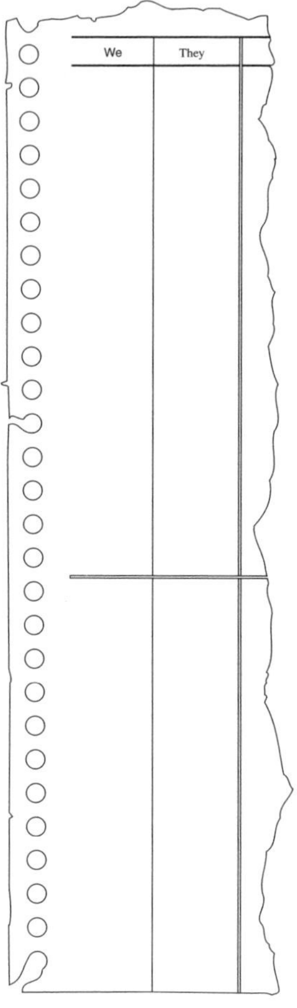

and if the opponents then score game the part-score cannot be carried forward towards the next game. When a partnership wins a game a line is drawn across the score sheet below it, and both partnerships begin the next game from a love score.

Tricks

If a partnership has bid and made its contract, it scores:

In No Trumps: 40 points for the first trick and 30 points for each subsequent trick.

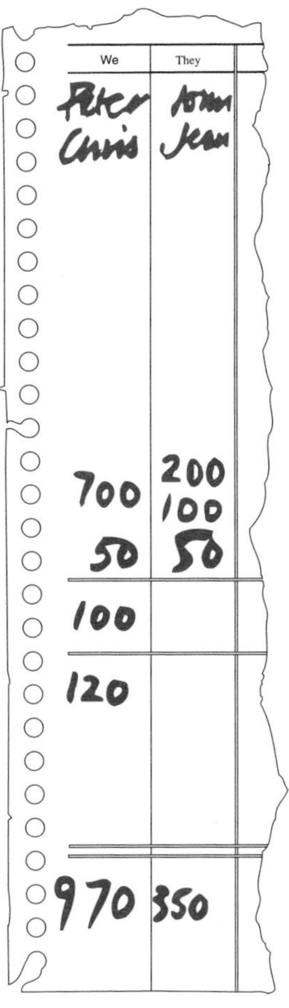

In Spades and Hearts:	30 points for each trick.
In Diamonds and Clubs:	20 points for each trick.

The scores for winning tricks are doubled if the contract has been doubled, and quadrupled if the contract has been redoubled.

If a partnership has made tricks in excess of its contract, it scores:

If undoubled:	trick value for each trick.
If doubled:	100 points for each trick if not vulnerable.
	200 points for each trick if vulnerable.
If redoubled:	200 points for each trick if not vulnerable.
	400 points for each trick if vulnerable.

If a partnership has failed to make its contract, it loses:

If undoubled:	50 points for each trick if not vulnerable.
	100 points for each trick if vulnerable.
If doubled:	100 points for the first trick; 200 points for each subsequent trick if not vulnerable.
	200 points for the first trick; 300 points for each subsequent trick if vulnerable.
If redoubled:	200 points for the first trick; 400 points for each subsequent trick if not vulnerable.
	400 points for the first trick; 600 points for each subsequent trick if vulnerable.

Bonuses

Winning rubber:	
in three games	500
in two games	700

Grand slam bid and made: vulnerable 1,500; not vulnerable 1,000.

Small slam bid and made: vulnerable 750; not vulnerable 500.
150 points if either partner holds all four Aces in a No-Trump contract, or all five honours in a suit contract.
100 points if either partner holds any four honours in a suit contract.
50 points if a partnership makes a doubled or redoubled contract.

BRINT

BRINT *was originated by J. B. Chambers in 1929. It is a hybrid of Bridge (see page 104) and Vint, the national card game of Russia.*

NUMBER OF PLAYERS

Brint is for four players.

CARDS

The full pack of 52 cards is used.

THE PLAY

Brint is played in the same way as Bridge. It has been described as Bridge with Vint scoring, because the score that counts towards game, and recorded below the line, depends entirely upon the level to which the bidding has been carried. No trumps and the suits retain their rank, but each trick (over six) at the level of One is worth 10 points, at the level of Two 20 points, and so on up to Seven when each trick is worth 70 points.

The full scoring table is set out at the top of the opposite page.

The score for tricks made is unaffected by a double, but if a doubled contract is redoubled the trick score, as well as the bonus and penalty for a doubled contract, is doubled. The bonuses and penalties are increased by 100 points each if the player is vulnerable.

A game is won by the pair that first reaches a trick score of 160 points.

The bonuses for bidding and making slams and games, and for holding honours, recorded above the line as at Bridge, are set out at the foot of the opposite page.

THE SCORING TABLE FOR BRINT

		When the declarer is not vulnerable		
		Undoubled	*Doubled*	
When the contract is at the level of:	*Each odd-trick (whether doubled or not) is worth:*	*Penalty for each undertrick*	*Bonus for contract and each overtrick*	*Penalty for each undertrick*
One	10	50	50	100
Two	20	50	50	100
Three	30	50	50	100
Four	40	100	100	200
Five	50	150	150	300
Six	60	200	200	400
Seven	70	250	250	500

THE BONUSES IN BRINT

Successful bid of Seven	1,000
Successful bid of Six	500
Successful bid of Five	250
Successful bid of Four	
vulnerable	500
not vulnerable	250
4 Aces in one hand in no trump contract	150
5 honours in one hand in a suit contract	200
4 honours in one hand in a suit contract	100

They are unaffected by vulnerability, doubling and redoubling.

CALYPSO

CALYPSO *was invented by R.W.Willis of Trinidad. It dates from the mid-1950s, and though designed on entirely new lines, inevitably borrows some of the best features of Bridge (see page 104) and Canasta (see page 128).*

NUMBER OF PLAYERS

Calypso is for four players playing in two partnerships, but can be played cut-throat by three, as described later.

CARDS

The game is played with four packs of cards (with identical backs) shuffled together, but the cards are shuffled only at the start of a game, and a player holds only 13 of them at a time.

It is a novel feature of the game that each player has his own trump suit. Spades and hearts play in partnership against diamonds and clubs. The players cut for seats and trump suits. The highest has the choice of both, and his partner takes the corresponding suit and sits facing him. The choice of a trump suit conveys no advantage; it is purely a matter of personal preference.

Thirteen cards are dealt to each player, and the dealer places the rest of the pack to his left, ready for the next dealer after the hand has been played.

THE PLAY

The object of the game is to build calypsoes. A calypso is a complete suit (from Ace to 2) in a player's trump suit.

The player on the left of the dealer leads to the first trick. Thereafter the lead is made by the player who wins a trick. When playing to a trick a player must follow suit if he can; otherwise he may either discard or trump by playing a card of his own trump suit.

A trick is won by the player who has played the highest card of the suit led, or by the player who has trumped it, or over-trumped it by playing a higher trump of his own trump suit. If two or more players play identical cards, the first played takes priority for the purpose of winning tricks, and, perhaps the most important feature of the game is that if a player leads a card of his own trump suit, he wins the trick automatically unless it is trumped by another player or overtrumped by another. To illustrate:

North ♣	East ♠	South ♦	West ♥
♥ 8	♥ J	♥ 10	♥ 3

North has led the ♥ 8, and East wins the trick because he has played the highest heart.

♦ 4	♠ 6	♦ 7	♦ 3

North has led the ♦ 4, and East wins the trick because he has trumped. South has merely followed suit to North's lead.

♥ 3	♠ 4	♦ 6	♥ J

North has led the ♥ 3, and South wins the trick, because although East has trumped, South has over-trumped. West has merely followed suit to North's lead.

♣ 9	♣ J	♣ 6	♣ 5

North has led the♣ 9 and wins the trick because clubs is his own trump suit. That East has played a higher club does not score.

♣ 6	♠ 7	♦ 9	♣ 5

North has led the ♣ 6, East has trumped, but South wins the trick because he has over-trumped.

♥ 6	♥ Q	♥ Q	♥ 10

North has led the ♥ 6, and the trick is won by East as his ♥ Q was played before South's.

When a player wins a trick, he leaves exposed on the table, in front of him, any cards that will help him to build a calypso, passes to his partner any cards that will help him to build a calypso, and discards the others, face downwards, on his right.

North (whose trump suit is clubs) leads the ♣ 4 and wins the trick:

♣ 4	♣ 6	♣ J	♣ 6

North places the ♣ 4, ♣ 6 and♣ J face upwards on the table in front of him, and discards the second ♣ 6. He then leads the ♣ 8 and the trick is:

♣ 8	♣ J	♣ 7	♦ 8

Again North wins the trick. He keeps the ♣ 7 and ♣ 8 for his calypso, passes the ♦ 8 to his partner for his calypso, and discards the ♣ J because he already has one.

The play continues until all 13 tricks have been played; the next player then deals another hand of 13 cards each.

A player may build only one calypso at a time, but once a calypso has been built the player may begin another. He may use any cards in the trick with which a calypso has been completed, but he cannot use any cards from his discard pile. These cards are dead and one object of his opponents will be to give him duplicate cards while he is building his calypso to prevent him building a second or third calypso.

The game ends when each player has dealt once. The score is then made up as follows:

For the first calypso – 500 points.

For the second calypso – 750 points For any subsequent calypso – 1,000 points	When obtained by the individual players.

For each card in an incomplete calypso – 20 points.
For each card in the discard pile – 10 points.

Partners add their totals together, and stakes are paid on the difference between the totals of the two sides.

A serious view is taken of revoking. A revoke does not become established until a player of the offending side has played to the next trick, and a revoke made in the 12th never becomes established, but if established a revoke suffers a penalty of 260 points.

SOLO CALYPSO

Solo Calypso is played by four players but each plays for himself. The play is more or less identical with the parent game, the main difference between the two is that, in Solo Calypso, the players draw cards for choice of seats and trump suits; the highest has first choice, the lowest takes what is left.

CALYPSO FOR THREE PLAYERS

This variation is played with three packs of cards and one complete suit (it does not matter which) removed from all three packs. The game consists of three deals. Each player plays for himself.

CANASTA

CANASTA *was invented in South America during the early part of the 20th century, and spread rapidly round the world soon after the Second World War. Recently it has declined somewhat in popularity, but it remains an entertaining game, and is easy to learn.*

NUMBER OF PLAYERS

Canasta is best for four players, but can be played by two or three, though not so satisfactorily.

CARDS

Two standard packs are used, together with four Jokers, making 108 cards in all.

If there are four players, each receives 11 cards. With three players each gets 13 cards, and two players get 15 cards each. Cards are dealt one at a time, clockwise round the table starting on the dealer's left. The top card of the remaining pack is then turned over to start the discard pile, and the player on dealer's left plays first. Before that, however, all the players holding red 3s put them down and draw replacement cards. The deal moves round to the left in subsequent hands.

If the card turned over by the dealer is a wild card (a Joker or a 2) or a red 3, then he turns another card to cover it, and the pack is frozen (so that wild cards and cards on the table may not be used to capture it).

THE PLAY

Canasta is a 'draw and discard' game, like Gin Rummy – each player in turn draws a new card from the pack, and then discards one card, trying to form his hand into matching sets while doing so. It is sometimes possible, instead of drawing a new card from the pack, to capture the entire discard pile, and much of the skill in the game goes towards manoeuvring so as to be able to do this.

If a player is able to form a legal combination including the top card (that most recently discarded) of the discard pile, then he may do so instead of drawing a new card from the pack, and having done so he takes the rest of the discard pile into his hand. The combination may involve the last discard, cards in the player's hand and combinations previously played on the table by him, but may not involve any of the previous discards. Having made his capture, and picked up the discard pile, the player may put down any further cards he wishes – these may include some of the cards he just picked up – and then discards to complete his turn. There is no restriction on discarding captured cards immediately.

It is illegal to make a capture using a wild card unless the player already has a wild card on the table before the start of his turn – otherwise the last discard must be matched with at least two plain cards of the same rank.

If a black 3 is discarded, it is always illegal for the next player to capture the pile – the main function of black 3s in the game is to act as safe discards.

If a wild card is discarded, then the pile is said to be 'frozen'. It is illegal for the next player to capture the pile, as with black 3s, but there are two additional restrictions which continue to apply while the pile is frozen (i.e. until it is next captured): it becomes illegal to combine the top discard with cards already played on the table – the combination must be with cards from the hand; and it becomes illegal to capture the pile using a wild card, even if a wild card has already been used.

It is normally illegal to put down a set of black 3s, but this may be done by a player on the turn in which he goes out. A set of black 3s may never contain any wild cards.

If the last card in the pack is a red 3, then the player drawing it does not discard on that turn.

Wild cards (see overleaf) may be added to completed canastas, provided that they do not break the law that no more than three wild cards should appear in one combination. If wild cards are added to a natural canasta, though, it becomes a mixed canasta and only scores 300 points (it may sometimes be necessary to do this in order to go out).

In the early part of the game, the main objective is to be the first to capture the discard pile. Having done this, a player can often continue capturing the pile for the rest of the hand – each time he picks up he recycles the safe discards that he has already used.

When a player has succeeded in making the first capture, and has the chance to go out, it is often good not to do so, but to keep going and make a really huge score. If, on the other hand, his opponent has made the first capture, he will often be stuck simply feeding him cards, and it is usually best to try to go out as soon as possible. Going out is a defensive tactic.

Black 3s should not be discarded too early. Capturing a pile of three of four cards is not very devastating, and it is usually better to hang on to black 3s until the pile gets bigger and a safe discard is really needed.

SCORING

The object of the game is to be the first to 5,000 points.

In order to score, a combination of cards must be laid face up on the table. The only combinations allowed are sets of cards of the same rank – there are no sequences in Canasta. A combination must contain at least three cards. Jokers may be used to substitute for 'plain' cards, and 2s may also be used like Jokers in this way. We refer to 2s and Jokers collectively as 'wild cards'. However, a set may never contain more than three wild cards, or fewer than two plain cards.

A set of seven or more cards is called a canasta, and scores a large bonus. 'Natural' canastas (containing no wild cards) score more than 'mixed' ones. Examples are illustrated in the above illustration opposite.

The 3s are covered by special rules. Black 3s may not normally be used for anything constructive – but are nevertheless good cards to hold – (see page 129). Red 3s are bonus cards - a player holding one should immediately lay it face up in front of him and draw another card to replace it.

The first time a player puts scoring cards on the table, they must add up to at least a minimum value, which depends on how close that player's side is to the target of 5,000 points. This total may be achieved using several combinations, for example a total of 50 can be achieved with a set of three 5s (15) and a set of two Kings with a 2 (40). If (as usually happens) the first scoring cards are played while capturing the discard pile, this total must be achieved using only the last discard and cards in the player's hand.

The requirements depend on the side's score as follows:

Negative score	*No restriction*
0–1,495	50 points required
1,500–2,995	90
3,000–4,995	120

This requirement is quite independent of any red 3s laid down. Examples of sets giving the points required are shown in the lower illustration opposite.

When the game ends, each side adds up the value of their cards face up on

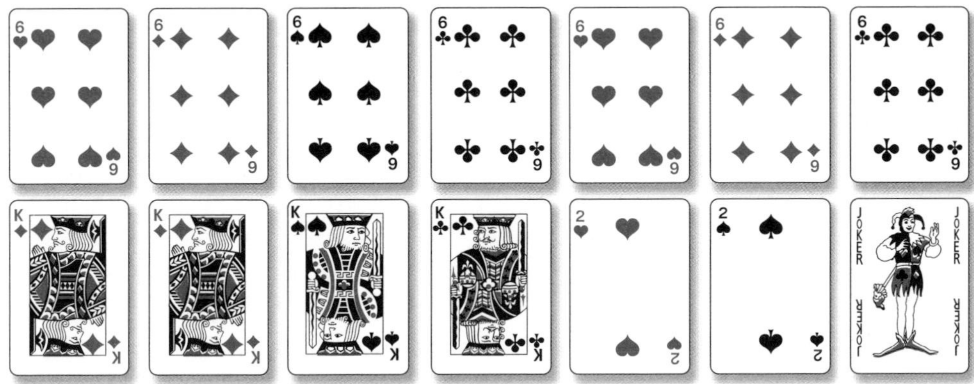

A natural canasta (this one worth 535 points) and a mixed canasta (worth 430).

the table, then subtracts the value of any cards remaining in their hand. Scores are as follows:

7, 6, 5, 4 or black 3	5
K, Q, J, 10, 9 or 8	10
Ace	20
2	20

(continued overleaf)

Sets satisfying the requirements of a first combination, worth 50, 90 and 120 points.

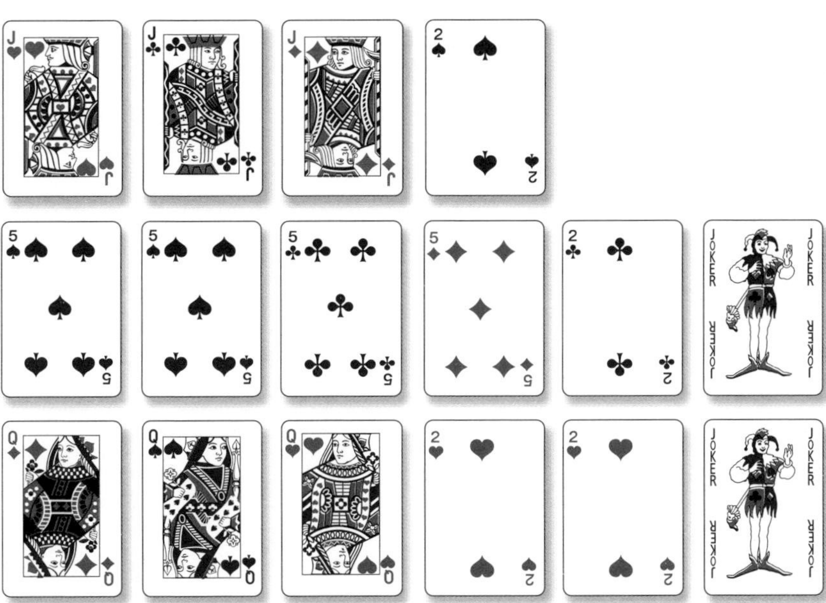

Joker	50
Red 3	100
All four red 3s	800
Mixed canasta	300
Natural canasta	500
Going out	100
Going out 'concealed'	200

FOUR PLAYERS

With two or three players, each plays individually, but four players play as two pairs of partners. Partners sit opposite each other. In this case partners keep their scoring cards separately, and they must meet the requirements to score a certain number of points with their first combinations and to make one canasta before going out separately, but they can add cards to each other's combinations. The end of the game comes when both partners on one side have gone out (or when the pack runs out). It is normally good play for the two partners to go out in immediate succession, and in order to be able to achieve this it is legal to say 'Shall I go out, partner?' before discarding. If your partner says 'Yes' then you are obliged to go out.

CINCH

CINCH *is a game from the All Fours family which was very fashionable in the USA before Bridge began to oust most other card games of the type. It has some of the attractions of Bridge, like the bidding, without all the conventions, and is a game of skill well worth playing. It is also called Double Pedro and High Five.*

NUMBER OF PLAYERS

Cinch is best as a game for four players, as described first, playing in two partnerships, with the partners sitting opposite each other. It can be played by two to six players, and there are variants such as Auction Cinch, described later.

CARDS

The full pack of 52 cards is used. Cards rank from Ace (high) to 2 (low), with the exception of the 5 of the same colour as the trump suit, which is also regarded as a trump and ranks between the 5 and 4. For example, if clubs are trumps, the trump suit ranks as follows:

♣ A, K, Q, J, 10, 9, 8, 7, 6, 5; ♠ 5; ♣ 4, 3, 2

The 5 of the trump suit is called Right Pedro and the 5 of the same colour is called Left Pedro. Cards in the trump suit have values to players winning them in tricks as follows: Right Pedro five points, Left Pedro five points, Ace (known as 'high') one point, 2 (known as 'low') one point, Jack one point and 10 (known as 'game') one point. On each deal there are thus 14 points at stake.

Players draw cards to determine partners, the two highest playing against the two lowest, the highest being dealer. The dealer shuffles, and the player to his right cuts. The dealer deals nine cards to each player in threes, clockwise from his left. The remaining cards are set aside face down for the moment - they will be used later.

THE PLAY

The object is to take tricks containing the scoring cards, and the trump suit is decided by the side which undertakes to make the most tricks, so the next stage is a round of bidding.

Beginning with eldest hand (to dealer's left), each player in turn makes a bid, or passes. Each player is allowed only one bid. A bid consists of the number of points that the player proposes to make in play, with his partner's help. He can decide which suit is to be trumps, but at the bidding stage he does not announce the suit. The minimum bid is one, and the maximum is 14 (the total points available). Once a player has bid, any subsequent bid must be for a higher number of points. When the round of bidding has finished, the player who bid the highest names the trump suit (he is not allowed to consult his partner, and no signals must pass between them). The side bidding highest has now contracted to make the stated number of points with the trump suit as specified.

As with Bridge, expert players have certain systems of bidding, of which the following is an example:

With a Pedro, bid five to show it.

With A, x, x, or A, x, x, x, bid six.
With A, K, bid seven.
With A, K, J, x, x, bid 11.
With A, K, Q, x or better, bid 12.

Should the first three players all pass, the dealer names the trump suit, but he is not obliged to contract to make a certain number of points.

The trick-taking part of the game commences with each player holding six cards, so the next stage is one of discarding, but each player is given the opportunity to improve his hand by drawing new cards from the remaining pack.

Beginning with the eldest hand, each player discards as many cards as he wishes, face up, and is given by the dealer, face down, enough cards from the top of the pack to bring his hand up to six cards. A player must make at least three discards (if he discards only three, he draws no new cards). No player may discard a trump, unless he is dealt with seven or more, in which case he must discard at least one to bring his hand to six cards.

When it is dealer's turn to discard, he simply 'robs the pack'. He is entitled to look at all the remaining cards and decide which he wishes to take into his hand and to discard accordingly. He announces how many cards he is taking but need not show his discards except that, should there be more than six trumps in his hand and the pack, he must show the other players the trumps that he is forced to discard or not to take into his hand.

In practice, each player will keep all his trumps and usually discard all his non trumps, because, as all the point-scoring cards are trumps, it is impossible to win any points with a plain card.

With all the players reduced to six cards, the trick-taking phase begins. The player who named the trump suit is called the maker. The maker leads to the first trick. Subsequently the winner of a trick leads to the next.

When a trump is led, each player must follow suit if able, and must discard if unable. When a plain suit is led, a player able to follow suit may do so or *trump*, but may not discard. A player unable to follow suit may discard or trump.

The object of each side is to take as many tricks containing point-scoring cards as possible, with particular reference to the contract.

When all six tricks have been played, each side counts the number of points won. If the making side has made its contract, i.e. has scored at least the number of points bid by the maker, the side with the higher total of points wins the difference. For example, if the maker bids six and scores nine against the opponents' five, his side scores four points. Notice that even when the maker achieves his contract, it is not necessarily his side which scores. If he bids six and makes six, his opponents having scored eight, his opponents score two points for the difference.

If the making side fails to make its contract, the opponents score the number of points they made, plus the value of the contract. For example, if a side contracts to make ten points, and makes only eight, the opponents score the six points they made plus the ten points of the contract, i.e. 16 points.

When all players have passed, and the dealer names trumps without bidding, the side scoring the more points scores the difference.

Game is to 51 points.

The illustration opposite shows the nine cards dealt to each hand by the dealer (South).

West bid five (to tell his partner he held a pedro); North, with ♣ A, K bid seven; East, with his strong diamonds, bid eight (if his partner's 5 was red, he was certain to make seven, and almost certain to make eight, even without any cards he might draw), while South could only pass.

East announced diamonds as trumps, much to the satisfaction of West, whose ♥ 5 was now certainly worth five points.

West, North and East each discarded all their non-trumps, and drew three, three and two cards respectively. South robbed the pack, finding only one trump, the ♦ 2, and drawing two cards.

The new hands are in the illustration on page 136.

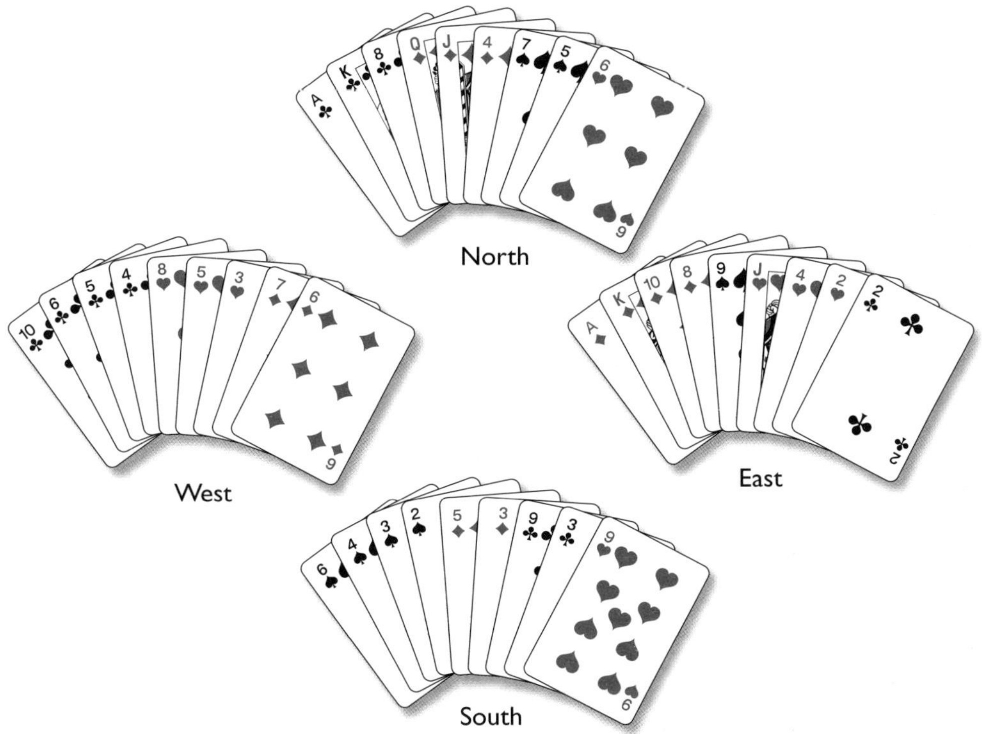

Play might proceeds as follows:

East	*South*	*West*	*North*
♠ 8	♠ 2	♦ 6	♠ 10
♦ A	♦ 3	♥ 5	♦ 4
♠ A	♥ 9	♦ 7	♣ Q
♦ 10	♣ 3	♠ J	♦ 9
♦ K	♦ 2	♥ Q	♦ Q
♦ 8	♦ 5	♣ J	♦ J

East led low and his partner West played ♦ 6 to prevent North winning the trick and five points should he hold a Right Pedro (West knows he himself has Left Pedro). This play, of third player playing a trump higher than 5 is known as 'cinching the trick'. Knowing that his partner held ♦ A, West led Left Pedro for East to take, and West cinched again at trick 3. East played ♦ 10 at trick 4, because he would not mind losing it to either ♦ Q or ♦ J in the South hand, as he would be sure then of taking the last two tricks and capturing Right Pedro. It would not have helped North to play ♦ Q or ♦ J at trick four – East would play low and win the last two tricks, conceding no more than six points. At trick 5 East leads the ♦ K knowing he will lose the last trick but that his opponents cannot contribute more than six points to it. East/West thus take eight points, achieve their contract, and score the difference between the two totals, i.e. two points.

It is as well to remember that of the 24 cards in play, 14 will be trumps, and that a player holding four trumps will find at least one other player holding as many. However, it is more important to hold the high trumps than length. A player whose hand consists of six low trumps might not win a point. It is necessary to win at least one Pedro to take the balance of points, and a player can lead a Pedro to a partner holding the master trump, as in the second trick in the example hand on page 135.

It frequently does not pay to draw trumps, a tactic that is frequently used in other trick-taking games, including Bridge. Had East, with his strong trumps, attempted to do so in the example hand, the play might have proceeded as follows:

East	*South*	*West*	*North*
♦ A	♦ 3	♥ 5	♦ 4
♦ K	♦ 2	♦ 6	♦ 9
♠ 8	♠ 2	♦ 7	♠ 10
♦ 8	♥ 9	♠ J	♣ Q
♠ A	♣ 3	♥ Q	♦ J
♦ 10	♦ 5	♣ J	♦ Q

Each side took seven points, meaning East/West failed to make their contract, and North/South therefore scored their points, seven, plus the value of the contract, eight, making 15.

It is as well to note that a side failing to make a contract must lose at least 15 points, while if it makes the contract it cannot score more than 14. This suggests bids should be made with

caution. On the other hand, naming the trump suit is a big advantage.

CINCH WITH A WIDOW

In this variation of the game, after the first three cards to each player, the dealer deals each player a widow of four cards, which remains on the table before them. Players bid as before, whereupon each player picks up his widow. The maker then names the trump suit, and each player discards seven cards to bring his hand to six. Any player who discards a trump or trumps must show them to the other players. Play then proceeds as before.

CUT-THROAT CINCH

Cinch can be played by two, three, five or six players, each playing for himself. With two or three players, the dealer does not rob the pack, but discards and draws like the other players. Obviously not all the trumps will be in play, which makes the bidding and play more of a gamble. With five or six players, each player is dealt six cards only, so draws the same number of cards as he discards.

In Cut-throat Cinch, the maker plays against the other players. With two players, scoring is as in the parent game, which has two sides. With three to six players, if the contract is made, the side with the most tricks (either the maker or the combined opponents) scores the difference between the two totals (each opponent of the maker scores the difference if his side wins). If the contract is not made, each opponent scores the amount of the bid plus the number of points scored by himself personally.

AUCTION CINCH

Auction Cinch, also called Razzle Dazzle, is for five or six players, each playing for himself. Six cards are dealt to each player in bundles of three. Bidding is as in the parent game described, and when the highest bidder has named trumps, each player in turn discards all his non-trumps, and takes cards sufficient to bring his hand back to six cards. The maker then specifies a card not in his hand (usually the highest trump he is missing). The holder of the card acknowledges that he has it, and the two play in opposition against the others. The partner does not change seats, even if sitting next to the maker. The scoring of the points in play is as in the parent game. If the maker and his partner make their contract, the side with most points scores the difference between the two totals. Each player on the winning side scores the difference. If the contract fails, each player on the noncontracting side scores the points specified in the contract plus the points he himself took in tricks.

Some schools prefer that the partner of the maker does not acknowledge that he holds the specified card. This brings surprise and uncertainty to the play while detracting from the skill factor.

EUCHRE

EUCHRE *is a game that has always been more popular in the New World than in the Old. It was made famous by Bret Harte's witty* Plain Language from Truthful James.

NUMBER OF PLAYERS

The standard game is suitable for from two to six players, but is best for four, two playing in partnership against the other two, as described first.

CARDS

The game is played with a 32-card or short pack, that is the standard pack from which the 6s and lower cards have been removed. The cards rank in the order from Ace (high) to 7 (low) with the exception that the Jack of the trump suit (Right Bower) takes precedence over all other trump cards, and the Jack of the suit of the same colour (Left Bower) ranks as the second highest trump.

There is some advantage in dealing. The players, therefore, must draw cards to decide who shall deal. The highest takes first deal, which, thereafter, passes round the table clockwise.

The dealer gives five cards to each player either in bundles of two then three, or three then two. It does not matter which, but he must be consistent throughout the game. The rest of the pack is placed face downwards in the centre of the table, and the top card is turned face upwards.

THE PLAY

The turned up card is the potential trump suit, and, beginning with the player on the left of the dealer, each player in turn has the option of either refusing or accepting it.

To accept it as the trump suit the opponents of the dealer say: 'I order it up'; the dealer's partner says: 'I assist'; and the dealer himself says nothing, but accepts by making his discard. To refuse the card as the trump suit, the opponents and partner of the dealer say: 'I pass'; the dealer signifies refusal by taking the card from the top of the pack and placing it, face upwards, partly underneath the pack.

If all four players pass on the first round, there is a second round. Beginning with the player on the left of the dealer, each player in turn may now either pass, or name any suit he likes (other than that of the turned up card) as trumps. If all four players pass on the second round, the hand is abandoned and the deal passes.

When the trump suit has been settled, the player who has named it (the maker) has the right to go it alone, but he must announce his intention to do so before a card has been led. His partner places his cards face downwards on the table, and takes no active part in the hand. The maker (he is the only one of the four who can go alone) plays his hand against the two opponents in partnership. If he wins the march (all five tricks) he scores four points; if he wins three or four tricks he scores one point; if he is euchred (i.e. fails to win at least three tricks) the opponents score two points each.

Euchre is a trick-taking game. The player on the left of the dealer (or the player on the left of the maker if he is going it alone) leads to the first trick. Thereafter the player who wins a trick leads to the next. A player must follow suit to the card led if he can, if not he may either discard or trump.

If the partnership that made the trump suit wins the march it scores two points; if it wins three or four tricks it scores one point; if it is euchred the opposing side scores two points. It is customary for each side to keep the score by using a 3 and a 4 (cards not needed in the game) as shown in the illustration. The side that is first to score five points wins.

TWO-HANDED EUCHRE

With two players, the game is played in exactly the same way as the parent game except that the pack is reduced to 24 cards by removing the 8s and all

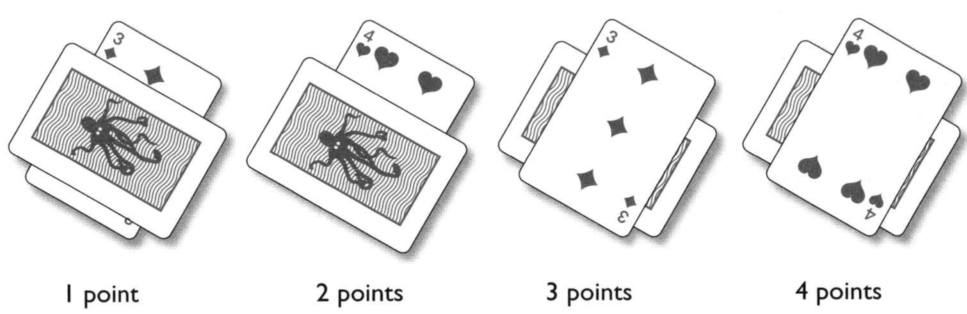

the lower cards, and, obviously, there is no declaration of going it alone.

THREE-HANDED EUCHRE

The game for three players is played in the same way as the parent game except that the maker of the trump suit plays against the other two in partnership. If the maker wins the march he scores three points; if he wins three or four tricks he scores one point; and if he is euchred each of his opponents scores two points.

CALL-ACE EUCHRE

This is a variation that may be played by four, five or six players, each playing for himself. It is played in the same way as the parent game with the exception that the maker has the option of either playing for himself or of calling for a partner by saying: 'I call on the Ace of …' and he names a suit. The player who holds the Ace of this suit then plays in partnership with the maker against the other players, but he does not reveal himself. It follows, therefore, that until the Ace is played, and it may not be in the deal, everyone except the holder of the Ace (if it is in play) is left to guess where his interest lies.

The scoring is rather different from that of the other variations as fundamentally the game is all against all. For winning the march a lone player scores one point for every player in the game; in a partnership hand the score is two points each if three or four players are in the game, and three points each if five or six players are in the game. For winning three or four tricks a lone player scores one point; in a partnership hand both players score one point. If a lone player or a partnership is euchred the other players score two points each.

HEARTS

HEARTS *and its several variations is very similar in principle to Black Maria (see page 72) because the object of the game is to avoid taking tricks that contain certain specified cards.*

NUMBER OF PLAYERS

The game may be played by any reasonable number of players, but it is at its most interesting and skilful as a game for four, each playing for himself.

CARDS

The full pack of 52 cards is used. However, when the game is played by three players or by more than four, low cards are removed from the pack to reduce it to a number that allows every player to be dealt the same number of cards.

All the cards are dealt out, singly and clockwise.

THE PLAY

The play follows the general principles of trick-taking games: the player on the left of the dealer leads to the first trick, and thereafter the winner of a trick leads to the next; a player must follow suit to the card led if he can, and if he cannot he may discard any card that suits him.

The ♠ Q and all cards of the heart suit are penalty cards. Every deal is a separate event, and the usual method of settling is to debit the player who wins the ♠ Q 13 points, and those who win hearts one point for each card.

A revoke is heavily penalized. A player may correct a revoke if he does so before a card is led to the next trick; otherwise the revoke is established, the hand is abandoned, and the revoking player is debited all 26 points.

The game is not a difficult one, but it calls for an ability to count the cards, read the distribution and visualize possibilities. It is instructive to consider the play in the deal illustrated overleaf if West has to make the opening lead and assumes that the best lead is the ♥ 2 because one of the other players will certainly have to win the trick.

Against West's opening lead of the ♥ 2 the play will be short and sharp, and West will come off worst of all because good play by his opponents will saddle him with the ♠ Q.

West	*North*	*East*	*South*
♥ 2	♥ 4	♥ 3	♥ 8
♥ 6	♥ 7	♥ 10	♥ 9
♥ Q	♥ K	♥ J	♦ A
♥ A	♥ 5	♠ Q	♦ Q

A more experienced West would have kept off leading a heart. It is probable that his best lead is the singleton diamond, because he has nothing to fear in the spade suit, and, once he has got rid of his diamond, he gives himself the best chance to get rid of the dangerous ♥ A and ♥ Q.

DOMINO HEARTS

In this version of the game, the players are dealt only six cards each, and the rest of the pack is placed face downwards in the centre of the table. The player on the left of the dealer leads to the first trick, and the game is played in the same way as the parent game except that if a player cannot follow suit to a card that has been led he must draw a card from the stock, and continue to do so until he draws a card of the suit led. Only after the stock has been exhausted may a player discard from his hand if he cannot follow suit to a lead.

Play continues until all the cards have been taken in tricks, each player

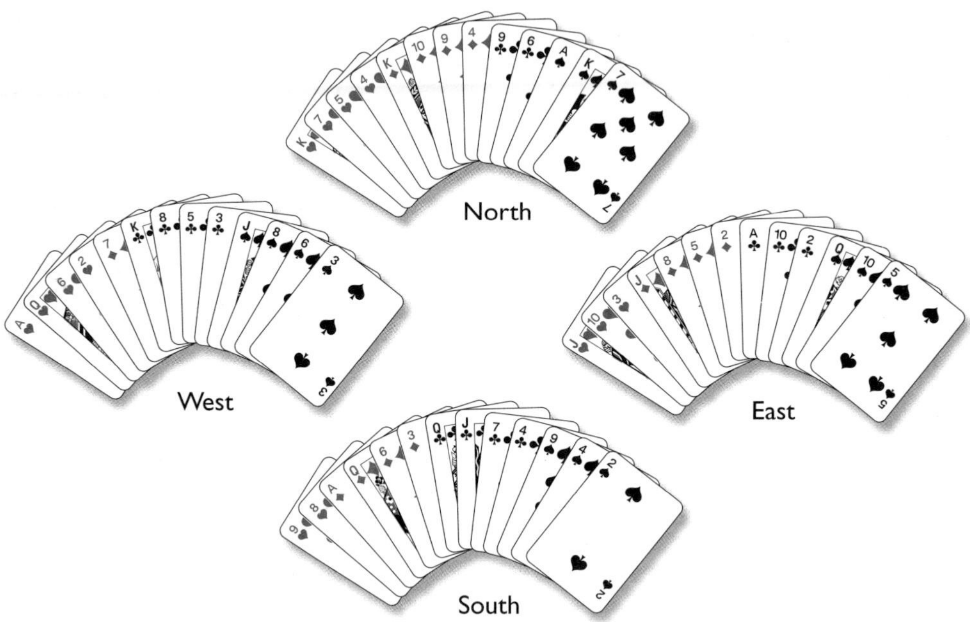

dropping out as his hand is exhausted. If a player wins a trick with the last card in his hand, the next active player on his left leads to the next trick. The last player to be left in the game retains all the cards left in his hand, and takes into it any cards that may be left in the stock.

The ♠ Q is not a penalty card; only cards of the heart suit are, and one point is lost for each one taken in a trick or left in the hand of the surviving player.

GREEK HEARTS

In this version, as in Black Maria (see page 72) each player, before the opening lead is made, passes three cards to his right-hand opponent and receives three from his left-hand opponent.

As in the parent game the penalty cards are the ♠ Q and all cards of the heart suit, and the penalties for winning them are the same; if, however, a player wins all the hearts and the ♠ Q, instead of losing 26 points, he receives 26 points from each of the other players.

The game calls for some considerable skill, because, before passing on his cards, a player has to decide whether he will take the easy road and play to avoid winning penalty cards, or try for the big prize by winning them all. The decision is never an easy one, because discarding a high heart one may be helping an opponent to a better score, and oneself lose a good score if one receives the ♠ Q and a couple of high hearts from one's left-hand opponent.

HEARTSETTE

This variation is played in the same way as the parent game, but with a widow hand. If three or four take part in the game the ♠ 2 is removed from the pack, and if five or six take part the full pack is used.

When there are three players, each one is dealt 16 cards; when four, 12 cards; when five, ten cards and when six, eight cards. The remaining cards are placed face downwards in the centre of the table.

The player on the left of the dealer leads to the first trick and whoever wins it takes the widow and discards from his hand to reduce it to the proper number of cards. No one else sees the widow nor the cards that have been discarded.

The play continues in the same way as in the parent game with the same penalty cards and penalties for winning them.

OMNIBUS HEARTS

Also called Hit the Moon, this version combines most of the features that have been added to the parent game. Like it, it is at its best when played by four people, each playing for himself.

Thirteen cards are dealt to each player, and before the opening lead is made each player passes three cards to his right-hand opponent and receives three from his left-hand opponent.

The play is the same as in the parent game. All the hearts and the ♠ Q are penalty cards, but a novel feature is that the ♦ 10 is a bonus card. A player loses one point for every heart that he wins and 13 points if he wins the ♠ Q. By contrast, he wins 10 points if he takes the ♦ 10, and if he wins all the hearts, the ♠ Q and the ♦ 10 (known as hitting the moon – no longer such a feat as it once was) he wins 26 points instead of losing 16.

The game is won by the player who has the highest plus score, or lowest minus score, when one player reaches a score of –100.

The game calls for skill both in discarding to the right-hand opponent and in the play. Good discarding is dictated by the fact that only the club suit is neutral and harmless. Every heart is a liability and top spades are dangerous (unless adequately supported by low cards) and though top diamonds are advantageous the low ones may simply be liabilities.

In play it is necessary to aim at forcing the lead into the hand of the least dangerous opponent. All the time temporary partnerships must be formed. If the score stands at: North – 83, East – 41, South + 32, West + 47, it is obvious that West will be doing his best to win the game by driving North to –100 as quickly as possible. A skilful South, therefore, will enter into a tacit partnership with North to try and save him by prolonging the game and so give himself more time to pull ahead of West. The strategy is perfectly proper because both players are acting in their own interests.

PIP HEARTS

This version is played in the same way as the parent game, but the ♠ Q is not a penalty card and the penalty for winning a heart is increased to the pip value of the card, the court cards counting Jack 11, Queen 12, King 13 and Ace 14.

PINOCLE

PINOCLE *(spelt without the 'h' as explained on page 58) has much in common with Bezique (see page 11) and it originated in Europe. It has, however, long since crossed the Atlantic, and, if we exclude the ubiquitous Bridge (see page 104) it shares with Poker (see page 177) the honour of being the national card game of the USA.*

NUMBER OF PLAYERS

In its original form, Pinocle is a game for two players and is described on page 58. American card-players, however, have developed a number of variations suitable for more than two. The most popular is Auction Pinocle, a rather remarkable game because though fundamentally a game for three it makes a better game when played by four. The four-handed game is described first. However, the game can be played by more than four players, and a version is described later.

CARDS

From two packs of 52 cards, the 8s and below are removed, leaving a pinocle pack of 48 cards. The cards rank Ace, 10, King, Queen, Jack, 9.

The dealer deals 15 cards face downwards to the (three) active players, either in five threes, or in three fours and one three, and after the first round, three cards face downwards to the table as a widow hand.

THE PLAY

In every deal only three players take an active part. If four play (as is recommended) the dealer deals no cards to himself; and if five wish to take part the dealer deals no cards to the second player on his left as well as none to himself. The inactive players, as they are called, take no part in the bidding and play, but participate in the settlement.

A bid is a contract to score either by melds, by cards won in tricks, or by both, the number of points named, and the player on the left of the dealer makes the first bid which must be at least 300. After this, each player in turn may either pass or make a higher bid. Bids must be in multiples of ten, and once a player has passed he cannot reenter the auction. When two players pass a bid the player who made it becomes the bidder, his bid the contract, and the other two players his opponents.

If the opening bid of 300 is passed by the other two players the bidder may concede defeat by throwing in his cards without looking at the widow. He pays three units to the kitty (but nothing to his opponents) and the deal passes to the next player.

If the bid is for more than 300, or if the bidder does not wish to concede defeat, he shows the widow to his opponents and takes the cards into his hand. He then names the trump suit, and places his melds on the table in front of him. They are scored for as follows:

Class A

A, 10, K, Q, J of trumps	150
K, Q of trumps (royal marriage)	40
K, Q of plain suit (common marriage)	20

Class B

Pinocle (♠ Q and ♦ J)	40
Dis (9 of the trump suit)	10

Class C

Ace of each suit	100
King of each suit	80
Queen of each suit	60
Jack of each suit	40

No card may be used twice in melds of the same class, but the same card may be used in two or more melds of different classes. Only the bidder melds. He then discards face downwards (buries) three cards from his hand in order to reduce it to 15 cards: later the cards that he discards will be counted for him as won in a trick. The discards must be made from the cards in his hand, not from those in his melds, but before he leads to the first trick he may change the cards that he has discarded, change the melds and the trump suit.

When the bidder and his opponents have agreed on the value of the melds and how many more points (if any) he needs to fulfil his contract, the bidder leads to the first trick. If, however, he thinks he will not be able to make his contract he may concede defeat (called *single bete*) and pay to the players, active and inactive, the value of his bid.

When playing to a trick a player must follow suit if he can, and if he cannot he must play to win the trick by trumping or overtrumping it. Only if he has no card of the suit led and no trump card may he discard. If a trump is led, the subsequent players must try to win it. A trick is won by the highest card of the suit led or the highest trump if the led card has been trumped. If two identical cards are played the one first to be played wins the trick, if the trick is to be won by the card.

When all the tricks have been played, the players score for each Ace 11 points, each 10 ten points, each King four points, each Queen three points, each Jack two points, and for winning the last trick ten points. It gives a total of 250 points to be won in tricks.

Every deal is a separate event and settlement is made before the next deal begins. It is usual to reduce the contract to units on which payment is made.

Contract	*Unit value*	
300–340	3	
350–390	5	If spades
400–440	10	are trumps
450–490	15	the unit
500–540	20	values are
550–590	25	doubled
600 and more	30	

The bidder pays double (called *double bete*) if his score for melds and cards taken in tricks fails to equal his contract; he receives if his score equals or exceeds his contract, but he does not receive more than the unit value of his contract.

Payment is made to and from all players, active and inactive, and to and from a kitty if the contract is for 350 or more.

The kitty is a separate account and is the common property of the players. They make good any deficiency if it owes, and divide any surplus when the game breaks up.

PARTNERSHIP PINOCLE

This game, as its name implies, is played by four players, two playing in partnership against the other two. The partners face each other.

The 48-card Pinocle pack is used. The dealer gives each player 12 cards in sets of three, and turns up the last card dealt to himself to determine the trump suit. In turn, beginning with the player on the left of the dealer, any player who holds the dis (9 of the trump suit) may exchange it for the turned-up card, and if the dealer turns up the dis as the trump card he scores ten points. Each original holder of a dis, whether or not he exchanges it with the turned-up card, scores ten points for it.

The players expose their melds on the table in front of them, and, in addition to the melds for Auction Pinocle, melds and the scores for them are as follows:

Double trump sequence A, 10, K, Q, J	1,500
Double pinocle	300
All eight Aces	1,000
All eight Kings	800
All eight Queens	600
All eight Jacks	400

When the players have shown their melds and scored for them, they return them to their hands. No meld, however, finally counts unless the partnership wins a trick, and when a trick is won both partners score for their melds.

The player on the left of the dealer leads to the first trick, and the play continues as in Auction Pinocle.

When all 12 tricks have been played, the players count ten for every Ace and 10 won, five points for every King and Queen, and ten points for winning the last trick. As in Auction Pinocle the total is 250 points.

The game is won by the partnership that first wins 1,000 points in melds and cards won in tricks, but if both partnerships reach 1,000 or more points in the same deal the game continues to 1,250 points, and, if it happens again, to 1,500 points, and so on.

At any time during the game a player may claim that he has scored 1,000 points or more and won the game. Play is brought to an end and the claim is verified. If the claim is found to be correct his partnership wins the game; if the claim is found to be wrong his partnership loses the game. In either case, what the opposing side has scored makes no difference to the result.

PARTNERSHIP PINOCLE FOR MORE THAN FOUR PLAYERS

This game is played with two 48-card Pinocle packs shuffled together. Six players form two partnerships of three players each sitting alternately at the table: eight players form two partnerships of four players each sitting alternately.

The dealer gives 16 cards to each player in bundles of four each (12 cards each if there are eight players) and turns up the last card dealt to himself to denote the trump suit.

The game is played in the same way as Partnership Pinocle, but in addition to the melds above, melds and the scores for them are as follows:

Meld	Score
Triple trump sequence A, 10, K, Q, J	3,000
Double trump sequence A, 10, K, Q, J	1,500
4 Kings and Queens of the same suit	1,200
3 Kings and Queens of the same suit	600
2 Kings and Queens of the same suit	300
Quadruple pinocle	1,200
Triple pinocle	600
Double pinocle	300
15 Aces, Kings, Queens and Jacks	3,000
12 Aces	2,000
12 Kings	1,600
12 Queens	1,200
12 Jacks	800
8 Aces	1,000
8 Kings	800
8 Queens	600
8 Jacks	400

FIREHOUSE PINOCLE

This version is played as a partnership game for four, two playing in partnership against the other two. Twelve cards are dealt to each player. As in Auction Pinocle the trump suit is bid for; the player on the left of the dealer bids first; each player has only one bid or pass, and the minimum bid is 200. The bidder makes the trump suit and leads to the first trick. Game is won by the partnership that first reaches 1,000 points. The score of the bidder's side is counted first, and the game is played to the end. A partnership cannot concede defeat.

CHECK PINOCLE

This version was developed some say in Texas, out of Firehouse Pinocle, and is considered one of the best and most skilful of all partnership games, not excluding Bridge.

The game is played by four players, two playing in partnership against the other two, with the regular 48-card Pinocle pack.

Twelve cards are dealt to each player three at a time, and each player in turn, beginning with the player on the left of the dealer, must either bid or pass. The lowest bid is 200, subsequent bids must be made in multiples of ten, and once a player has passed he may not re-enter the bidding. None of the first three players may make a bid unless he holds a marriage (King and Queen of one suit) but if all three pass the dealer must bid at least 200 and he does not need a marriage to do so; if, however, he wishes to make a higher bid than 200 he must hold one. The bidding ends when a bid has been passed by the three other players, and the bidder then names the trump suit.

The players then expose their melds on the table. The melds and the scores for them are the same as in Auction Pinocle (see page 145) and the partners add the values of their melds together and record the total as a single score.

Some melds have what is known as a check (chip) value: a trump sequence (Ace, 10, King, Queen, Jack) and four aces each of a different suit are each worth two checks, four Kings, four Queens, four Jacks each of a different suit, and double pinocle are all worth one check. Check values are paid across the table as the game proceeds.

The players return the melds to their hands, and the play is the same as in Partnership Pinocle. When all 12 tricks have been played a partnership scores 10 points for every Ace and 10 that it has won, 5 points for every King and Queen, and 10 points if it has won the last trick.

The bidding side adds these points to those that it has already scored for its melds, and if the total is at least equal to the bid the contract has been made and the partnership scores for everything that it makes; if its total is less than its bid the amount of its bid is deducted from its score. In all cases the opposing side scores for everything that it makes.

At the end of each deal a partnership is entitled to checks on the following scale:

Contract	*If made*	
200–240	2 checks	If the contract is defeated the bidding partnership pays double checks to the opposing partnership
250–290	4 checks	
300–340	7 checks	
350–390	10 checks	
400–440	13 checks	
and 3 added checks for each series of 50 points.		

A partnership that wins all 12 tricks in a deal receives four checks; for winning the game it receives seven checks and one check for each 100 points (or part thereof) by which the score of the winning partnership exceeds that of the losing partnership; and if the losing partnership has a net minus score, the winning partnership receives an additional four checks.

The game is won by the partnership that first scores 1,000 points. The score of the bidding partnership is counted first, and as the game is over when it reaches 1,000 points, the opposing partnership scores nothing in the final deal.

POLIGNAC

POLIGNAC *is sometimes called Quatre Valets or Four Jacks.*

NUMBER OF PLAYERS

Polignac is for four players.

CARDS

A 32-card pack is used, i.e. a standard pack with 6s, 5s, 4s, 3s and 2s removed.

Eight cards are dealt face downwards to each player.

THE PLAY

The player on the left of the dealer leads to the first trick. Thereafter the player who wins a trick leads to the next. A player must follow suit to the card led, if he can, otherwise he may discard.

The object of the game is to avoid taking tricks that contain a Jack, and one point is lost for every Jack taken, with the exception of the ♠ J (Polignac) which costs the winner two points.

The usual method of scoring is to play a pre-arranged number of deals (that should be a multiple of four) and he who loses the least number of points is the winner.

It is a very simple game, but some skill is called for particularly in choosing the best card to lead after a trick has been won, correct discarding when unable to follow suit, and deciding whether or not to win a trick when the choice is available.

SLOBBERHANNES

If we may judge by its name, Slobberhannes is either of Dutch or German origin. It is a very simple game played in the same way as Polignac. The only difference is that a player loses one point if he wins the first trick, one point if he wins the last, one point if he wins the trick containing the ♣ Q, and a further one point (making four points in all) if he wins all three penalty tricks.

QUINTO

QUINTO *is unusual in that three of the suits are trumps. It is a trick-taking game which gives the opportunity for skilful play.*

NUMBER OF PLAYERS

Quinto is for four players, who play in two partnerships, partners sitting opposite each other. It can be adapted for three players, as described later.

CARDS

The standard pack of 52 cards plus the Joker is used. The cards rank from Ace (high) to 2 (low). The Joker has a points value, as will be seen, but does not rank in trick-taking value. The suits also have their rank as follows: hearts (high), diamonds, clubs, spades. Each card in a suit can be used to trump over a card in a lower suit. Thus only spades cannot be used as trumps, spades being the lowest suit. In other words the cards rank from ♥ A (high) down to ♠ 2.

The dealer deals the top five cards to the table in front of him. These are known as the 'cachette'. The remaining 48 cards are dealt clockwise one at a time to the four players, so each has 12 cards.

THE PLAY

Players draw for partners, the two lowest playing against the two highest, the lowest of all being the dealer (cards for this purpose rank as above, so there cannot be any ties). The dealer shuffles and the opponent to his right cuts. After each hand the deal passes to the left.

After examining his hand, each player in turn, beginning with eldest (the player to dealer's left), may double, which doubles the value of all the tricks. When a player has doubled, a succeeding opponent may redouble, which has the effect of quadrupling the value of each trick. A player cannot redouble a double by his partner.

Each trick, if undoubled, is worth five points, if doubled 10, and if redoubled, 20.

Once the value of a trick is decided, eldest leads to the first. Each player in turn must follow suit if possible. If unable to, he may trump with a card of any higher suit or he may discard. It is, of course, impossible to trump a heart, since hearts is the highest ranking suit, or, by the same token, to discard on a spade.

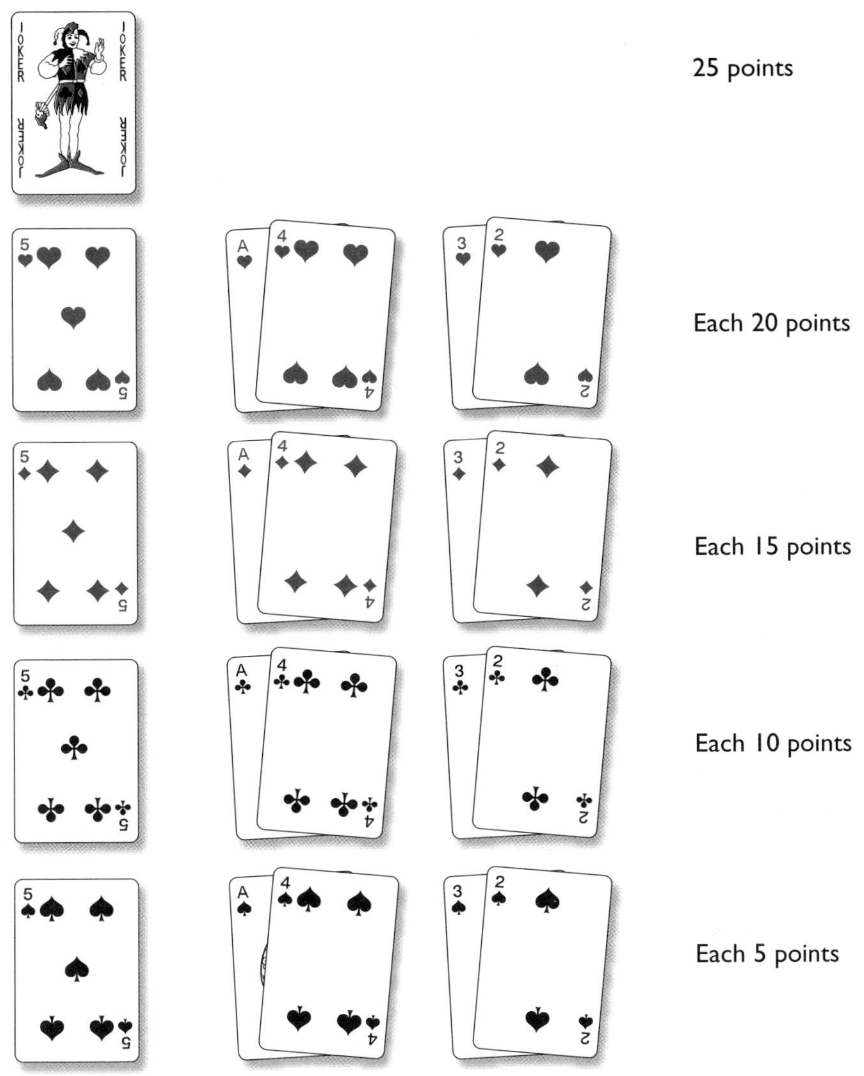

A trick is won by the highest value card it contains. The Joker has no trick-taking value, and can be played by its holder whenever he wishes, irrespective of whether or not he can follow suit. If the Joker is led, succeeding players can play whatever card they wish, the trick, as usual, being won by the highest card played.

As well as points for each trick, there are bonus points for taking tricks containing certain cards. The Joker, known as Quint Royal, is worth 25 points. The 5 of each suit, or any pair of cards totalling five, are Quints (for which purpose Ace counts as one, thus Ace, 4 and 2, 3 are Quints) and winning a Quint in a trick scores points according to the suit. The illustration on page 151 gives the values of each of the bonuses. To score for the Quints Ace, 4 and 2, 3 the cards must be taken in the same trick.

The winner of a trick leads to the next. The winner of the last trick takes the cachette, which is regarded as an extra trick and scores accordingly, including scoring for any Quints or Quint Royal it might contain.

Two running scores are kept, one for each partnership. All scores for Quint Royal or Quints are entered on the score sheet as they are made, while the scores for tricks are added at the end of each hand. The partnership which scores 250 points first wins the game. It is usual to play a rubber of best of three games. The scores of each game in the rubber (which might be of two or three games) are added together for each partnership and the side which won the rubber adds 100 points. If the game is played for stakes, the losing partnership pays the winning partnership according to the difference between the two totals at an agreed unit per ten points, any odd five points being disregarded.

An example deal is shown in the illustration opposite. Dealer is South. None of the players has a very strong hand, but East, with prospects of making four tricks himself (with ♥ K, Q, J, and ♠ A, and a possible small trump on a diamond lead) and also of taking the cachette, decides to take a chance and double. South does not redouble.

West, assuming that his partner holds ♥ A, is tempted to lead the Joker immediately and score his side 25 points, but luckily decides it would be more prudent to wait until he knows his partner is certain to win a trick. So he can do no better than lead an unadventurous spade. In view of North's spade holding, this works beautifully for East, who is able to score a Quint on the first lead. Play proceeds as follows:

West	*North*	*East*	*South*
♠ 8	♠ 4	♠ A	♠ 7
♣ Q	♣ K	♣ 2	♣ 7
♣ 6	♣ A	♣ 3	♣ 4
♣ 10	♣ 9	♠ 3	♣ J
♠ 10	♠ 5	♠ 6	♠ 2
♥ 6	♥ A	♥ K	♥ 3
♦ 4	♦ A	♥ 5	♦ 7
♠ J	♣ 8	♠ Q	♦ 5
♦ K	♦ 3	♠ 9	♦ Q
Joker	♦ 6	♥ Q	♥ 7
♥ 8	♦ 8	♥ 4	♥ 10
♦ 2	♦ 9	♥ J	♥ 9

East's double was fully justified, as by making sure of the last trick he picked up the cachette, making seven tricks to six in his side's favour. The last trick also contained a Quint, the ♣ 5.

Eight Quints were scored. To East/West: Joker; ♥ 5; ♣ 5; ♠ 5; ♦ A, 4; ♠ A, 4; total 80 points. To North/South: ♦ 5; ♣ A, 4; total 25.

So on the first hand, East/West, with tricks worth ten points each, made a total of 150 points to North/South's 85.

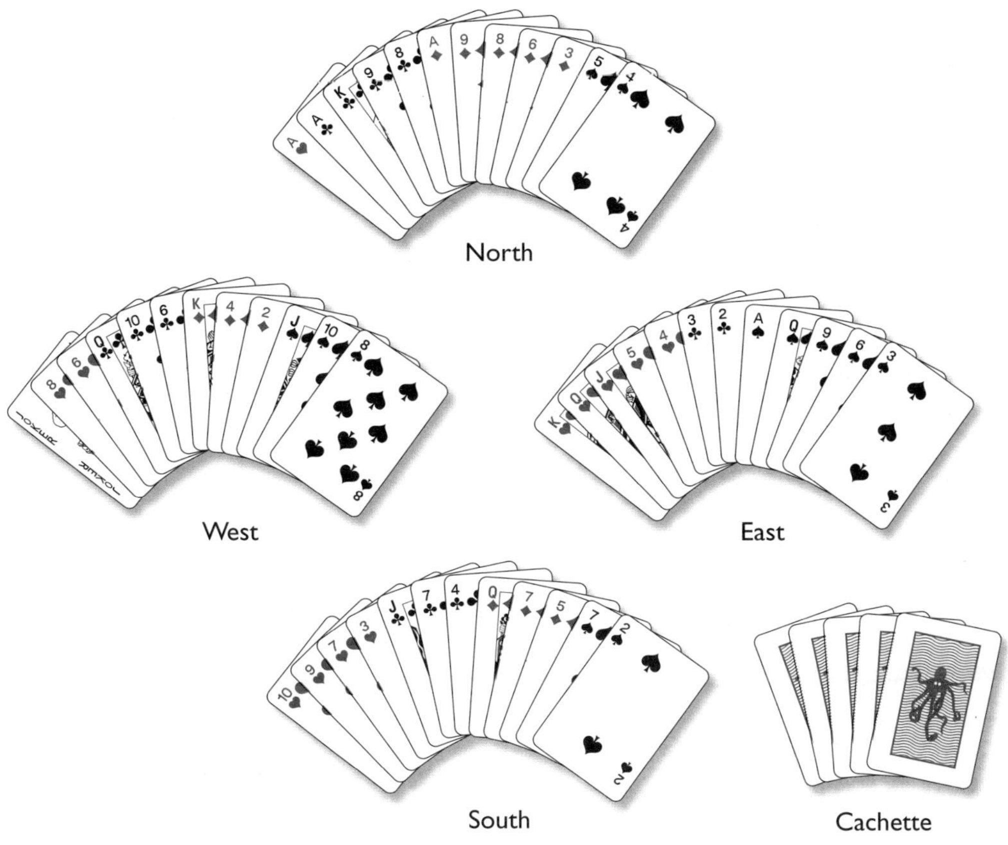

QUINTO FOR THREE PLAYERS

Quinto is one four-handed game which can be played very well by three: indeed some people prefer the game with three. Two players play in partnership against a third. Dealer is decided by the method described above, and the first dealer is the player with the dummy, and he remains the player with the dummy for the whole game. The dummy is the hand opposite him, his opponents sitting either side of him and dummy. After the first hand, the deal passes clockwise.

The dealer, on the first hand, must look at his dummy hand first, and can double or redouble either of his opponents on the strength of it. He cannot double or redouble on his own hand, because he will by then have seen both his hands. Similarly, when one of his opponents deals, the player with the dummy must look first at the hand which will lead to the first trick, and can double on it but any doubling or redoubling must be completed before the player with the dummy looks at his second hand.

Before the lead to the first trick, the dummy is displayed on the table, and the player with the dummy operates both his hands.

Because the player with dummy is regarded as having an advantage, his opponents are given a start of 25 points towards game. Each game is regarded as separate (i.e. rubbers are not played) and it is usual to play games in sets of three, so that each player has a turn to have the dummy.

SOLO WHIST

SOLO WHIST, *usually just called Solo, is based on the ancient game of Whist (see page 158) but it includes a bidding principle and each player plays for himself. It is a betting game.*

NUMBER OF PLAYERS

Solo Whist is a game for four players, and cannot satisfactorily be played by any other number.

CARDS

The full pack of 52 cards is used.

Thirteen cards are dealt to each player in three bundles of three cards each, and the last four cards singly. The dealer turns up the last card to indicate the trump suit.

THE PLAY

Each player in turn, beginning with the player on the left of the dealer, must either pass or make a bid. The bids (declarations) are:

Proposal. The player who makes a Proposal asks for a partner with the object of making eight tricks in partnership with him against the other two players. In turn, any other player may Accept, and the two play as partners from the seats in which they are sitting. The declaration of Proposal and Acceptance is usually called Prop and Cop.

Solo is a declaration to win five tricks against the other three players.

Misère is a declaration to lose all 13 tricks. The hand is played without a trump suit.

Abundance is a declaration to win nine tricks against the other three players; the declarer chooses his own trump suit. A player who wishes to play abundance with the turned-up suit as trumps may overcall with Royal Abundance, but the stake value of the bid remains unchanged.

Open misère is a declaration to lose every trick, and after the first trick has been played with his cards exposed on the table in front of him. There is no trump suit.
Declared abundance is a declaration to win all 13 tricks with a trump suit of his own choice.

Every bid must be higher than the previous one, and with the exception of the player on the left of the dealer, who may accept a proposal after passing, no player may re-enter the bidding once he has passed. The bidding ends when a bid has been passed by the other three players.

If the final bid is Declared abundance, the declarer leads to the first trick. Against any other declaration the opening lead is made by the player on the left of the dealer. The play follows the general principles of trick-taking games: a player must follow suit if he is able to, otherwise he may either discard or trump, and the winner of a trick leads to the next.

Stakes are scaled to the value of the bids:

Proposal and Acceptance	2 units*
Solo	2 units
Misère	3 units
Abundance	4 units
Open misère	6 units
Declared abundance	8 units

* Proposal and Acceptance does not carry equivalent stakes to Solo because they are paid by and received from two players, whereas in Solo (and higher declarations) they are paid to and received from three players.

Solo is a combination of whist and nap(oleon). It is a fairly simple game, and by far the simplest of the declarations is Proposal and Acceptance. As no player will propose without some strength in trumps, the partnership hardly ever fails to make eight tricks. It is a notoriously dull contract, therefore, and most modern players reject it.

The declaration of Solo is another that is fairly easy to win, though it must never be forgotten that the player has to compete against three. It is unwise to bid Solo without a good trump suit, and the dealer is in the ideal position to bid it with success because he plays last to the first trick: it gives him the best chance to win it and make an immediate attack on the trump suit.

Misère is not such an easy declaration as it may seem. A five-card suit, unless it contains the 2, is likely to spell defeat. If a player holds 7, 6, 5, 4, 3 of a suit he will usually be defeated if another holds four of the suit including the 2.

Abundance should not be attempted without a very good trump suit, and Declared abundance is best avoided by any except an experienced player.

South deals the cards in the illustration overleaf and turns up the ♠ 2.

West	*North*	*East*	*South*
Solo	Misère	Abundance	Open misère
Pass	Pass	Pass	

West's Solo is the obviously correct bid. He cannot fail to win at least five

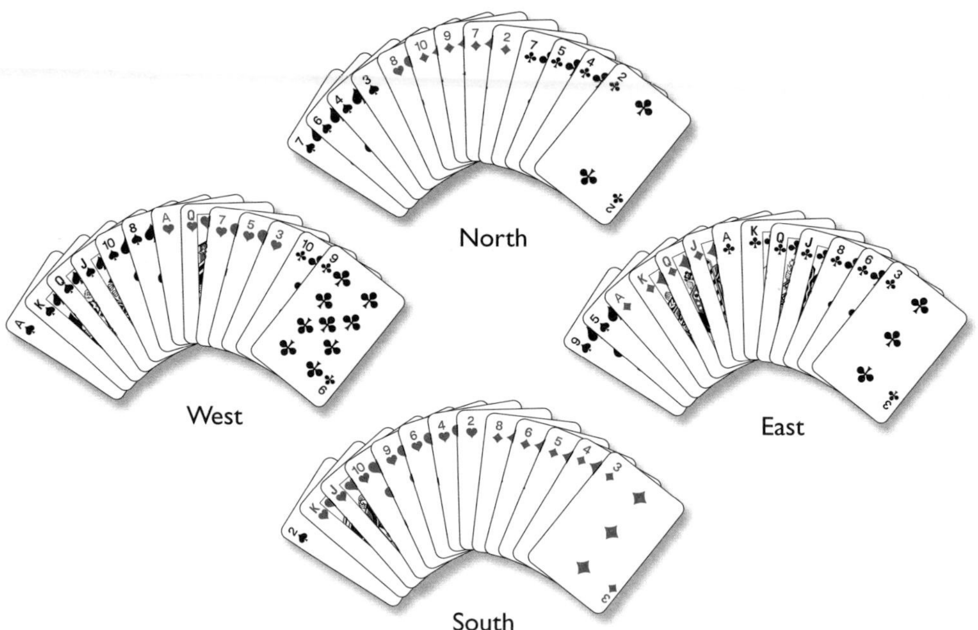

tricks and it is too much to expect the hearts to develop three tricks to make Abundance a good call.

North's Misère is optimistic. Had he been left to play it, the opening lead of a heart would have broken him out of hand.

East's Abundance is a certainty with 11 tricks (and needing only nine) for the taking of them.

South's Open misère is not to be advised. As already pointed out, a five-card suit missing the 2 is a danger spot. As it happens it is the heart suit that proves his downfall.

West leads the ♣ 10, and the play is:

West	*North*	*East*	*South*
♣ 10	♣ 7	♣ J	♥ K
♣ 9	♣ 5	♣ A	♥ J
♠ A	♣ 4	♣ 3	♥ 10
♥ A	♥ 8	♦ A	♥ 6

The position is down to the situation shown in the illustration opposite.

South is doomed because West wins the ♥ 7 and ♥ 5 (on which South plays the ♥ 4 and ♥ 2) and continues with the ♥ 3 which South must win with the ♥ 9.

AUCTION SOLO

As Solo is limited to a mere handful of declarations, the variation known as Auction Solo is much to be preferred, because it permits of a larger number of declarations and, therefore, makes a more interesting and skilful game. In ascending order the declarations are:

Proposal and Acceptance.
Solo of Five in own suit.
Solo of Five in trump suit.
Solo of Six in own suit.
Solo of Six in trump suit.
Solo of Seven in own suit.

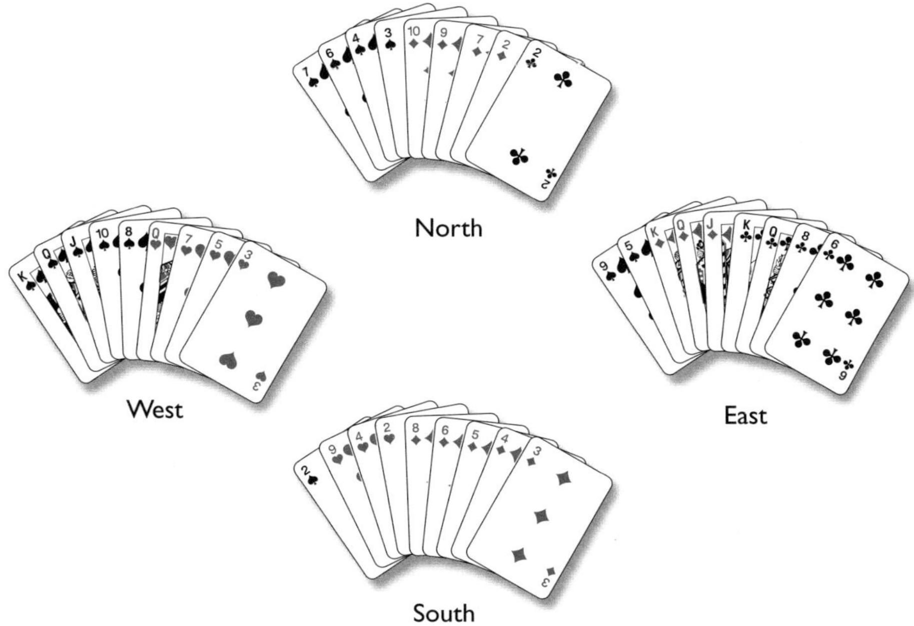

Solo of Seven in trump suit.
Solo of Eight in own suit.
Solo of Eight in trump suit.
Misère.
Abundance of Nine in own suit.
Abundance of Nine in trump suit.
Abundance of Ten in own suit.
Abundance of Ten in trump suit.
Abundance of Eleven in own suit.
Abundance of Eleven in trump suit.
Abundance of Twelve in own suit.
Abundance of Twelve in trump suit.
Open misere.
Declared abundance with no trump suit (bidder has the lead).
Declared abundance in the original trump suit (bidder does not have the lead).

Such, at least, are the declarations in the original version of the game, but modern players do not recognize all of them. Proposal and Acceptance are nearly always omitted, as are Solo of Five in own suit, and Declared abundance in the original trump suit.

Once the players have agreed on which declarations are admissible and which not, the game is played in the same way as the parent game.

Settlement is made in the following way:

Proposal and Acceptance

For success: receive 6 units each plus 1 unit for each overtrick.

For failure: pay 6 units each plus 1 unit for each undertrick.

Solo

For success: receive 6 units from each player plus 3 units for each overtrick.

For failure: pay 6 units to each player plus 3 units for each undertrick.

Misère

For success: receive 12 units from each player.

For failure: pay 12 units to each player.

Abundance

For success: receive 18 units from each player plus 3 units for each overtrick.

For failure: pay 18 units to each player plus 3 units for each undertrick.

Open misère

For success: receive 24 units from each player.

For failure: pay 24 units to each player.

Declared abundance

For success: receive 36 units from each player.

For failure: pay 36 units to each player.

The stake values of Solo and Abundance are unchanged whether the contract is for five, six, seven or eight, or nine, ten, eleven or twelve tricks.

Overtricks and undertricks count from the number of tricks that are contracted for.

The method of scoring appears to encourage underbidding. In practice, however, it is not so and as first bidder a player would be well advised to declare his full strength at once, especially if his hand is worth no more than six tricks. With six tricks in a plain suit a player should bid it at once, no matter what his position at the table, but if the tricks are in the original trump suit it is reasonable to bid only a Solo of Five: he may get away with it, and, if not, a Solo of Six in the trump suit will overcall an opponent's Six in a plain suit. The penultimate player should make it a rule to bid his hand to the limit; if he does not the last player will do so and then there may be no second chance.

WHIST

WHIST *developed out of the 16th century game of Triumph. At first its practice was confined to the lower classes, but in 1718 it was taken up by a party of gentlemen, Lord Folkestone among them, who met at the famous Crown Coffee House, and they, with the help of Edmond Hoyle, introduced the game to fashionable society. At this time the game was known as whisk: soon after it was changed to whist in order to underline the silence in which it was proper to play the game.*

During the 18th and 19th centuries it was by far the most popular card game of the English-speaking nations, but at the close of the 19th century it lost much of its popularity because of the introduction of Bridge. It is, however, still extensively played.

NUMBER OF PLAYERS

Whist is played by four players, in two partnerships.

CARDS

The standard pack of 52 cards is used, the cards ranking from Ace (high) to 2 (low).

The partners sit facing each other. The deal passes in clockwise rotation. Thirteen cards are dealt singly to each person, and the dealer exposes the last card to denote the trump suit. He takes it into his hand after he has played to the first trick.

THE PLAY

The player on the left of the dealer leads to the first trick. Thereafter the player who wins a trick leads to the next. A player must follow suit to the card led if he can; if not he may either discard or trump.

The object of the game is to win a rubber (best out of three games), and a game is won when one side has won five points. The first six tricks (the book) do not count for scoring: a side scores one point for each trick that it wins over six. The Ace, King, Queen and Jack of the trump suit are known as honours, and any side that is dealt all four of them scores four points, and any three two points. If, however, at the beginning of a deal a side has a score of four points it cannot score for honours.

Skill at whist is largely a matter of playing in close collaboration with one's partner, and estimating from the cards held and those that have been played, the most likely position of those that remain to be played.

To this end, there are a number of recognized plays which should be departed from only under special circumstances, to be learnt by experience. It is, for example, good tactics for the second player to play low and the third high; a player should not finesse against his partner; and if an opponent plays an honour it is usually profitable to play a higher honour on it.

A player who holds five or more trumps in his hand should make it a rule to lead one; and if a player fails to lead a trump and wishes his partner to do so, he calls for the lead of one by first playing an unnecessarily high card in a suit and following it with a low card in the same suit.

The lead is a good opportunity for a player to give his partner information about his hand, and the leads listed in the table overleaf are standard practice and should be known to all players.

In plain suits

Holding	*1st lead*	*2nd lead*
A, K, Q, J	K	J
A, K, Q	K	Q
A, K, x and more	K	A
A, K	A	K
K, Q, J, x	K	J
K, Q, J, x, x	J	K
K, Q, J, x, x and more	J	Q
A, x, x, x, and more	A	4th best of remainder
K, Q, x and more	K	4th best of remainder
A, Q, J	A	Q
A, Q, J, x	A	Q
A, Q, J, x, x and more	A	J
K, J, 10, 9	9	K (if A or Q falls)
Q, J, x	Q	
Q, J, x, x and more	4th best	

In the trump suit

Holding	*1st lead*	*2nd lead*
A, K, Q, J	J	Q
A, K, Q	Q	K
A, K, x, x, x, x, x and more	K	A
A, K, x, x, x, x	4th best	

Lacking any of these combinations the fourth highest of the longest suit should be led.

With the hands shown opposite the mechanics of the game can be illustrated (opposite).

South deals and turns up the ♠ 4 to denote trumps.

West leads the ♦ 5, and the play is:

West	*North*	*East*	*South*
♦ 5	♦ J	♦ A	♦ 3

West leads the fourth highest of his longest suit, commonly called fourth-best. East wins with the ♦ A. It would be finessing against his partner if he played the ♦ Q. In the event it makes no difference, because East has no better play than to return his partner's suit, and it is proper to lead the highest from an original holding of three.

♦ 2	♦ 7	♦ Q	♦ K

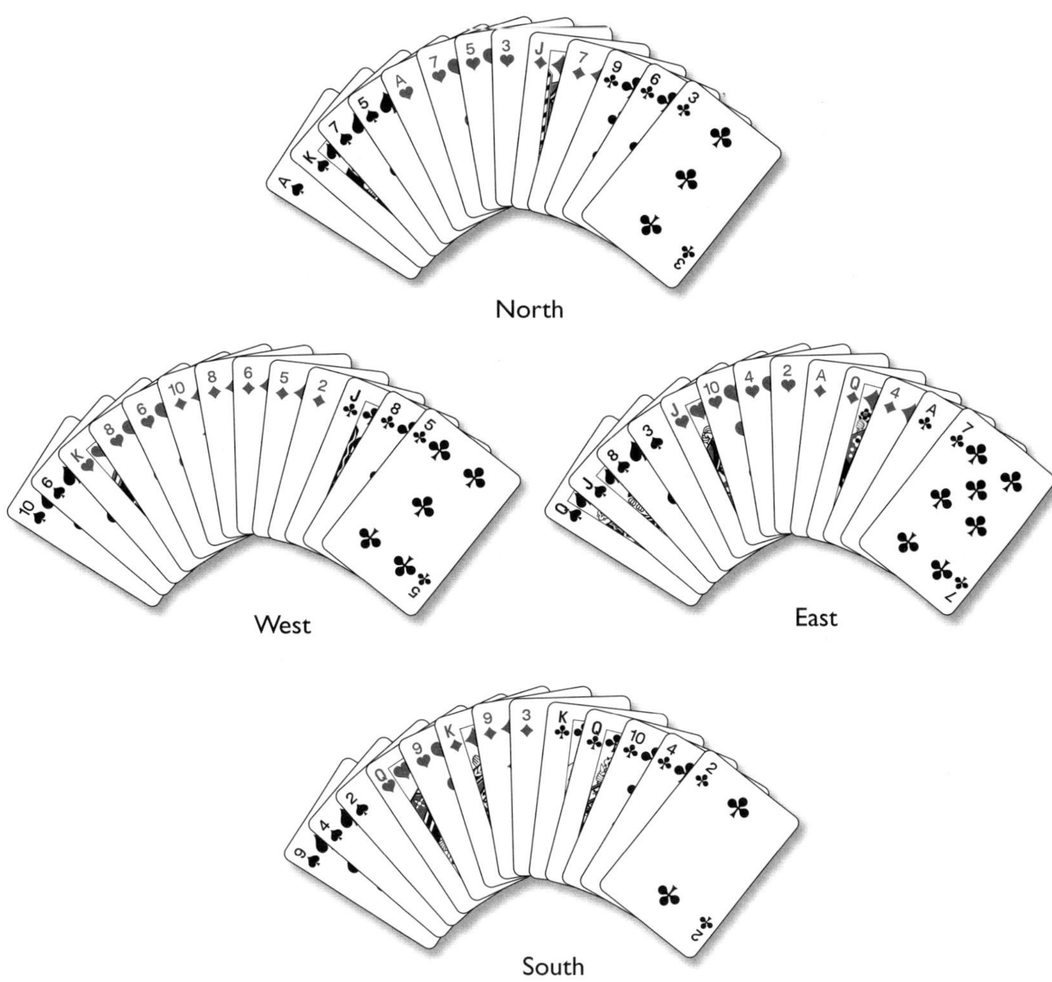

South, therefore, wins the second trick, instead of the first, with the ♦ K.

West	*North*	*East*	*South*
♣ 5	♣ 3	♣ A	♣K
♣ 8	♣ 6	♣ 7	♣ Q

East has no better lead than the ♣ 7. He knows that South holds the ♣ Q, because without it South would not have led the ♣ K at the previous trick, but it offers a chance of trumping if West can take the lead early in the play.

West	*North*	*East*	*South*
♦ 10	♠ 5	♦ 4	♦ 9
♠ 6	♠ A	♠ 3	♠ 2
♠ 10	♠ K	♠ 8	♠ 4
♣ J	♣ 9	♥ 2	♣ 2

North has no better lead than the ♣9.

West	*North*	*East*	*South*
♦ 8	♥ 3	♠ J	♣ 4
♦ 6	♠ 7	♠ Q	♠ 9

East pulls the remaining trumps.

♥K	♥ A	♥ J	♥ Q

The end position is now as below.

It is North's lead. North and South have won six tricks, East and West five tricks. North, therefore, leads the ♥ 5. If East wins with the ♥ 10 his side will win the odd trick as West will win the last trick with the ♥ 8. North's only hope is that East will make the mistake of playing the ♥ 4, because then South will win with the ♥ 9 and the last trick with the ♣ 10.

West	*North*	*East*	*South*
♥ 6	♥ 5	♥ 10	♥ 9

East makes no mistake.

♥8	♥ 7	♥ 4	♣ 10

East and West, therefore, have won the odd trick and score one point. There is no score for honours as both sides held two.

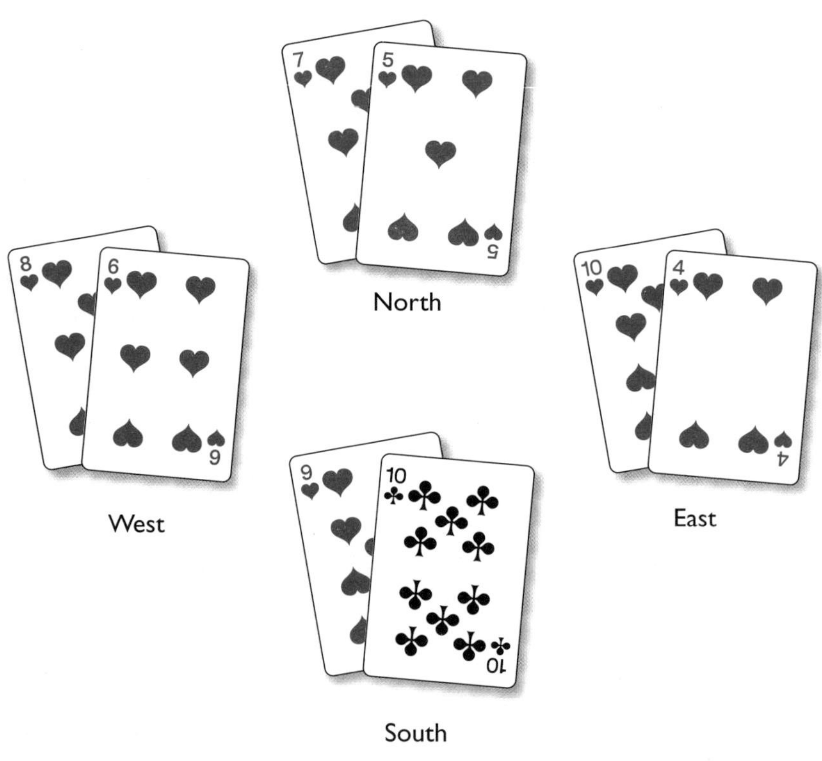

BRAG

BRAG *is almost certainly the ancestor of Poker (see page 177) and itself probably derived from the Spanish game of Primero, the popular card game of Tudor England and, so far as we can trace, the first card game to be played scientifically in that country. It is purely a gambling game.*

NUMBER OF PLAYERS

Any number of players can play, from five to eight being best.

CARDS

The full pack of 52 cards is used. Cards rank from Ace (high) to 2 (low).

THE PLAY

The general principle of the game is quite simple. The players stake on the respective merits of their cards, and the best hand is determined by certain arbitrary rules. Bluffing is an important feature of the game. The ♦ A, ♣ J and ♦ 9 are known as braggers, and rank as Jokers or wild cards. There are two versions of the game: Single-Stake Brag and Three-Stake Brag.

SINGLE-STAKE BRAG

In this version of the game the dealer puts up a stake to the agreed limit, and deals three cards face downwards to each player. In turn, beginning with the player on the left of the dealer, each player must either drop out of the game for the round in progress, or put up a stake at least equal to that of the dealer's. If he chooses he may raise the stake, in which event any player coming into the game, or already in the game, must raise his bet to as much as the highest individual stake, or drop out of the game and lose what he has already staked. If no one meets the dealer's stake he withdraws it, and receives an agreed amount from the other players. The deal then passes to the next player.

Unlike at poker, there is no discarding and drawing more cards. When all those who wish to play have raised their bets to an equal amount, the cards are shown and the player with the best hand collects all the stakes.

Flushes and sequences are of no value. The best hand is a pair-royal; it consists of three cards of equal rank (Aces high, 2s low) and a hand of three

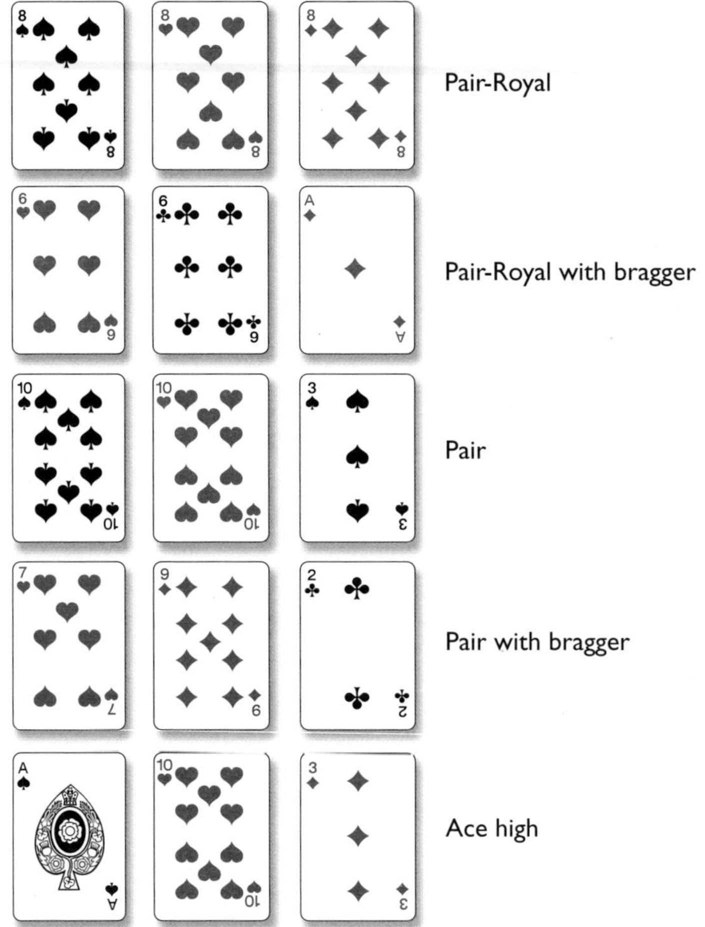

The classes of Brag hands, the highest at the top.

natural cards takes precedence over one with braggers. The next best hand is a pair, with a preference for a natural pair over one with a bragger, and if two players have equal pairs the one with the higher third card wins. If no player holds either a pair-royal or a pair, the player with the highest single card wins and if two players hold exactly equal hands the winner is the person who was first to stake.

THREE-STAKE BRAG

This game begins by each player putting up three separate stakes; the dealer then deals two cards face down and one card face up to each player.

The first stake is won by the player who is dealt the highest face-upwards card. For this round of the game the braggers take their normal position in the pack, and if two or more players are dealt cards of equal rank, precedence is determined as in the single-stake game.

The hand is next played as in single-stake, and the winner takes the second stake. If no one bets, the hands are exposed and the highest hand wins.

Finally, the players expose their cards and the third stake is won by the player whose cards most nearly total 31 (over or under), the Aces counting 11, the court cards 10 each and the other cards at their pip values. A player whose hand totals less than 31 may draw a card from the remainder of the pack, but if his total then exceeds 31 he automatically loses the game.

COON CAN

IN THE USA *Coon Can is known as Double Rum. It is not a bad name for it because it is a variation of Rummy (see page 184), played with two packs of cards shuffled together with two Jokers.*

NUMBER OF PLAYERS

The game may be played by any number of players up to eight; each plays for himself.

CARDS

Two identical packs are used, with two Jokers, making a pack of 106 cards. Ace can rank either high or low, and the Jokers are wild.

Ten cards are dealt face downwards to each player. The rest of the pack (the stock) is placed face downwards in the centre of the table, and the top card of it is turned face upwards and placed alongside it to start the discard pile.

THE PLAY

The object of the game is to get rid of all the cards held, by melding them face upwards on the table, either in sets of three or more of the same rank, or in sequences of three or more of the same suit, with the Ace either high or low but not round-the-corner. A Joker may be used to represent any card that the holder chooses.

Each player, beginning with the one on the left of the dealer, plays in turn. He is under no obligation to meld, but he must take into his hand either the top card of the stock or the top card of the discard pile, and discard a card to reduce his hand to ten cards. If he chooses to meld he must do so between drawing a card and discarding one, and as well as melding, at the same time he may add cards to melds that he has already made, and to those of his opponents.

A Joker may be moved from one end of a meld to the other, provided the player has the natural card to replace it. If, for example, a sequence is: ♠ 6, 7 8, Joker, a player who holds a ♠ 9 may play it in place of the Joker and transfer the Joker to represent the ♠ 5. Once moved, however, a Joker cannot be moved a second time and a player who holds a ♠ 5 cannot play it in place of the Joker and place the Joker elsewhere. Nor can a Joker be moved if it is in the interior of a sequence, as in ♠ 4, 5, 6, Joker, ♠ 8. The Joker cannot be replaced by a ♠ 7. When a Joker cannot be moved it is customary to place it crosswise, as a reminder to the other players.

The game is won by the player who is first to meld all his cards. The remaining players pay him the same number of units as the pip value of the unmelded cards left in their hands - a Joker counting 15, an Ace 11, the court cards 10 each, and all other cards their pip values.

It rarely happens that the stock will be exhausted before the game has been won. In this event the game continues and the players draw cards from the discard pile, discarding a different card to that drawn. If this proves insufficient to finish the game, the pip values of the hands are counted and placed into a pool to be scored by the winner of the next hand.

CRAZY EIGHTS

THIS IS *a very simple game, not to be confused with the game of Eights described earlier. Crazy Eights is a gambling game.*

NUMBER OF PLAYERS

The game can be played by any number of players from two to eight, but is best for four or more, each player playing for himself.

CARDS

The full pack of 52 cards is used. The ranking of the cards is immaterial, but cards have a point-scoring value, as described below.

Any player picks up the cards, shuffles, and begins dealing them one to each player face up - the first player to be dealt a Jack becomes first dealer. Subsequently the deal passes clockwise to the left.

Before the deal, each player puts a stake into the centre. The dealer then deals five cards to each player, one at a time to the left, then lays out eight cards face up in the centre of the table, arranged in two rows of four. The remainder of the pack is set aside.

THE PLAY

Beginning with the player on the dealer's left, each player in turn may lay a card from his hand face up on one of the eight cards in the centre. The card must match in rank the card onto which it is played. A card in the centre may be covered as many times as required,

i.e. if two players are dealt an 8, and there is an 8 in the centre, each player can play his 8 onto it in turn. A player who cannot go says 'pass'.

Should a player get rid of all his cards, he shouts 'crazy eights' and collects the whole pool of stakes. Frequently the game ends with every player being forced to pass while still holding a card or two. In this case, every player counts the points still held in his hand according to the following scale: Aces 15 points, Kings, Queens, Jacks 10 points, and all other cards their pip value. The pool is then divided between the high player (whose points total is highest) and the low player (whose points total is lowest).

In the illustration on page 167, players A, B, C, D, E and F have each contributed two chips to a pool of 12 chips. Player A dealt the hands as shown, and the eight cards in the centre of the table.

Player B plays first and lays his ♦ J on the ♣ J, player C plays his ♠ 8 on ♣ 8 and so on. All players can play to the first round, but player D must pass in the second, players C and A in the third, players B and F in the fourth, and finally player E passes on the fifth round. Player A is left with K, 5, 3 = 18 points; B with K, 7 = 17 points; C with K, 9, 5 = 24 points; D with 7,5, 3, 3 = 18 points; E with the ♠ 9 only = 9 points; and F with K, 10 = 20 points. So player C collects six chips for high, and player E six chips for low.

LIFT SMOKE

LIFT SMOKE *is a simple English game. It can be played for stakes by each player putting an amount into a kitty before each deal.*

NUMBER OF PLAYERS

The game is for four to six players, six perhaps being the best. Each player plays for himself.

CARDS

The full pack of 52 cards is used. The cards rank from Ace (high) to 2 (low).

One player picks up the cards and deals them round face up – the first player to be dealt a Jack becomes the first dealer. Thereafter the winner of each game deals for the next.

The dealer deals the cards one at a time in a clockwise direction to each player beginning with the player on his left. Each player receives the same number of cards as there are players in the game, i.e. with six players each player receives six cards. The last card dealt to the dealer is turned face up to establish the trump suit. The cards not dealt are placed in the centre of the table to form a stock.

THE PLAY

When all players have seen the trump suit, the dealer takes his cards into his hand, and the trick-taking phase of the game begins. The player to the left of dealer leads to the first trick, leading any card he likes. Subsequent players must follow suit if able, and if unable may trump or discard. The trick is won by the highest trump, or failing a trump by the highest card in the suit led.

When a trick is won, it is placed face down to one side, and the winner of the trick takes into his hand the top card of the stock. No other player takes a card, so the hands are now unequal. The winner of a trick leads to the next.

Each time a player fails to win a trick, his hand will diminish by one card. When a player is reduced to no cards, he drops out of the game. The last player remaining wins the game and if there is a kitty he takes it.

If the last card is taken from the stock while two or more players still have cards, the winner is the player who takes the next trick.

LOO

THE MODERN PLAYER *may be forgiven if he mistakes the meaning of the name which has been attached to this game. In fact it is a truncation of the now obsolete lanterloo, from the French* lanturlu, *a word best translated by our succinct, if vulgar, fiddlesticks. There are several variations of the game, of which Three-card Loo, Five-card Loo and Irish Loo are described here.*

NUMBER OF PLAYERS

Loo is suitable for any number of players, though the best number is six or seven.

CARDS

The standard 52-card pack is used, with the cards ranking from Ace (high) to 2 (low), except in Five-card Loo, in which the ♣ J is the highest ranking card (see opposite).

The first player to deal puts into a pool an agreed number of units. It may be any number divisible by three. Three cards are then dealt, one card at a time, to each player, and to an extra hand that is known as 'miss'. The top card of the remainder of the pack is turned up to denote the trump suit.

THE PLAY

The dealer offers the player on his immediate left the choice of refusing to play, playing with the cards dealt to him, or exchanging his cards for miss and playing with those. In turn, each player is offered the same choice, though, of course, once a player has chosen to exchange his hand for miss, a subsequent player is reduced to choosing between playing with the cards dealt to him or not playing the hand. Once a player has made a decision he must stand by it, and if he has chosen not to play he throws his cards face downwards to the centre of the table.

The player who first chooses to play leads to the first trick. Thereafter the player who wins a trick leads to the next. The play is governed by the following rules:

> A player must follow suit if he can, and must head the trick if he can.
> If a player cannot follow suit he must trump if he can, and if the trick has already been trumped he must overtrump if he can.
> If the player on lead holds the Ace of trumps (or the King if the Ace has been turned up) he must lead it.
> If the player on lead holds two or more trumps he must lead one of them, and if there are only two players in the game he must lead the highest.

A player who fails to comply with any of these rules, when able to do so, is deemed to have revoked; the pool is divided among the non-offenders, and the offender pays the full amount back to the pool.

When the hand has been played those who have won tricks divide the pool between them: one-third of the amount in it to the winner of each trick.

Those who have not won a trick are looed, and must put into the pool as many units as there were in it at the beginning of the deal. Unlimited loo, however, can come very expensive, and in practice it is essential for the players to agree upon limiting the losses of looed players.

If no player is looed, the next dealer replenishes the pool as at the beginning of the game.

If every player refuses to play, the dealer takes the entire pool and the next dealer replenishes it.

If only one player chooses to play the dealer must come into the game against him, but if he holds a weak hand, he may protect himself against loss by announcing that he will play for the pool. In this event he is not looed if he fails to win a trick, and, in return for the concession, he leaves in the pool any amount to which he may be entitled by reason of his having won tricks.

FIVE-CARD LOO

This is a variation of the parent game that differs from it in the following five particulars:

Every player is dealt five cards, and as there are five tricks to be won the number of units paid into the pool must be divisible by five.

There is no miss.

A player may exchange cards by drawing them from the stock. He may exchange any number of cards that he chooses, and once he has exchanged a card he must enter the game.

The highest card in the pack is the ♣ J. It is known as Pam. It ranks as a trump and takes precedence even over the Ace; if, however, a player leads the Ace of trumps and announces 'Pam be civil' the holder of Pam is debarred from playing it to the trick.

If a player holds five cards of a suit, or four cards of a suit and Pam, he is said to hold a flush and must expose his hand at once. He wins the pool and all the other players, except those who may hold flushes or Pam, are looed. If one or more players hold flushes, one in the trump suit wins over one in a plain suit, and between two or more in a plain suit, the one with the highest card wins. If two or more in plain suits are exactly equal the pool is divided.

IRISH LOO

This game is a combination of the three-card and five-card games, and is considered by competent players to be the best of the several variations.

Every player is dealt three cards, there is no Pam and no miss, but a player is allowed to exchange cards by drawing from the stock. The game is played in the same way as the parent game, with the added novelty that if clubs are trumps everyone must enter the game. It is known as Club Law and makes it imperative that the penalty for being looed must be limited to a reasonable amount.

Loo, in all its variations, is so bound up by hard and fast rules of play, already mentioned, that there is very little to be said about the play of the cards. At best one can only say that the most successful player is not he who knows how to play, but he who knows when to elect and when to refuse to play.

The most important point to note is that, apart from Pam at Five-card Loo, there are only three certain tricks, i.e. the Ace, the King-Queen combination and the Queen-Jack-10 combination of trumps. Usually the player who holds the Queen, Jack and 9 of trumps will win a trick, but it is not certain, and he may be looed if in an unfavourable position at the table. It is the same if a player holds the King and 3 of the trump suit. He will certainly win a trick if the suit is led and he is the last to play, but if he is not, he may not win a trick, because if the 4 is played he is compelled to play the King and a later player may win with the Ace. It leaves him only with the remote possibility of winning a trick with the lone 3 of trumps.

Perhaps in practice the picture is not so depressing as it appears in theory, because, even if there are seven players in the game, a large number of cards remain in the stock. Some of the high cards, therefore, may not be active and a combination such as a Jack and 10 of trumps, or even a Jack, 10 and a card in a plain suit, may win a trick.

In general a player is advised not to be too cautious about electing to play if he holds a weak hand, but he is advised to be careful. In practice he should keep a close watch on the number of units in the pool and weigh up the possible loss against the possible gain. If, for example, there are 15 units in the pool at Five-card Loo and the cost of being looed is 10 units it is not worth entering the play with a weak hand because, look at it which way you like, the cost of being looed is three times more than the possible gain that will accrue by winning one trick. It is not a good bet.

NAPOLEON

NAPOLEON, *usually called Nap, is one of the simplest of all card games. It is entirely a game for betting.*

NUMBER OF PLAYERS

Any number up to six may play, each playing for himself.

CARDS

The full pack of 52 cards is used, cards ranking from Ace (high) to 2 (low).

Each player is dealt five cards.

THE PLAY

Beginning with the player on the left of the dealer, every player in turn must either pass or declare to win a specified number of tricks in the ascending order: Two, Three, Four and Nap (a declaration to win all five tricks).

The player who has contracted to win most tricks leads to the first trick and the card that he leads determines the trump suit. Play follows the usual routine of trick-taking games: a player must follow suit if he can, otherwise he may discard or trump, and the player who wins a trick leads to the next.

Stakes are paid only on the number of tricks contracted for. Those won above, or lost below, the number contracted for are ignored. The usual method of settlement is by means of a level-money transaction:

Declaration	*Declarer wins*	*Declarer loses*
Two	2 units	2 units
Three	3 units	3 units
Four	4 units	4 units
Nap	10 units	5 units

Payment is made to, and received from, all players at the table.

Nap(oleon) is such an elementary game that in some circles interest is added to it by introducing a number of extraordinary declarations:

Misery is a declaration to lose every trick. It ranks between the declaration of Three and Four, and though normally it is played without a trump suit, some play it with a trump suit, determined as in the parent game by the opening lead. It pays and wins three units.

Wellington is a declaration to win all five tricks at double stakes. It cannot be declared, however, except over a declaration of Nap.

Blücher is a declaration to win all five tricks at triple stakes. It cannot be declared, however, except over a declaration of Wellington.

Peep nap sanctions the player who has declared Nap (or Wellington or Blücher if these declarations are permitted) to exchange the top card of the pack for a card in his own hand.

Purchase nap sanctions each player before declaring to exchange any number of cards in his hand for fresh cards, by paying into a pool one unit for every card exchanged. The pool is carried forward from deal to deal and taken by the first player to win Nap (or Wellington or Blücher if these declarations are permitted).

SEVEN-CARD NAPOLEON

In this variation seven cards are dealt to each player, and a player cannot contract to win fewer than three tricks. There is no Wellington and no Blücher. Misery is optional and, if permitted, ranks between Nap and Six.

Apart from these amendments, the game is played in the same way as the parent game.

Settlement is made as follows:

Declaration	*Declarer wins*	*Declarer loses*
Three	3 units	3 units
Four	4 units	4 units
Nap	10 units	5 units
Misery	10 units	5 units
Six	18 units	9 units
Seven	28 units	14 units

Payment is made to, and received from, all players at the table.

PANGUINGUE

PANGUINGUE *is one of the best games of the Rummy type for a large number of players. It arises from the Spanish game of Conquian, and retains the characteristics of using the Spanish 40-card pack and of play rotating to the right. It was very popular in the first half of the 20th century on the west coast of the USA. It is played for small stakes.*

NUMBER OF PLAYERS

Any reasonable number may play – perhaps six to eight is best, but the game can in fact accommodate twice this number.

CARDS

Eight of the 40-card packs are used, making a pack of 320 cards. The 40-card pack is formed by removing from a standard pack the 10s, 9s and 8s. It is possible to use fewer packs, but fewer than five should not be used. The cards rank in the order: King, Queen, Jack, 7, 6, 5, 4, 3, 2, Ace. Players may remove the Kings, Queens and Jacks instead of the 10s, 9s and 8s, so that the cards are in their natural sequence and there is no need to remember that 7 and Jack are in sequence.

The 320-card pack is shuffled by many hands and amalgamated. Each player draws a card, and the lowest becomes eldest hand. The second lowest becomes dealer and sits on eldest's left (this is because the dealing and the play rotates to the right, i.e. anti-clockwise).

The final shuffle before the deal is made by the player at the dealer's left. It is unusual for all the cards to be used during one hand, and after the first deal the practice between deals is to shuffle only the cards which have been used together with a batch from the unused cards, these going to the bottom of the total pack. The deal does not rotate - the winner of a hand becomes eldest hand for the next, i.e. the player to the left of the winner deals the next hand.

Without holding the whole pack in his hand, the dealer deals ten cards to each player in bundles of five. The remaining cards are placed face down to form the stock. Here again it is usual to divide the pack in two so that the stock is not unmanageable. The upper part, called the 'head' is used, while the lower part, the 'foot', is put to one side to be used if necessary.

THE PLAY

The top card of the stock is turned face up to begin a discard pile. Beginning with eldest (the player to the dealer's right) and proceeding anti-clockwise, each player in turn announces whether he will stay in the game or drop out. A player who drops out pays a forfeit of two chips. The chips are placed on that part of the stock called the foot, and the player who drops out thus says that he is 'going on top'. His cards are placed face down below the foot, but crosswise, because they do not become part of the stock and must not be used in the hand.

After all those who wish have dropped out, those remaining, in turn anti-clockwise, draw a card either from the top of the discard pile or from the top of the stock. The card from the discard pile can be taken only if it can be melded with immediately. A meld, usually called a 'spread', is either of a group or of a sequence, as in the more familiar Rummy, and consists of three cards.

A group consists of three cards of the same rank, but to be valid there are restrictions as to suits. If the rank is King or Ace (called 'non-comoquers') there are no restrictions; any three cards are valid. However, for other ranks, the cards must be either all of the same suit or all of different suits.

A sequence (usually called a 'stringer') consists of three cards of the same suit in sequence (remembering that a sequence continues from 7 to Jack).

A player may lay down any melds on his turn (if taking the card from the top of the discard pile, he must meld with it, as stated). Subsequently, on his turn, he may add to any of his melds, called 'laying off'. A player may lay off on his own melds only – not on his opponents'. A sequence may be added to by laying off additional cards in sequence. A group of the same suit may be added to by laying off cards of the same rank and suit. A group in different suits may be added to by laying off cards of the same rank in any suit (this means that such a meld is not restricted to four cards only).

A player may take the top of the discard pile in order to lay off on one of his melds.

Certain melds are called 'conditions', and a player who makes one immediately collects chips from all other players. So far as groups are concerned, certain ranks (7s, 5s and 3s) are called 'valle cards' or value cards. The five classes of condition melds are as follows:

A group of valle cards of different suits (worth one chip from each player).

A group of valle cards in the same suit (worth four chips in spades, two in other suits).

A group of non-valle cards in the same suit (worth two chips in spades, one in other suits).

A sequence of Ace, 2, 3 (worth two chips in spades and one in other suits).

A sequence of King, Queen, Jack (worth two chips in spades and one in other suits).

A player who lays off on a condition collects again from each player its value, except that in the case of three valle cards in the same suit he collects only two chips in spades and one in other suits. A player collects each time he lays off on a condition.

If a player lays off three or more cards on a meld, he may split it into two separate melds, provided that each half is valid. By doing so he may create a condition. For example, if he adds to a sequence of ♦ 5,4,3 the ♦ 2, the ♦ 6 and the ♦ A, he may split the sequence of six cards into two sequences: ♦ A, 2, 3 and ♦ 6, 5, 4. This creates a condition (Ace, 2, 3) and the player collects one chip from every other player (or two if it is in spades).

A player may also take a card or cards from a meld to which he has laid off to form a new meld, provided that he leaves a valid meld. This is called 'borrowing'. For example, if he makes a meld of ♥ J, 7, 6 to which he adds ♥ 5, 4, he may later borrow the ♥ 5, 4 to make a new meld with ♥ 3 or another ♥ 6. Or he may borrow the ♥ J to make, for example, a meld of ♥ J, ♣ J, ♠ J. But he could not borrow the ♥ 7, or ♥ 6, or ♥ 5, because to take one of those cards would destroy the sequence, i.e. it would not leave a valid meld.

The object of each player is to meld all his cards, called 'going out', whereupon he wins the game.

A player's turn consists of taking either the top card of the discard pile or stock, melding or laying off, if he wishes, and, except when going out, discarding. A player who goes out may not discard; thus to go out a player needs 11 cards melded on the table.

If the top card of the discard pile can be laid off on a meld of the player whose turn it is, any other player can demand that he take the card and lay it off. This might be done to disrupt the hand of the player in play, since having laid off the card he is forced to discard.

It follows that a player with nine cards melded and one in his hand still requires to find two cards to lay off. Should he draw a card from stock which he lays off on his melds, he must still discard the card in his hand. This leaves him with ten cards melded and none in his hand, but he has not gone out. He must continue to draw, on his turn, from the discard pile or the stock until he draws a card which he can lay off, and thus go out with 11 cards melded.

If a player is in the situation of having ten cards melded, the previous player must not discard a card which would allow him to go out (unless the previous player has no alternative, i.e. he cannot make a safe discard).

The winner of the game (i.e. the player who goes out) wins one chip from all the others remaining in the game (in some schools he collects two chips from any player who has not melded). He also collects from each player chips representing the values of his conditions. (As a player collects for conditions as he melds them, the winner therefore collects twice for his conditions.) The winner also takes the chips of those players who dropped out, i.e. those chips stacked on the foot of the stock.

In the unlikely event of the stock (both head and foot) being exhausted before any player has gone out, the discard pile is turned over and becomes the stock, play continuing as usual.

So far as strategy is concerned, the usual principles of good play at all Rummy-type games apply, i.e. a player should try to hold cards giving multiple options of melding rather than isolated pairs or possible sequences with gaps in the middle. As the number and rank of cards held in the hand are immaterial in the settling when an opponent goes out, there is no point in laying down melds prematurely. However, a player should lay down and collect for conditions and get down a first meld if there is a double payment to the winner by players who have failed to meld.

POKER

POKER *is not a difficult game to learn, but by no means is it an easy one to play well because skill at the game is born only of experience coupled with some knowledge of arithmetic. Fundamentally, Poker is a game of calculating chances. It is a gambling game and cannot be played without betting.*
The parent game, described first, is commonly called Straight Poker, but is more correctly Straight Draw Poker.

NUMBER OF PLAYERS

Any reasonable number may play; five, six or seven are considered the ideal numbers.

CARDS

The full pack of 52 cards is used. The cards rank from Ace (high) to 2 (low).

THE PLAY

Each player is dealt five cards face downwards, and the object of the game is to make the best hand by an exchange of cards, and then bet on it against the other players.

In ascending order the nine classes of poker hands, together with the approximate odds against their being dealt to a player, are:

Highest card: any five odd cards. Evens.

One pair: two cards of the same rank and three odd cards. 15 to 11

Two pairs: two cards of the same rank, two other cards of the same rank and an odd card. 20 to 1

Threes: three cards of the same rank and two odd cards. 46 to 1.

Straight: any five cards in sequence, not of the same suit; an Ace may be either high or low. 254 to 1

Flush: any five cards of the same suit. 508 to 1.

Full house: three cards of the same rank and two other cards of the same rank. 693 to 1.

Fours: four cards of the same rank and an odd card. 4,164 to 1.

Straight flush: a sequence of five cards all of the same suit: an Ace may be either high or low. 64,973 to 1.

Examples of each hand are illustrated opposite. They are valued on the highest combination, and if the combination of two or more players is equal, by the highest odd card. In the event of two or more players holding exactly equal hands the stakes are divided.

The player on the left of the dealer begins the game by putting up an agreed amount, known as the ante. For convenience we will assume that it is one chip. The player on his left then puts up a straddle of two chips. Throughout the game every player puts his chips on the table in front of him.

The dealer now deals, face downwards, five cards to each player. After looking at his cards, the player on the left of the straddle has the option of playing or not. If he decides not to play he throws his cards face downwards towards the centre of the table, and takes no further interest in the deal in progress. If he decides to play he puts up four chips. The player on his left now has the choice of throwing in his hand, coming into the game for four chips, or doubling (i.e. coming into the game for eight chips). In the same way, in turn, every player has the choice of throwing in his hand, coming into the game for the same stake as the previous player, or raising the stakes until the agreed maximum is reached.

When staking reaches the ante and the straddle, they can either throw in their hands and sacrifice what they have already put up, or come into the game by raising their stakes to the appropriate amount.

If no player comes into the game, the straddle recovers his two chips and takes the one chip put up by the ante.

Staking continues for some little time, because if a player has come into the game and a subsequent player has doubled, it is open to those who have already staked to increase their stakes, and this progressive staking continues until no one increases the stakes or the agreed limit is reached.

When everyone has staked, those left in the game have the chance to improve their hands by exchanging cards. The dealer ignores those who have already

The classes of Poker hand, the highest at the bottom. The numbers of possible ways in which each hand can be made up are as follows:

highest card:	1,302,540
one pair:	1,098,240
two pairs:	123,552
threes:	54,912
straight:	10,200
flush:	5,108
full house:	3,744
fours:	624
straight flush:	40

thrown in their hands, but gives all the other players in turn as many cards as they wish after they have discarded those cards that they do not wish to retain. A player may discard any number of his cards, but no experienced player would remain in the game to exchange four cards, and only one who has taken leave of his senses will do so to exchange all five cards. Most players will exchange one, two, or three cards.

When cards have been exchanged, the player who was first to come in begins the betting. Either he throws in his hand (sacrificing the stake he has already made to come in), checks (signifies his intention to remain in the game without increasing his stake) or raises (increases his stake to any amount up to the agreed limit).

If he checks, all the players who follow him have, in their turn, the same choice. If no one raises those left in the game show their cards and the player with the best hand takes all that has been staked. If a player raises, the subsequent players, in turn, have the option of throwing in their hands, putting up sufficient chips to meet the raise, or raise still further.

In this way the betting continues, until the final bet is either called or not. If the final bet is called, the players left in the game show their cards and the player with the best hand wins all that has been staked: if the final bet is not called, the player whose bet has not been called wins all that has been staked with no need to show his hand.

Poker falls naturally into two parts: the staking and the betting. The staking is the easier part of the game because it is open to a precise arithmetical analysis. We may suppose that a player is dealt:

♠ 10, ♠ 6, ♠ 5, ♠ 2, ♥ 9

Since a pair of 10s is of small value, the player's aim must be to discard the ♥ 9 hoping to draw a spade to fill the flush.

There are 47 cards from which to draw, and of them only nine are spades. It follows, therefore, that the odds against drawing a spade are 38 to 9, or approximately 4¼ to 1. If three players have come into the game with four chips each, making 15 chips on the table with the ante and straddle, it is not worth while playing because it costs four chips to come in so that the table is offering odds of 15 to 4 (3¾ to 1) and the chance of improving is 4¼ to 1. If, however, four players have come in it will be just worth while coming into the game, because now there will be 19 chips on the table so that the table is offering odds of 4¾ to 1, which is better than the odds against improving.

Poker players should study very carefully the mathematical chances, because the whole theory of staking may be summed up by asking oneself two questions: What are the chances of improving my hand? What odds are the table laying me? Then, if the answer to the first question is greater than to the second, the player should come in; if it is not he should throw in his hand.

The betting is the more difficult part of the game because it is largely psychology. At the same time a player has to be gifted with the quality that we call judgement because his betting must be dictated by the manner in which the other players are betting, and how they, on their part, will interpret his betting. Particular note should be taken of the number of cards drawn by each of the other players and deductions drawn from the information gained. The subsequent betting should go a long way towards confirming whether the deductions are correct or not, and whether the player has improved on the draw.

A good poker player is inscrutable and unpredictable, because he varies his game to make the most with his good hands and lose the least with his bad ones. He profits by the advice of Saint Matthew - 'let not thy left hand know what thy right hand doeth' - and he is always imperturbable, because there is no future in gloating over a win and wailing over a loss. If he thinks that he holds the best hand he bets on it boldly: if he thinks that he is beaten he throws in his cards and cuts his losses.

Pot-deals, commonly called pots, are widely played, and are an important feature of all variations of the game. When a pot is played there is no ante and no straddle; instead every player contributes an agreed amount to a pot, or pool, that is independent of the staking and betting. The player on the immediate left of the dealer has first decision whether to open the game by staking or not. If he does not open, the option passes to the player on his left, and so on.

The essence of a pot is that a player is debarred from opening the game, by putting up a stake, unless his hand qualifies him to do so by a prearranged standard. If no player opens, the deal passes, and the players sweeten the pot, by adding to it, for the next deal. If the pot is opened, other players may come in even if their hands are below standard, and he who wins the deal also wins the amount in the pot as well as all the stakes put up by the other players. The player who opened the game must show that his hand qualified for opening.

In a *Jackpot* a player must have a pair of Jacks, or better, to qualify for opening.

In a *Progressive jackpot*, if no-one opens the first deal, the second deal is a Queenpot, and if no one opens it the next is a Kingpot, and so on. Some stop at Acepots, others continue to two pairs before beginning again at a Jackpot if no one has opened the game.

In a *Freak pot*, sometimes called Deuces wild, all the 2s are wild cards and may be used to represent any cards that the holder chooses. Fives (five cards of the same rank) is now a possible hand, and it is classed above a straight flush, but is beaten if the straight flush is headed by an Ace.

In a *Double pot*, or Legs, any type of pot is chosen, but a player must win it twice before he may take his winnings.

WILD WIDOW

This is a variation of the parent game, but, after four cards have been dealt to each player, a card is turned face upwards in the centre of the table and is left there for the duration of the deal. The dealer then gives each player one more card, and the game is played with the three other cards of the same rank as the exposed card as wild.

SPIT IN THE OCEAN

In this variation, only four cards are dealt to each player. A card is then dealt face upwards in the centre of the table. Each player considers this card as the fifth card of his hand. It is a wild card, as also are the other three cards of the same rank.

STUD POKER

In this variation of the parent game the main feature is that some of the cards are dealt face upwards and some face downwards. There are several ways of playing the game.

In *Five-card stud* there is no ante unless agreed on. The dealer gives each player a card face downwards (it is known as the hole card) and then a card face upwards. The deal is then interrupted for a betting interval. After the betting interval the dealer gives each active player another three cards face upwards, and after each there is a betting interval. If two or more players remain in the game after the last betting interval, they turn up their hole cards and the player with the best hand wins.

Each betting interval begins with the player who holds the best combinations of cards exposed, and if two or more players have equal combinations the one nearest to the dealer's left bets first. At the first betting interval the player who opens must make a bet; at subsequent intervals he may check. Any player who drops out of the game must turn his exposed cards face downwards.

Seven-card stud, sometimes called Down the River, or Peek Poker, is played in the same way as five-card stud, except that the dealer first deals to each player two cards face downwards and one card face upwards. There is a betting interval, and, after this, the active players are dealt three cards face upwards and one face downwards, with the deal interrupted for a betting interval after each round of dealing. At the showdown, a player exposes his hole cards and selects five of his seven cards to form his hand.

WHISKEY POKER

This variation is so called because it was originally played in the American lumber camps to decide who should pay for the drinks.

Every player contributes an agreed amount to a pool. The dealer deals an extra hand (widow) to the centre of the table, immediately before dealing cards to himself. The player on the left of the dealer, after looking at his cards, may either exchange his hand for the widow, pass (in which case the option of taking the widow passes to his left-hand neighbour) or indicate, by knocking the table, that he will play with the cards dealt to him.

If the player on the left of the dealer (or any subsequent player) takes the widow, he puts his own cards face upwards on the table as a new widow. The player on his left may now either take the whole of the exposed widow in exchange for his own hand, take one or more cards from it in exchange for cards in his hand, or knock. A player, however, cannot draw cards from the widow and knock at the same turn, and the option to exchange the widow or cards with it continues until a player knocks. As soon as a player does so, the remaining players have one turn each to exchange their hands or cards for it. After the player on the right of the knocker has had his turn, the players expose their hands and the best hand wins the pot.

If no one takes the widow before it is the turn of the dealer, he must either take the widow or turn it face upwards on the table. Even if he decides to knock, without making an exchange, he must still turn up the widow.

KNOCK POKER

In this variation, every player puts up an ante. The dealer gives every player five cards, as in the parent game, and the rest of the pack (the stock) is placed face downwards in the centre of the table. The player on the left of the dealer draws the top card of the stock and discards a card from his hand. Thereafter each player in turn draws either the top card of the stock or the top card of the discard pile, and discards a card from his hand.

At any time after drawing a card and before discarding one, a player may knock the table. He then discards a card from his hand. The other players have one more turn each to draw and discard a card, or drop out of the game by paying the knocker the amount of the ante. After the player on the right of the knocker has drawn and discarded, or dropped out of the game, all players remaining in the game show their cards and settlement is made as follows:

If the knocker has the best hand, all who are in the game pay him twice the ante.

If the knocker and one or more other players have equal hands they divide the winnings except for the amount paid to the knocker by those who dropped out of the game.

If the knocker does not have the best hand he pays twice the ante to every player remaining in the game, and the player with the best hand wins the antes.

HIGH-LOW POKER

Any variation of poker may be played high-low. As a rule the hand is played as a pot. The player plays his hand for either high or low, but does not have to announce which until the last card is dealt. The highest and the lowest hands divide the pot between them. An Ace is always high and cannot be counted as a low card except as part of a sequence in the high hand.

STRIP POKER

In this version of the game the dealer deals five cards, face downwards, to each player. There is no ante and no straddle. After an exchange of cards (as in the parent game) the players expose their cards and the one with the worst poker hand pays the table by removing an article of clothing.

The game, with all its voluptuous prospects, is said to be at its best in mixed company during a heatwave!

RUMMY

RUMMY, *or Rum, as the name is frequently abbreviated to, is one of the most popular of all card games. Derivatives to be found elsewhere in this book include Gin Rummy and Canasta. Coon Can is another game of the type but that predates even Rummy.*

NUMBER OF PLAYERS

Any number up to six may play. More than six should prefer Coon Can (see page 165).

CARDS

The full pack of 52 cards is used. They rank from King (high) to Ace (low).

Ten cards are dealt to each player if only two play; seven cards if three or four play; and six cards if five or six play. The rest of the pack (the stock) is placed face downwards in the centre of the table, and the top card of it is turned face upwards and laid alongside it to start the discard pile.

THE PLAY

The object of the game is to make sets of three or more cards of the same rank, or sequences of three or more cards of the same suit (the Ace being low) and declare them by exposing them on the table, after drawing a card from the stock or discard pile and before discarding a card from the hand. At the same time a player may add one or more proper cards to sequences and sets already declared either by himself or the other players.

Each player in turn, beginning with the one on the left of the dealer, must take into his hand either the top card of the stock or the top card of the discard pile, and discard a card from his hand, but if he has drawn the top card of the discard pile he must not discard it in the same turn.

If the stock is exhausted before any player declares all his hand, the discard pile is turned face downwards and becomes the stock.

The player who is first to declare all his cards wins the hand, and the other players pay him ten points each for every court card left in their hands, one point for every Ace, and its pip value for every other card. If a player declares all his cards in one turn he scores rummy and is paid double.

Rummy is a simple game that has acquired a number of improvements.

BOATHOUSE RUMMY

In this version, a player may draw the top card of the stock; or he may draw the top card of the discard pile and then either the top card of the stock or the next card of the discard pile. He may, however, discard only one card.

In a sequence the Ace may be either high, low, or round the corner.

The play does not come to an end until a player can declare his entire hand in one turn.

A losing player pays only for the unmatched cards in his hand, but Aces are paid for at 11 points each.

CONTINENTAL RUMMY

This variation of the parent game is suitable for any number of players up to 12. If two to five play two packs with two Jokers are used; if six to eight play three packs with three Jokers are used; and if nine to 12 play four packs with four Jokers are used.

Each player receives 15 cards. A player may not declare until all 15 of his cards are melded either in five three-card sequences, or in three four-card sequences and one three-card sequence, or in one five-card, one four-card and two three-card sequences. Sets of three or more cards of the same rank are of no value. A Joker may be used as any card. The Ace may be high or low, but not round the corner.

There are many ways of scoring, but generally the winner collects from all the other players one unit from each for winning, and two units from each for every Joker in his hand.

GAMBLER'S RUMMY

This version is so called because it is the variation of the parent game that is most frequently played for high stakes.

Only four players take part and each is dealt seven cards. The Ace is low and, as in the parent game, counts only one point in the settlement. A player is not allowed to declare all his hand in one turn. He must declare it in at least two turns, but he is not debarred from going out during his second turn even if on his previous turn he played off only one card on another player's declaration.

The stock is gone through only once. When it is exhausted the players must draw the top card of the discard pile, and the game ends when a player refuses it.

KNOCK RUMMY

This version is also called Poker Rum, and is played in the same way as the parent game, but a player does not declare his sequences and sets by exposing them on the table. Instead, after drawing a card, he knocks on the table, and then discards. Play comes to

A good rummy player will maximize his opportunities. With the hand above, the player should take the ♠5 and discard ♣9, as ♠5 offers alternative chances of melding: either with ♥5 or ♠6.

an end. The players separate their matched cards from their unmatched ones, and each announces the count of his unmatched cards, as reckoned in the parent game. The player with the lowest count wins the difference in counts from all the other players. If a player ties with the knocker for the lowest count he wins over the knocker. If the knocker does not have the lowest count he pays a penalty of an extra ten points to the player with the lowest count. If the knocker goes rummy (has all his cards matched when he knocks) and wins, he receives an extra 25 points from all the other players.

SCOTCH WHIST

SCOTCH WHIST *is sometimes called Catch the Ten because one of the objects of the game is to win the trick that contains the 10 of the trump suit.*

NUMBER OF PLAYERS

Any number from two to eight may play. If two, three, five or seven play, each plays for himself. If four, six or eight play they may either play each for himself, or form into partnerships.

CARDS

Scotch Whist is played with a pack of 36 cards. The 2s, 3s, 4s, and 5s are removed from the standard pack. The cards rank from Ace (high) to 6 (low) with the exception that the Jack of the trump suit is promoted above the Ace.

Every player must begin with the same number of cards: if five or seven players take part the ♠ 6 is removed from the pack, and if eight take part all four 6s are.

Dealing varies with the number of players taking part in the game. If two play each receives 18 cards that are dealt in three separate hands of six cards each, to be played independently; if three play each receives 12 cards that are dealt in two separate hands of six cards each, to be played independently; if four or more play the cards are dealt in the normal clockwise rotation. In every case the dealer turns up the last card to indicate the trump suit.

THE PLAY

The player on the left of the dealer leads to the first trick. Thereafter the player who wins a trick leads to the next. Play follows the usual routine of trick-taking games: a player must follow suit, if he can, to the suit led and if he cannot he may either trump the trick or discard on it.

The object of the game is to win tricks containing the five top trump cards, and the player, or partnership, that does so scores 11 points for the Jack, four points for the Ace, three points for the King, two points for the Queen, and ten points for the 10. Over and above this, each player, or partnership, counts the number of cards taken in tricks, and scores one point for every card more than the number originally dealt to him, or it.

The game ends when a player, or partnership, has reached an agreed total, usually 41 points.

It stands out that a player must direct his play towards winning tricks that contain the top cards of the trump suit, particularly that which contains the 10, since the Jack can only go to the player to whom it has been dealt, and usually the luck of the deal determines who will win the tricks that contain the Ace, King and Queen.

In a partnership game the player who has been dealt the 10, either singleton or doubleton, would be well advised to lead it. It gives a good score if his partner is able to win with the Jack; if an opponent wins the trick the partnership must hope to recover by aiming to win as many tricks as possible. If the game is being played all against all, the player who has been dealt the 10 should try and get rid of all the cards in his shortest suit, so that he can win the 10 by trumping with it.

SPOIL FIVE

SPOIL FIVE, *sometimes called Forty-five, is an excellent game of the Euchre family, sometimes regarded as the national card game of Ireland. It calls for a show of skill and is usually played for stakes.*

NUMBER OF PLAYERS

Any reasonable number may play, but the game is best for five or six.

CARDS

Spoil Five is played with the full pack of 52 cards, but that it is rarely, if ever, played outside its native Ireland may be ascribed to the eccentric order of the cards. The 5 of the trump suit is always the highest trump, the Jack of the trump suit is the second highest, and the Ace of hearts the third highest. Thereafter, if a black suit is trumps the cards rank in the order Ace, King, Queen, 2, 3, 4, 6, 7, 8, 9, 10 and if a red suit is trumps in the order Ace (if diamonds are trumps), King, Queen, 10, 9, 8, 7, 6, 4, 3, 2. In plain suits, the black suits rank in the order King, Queen, Jack, Ace, 2, 3, 4, 5, 6, 7, 8, 9, 10; the red suits in the order King,

Queen, Jack, 10, 9, 8, 7, 6, 5, 4, 3, 2, Ace (except in hearts). It is concisely expressed as 'highest in red; lowest in black', but even with this help it is all rather involved.

Five cards are dealt to each player either in bundles of two then three, or three then two. The next card is exposed to determine the trump suit.

THE PLAY

A pool is formed to which every player contributes an agreed amount, and it is usual to fix a maximum and, after the first deal, only the player whose turn it is to deal contributes to the pool.

The object of the game is to win three tricks, or to prevent another player from winning them.

The player on the left of the dealer leads to the first trick. Thereafter the winner of a trick leads to the next. The rules of play are precise and peculiar to the game:

> If the card turned up to denote the trump suit is an Ace, the dealer may rob. He may, that is, exchange the Ace for a card in his hand, but he must do so before the player on his left leads to the first trick.
>
> Any player who has been dealt the Ace of the trump suit may exchange any card in his hand for the turn-up card, but he need not do so until it is his turn to play.
>
> If a trump is led a player must follow suit if he can, but the 5 and Jack of the trump suit and the ♥ A are exempt from following suit to the lead of a lower trump. It is called reneging. It means that the 5 of the trump suit need not be played if the Jack of the trump suit is led, and the Jack of the trump suit need not be played if the ♥ A is led; if, however, the 5 of the trump suit is led no trump can renege.
>
> If a plain suit is led a player may follow suit or trump as he chooses, but he must not discard from another plain suit if he is able to follow suit or trump.
>
> If a player misdeals the deal passes to the next player.

The player who wins three tricks takes the pool; if no-one wins three tricks (a spoil) the deal passes to the next player. When a player has won three tricks the hand ends and the deal passes, unless the player who has won them declares 'Jinx'. This is an undertaking to win the remaining two tricks. Play then continues and if he fails to win the two tricks he loses the pool; on the other hand, if he wins the two tricks not only does he take the pool but the other players each pay him the amount that they originally contributed to the pool.

In the four-handed game illustrated overleaf, South deals and turns up the ♦ 9.

West leads the ♦ J. North may renege the ♦ 5, but it would hardly be good play not to use it to win the second highest trump, so he plays it. East, who holds the ♦ A, robs by exchanging the ♣ 8 for the ♦ 9 and, of course, plays it. West, who started with the hope of a jinx, is now not so sure that he will win even three tricks. His

East is dealt the ♣ 8, but exchanges it for the ♦ 9.

prospects, however, improve when South, perforce, plays the ♥ A.

North leads the ♣ J, East plays the ♣ 5, South the ♣ 7, and West wins with the ♦ 2.

West leads the ♠ K, North plays the ♠ 6, and East sees the possibility of himself winning three tricks. He trumps with the ♦ A, and South plays the ♠ 9. With any luck East should be able to win the last two tricks with the ♠ J and ♠ 5.

As it happens, however, East's play has enabled West to win three tricks, because when East leads the ♠ J, West wins with the ♦ 3 and the last trick with the ♠ 6.

FAN TAN

FAN TAN *is also known as Card Dominoes, Parliament and Sevens, and must not be confused with the gambling game that is played in China under the same name. In fact, the well-known Chinese game is not a card game.*

NUMBER OF PLAYERS

Any reasonable number may play, with perhaps four to six being the best.

CARDS

The standard 52-card pack is used, with cards ranking from King (high) to Ace (low).

Players cut for deal, the drawer of the highest card being first dealer. Thereafter the deal passes to the left.

Before each deal an agreed amount is placed by each player into a pool. The cards are dealt one by one, face downwards, until the pack is exhausted.

THE PLAY

Play begins by the player on the left of the dealer placing a 7 face upwards in the centre of the table. If he has no 7 he contributes one unit to the pool, and the player on his left now has to play a 7 to the centre of the table or contribute one unit to the pool, and so on.

As soon as a 7 has been played to the centre of the table, the next player must play either the 6 of the same suit on its left, or the 8 of the same suit on its right, or the 7 of another suit below it. The game continues clockwise round the table, the players building up to the Kings on the right of the 7s and down to the Aces on the left of them.

Any player who is unable to play in his turn contributes one unit to the pool, and if he revokes, by failing to play when he could do so, he forfeits three units to the pool, and five units each to the holders of the 6 and 8 if he fails to play a 7 when he could and should have played it.

The game is won by the player who is first to get rid of all his cards. He receives all that is in the pool and from each of the other players one unit for every card that the player holds.

Skill comes into the game by holding up the opponents. As a general rule a 7, unless it is accompanied by several cards of the same suit, should be kept in hand for as long as possible; and, if a player has a choice of plays, he should prefer the card that will allow him later to play a lower or higher one of the same suit, rather than one that can only help the opponents.

With the situation of the game as in the illustration, the player plays the ♣ 10 because when the ♣ J is played he can follow with the ♣ Q. It would be an error of judgement to play the ♥ 6, because it doesn't help him, but might help the opponents.

The game can, of course, be enjoyed by children (or adults) without the need for a pool.

PLAY OR PAY

The original version of Fan Tan was called Play or Pay and may still be enjoyed. The eldest hand may lead any

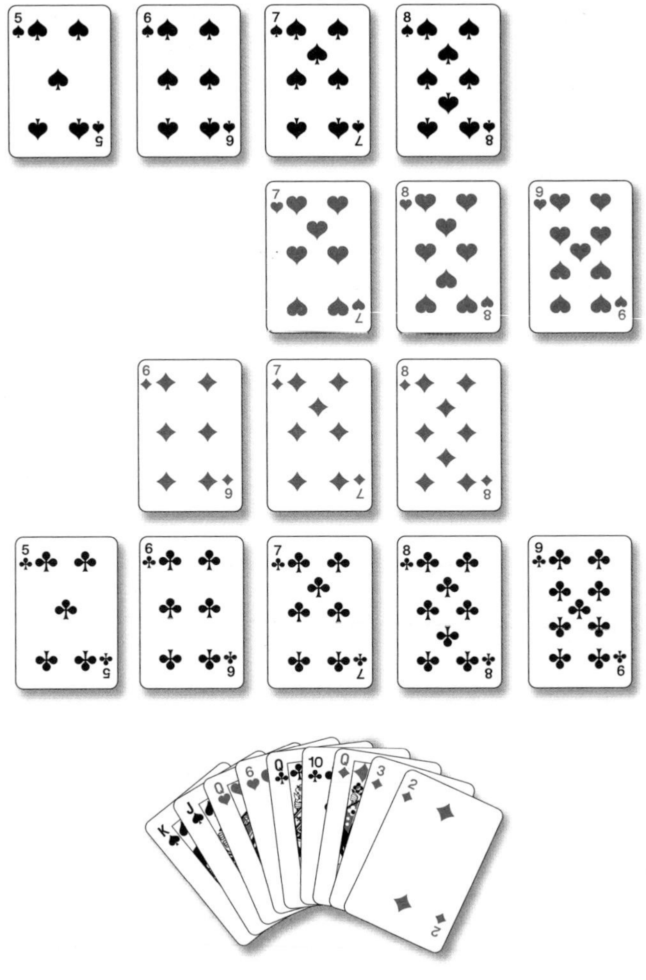

card (not necessarily a 7). The next player must play the next higher card in the same suit, or, if unable to, pay a chip to a pool. The sequence is built upwards only, and is regarded as continuous, i.e. Ace follows King. Only one suit is played at a time, and only when the first suit is finished is a second begun. The player who lays the last card in the first suit also plays the first card to the next – the suit and the rank are of his choice. The first person to get rid of his cards wins the pool.

The first player to play might choose a suit in which he has two consecutive cards, and lay the higher. By this means he is certain to lay the last card in the suit and thus begin the next. It is clearly an advantage to play first to the final suit, when opposite rules apply, and the player will decide which of his cards provide the biggest gap and lead so that his own cards are played before this gap is filled.

If the hand in the illustration above is held by the player to play first, its holder has an excellent chance of winning. He should begin with ♥ K, and will play the last card in the heart suit with ♥ Q. He then begins spades with ♠ 8 and plays the last card with ♠ 7. He then lays ♣ 4 and ends the suit with ♣ 3. Then he plays ♦ 10 and wins provided each of his opponents holds one of the cards ♦ 9, 8, 7, 6, 5, 4, 3. An alternative plan would be to play the diamond suit second, and hope that the last suit, whether it be spades or clubs, will begin at such a level that he can play his two consecutive cards before any other player has gone out.

It should be pointed out that if players put in chips for each pass, each player might easily pass 40 times in one deal, so stakes should be geared accordingly. An alternative method of settling up debts would be for each loser to pay the winner at the end of the deal one chip for each card remaining in his hand. Like Fan Tan, the game can, of course, be played for enjoyment only.

NEWMARKET

NEWMARKET *is a modern variation of the old game of Pope Joan and is known by a number of other names – Boodle and Stops in England; Chicago, Michigan and Saratoga in the USA. It is an excellent gambling game that is easy to learn and contains an element of skill that guarantees the better player winning in the long run.*

NUMBER OF PLAYERS

From three to eight players may play.

CARDS

The game is played with a full pack of 52 cards, ranking from Ace (high) to 2 (low), and an Ace, King, Queen and Jack (each of a different suit) from another pack. These four extra cards are known as the boodle cards, and are placed, face up, in a row in the centre of the table.

THE PLAY

Before the deal each player has to stake an agreed number of chips (usually, but not necessarily, 10) on the boodle cards. He may stake his chips as he pleases, but he must not stake more nor less than the agreed number.

The dealer then deals the cards one at a time to each player in rotation, and to an extra hand or dummy. As the players must each receive the same number of cards, any over-cards are dealt to the dummy hand which remains face downwards on the table throughout the deal.

The player on the left of the dealer makes the first lead. He may lead a card from any suit, but it must be the lowest card that he holds in the suit. The players do not play in rotation round the table. The next play is made by the player who holds next higher cards in the suit, then the next higher card is played by the player who holds it, and so on, until the run is stopped either because a player plays the Ace of the suit, or the next higher card is in the dummy hand. Either way, the player who played the last card leads the lowest card of another suit, and if he has no other suit the lead passes to the player on his left.

When a player plays a card that is identical with one of the boodle cards he collects all the chips from it.

The object of the game, however, is not only to win the chips that have been staked on the boodle cards, but to get rid of all one's cards, because the

player who is first to do so receives one chip from each of the other players. If no player gets rid of all his cards, the one who holds the fewest cards wins the hand, and if two players are left with an equal number of fewest cards they divide the winnings.

If when a deal comes to an end the chips on one or more of the boodle cards have not been claimed, because the corresponding cards to the boodle cards are in the dummy hand, they are simply carried forward to the next deal of the game.

PIP-PIP!

PIP-PIP! *can be quite a noisy game, and is an enjoyable one for a party.*

NUMBER OF PLAYERS

Any reasonable number may play up to about 12, but maybe six to eight players is best.

CARDS

Two standard packs are required, shuffled together. The cards rank as follows: 2, Ace, King, Queen, Jack, 10, 9, 8, 7, 6, 5, 4, 3, in other words in the usual order except that 2 is promoted to be the top card in each suit.

The players draw cards. He who shows the highest deals first, and the card drawn determines the trump suit. Thereafter the deal passes to the left, and the trump suit is determined by the player to the right of the dealer cutting the pack.

Seven cards are dealt face down to each player, and the remainder of the pack is placed face downwards in the centre of the table (the stock).

THE PLAY

The object of the game is to win tricks containing 2s, Aces, Kings, Queens and Jacks, and for winning them a player scores 11 points for each 2, 10 points for each Ace, five points for each King, four points for each Queen and three points for each Jack.

The player on the left of the dealer leads to the first trick. Thereafter the player who wins a trick leads to the next. A player must follow suit if he can; if not he may either discard or trump. If two players play identical cards, the player of the second is deemed to have played the higher card.

Immediately after a player has played to a trick he draws a card from the stock; if he now holds in his hand the King and Queen of the same suit, other than of the trump suit, he may call 'Pip-Pip', and place the two cards face upwards on the table in front of him. For calling 'Pip-Pip' a player scores 50 points and, at the end of the current trick, the trump suit changes to that of the exposed King and Queen.

'Pip-Pip' may be called and 50 points scored if a player is dealt the King and Queen of a suit – other than of the trump suit. The trump suit is then changed before the first trick is played. If two or more players are dealt the King and Queen of a suit – other than of the trump suit – each scores 50 points if he calls 'Pip-Pip'. The trump suit is changed to that of the player who was first to call. 'Pip-Pip' may be called twice in the same suit provided the player has both Kings and both Queens of it. A King or a Queen once paired cannot be paired a second time. It is not compulsory to call 'Pip-Pip' if a player holds the King and Queen of a suit, but if he does not call he cannot score the bonus of 50 points.

Drawing cards from the stock continues until it contains insufficient cards to enable every player to draw one. The remaining cards in the stock are then turned face upwards and the players play the last seven tricks with the cards left in their hands.

The game ends when every player has dealt an equal number of times.

POPE JOAN

POPE JOAN *is a very old card game that at one time was exceptionally popular in Scotland. The ♦ 9 is given the name of Pope and as the Pope was the Antichrist of Scottish reformers, there is reason to think that it was for this reason that the nickname of Curse of Scotland became attached to the card. Pope Joan is a gambling game.*

NUMBER OF PLAYERS

Any number from three to eight may play, with four to six being best.

CARDS

The game is played with a standard pack of 52 cards from which the ♦ 8 is removed.

THE PLAY

Originally a special board, consisting of a circular tray divided into eight compartments, and revolving about a central pillar, was used with counters. Today these boards are museum pieces, and modern players must make do with eight saucers labelled: *Pope* (♦ 9), *Ace, King, Queen, Jack, Matrimony, Intrigue, Game*, placed in the centre of the table.

Each player begins with the same number of counters of an agreed value, and the dealer places six in the saucer labelled Pope (♦ 9), two each in Matrimony and Intrigue, and one each in Ace, King, Queen, Jack and Game. It is called dressing the board.

Cards are dealt to the players and to an extra hand (widow) in the centre of the table. The number of cards dealt to each player and the widow depends on the number of players in the game. The players must each hold the same number of cards, so any over-cards go to the widow. The last card is turned face upwards to denote the trump suit, and if it is either the Pope (♦ 9) or an Ace, King, Queen or Jack, the dealer wins the counters in the corresponding saucer.

The player on the left of the dealer leads to the first trick. He may lead any card he chooses, and at the same time he announces it. Suppose it is the ♣ 6. Then the player who holds the ♣ 7 plays it and announces it, the player who holds the ♣ 8 plays it and announces it, and so on, until the run comes to an end.

The four Kings are stop cards, and in the diamond suit the 7 is as well, because the ♦ 8 has been removed from the pack. In practice, of course, any card may be a stop card on account of the cards in the widow hand, and because the next higher card may already have been played.

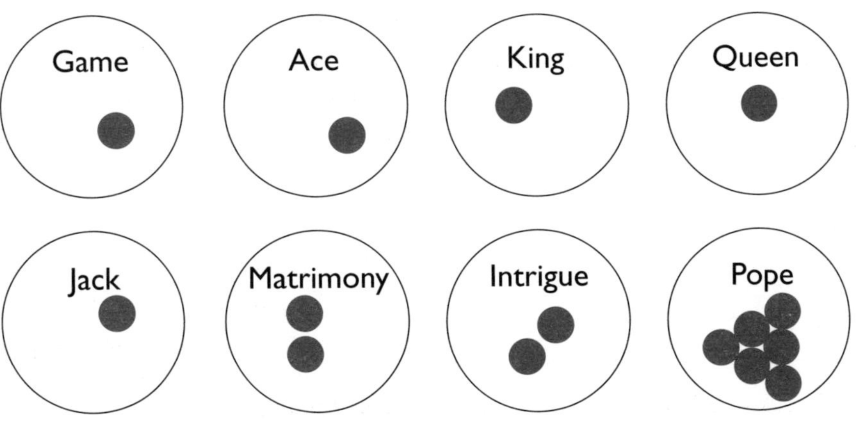

When a run comes to an end, the player of the stop card starts a fresh run by leading any card he likes. In this way the game continues until one of the players has played all his cards. He is then entitled to the counters in the Game saucer, and, in addition, he receives from each player one counter for every card left in his hand. The player who is left with the Pope (♦ 9), however, is exempt from paying the winner so long as he holds the card in his hand. If he has played it in the course of the game he loses this advantage.

During the course of the game, any player who plays the Ace, King, Queen or Jack of the trump suit, or the Pope (♦ 9), wins the counters in the corresponding saucers; if the same player plays the King and Queen of the trump suit he wins the counters in Matrimony, and if the same player plays the Queen and Jack of the trump suit he wins those in Intrigue.

The deal passes round the table clockwise, and any counters that have not been won in a deal are carried forward to the next.

RANTER GO ROUND

RANTER GO ROUND *is an old Cornish game with the rather more appropriate alternative name of Cuckoo. It is a game that children enjoy.*

NUMBER OF PLAYERS

Ranter Go Round can be played by any reasonable number of players.

CARDS

The full pack of 52 cards is used, cards ranking from Ace (high) to 2 (low).

THE PLAY

Each player begins with an agreed number of units, which is usually three. The dealer deals one card face downwards to each player. The object of the game is to avoid being left with the lowest card.

The player on the left of the dealer begins the game. He may either retain his card or offer it to his left-hand neighbour with the command 'Change'. There is no choice about it. The player so commanded must exchange cards with his right-hand neighbour unless he holds a King, when he says 'King', and the game is continued by the player on his left.

When an exchange has been made, the player who has been compelled to do so may pass on the card he has received in the same way, and so on, clockwise round the table, until the card is brought to a halt either by a King or by a player receiving a higher card in exchange, so he has nothing to gain by passing it on.

Any player giving an Ace, 2 or 3 in obedience to the command 'Change' must announce the rank of the card.

The dealer is last to play, and if he wishes to exchange his card, he does so by cutting the remainder of the pack and taking the top card of the cut.

If in doing this he draws a King he loses the hand and contributes one unit to the pool. If he does not draw a King, all the players expose their cards and the one with the lowest contributes one unit to the pool. If two or more tie for lowest card, all contribute to the pool.

When a player has contributed all his units to the pool, he retires from the game. The others continue, and the game is won by he who is left with at least one unit in hand.

RED DOG

ALTHOUGH *in Red Dog, or High-card Pool, players stake on their cards, it is usually accepted as a party game, rather than a banking game, because the players stake against a pool and not against a banker.*

NUMBER OF PLAYERS

Any number up to ten may play.

CARDS

The full pack of 52 is used, cards ranking from Ace (high) to 2 (low).

THE PLAY

The players contribute to the pool an agreed number of units, and each player is dealt five cards (or only four cards if nine or ten players are in the game). Beginning with the player on the left of the dealer, each in turn bets a minimum of one unit and a maximum that must not exceed the number of units in the pool, that he holds a card that is higher than, and in the same suit as, the top card of the stock when it is his turn to play.

The dealer turns up the top card of the stock. If the player can beat it, he shows his card and is paid out of the pool. His remaining cards are not seen. If he cannot beat it, his stake is added to the pool and his cards are shown to the other players.

If at any time a player's winning bet takes everything in the pool, a new pool is started.

ROCKAWAY

ROCKAWAY *or Go Boom is a game that may be played by children.*

NUMBER OF PLAYERS

Any reasonable number may play.

CARDS

Two standard packs of 52 cards are shuffled together, making a pack of 104 cards. Cards rank from Ace (high) to 2 (low).

The dealer deals seven cards, face downwards, to each player. The next card (the widow) is placed face upwards in the centre of the table, and the rest of the pack (the stock) is placed face downwards on the table.

THE PLAY

In turn, and beginning with the player on the left of the dealer, each player covers the widow either with a card of the same rank, of the same suit, or with an Ace, drawn from his hand. If he has no suitable card in his hand he draws a card from the stock and continues to draw one until he draws a card that permits him to cover the widow.

The card that covers the widow then becomes the widow for the next player, and so on, round the table in a clockwise direction.

When the stock is exhausted, the players play out the cards in their hands, and a player who cannot cover the widow misses his turn.

The hand comes to an end when a player has exhausted the cards in his hand. The remaining players expose their cards, which are scored against them, an Ace counting 15 points, a court card 10 points, and all other cards their pip value.

The deal passes round the table in a clockwise direction, and the game comes to an end when every player has dealt an equal number of times, by arrangement between the players before the game begins.

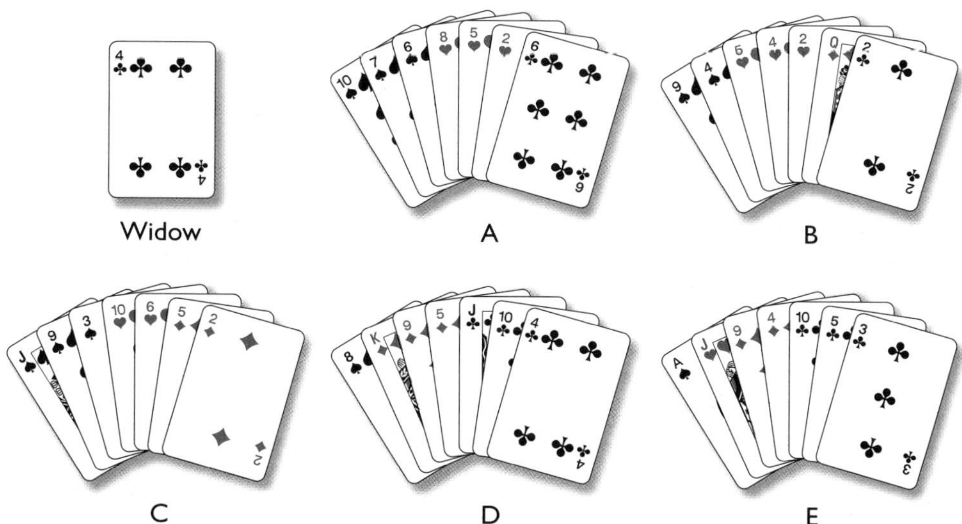

E dealt the hands illustrated. A, therefore, leads first, and the play is:

A	*B*	*C*	*D*	*E*
♣ 6	♣ 2	♦ 2	♦ K	♠ A

As an Ace counts 15 points against a player who is left with it, E plays ♠ A rather than one of his diamonds.

♠ 10	♠ 9	♠ J	♠ 8	?

As E has no spade, no 8 and no Ace in his hand, he must draw from the stock, and continue to do so until he draws a playable card.

E was foolish to play his Ace first round. As no opponent can go out in fewer than seven rounds, E would have been wise to keep his Ace for six rounds at least. He would not then have found himself in such a bad position on the second round. Usually, an Ace should not be played if another choice is available.

SPINADO

SPINADO *is a less complicated version of Pope Joan (see page 196). It is a mild gambling game. No board is necessary and there are only three pools: Matrimony, Intrigue and Game.*

NUMBER OF PLAYERS

Any number from two to seven may play, four or five being best.

CARDS

From a standard pack of 52 cards, the four 2s and the ♦ 8 are removed, leaving a pack of 47 cards. Cards rank from King (high) to Ace (low).

The dealer deals the cards to the players and to an extra hand (widow). As the players must each hold the same number of cards, over-cards go to the widow hand.

THE PLAY

Before dealing the dealer contributes 12 counters to the Matrimony pool, and six each to the Intrigue and Game pools. The other players contribute three counters each to the Game pool.

Matrimony is the King and Queen of Diamonds, Intrigue is the Queen and Jack of Diamonds.

The player on the left of the dealer starts the game by playing any card that he chooses, and the other players continue by playing the next higher cards in the chosen suit in succession until a stop is reached. The player who plays the stop card then starts a new run by playing any card that he chooses.

The ♦ A is known as Spinado, more usually abbreviated to Spin, and whoever holds it may play it at any time that he chooses provided that he accompanies it with the proper card, and announces that he is playing Spinado. It constitutes a stop, and he receives three counters from each opponent.

During the game, the player who plays the ♦ K receives two counters from each of the other players, and if he plays the ♦ Q as well he wins the Matrimony pool. The player who plays the ♦ Q and the ♦ J wins the Intrigue pool, and those who play the Kings of spades, hearts and clubs receive one counter from each of the other players.

The game is won by the player who is the first to play all his cards. He takes the counters in the Game pool and is exempt from contributing to the pools in the next deal, unless it is his turn to deal.

A player who is left with Spinado in his hand pays the winner of the game double for each card he is left with.

Spinado, therefore, should not be kept back too long. On the other hand,

Top: matrimony
Centre: intrigue
Bottom: spinado

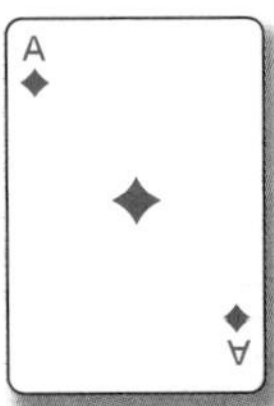

it is not always advisable to play it with one's first card. If, for example, a 10 is led, and the player who holds Spinado also holds the King and Jack, it is an error of judgement to play Spinado with the Jack, because if the Jack proves to be a stop there was no need for the play of Spinado, and the King is the natural stop if another player follows with the Queen.

It is better to hold up Spinado to be played with some card that is not known to be a stop.

THIRTY-ONE

THIRTY-ONE *may be played by any number of players up to 15. It is a gambling game.*

NUMBER OF PLAYERS

Any reasonable number may play.

CARDS

Thirty-One is played with the full pack of 52 cards, the Aces ranking high, the 2s low.

Three cards are dealt face downwards to each player, and three

The player might be advised to exchange his ♦ 5 with the ♥ 7 and rap, since 25 is not a bad score.

Widow

Hand

cards are placed face upwards in the centre of the table. It is known as the widow hand.

THE PLAY

Before each deal the players contribute an agreed amount to a pool.

In turn each player, beginning with the one on the left of the dealer, must exchange one of his cards with a card from the widow. He cannot pass, nor can he exchange more than one card. Counting the Ace as 11, the court cards as 10 each and all the other cards at their pip values, the object of the game is to hold three cards of the same suit which will add up to 31. Next in value is a hand that contains three cards of the same rank. Failing either, the pool is won by the player who holds the highest total in any one suit.

The exchange of cards with the widow hand continues until a player has obtained a 31 hand. When a player holds such a hand he exposes it on the table, claims the pool, and the deal passes. At any stage of the game, however, a player who thinks he has a hand good enough to win, may rap the table. The other players now have the right, in turn, either to stick with the cards that they hold, or exchange one more card with the widow. The players then expose their cards and the one with the best hand wins the pool.

BANKING GAMES

BACCARAT

BACCARAT, *more correctly Baccarat Banque, is a game of chance that is played in casinos everywhere.*

NUMBER OF PLAYERS

The game may be played by any number up to 30 or more.

CARDS

Six packs of cards are shuffled together (in Las Vegas eight packs are used) cut and placed in an open-ended box known as a shoe, designed to release only one card at a time. The court cards rank in value at 10 points each; all other cards at their pip values.

THE PLAY

The banker sits midway down one of the sides of a long, oval table (see bottom illustration opposite), and the players sit in equal numbers on both

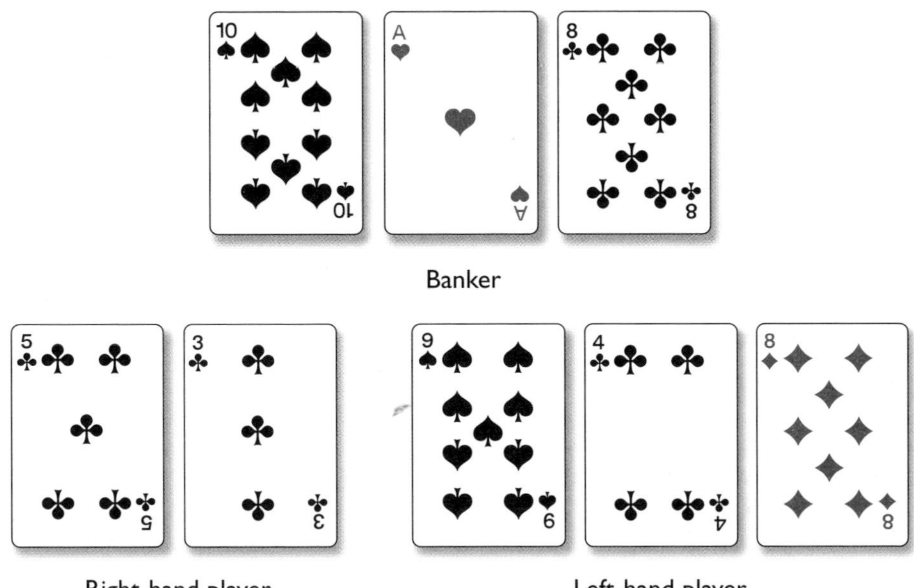

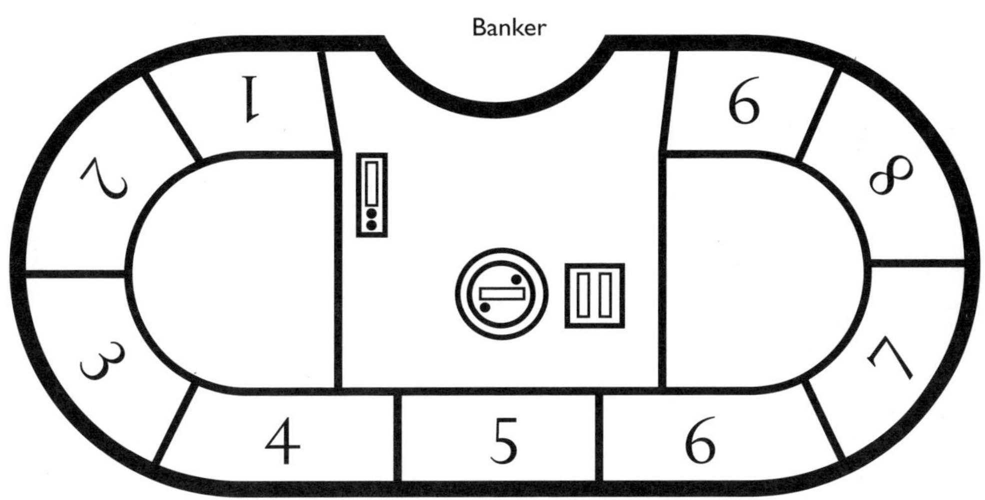

The layout of the staking table used in baccarat and *chemin de fer*.

sides of him. Those for whom there is no room to sit, stand behind them.

The banker, who is also the dealer, puts his stake on the table in front of him, and any player who wishes to bet against the whole of it calls 'Banco'. If two or more call, the one nearest to the banker's left makes the bet. If no one calls, the players combine their bets to equal the stake put up by the banker.

The banker then gives a card face downwards to the player on his right, a card to the player on his left and a card to himself. He repeats the operation so the three of them have two cards each.

The object of the game is to form in two or three cards a combination counting as nearly as possible to 9. In counting the total, ten is disregarded; if, for example, a player's two cards total 15 it counts as a point of 5.

The banker looks at his two cards and if he has a point of 8 or 9 he shows his cards (a natural). If he has not got a point of 8 or 9, he announces that he will give and the player on his right looks at his cards. If he has a point of 8 or 9 he shows his cards and announces his natural. If he has not got a point of 8 or 9 he may ask for one more card which the banker gives to him face upwards. The player on the left of the banker goes through the same performance, and then the banker may, if he chooses, take one more card. Finally, the banker wins or loses to each player according to whose point is nearer to 9; equality neither wins nor loses. A natural beats a three-card hand.

To illustrate (see top illustration on page 205). The banker holds ♠ 10 and ♥ A, making a point of 1, and he, therefore, must give. The right-hand player holds ♣ 5 and ♣ 3. He faces his cards, announces his natural point of 8, and must win. The left-hand player holds ♣ 9 and ♣ 4, making a point of 3. He must draw and the banker gives him ♦ 8, reducing his point to 1. For the moment, however, the left-hand player does not announce his point. The banker faces his cards, and, as he holds no more than a point of 1, he draws a card. It is the ♣ 8, which raises his point to 9.

The banker, therefore, wins from the left-hand player, but loses to the right-hand player because though the banker has a point of 9, against the point of 8 held by the right-hand player, a natural beats any point made by the addition of a drawn card.

The rules of play are strict and should never be deviated from because the player who is holding the cards is playing for all on his side of the table. If he deviates from the rules, and thereby loses the hand, he is liable to make good all losses incurred through his error. A player must not look at his cards until the banker has either announced that he holds a natural or that he will give cards. When a player looks at his cards, if he holds a natural he must expose his cards and declare his natural at once. If a player does not hold a natural, he must draw a card if he holds a point of 4 or less, stand if he holds a point of 6 or 7, and use his discretion to draw or stand only if he holds a point of 5.

BLIND HOOKEY

BLIND HOOKEY *is the simplest of all gambling games.*

NUMBER OF PLAYERS

Any number may play.

CARDS

The full pack of 52 cards is used.

After the pack has been shuffled by one player and cut by another to the banker, it is passed to the player on the left of the banker, who removes a few cards (not fewer than four) from the top of the pack, and places them in a pile face down on the table in front of him. He passes the pack to his left-hand neighbour who does the same, and so on until all the players (the banker last) have placed a small pile of cards in front of them.

THE PLAY

Without looking at the cards, all the players (except the banker) stake to an

The banker wins from A, B, C and F and loses to D, E and G. Overall he loses 3 units and, therefore, the bank passes to the next player.

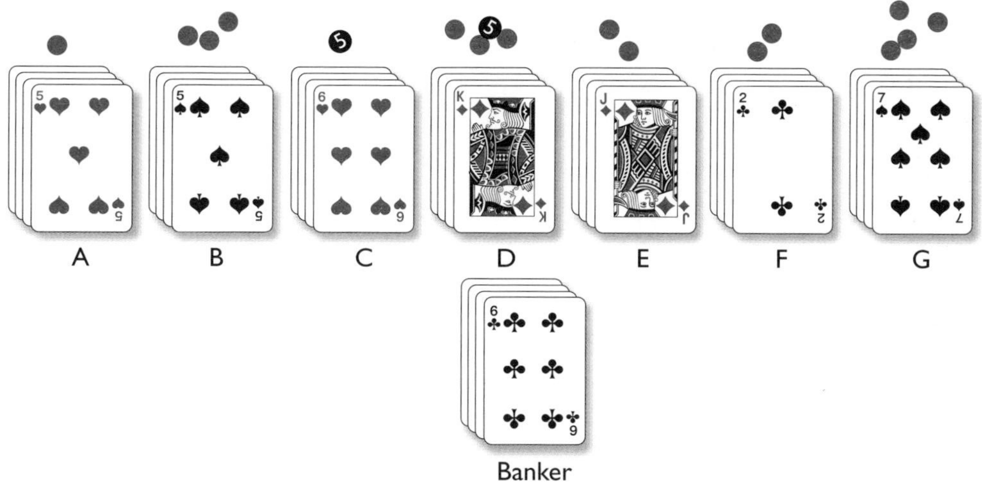

agreed limit and turn their piles face upwards to expose the bottom card. The banker wins from all whose exposed card is lower than or equal with his and loses to all whose card is higher. By agreement, the Ace may be high or low.

Play continues with the same banker if he wins more than he loses, or if he finishes level, but passes to the next player as soon as the banker loses more than he wins.

Another way of playing the game is for the banker to cut the pack into three piles. The players place their stakes on either of two piles, and the third pile is taken by the banker. The three piles are turned face upwards and the players receive from the banker or lose to him according to whether the bottom cards of their piles are higher or lower than the bottom card of his pile.

CHEMIN DE FER

CHEMIN DE FER, *nearly always called Chemmy, is the same game as Baccarat (see page 204) modified for social play, because in all games of chance the banker has an advantage to a greater or lesser degree, and his advantage at Chemin de fer is nothing like it is at Baccarat because he plays against one hand instead of against two.*

NUMBER OF PLAYERS

Any reasonable number can play.

CARDS

The full pack of 52 cards is used, although two or three packs shuffled together is better. In a casino, a number of packs will be used.

THE PLAY

For all practical purposes the difference between Baccarat and Chemin de fer is that at the latter game the bank passes in rotation round the table, the banker holding the bank until he loses a coup, when it is passed to the player on his left; and the banker deals only one hand, not two, to the players, the hand being held by the one who has made the largest bet.

As the banker plays against only one hand, he may not use his judgement whether to draw or stand. The rules for play are precise and strict:

If his point is 8 or 9 he declares a natural.

If his point is 7 he stands whether the player draws any card or stands.

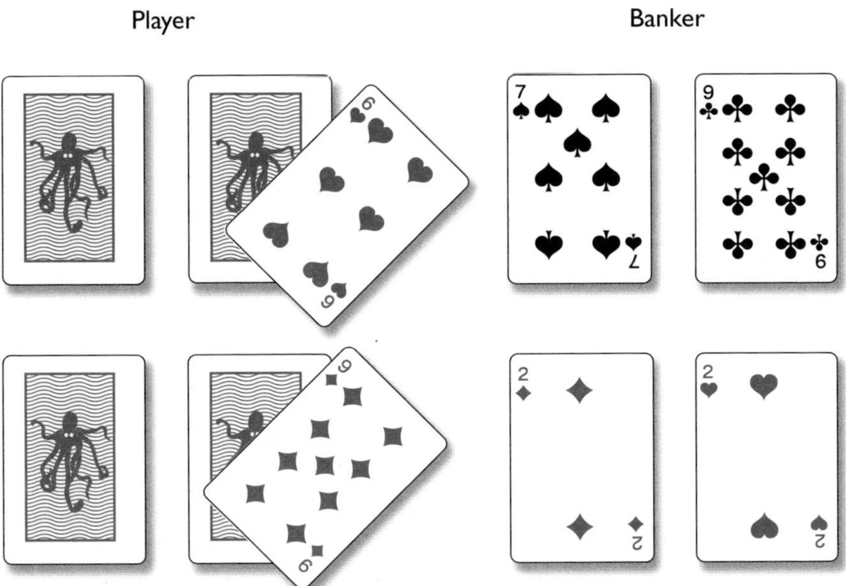

Top: Banker's point is 6. Player has drawn a 6, so banker must draw.
Above: Banker's point is only 4, but as player has drawn a 9 he must stand.

If his point is 6 he draws if the player draws a 6 or a 5, but stands if the player draws any other card or stands.

If he holds a point of 5 he draws if the player draws a 7, 6, 5, 4, 3, or stands, but stands if he draws any other card.

If he holds a point of 3 or 4 he draws if the player draws a 7, 6, 5, 4, 3, 2, or Ace or if he stands, but stands if he draws any other card.

If he holds a point of 0, 1 or 2 he draws whether the player draws any card or stands.

EASY GO

EASY GO *is a very simple game of chance, requiring no skill or concentration.*

NUMBER OF PLAYERS

Any number up to nine may play.

CARDS

The full pack of 52 cards is used.

THE PLAY

The banker deals five cards face upwards to every player, except himself. He now turns up a card and any player who holds a card of the same rank pays into a pool two units if it is the same colour and one unit if it is different. In all the banker turns up five cards in turn, and for the second card the players pay into the pool three units if the cards are of the same colour and two if they are different; for the third card they contribute five units if the cards are of the same colour and four if they are different; for the fourth card they contribute nine units if the cards are of the same colour and eight if they are different; for the fifth card they contribute 17 units if the cards are of the same colour and 16 if they are different.

There is now a second show of five cards by the banker, but this time the players take out of the pool at the same rate as they paid into it.

After this, anything left in the pool is taken by the banker, but if there is not enough in the pool to meet the requirements of the players he must make it good.

The bank passes clockwise.

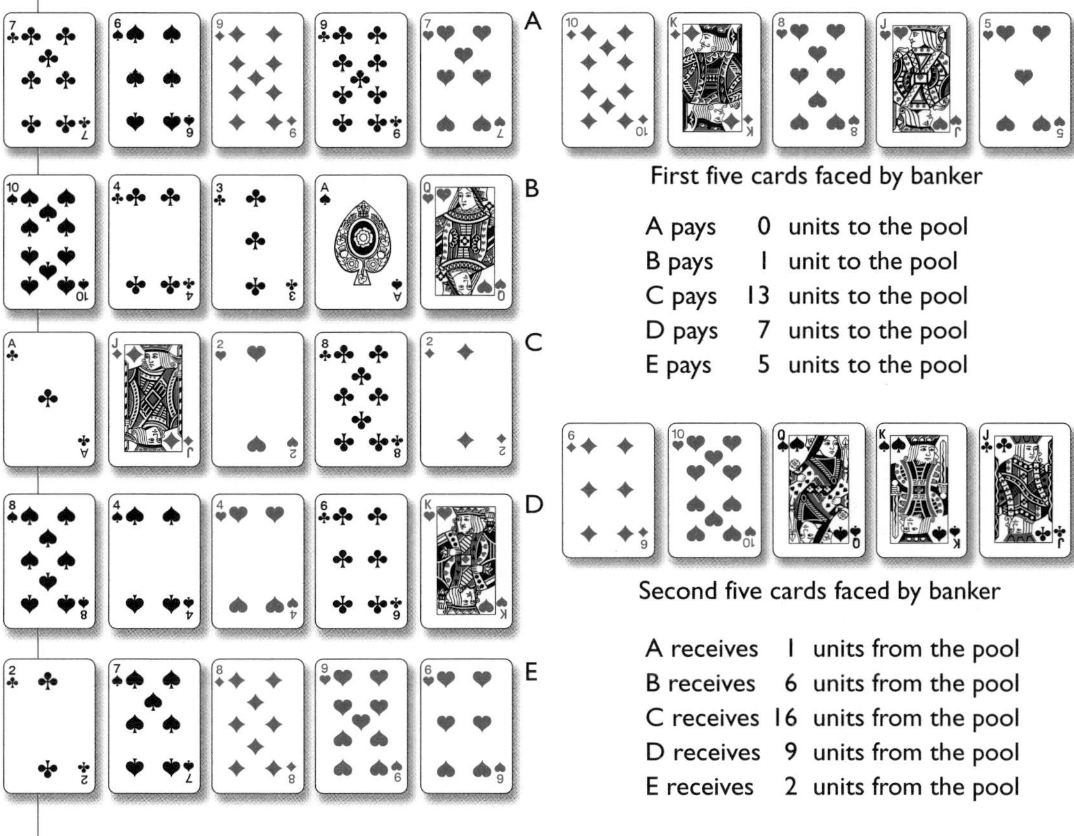

First five cards faced by banker

A pays 0 units to the pool
B pays 1 unit to the pool
C pays 13 units to the pool
D pays 7 units to the pool
E pays 5 units to the pool

Second five cards faced by banker

A receives 1 units from the pool
B receives 6 units from the pool
C receives 16 units from the pool
D receives 9 units from the pool
E receives 2 units from the pool

Overall result of this game of Easy Go: A wins 1 unit; B wins 5 units; C wins 3 units; D wins 2 units; E loses 3 units; banker loses 8 units.

HOGGENHEIMER

HOGGENHEIMER *is known as English Roulette, because the bets and staking bear a similarity to the French gambling game.*

NUMBER OF PLAYERS

Any number may play.

CARDS

Hoggenheimer is played with a pack of cards from which all of the 2s, 3s, 4s, 5s and 6s have been removed, and the Joker (or one of the rejected cards) added.

THE PLAY

After the pack has been shuffled and cut, the banker deals the cards, face downwards, in four rows of eight cards each, and places aside, also face downwards, the 33rd card. Great care must be taken when dealing that no one sees the face of any of the cards.

The top row is for spades, from Ace to 7; the second row for hearts, from Ace to 7; the third row for diamonds, from Ace to 7; the bottom row for clubs, from Ace to 7.

The players now stake their money. They may stake on a single card being turned up (even chance), or two touching cards being turned up (2 to 1 chance), or all four cards in a column or any group of four touching cards being turned up (4 to 1 chance), or all eight cards in a row being turned up (8 to 1 chance).

Hoggenheimer in progress. Stake 1 is on ♠ 10 being turned up; Stake 2 on ♠ 9, ♠ 8; Stake 3 on all four Queens; Stake 4 on ♦ 10, ♦ 9, ♣ 10, ♣ 9; Stake 5 on all clubs; Stake 6 on ♥ 7 and ♦ 7.

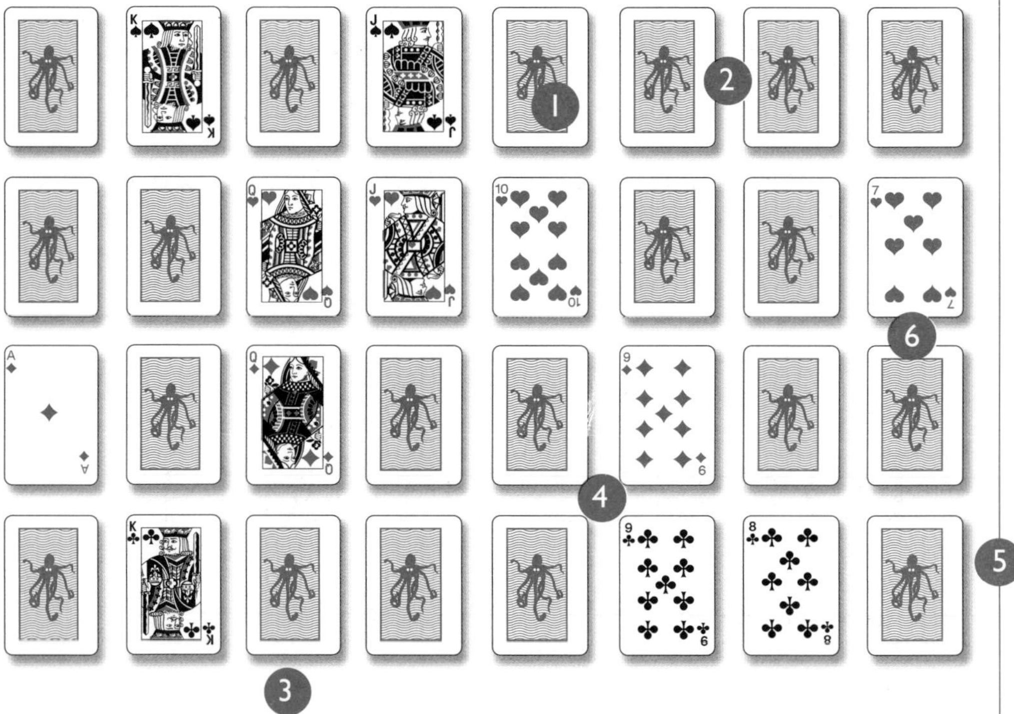

When the players have placed their bets, the banker picks up the 33rd card and shows it. If it is the Joker he wins all the money on the table and there is a redeal. If, as is more likely, it is another card, he places it in its appropriate place in the layout, exposes the card that it replaces and transfers this card to its place in the layout; and so on until the game is brought to an end when the he exposes the Joker.

The banker then collects the money on the chances that have not materialized in full, and pays out on those that have.

LANSQUENET

LANSQUENET, *of German origin, is a game of pure chance that derives its name from the 17th-century German mercenary (landsknecht) with whom the game is said to have been popular.*

NUMBER OF PLAYERS

Any number may play.

CARDS

The full pack of 52 cards is used.

The banker places the two top cards of the pack (hand cards) face upwards on the table. He then deals a card face upwards to himself, and one face upwards to the players. If either card is of the same rank as one of the hand cards it is put with them and another card dealt in its place.

THE PLAY

The players place their bets, and the banker covers them. He then draws cards from the pack, face upwards, one at a time. If he draws a card of the same rank as the players' card he wins the bets on it; if he draws a card of the same rank as his own card he loses all the bets on the other card; and if he draws a card that matches neither card nor the two hand cards it is placed on the table and the players may bet on it.

When the players' card is matched the banker withdraws both cards and deals another card to the players. Cards that match the hand cards are placed with them. The game ends when the pack is exhausted unless the banker matches his own card first.

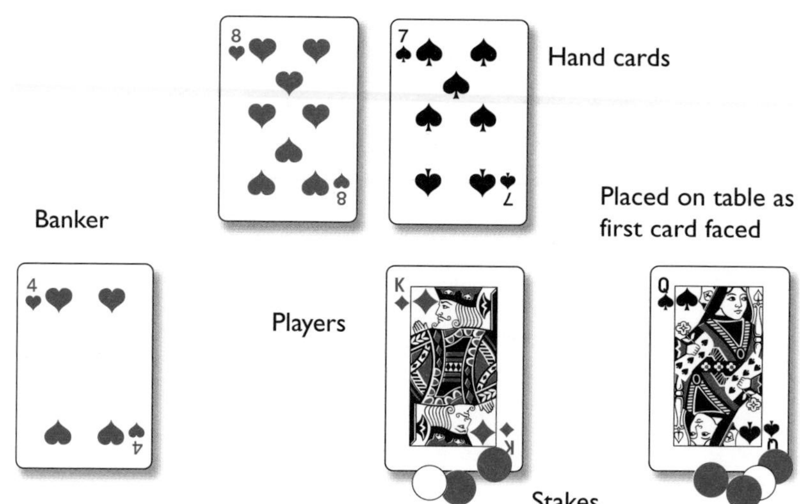

First card drawn from pack: ♠ Q. The card is placed on the table and players may bet on it. Second card drawn: ♦ 8. the card is hadded to the hand card pile. Third card drawn: ♥ K. the banker wins the two units staked on ♦ K.

MONTE BANK

IN PRINCIPLE *Monte Bank is a game of chance that is very similar to Lansquenet.*

NUMBER OF PLAYERS

Any number may play.

CARDS

The game is played with a pack of cards withthe 8s, 9s and 10s removed.

After the cards have been shuffled and the pack cut by one of the players, the banker draws the two cards from the bottom of the pack and places them face upwards on the table (the bottom layout), and then the two cards from the top of the pack and places them face upwards on the table (the top layout).

THE PLAY

The players place their bets up to an agreed maximum on whichever layout they choose. The banker then turns the pack face upwards and if the exposed

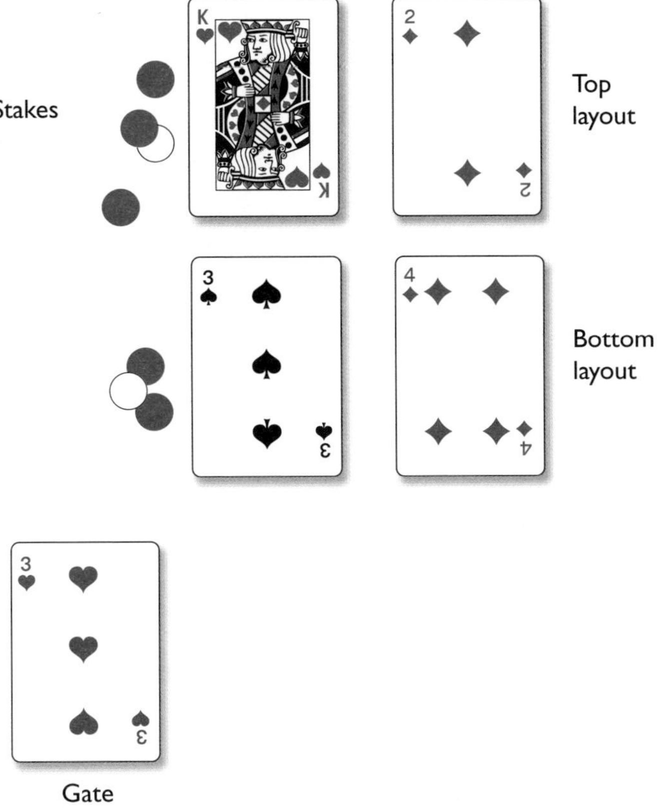

Banker pays four units to players who stake on the top layout and collects the three units on the bottom layout. If the gate had been a diamond, all players would have won; if a club all would have lost

bottom card (known as the gate) is of the same suit as any of the four cards in the layouts, he pays all bets on that layout, and collects all bets on a layout that shows no cards of the same suit as the gate.

The layouts and gate are then discarded, and the game is continued with new layouts and another gate. The bank passes to the next player in line after five coups.

RACING

RACING *is a simple gambling game.*

NUMBER OF PLAYERS

Any number may play.

CARDS

Racing is played with the standard pack of 52 cards.

THE PLAY

The four Aces are placed in a row on the table. The remainder of the pack is shuffled and cut, and the banker draws the top seven cards from the pack and lays them in a vertical column immediately below the Aces, so that the layout takes the form of a T (see illustration).

The banker deals the remaining cards one at a time, and each time that the card of a suit is dealt the Ace of the same suit is moved one card forward, the winner being the Ace that is first to pass the seventh card.

Players place their stakes on whichever Ace they choose. The race ends when an Ace passes the seventh card.

SLIPPERY SAM

SLIPPERY SAM, *or Shoot, as it is sometimes called, is probably the only banking game which favours the player rather than the banker, because the player has the advantage of seeing his cards before he bets and, therefore, can calculate whether the odds are in his favour or against him. Provided he bets with intelligence he should come out a winner.*

NUMBER OF PLAYERS

Any number up to ten may play, with six to eight the best.

CARDS

The full pack of 52 is used, the cards ranking from Ace (high) to 2 (low).

Racing layout (opposite). The banker might offer evens on a suit if there are no cards in the layout, 2-1 if there is one card (as with clubs and hearts here), 3-1 if there are two cards (diamonds here), 5-1 if there are three cards (spades here) and 10-1 if there are four cards. If there are five or more cards of a suit in the layout, it is impossible for that suit to win, and there must be a redeal.

THE PLAY

The banker places an agreed sum in a pool and then deals three cards, one at a time, face downwards, to each player. The remainder of the pack (the stock) he places face downwards on the table in front of him and topples it over to make it easier to slide off the top card.

The player on the left of the dealer, after looking at his cards, bets that at least one of them will be in the same suit as, and higher than, the top card of the stock. He may bet all that is in the pool or any part of it, but he may not bet less than an agreed minimum. When he has made his bet, the banker slides the top card off the stock and exposes it. If the player has won his bet he exposes his card and takes his winnings out of the pool. If he has lost his bet he pays the amount that he betted into the pool and does not expose his card. The four cards are then thrown into a discard pile, and the opportunity to bet passes to the next player.

Meanwhile, a player must not look at his cards until it is his turn to bet; if the pool is exhausted the bank immediately passes to the next player, otherwise the banker holds the bank for three full deals round the table, and then he may either pass the bank to the player on his left or hold the bank for one more, but only one more, deal round the table.

Since the player wins if a red card or a club lower than the 10 is exposed, and loses only if a spade or the Ace, King, Queen or Jack of clubs is exposed, he has 32 chances of winning and 17 of losing: he should stake heavily.

TRENTE ET QUARANTE

TRENTE ET QUARANTE, *or* Rouge et Noir, *is a game of pure chance and, like Baccarat (see page 204) is essentially a casino game. It is played on a long table, each end marked as in the accompanying diagram. The banker sits midway down one of the sides, the players sit, and some stand behind them, at each end.*

NUMBER OF PLAYERS

Any number of players may play.

CARDS

Six full packs of 52 are used, shuffled together.

THE PLAY

The six packs of cards are shuffled together, cut, and – with the Ace counting as one, the court cards 10 each, and other cards their pip values – the banker deals a row of cards until the total exceeds 30. He then deals a second row immediately below it in a similar manner. The top row is *noir* black) the lower *rouge* (red) and whichever row adds up to the lesser total wins. Apart from these two chances the players can bet on whether the first card dealt will be the same colour as the winning row (*couleur*) or the opposite colour (*inverse*). All four are even chances, but if both rows add up to 31 it is a *refait* (drawn game) and the player may either halve his stake with the bank, or allow the whole of it to be put in prison. He has the right to choose between the red and black prisons, and if his stake wins on the next deal he withdraws it.

All other identical totals end in the deal being declared void, and leave the player at liberty to withdraw his stake or leave it on the table to win or lose the next deal.

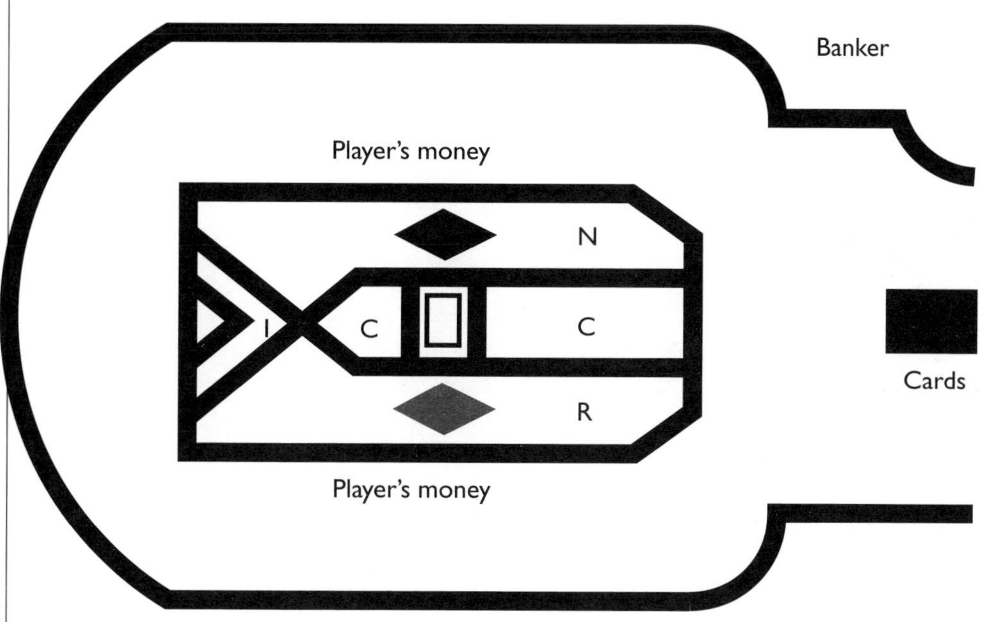

VINGT-ET-UN

VINGT-ET-UN *or Twenty-one, is a leading game in the casinos of USA where it is known as Black Jack. Although it is a game of chance, in which the odds on winning are heavily in favour of the banker, in Great Britain it is far more of a social pastime and, under the name of Pontoon (almost certainly a corruption of punting) it was exceptionally popular in the trenches during the First World War.*

NUMBER OF PLAYERS

Any number up to ten may play (or more if two packs of cards are used).

CARDS

The full pack of 52 cards is used (but see above).

THE PLAY

The banker deals one card face downwards to each player and to himself, and the players, after looking at their cards, stake any amount up to the agreed maximum.

The object of the game is to obtain a total of 21, or as near to it as possible, but without exceeding it. For this purpose an Ace counts 11 or 1 (at the option of the holder) a court card 10, and any other card its pip value.

When the players have made their bets, the banker looks at his card, and has the right to double. In this event the players must double their bets.

The banker then deals another card, face downwards, to all the players and to himself. If a player holds a pair he may announce his intention to split. He stakes the same amount as his original bet on both cards, and the banker deals a second card to each. The player plays both hands separately. The banker may not split pairs.

If the banker holds a natural (an Ace and a court card or a 10) he turns the two cards face upwards and receives from the players double what they have staked, except that if a player also holds a natural he loses only his original stake. The hands are thrown in, and the banker deals another hand.

If the banker does not hold a natural, but a player does, the banker pays him double his stake, and, after the deal has been completed, the bank passes to him. The bank, however, does not pass on a split natural. If two or more players hold naturals, the one nearest to the banker's left takes the bank.

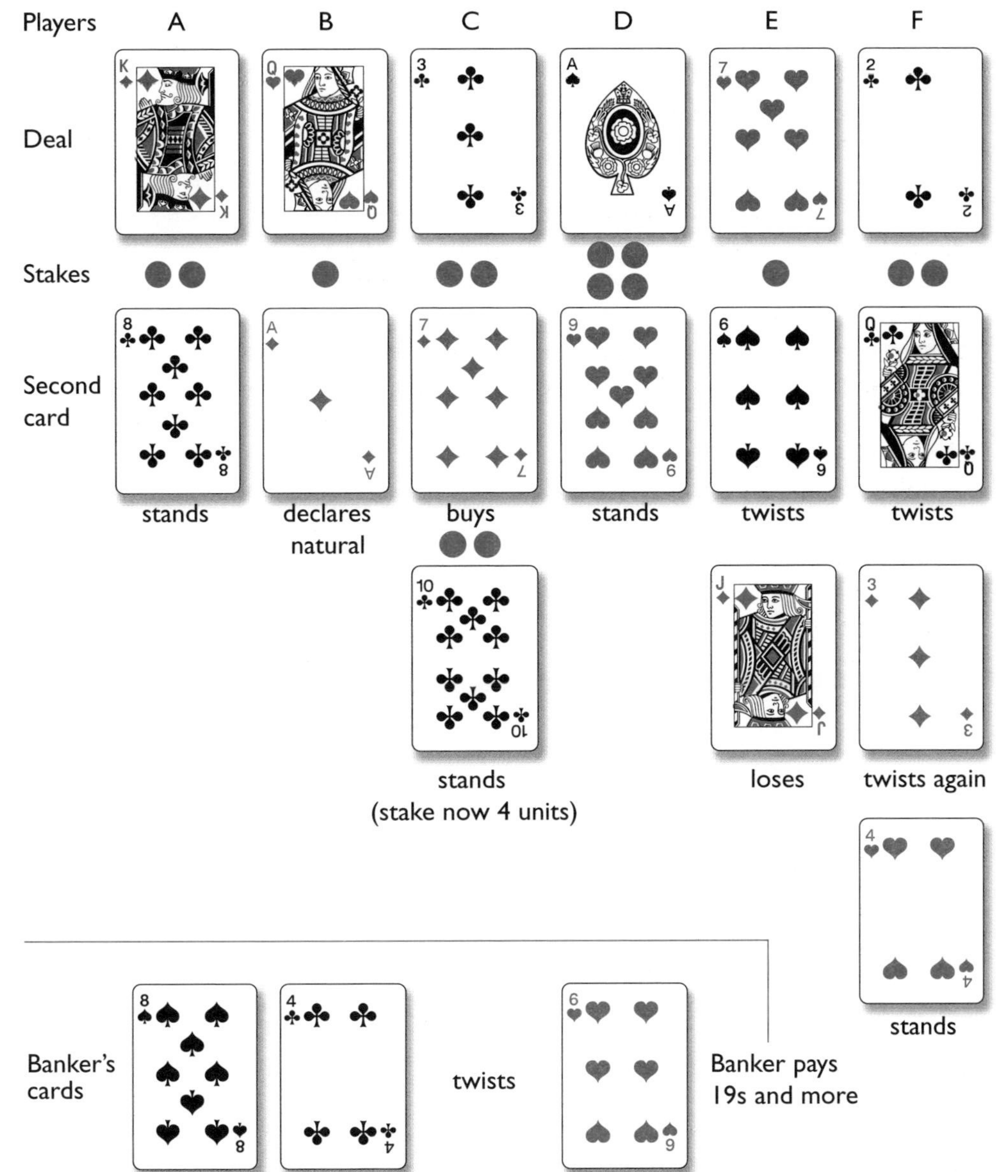

Banker pays B (double), C, D and F. Banker wins from A and E. Banker loses 9 units on deal.

When all naturals (if any) have been declared and settled, the banker asks each player in turn (beginning with the one on his left) whether he wants more cards or not. The player has three options. He may Stand; that is he elects to take no more cards. He may Buy; that is he increases his stake for the advantage of receiving a card face downwards. He may Twist; that is he does not increase his stake and receives a card face upwards. The rules to be observed are:

A player may not stand if he holds a count of 15 or less.

A player may not buy for more than his original stake.

If a player has twisted a third card he may not buy a fourth or fifth, though a player who has bought a third card may twist subsequent cards.

A player may not increase, though he may decrease, the amount for which he bought a previous card.

If a player has received four cards he may not buy a fifth if the total of his four cards is 11 or less.

Five cards is the most that a player may hold, and if they total 21 or less the banker pays him double, unless the banker also holds five cards that total 21 or less when the banker wins.

The player who makes a total of 21 with three 7s, receives triple his stake from the banker. The banker does not have this privilege.

When the total of a player's cards exceeds 21 he turns his cards face upwards and the banker wins all that he has staked.

When all the players have received cards, the banker turns his two cards face upwards and deals himself as few or as many cards as he chooses. If when doing so he exceeds a total of 21 he pays the players their stakes. At any time, however, he may elect to stand and agree to pay those players who have a higher total and receive from those who have a lower or equal total.

PATIENCE GAMES

BELEAGUERED CASTLE

SINGLE PACK

Beleaguered Castle, also called Laying Siege and Sham Battle, has a pleasing tableau although it must be admitted that it can be a frustrating game.

The four Aces are removed from the pack and placed in a column in the centre of the table to form the foundations. The remainder of the pack is shuffled and a column of four cards is dealt to the left of the Aces, followed by a column to the right of the Aces. Succeeding columns are dealt on these successively, each column overlapping the last until the whole pack is dealt and

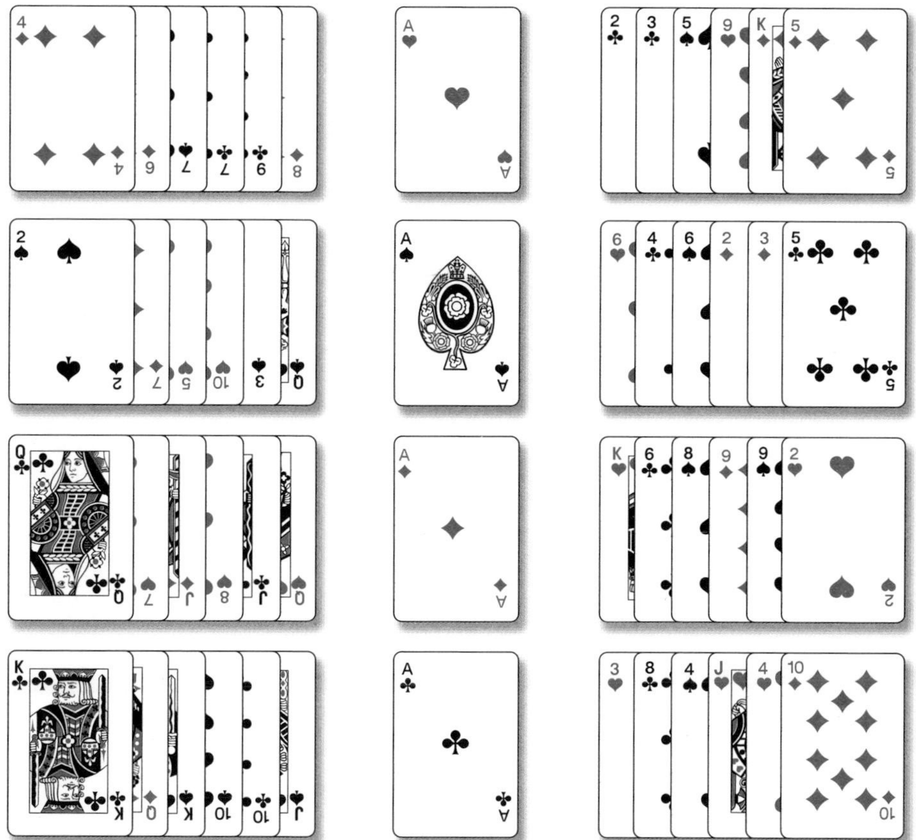

the tableau resembles that in the illustration. The cards to the left of the Aces are called the left wing and those to the right the right wing.

The object is to build on the foundations suit sequences up to the Kings. The cards available for play are those at the far end of each row, i.e. those whose faces are fully exposed. They can be built directly onto the foundations or packed onto another available card in descending order of rank, irrespective of suit, e.g. a 6 can be packed on any 7. When one of the rows is emptied, it can be filled by any available card. There are thus always eight available cards for play.

In the illustration, the ♥ 2 and ♠ 2 can be played to the foundations; the ♦ 4 to ♦ 5; ♣ 5 to ♦ 6; ♦ 3 to ♦ 4; ♦ 2 to foundation; ♦ 3, 4, 5 to foundation; ♠ 6 to ♦ 7; ♣ 4 to ♣ 5; ♣ Q to ♣ K; ♥ 6 to ♥ 7; ♦ K to the space created in the rows; ♥ 9 to ♦ 10; ♠ 5 to ♠ 6; ♣ 3 to ♣ 4; ♣ 2 to foundation, thus clearing another row and allowing the club foundation to be built on. But the game is soon doomed to failure, there being too many high cards burying the lower ones. The game is a quick one and the player will soon be optimistically redealing, which is the usual way with patience games.

BISLEY

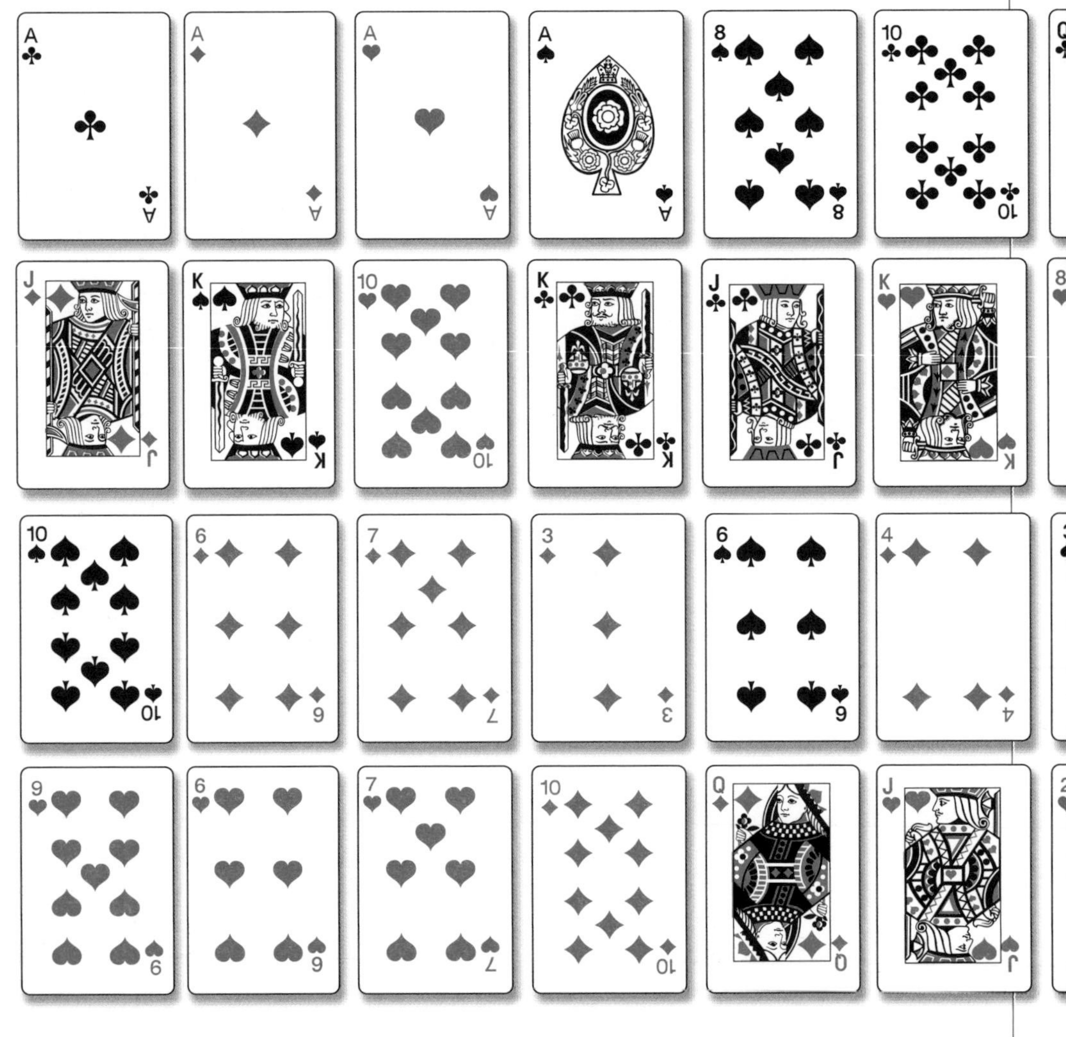

SINGLE PACK

Remove the Aces from the pack and place them face up in a row on the table. Deal nine cards in a row to the right of them, and the rest of the pack in three rows of 13 cards, below them (see illustration). When the four Kings become available, placed them above their Aces.

The Aces are built on upwards and the Kings downwards in suit-sequences. It does not matter where the two sequences meet.

Only the bottom card of a column is available for play. It may be built either on its Ace or King foundation, packed on the bottom card of another column, or itself be packed on. Packing may be

either upwards or downwards in suit sequence, and the player may change this at his convenience. A space left vacant in the layout, by the removal of a card, is not filled.

In the layout illustrated on page 225, the ♦ K is played above the ♦ A, the ♠ 2 is built on the ♠ A, and the ♥ 2 on the ♥ A. This exposes the ♠ 3 which is built on the ♠ 2. The ♦ Q is built on the ♦ K. The ♦ 9 is packed on the ♦ 10, and the ♦ 8 on the ♦ 9. Now the ♣ 8 is packed on the ♣ 9, exposing the ♣ 2 which is built on the ♣ A. And so on.

CALCULATION

SINGLE PACK

Calculation, or Broken Intervals, is a one-pack patience that is well-named, because it is necessary to calculate at the turn of every card, and it offers more scope for skilful play than any other patience.

Any Ace, any 2, any 3 and any 4 are placed in a row on the table to form four foundations. The object of the game is to build, regardless of suits, the remaining 48 cards on them, as follows:

On the Ace in the order Ace, 2, 3, 4, 5, 6, 7, 8, 9, 10, Jack, Queen, King.

On the 2 in the order 2, 4, 6, 8, 10, Queen, Ace, 3, 5, 7, 9, Jack, King.

On the 3 in the order 3, 6, 9, Queen, 2, 5, 8, Jack, Ace, 4, 7, 10, King.

On the 4 in the order 4, 8, Queen, 3, 7, Jack, 2, 6, 10, Ace, 5, 9, King.

The cards are dealt from the pack one at a time, and every card must either be built on a foundation or played to any one of a waste heap below each foundation. The pack is dealt only once, but play from a waste heap may continue after it has been exhausted. Only the top card of a waste heap may be played; it may be built on a foundation and may not be played to another waste heap.

The cards in the pack are now dealt one at a time. Suppose a 10 is dealt, as it cannot be built on a foundation it is best played to waste heap B. Next a 6 is dealt; it is built on the 3-foundation. Next comes an 8, and, of course, is built on the 4-foundation. The next card is a King. It must be played to a waste heap, but as a King is the last card to be built on a foundation it would be wrong to play it to waste heap B and so cover the 10. It should be played to another waste heap, and experienced players would now reserve

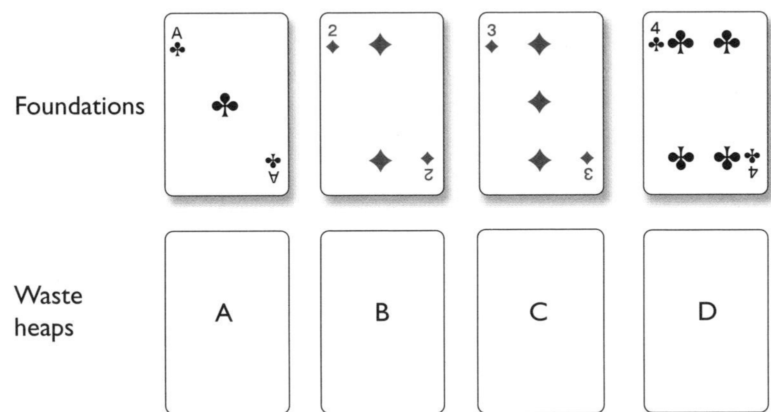

this for Kings. Play continues in this way until all 48 cards have been dealt.

If the play is carefully thought out, by building on the waste heaps descending sequences of two to four or, hopefully, more cards, towards the end of a game excellent progress will be made.

DEMON

SINGLE PACK

Demon is probably the best known of all the many one-pack patiences. It is sometimes known as Fascination, sometimes as Thirteen, and, in the USA, as Canfield, because it was reputedly invented by Richard A. Canfield, a well-known gambler of the late 19th century, whose practice it was to sell the pack for $52 and pay $5 for every card in the foundation row when the game came to an end. It was not altogether as profitable as it may seem, because for every player he had to employ a croupier to keep an eye on him during the play.

Thirteen cards are dealt face downwards in a pile and the top card is faced. The pile is known as the heel, and four cards are dealt face upwards in a row to the right of it. The next card of the pack is dealt face upwards and placed above the first card of the row. It indicates the foundations.

In the illustration overleaf, the ♦ 10 is the first of the four foundations, and the ♦ 3 is the top card of the heel. As they become available, the other three 10s are played to the right of the ♦ 10, and the object of the game is to build on them round-the-corner suit sequences up to the 9s. The four cards to the right of the heel are packed in descending sequences of alternate colours. As a start, therefore, the ♦ J is built on its foundation card; the ♣ 4 is packed on the ♥ 5 and the ♦ 3 on the ♣ 4. The card in the heel below the ♦ 3 is turned and, if it cannot be built on a foundation or packed on a card in the layout, is played to the space left vacant by the ♦ J. The next card in the heel is then exposed.

The bottom card of the four columns may be built on a foundation, but a sequence may be moved from one column to another only as a whole, and then only if the sequence can be packed on the next higher card of a different colour.

The stock is dealt to a waste pile in batches of three cards at a time, but if there are fewer than three cards at the end of the stock they are dealt singly.

The stock is dealt and redealt until the game is won, or lost because no further move can be made.

When all the cards in a column have been played, the space that is left must be filled at once with the top card of the heel and the next card of the heel exposed. A space must not be filled from the cards in hand, and when the heel is exhausted, spaces are filled from the waste heap, and the player need no longer fill a space at once, but leave it vacant until a suitable card is available.

GOLF

SINGLE PACK

Golf is a patience game, but addicts of the real game of golf might like to play it against an opponent, as described later.

Seven cards are dealt face up in a row, and second, third, fourth and fifth rows are dealt, each overlapping the previous row, until 35 cards are dealt in a tableau as shown in the illustration. This tableau is known as the 'links'.

The remainder of the cards are held in the hand and dealt one at a time to a talon or waste heap. Any of the cards exposed in the bottom row of the links are available to play onto the top card of the talon in either ascending or descending order, irrespective of suit. As many cards as possible may be played onto the talon at a turn, and the sequence may go up and down at will. However, the sequence does not go 'round-the-corner', i.e. Aces cannot be played onto Kings and vice-versa.

When a card has been removed from the bottom row, the card below it becomes available for play, i.e. a card fully exposed is available.

The object is to clear as many cards from the links as possible by the time the cards in the hand have run out. The number of cards remaining in the links is the score for the hole. Eighteen such holes are played to establish a player's score for the round. Sometimes the links will be cleared before all the cards in hand are exhausted, in which case the cards in hand represent a minus score for the hole, and can be deducted from a player's total. The object when played purely as a patience game is to beat par: 72 'strokes'.

In the layout in the illustration the ♦ 7 is turned over as the first card from hand onto the waste heap. Cards from the links can be played onto the ♦ 7 as follows: ♠ 8, ♦ 9, ♦ 10, ♥ J, ♥ Q, ♣ J, ♣ 10. A good start. The next card is turned over and so on.

COMPETITIVE GOLF

Golf Patience can be played as a competitive game by two or more players. Each player has his own pack, and each deals 35 cards into a links as related. Each player plays a hole simultaneously so that each records a score for each of the 18 holes, the lowest being the winner.

Two players can play 'match-play', in which instead of recording the score for each hole, each hole is either won, lost

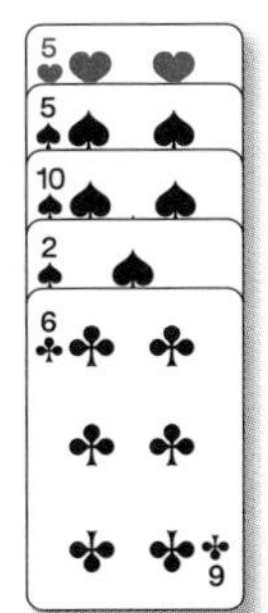

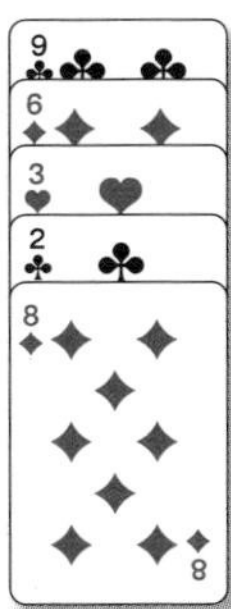
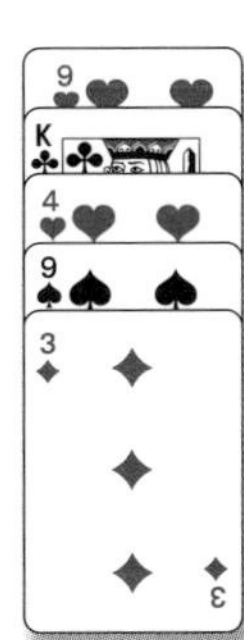

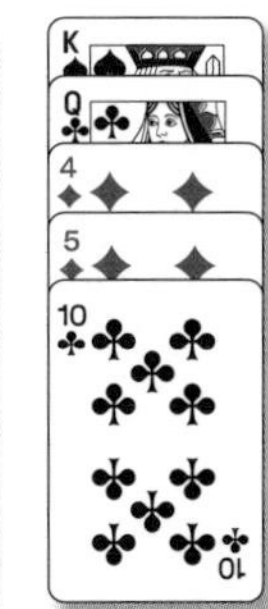

or halved, so that at any stage a player is 'two-up', 'three down', etc, as in the real game. Four can play as a 'four-ball', i.e. in two partnerships, each player using his own pack and only the lower score of each pair counting.

It is well known that patience players face a great temptation to cheat from time to time. Of course, players taking part in Competitive Golf must be as scrupulous over the rules as their counterparts out on the course.

KLONDIKE

SINGLE PACK

The Demon (see page 227) and the Klondike are probably the two best-known and most popular of the one-pack patience games. In England the name of Canfield is sometimes attached to the Klondike. This name, however, is a misnomer, and to be corrected, because Canfield is the name

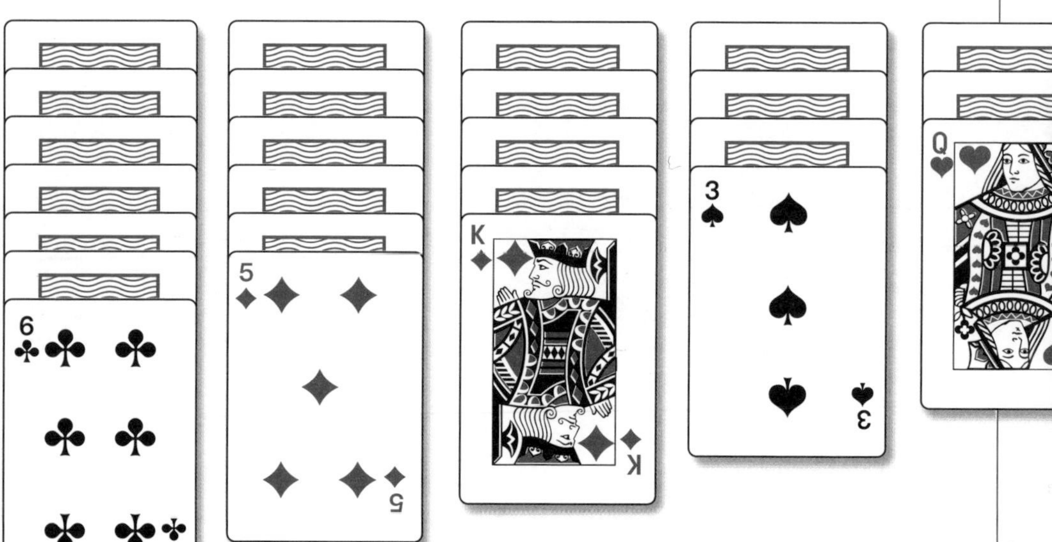

that in America is given to the patience that in England is called the Demon.

Twenty-eight cards are dealt face downwards in slightly overlapping rows of seven cards, six cards, five cards, four cards, three cards, two cards and one card. The bottom card of each row is turned face upwards (see illustration).

As they become available, Aces are played as foundations to a row above the layout; the object of the game is to build on the Aces ascending suit sequences to the Kings.

An exposed card at the bottom of a column is available to be built on a foundation, or it may be packed in a descending sequence of alternate colour. A sequence may be moved from one column to another, but only as a whole and when the highest card of the sequence may be placed on the next higher card of another colour. When an exposed card is played, the face-downwards card immediately above it is turned face upwards; when a whole column is moved, the space must be filled by a King which may or may not have a sequence attached to it.

The stock is dealt one card at a time to a waste heap, of which the top card is available for building on a foundation or packing on a column in the layout. Only one deal is allowed.

An Ace must be played to the foundation row as soon as it becomes available, but all other cards may be left in position if the player prefers to wait on the prospect of finding a better move later in the game.

In the layout shown the ♦ 5 is packed on the ♣ 6, and the card under the ♦ 5 is turned face upwards. The ♣ J

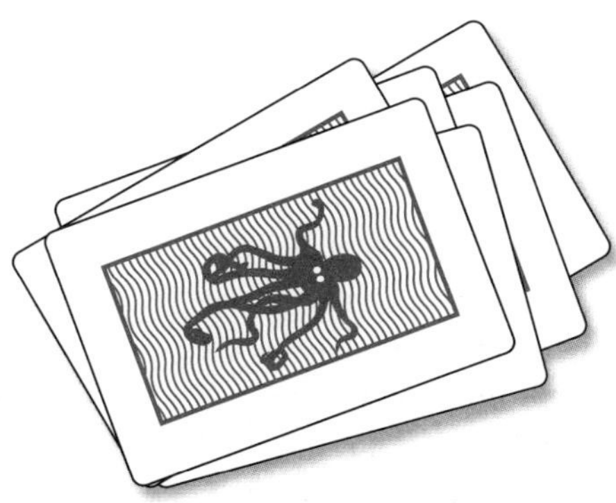

is packed on the ♥ Q, and the ♦ K moved to fill the space vacated by the ♣ J. The card under the ♦ K is now turned face upwards. And so on.

JOKER KLONDIKE

Klondike has been the subject of several variations. One of the best is Joker Klondike. It is played in the same way as the parent game, but with the Joker added to the pack. Whenever the Joker becomes available for play it must be built on a foundation as the next card in sequence. Other cards, if they are in correct sequence, are built on it, but when the natural card that it replaces becomes available it is substituted for the Joker which is built on another foundation.

A player may choose on which foundation he will build the Joker. If it becomes available for play before a foundation has been started it must remain in its position until an Ace turns up and a foundation started.

LA BELLE LUCIE

SINGLE PACK

La Belle Lucie, or the Fan, is one of the classic one-pack patiences; it has a very pleasing layout. The entire pack is spread on the table in 17 fans of three cards each and one of a single card, as illustrated opposite.

As the Aces become available they are placed above the layout as foundations, to be built on in ascending suit sequences to the Kings. Only the end card of each fan and the single card are available for play. They may be built on a foundation, packed on the end card of another fan in descending suit sequence, or themselves be packed on in descending suit sequences. A space made by playing off a complete fan is not filled.

When all possible moves have been made, all the cards except those played to the foundations are picked up, shuffled, and redealt in fans of three. If one or two cards are left over they make separate fans. Two redeals are allowed.

In the layout illustrated opposite the ♥ A and ♣ A are played to the foundation row. The ♥ 2 is built on the ♥ A, and the ♣ 7 is packed on the ♣ 8. This releases the ♣ 2 that is built on the ♣ A. The ♦ J is packed on the ♦ Q, the ♥ J on the ♥ Q, and the ♠ A followed by the ♠ 2 go to the foundation row. And so on.

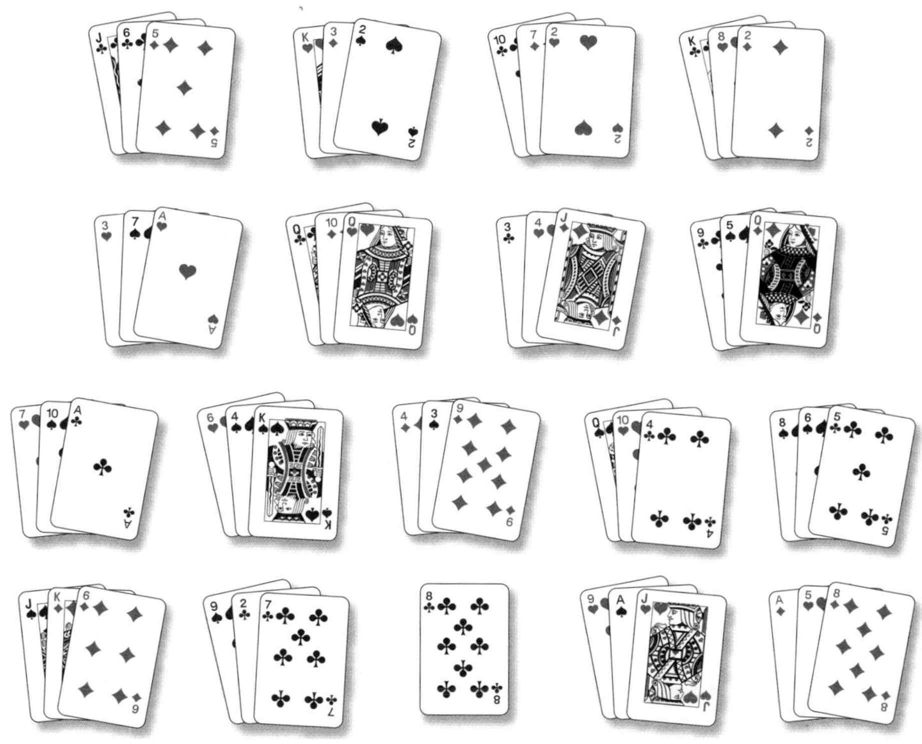

LITTLE SPIDER

SINGLE PACK

The red Aces and the two black Kings (or the two black Aces and the two red Kings) are placed in a row on the table to serve as foundations. The remaining 48 cards are dealt, face upwards, in two rows of four cards each, one above the foundation cards, the other below them, as illustrated overleaf.

The object of the game is to build ascending suit sequences on the Aces to Kings, and descending suit sequences on the Kings to Aces.

During the deal (i.e. after each round of eight cards) a card may be built from the upper row on any of the four foundation cards, but from the lower row only on the foundation card directly above it.

After every batch of eight cards has been dealt, the top cards of all eight piles are playable and may be built on any foundation cards or packed on any other pile in the layout. The piles are packed in ascending or descending, continuous sequences (an Ace ranks below a 2 and above a King) regardless of suit. A space made by removing an entire pile is not filled.

In the layout illustrated, the ♣ Q may be built on the ♣ K and the ♥ 2 on the ♥ A. The ♣ 10 may be packed on the ♠ J, and the ♣ 5 on the ♠ 6. And so on.

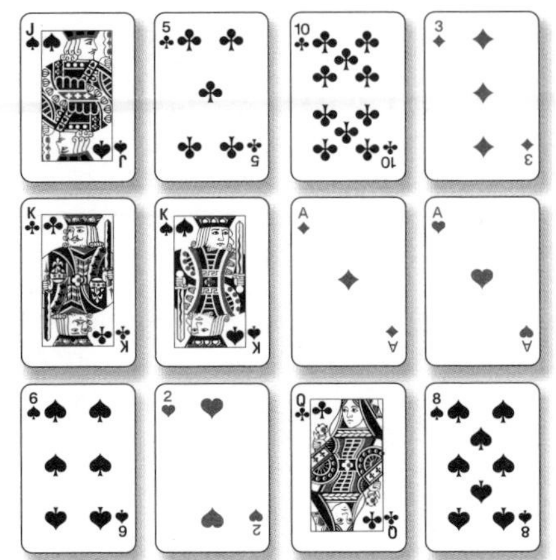

MAZE

SINGLE PACK

Maze is an excellent patience because some skill is necessary if it is to be successful.

The 52 cards of the pack are dealt face upwards in two rows of eight cards each, and four of nine cards each.

The four Kings are then discarded. This leaves four spaces, or six in all, because as well as the spaces left by the discard of the Kings, the spaces at the end of the first and second rows are taken into the layout for the play (see illustration opposite).

The object of the game is to arrange the 48 cards in four ascending suit sequences, from Aces to Queens, beginning with an Ace at the extreme left of the top row and ending with a Queen at the extreme right of the bottom row. The sequences follow on, from the end of one row to the beginning of the next, as in reading. Only one card may be moved at a time.

The rules for moving a card into a space are:

The card must be in suit sequence one higher than the card on the left of the space or one lower than the card on the right of the space, and it is to be assumed that not only are the rows continuous but that the bottom row is continuous with the top row.

When a space occurs on the right of a Queen it may be filled with any Ace,

as an alternative to the card one lower in suit sequence than the card on the right of the space.

Suppose the layout is as in the illustration. After the four Kings have been discarded, the space left vacant by the ♥ K may be filled by any Ace, or with the ♠ 9 (by reason of the ♠ 10 on the right of the space) or the ♠ 8 (by reason of the ♠ 7 at the end of the bottom row). The space at the extreme right of the top row may be filled either with the ♥ 2 or ♥ 4, that at the extreme right of the second row either with the ♥ 10 or ♠ 10. The space left vacant by the ♦ K may be filled either with the ♣ Q or ♠ 5.

To begin the game play the ♠ A to the top left corner of the layout, and the ♥ 10 to its vacant place. Play the ♦ 5 to the left of the ♦ 6 in the top row, and the ♦ J to the left of the ♦ Q in the bottom row. Play the ♠ 10 to the extreme right of the second row, and the ♠ 2 followed by the ♠ 3 to the right of the ♠ A in the top row. Play the ♠ 5 to the left of the ♠ 6, the ♣ J to the left of the ♣ Q and the ♠ 4 to the left of the ♠ 5. The ♥ 5 is played to the left of the ♥ 6, the ♥ 9 to the left of the ♥ 10 and the ♠ 9 to the left of the ♠ 10. Now the ♦ 5 in the top row may be played to the right of the ♦ 4 and the ♠ 4 to the right of the ♠ 3 in the top row. With the ♠ A, ♠ 2, ♠ 3 and ♠ 4 in position, the game progresses well.

MISS MILLIGAN

DOUBLE PACK

This is a classic patience, the enduring popularity of which must be due, in part, to its amazing ability to turn out from apparently hopeless positions.

Use two packs shuffled together, and deal out eight cards side by side, face up. Take out any Aces to start the building - the object of the game is to build all eight Aces in sequence and in suit up to their Kings. Having taken the Aces out, pack the remaining cards in descending sequence, red on black (or black on red) wherever they fit. You may also build any 2s which fit onto their Aces, and 3s on the 2s etc. Kings may be moved into spaces.

When no further building or packing can be done, deal out another eight cards on top of the piles (or into the spaces where piles have been emptied), then pause for another session of building and packing. Any card or properly packed sequence which fits may be moved from the top of one pile and packed onto the top of another pile. Aces are taken out as they appear, and building onto these Aces is allowed during the packing.

The illustration shows a position reached after three deals and some packing. From this position we can pack the sequence from ♦ J down to ♠ 6 onto the ♠ Q, then build the ♠ 2 onto the ♠ A, and the ♠ 3 onto the ♠ 2. No more packing can be done, so eight more cards are then dealt out.

Continue to alternate phases of packing and dealing until all the cards have been dealt out. You will probably have reached a pretty hopeless looking position, with all the cards you really need buried under something else, but at this point we introduce a new rule.

The rule is called 'waiving' and the process of waiving is simply to pick up the top card from one of the piles and

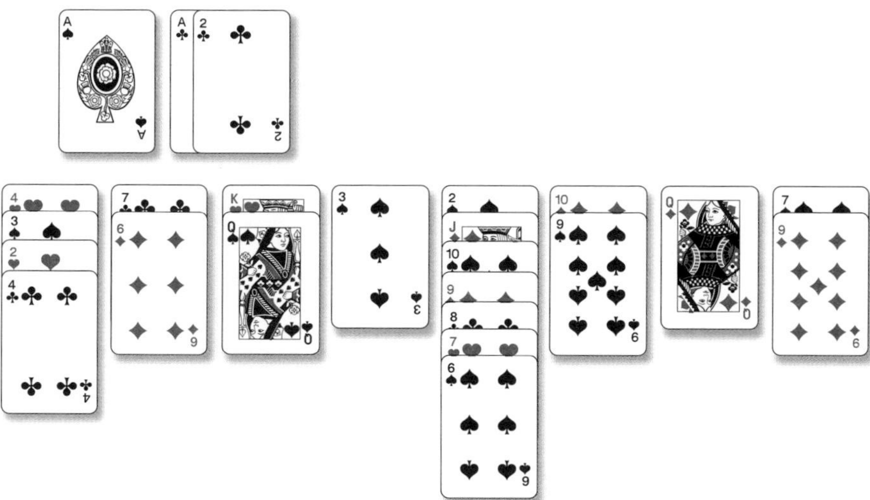

hold it in your hand, continuing the play as if it didn't exist until you find somewhere to build or pack it. You may only waive one card at a time, but this is often enough to bring the patience out. Some people allow a whole sequence to be waived at once so long as it is properly packed.

A technique which is particularly useful in Miss Milligan is the transfer of parts of sequences. Suppose, for example, that you have an awkward sequence with a black Jack at the top of it blocking one of the piles, and that there is another black Jack exposed elsewhere. Then you can transfer the bottom part of the sequence, from the red 10 downward, to the other Jack, then waive the offending Jack and start work on the rest of the pile.

PAGANINI

DOUBLE PACK

Paganini is a double-pack patience game, similar in principle to the single-pack game known as Spaces. It was composed by Mr Charles Jewell.

The entire pack is dealt face upwards on the table in eight rows of 13 cards each, as shown in the illustration overleaf.

The object of the game is to arrange the cards so that each row consists of one

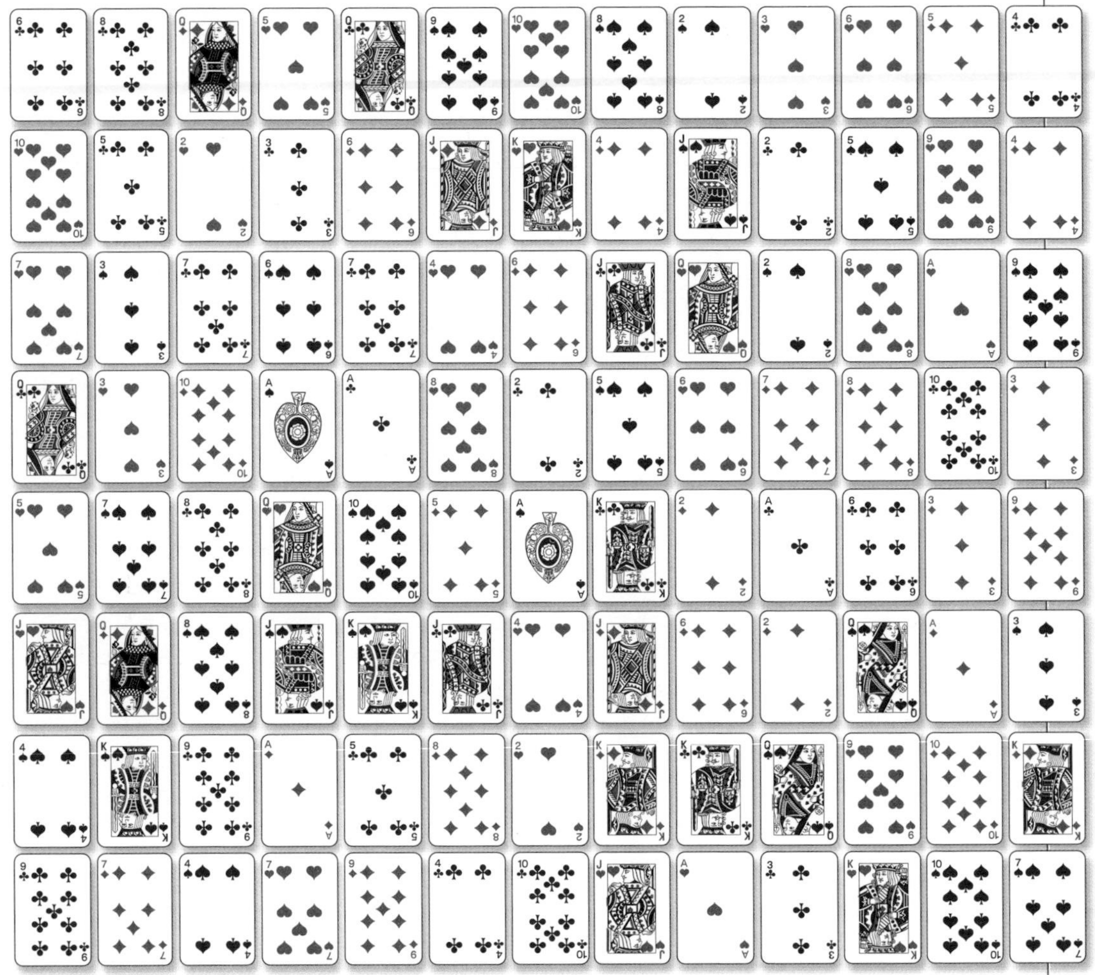

The pack as first dealt out for Paganini

suit beginning with an Ace (on the left) and ending with a King (on the right). No row is singled out for any particular suit; the player makes his own decision but, having made it, he must not alter it.

Play begins by moving one of the Aces to the extreme left of a row. It will be appreciated, therefore, that as the game proceeds the whole of the layout is moved one space to the left so to speak. When a card is moved it leaves a space in the layout which is filled with the next higher card of the same suit as the card on the left of the space. Filling a space leaves another space in the layout. In turn this is filled in the same way, and so on, until a run is brought to an end by removing a card from the right-hand side of a King, because no card is available to be played to the space on the right of a King.

The game calls for a show of skill. To begin, a player has to decide which of the eight Aces he will move first and to the extreme left of which of the eight rows he will move it to. Then, whenever a card is moved in the layout, there is, at all events early in the play, a choice of two cards to fill the available space. It will be seen, therefore, that when all eight Aces have been moved to the extreme left of the layout, each move will offer the choice of filling one of eight spaces with either of the two suitable cards.

The layout in the illustration is not as difficult as it may appear. Indeed, with a little care the game should be won.

After a general survey of the possibilities in the game, the ♥ A in the bottom row should be moved to the extreme left of the row; the ♥ Q in the fifth row is moved to the space left vacant by the ♥ A; and the ♣ 9 in the bottom row is moved into the space left vacant by the ♥ Q. The space left vacant by the ♣ 9 may be filled either with the ♥ 2 in the second row or the one in the seventh row. Consideration shows that it should be filled with the one in the second row, because the ♣ 6 in the top row can be moved into the vacant space, the ♣ A in the fifth row can be moved to the extreme left of the top row, the ♣ 6 in the top row can be moved to the space in the second row left vacant by the ♥ 2, and either the ♣ 2 in the second row or that in the fourth row can be moved into the space (alongside the ♣ A) left vacant by the ♣ 6. And so on.

ROYAL PARADE

DOUBLE PACK

Royal Parade is a popular two-pack patience with the alternative names of Financier, Hussars and Three Up.

Twenty-four cards are dealt in three rows of eight cards each (see illustration). Aces take no part in the game and are discarded. The cards in the layout must be arranged so that the top row consists of eight 2s, the middle row of eight 3s, and the bottom row of eight 4s, and these cards must be built on in suit sequences at intervals of three cards, namely:

2	3	4
5	6	7
8	9	10
J	Q	K

In the layout illustrated the ♦ A, in the top row, and the ♣ A, in the bottom

row, are discarded; the ♠ 4, in the middle row, is moved to the space in the bottom row left vacant by the discard of the ♣ A, and the ♠ 7, in the top row, built on it. Either the ♥ 3 or ♣ 3, both in the top row, may be moved to fill the space in the middle row left vacant by the ♠ 4, and clearly the ♥ 3 should be chosen because the ♥ 6 in the bottom row may be built on it. And so on.

When all moves have been made, eight cards are dealt to waste heaps below the layout. Aces, as they are dealt, are discarded; other cards are used to build on the foundations or to fill spaces in the layout. Play continues in this way, making moves after each deal of eight cards to the waste heaps, until the pack is exhausted. Only the top cards of the waste heaps may be moved to the layout.

SAINT HELENA

DOUBLE PACK

Saint Helena, or Napoleon's Favourite, is a two-pack patience in which the packs are not shuffled together but used one after the other. Although the game gives a player some scope for ingenuity and the exercise of his memory, it is

such a simple game that one rather doubts that it received its name because it was Napoleon's chief amusement during his last years.

An Ace and a King of each suit are arranged in two rows, the Kings above the Aces. Twelve cards are then dealt, clockwise, beginning above the left-hand King, as shown in the diagram above.

The Kings are built on in descending suit sequences to the Aces, and the Aces in ascending suit sequences to the Kings; with the restriction that cards dealt to spaces 1, 2, 3, 4 may be built only on the Kings, cards dealt to spaces 7, 8, 9, 10 only to the Aces, and cards dealt to spaces 5, 6, 11, 12 to either Aces or Kings.

When all moves have been made the spaces are filled from the pack, and when no further moves are to be made, another 12 cards are dealt to cover the cards in position.

When the pack has been exhausted, the restriction of play is lifted, and cards may be built on any foundation from any one of the 12 surrounding waste heaps. Also, the top card of each waste heap may now be packed on any other waste heap either in ascending or descending suit sequence.

Three deals in all are allowed. The waste heaps are picked up in reverse order 12 … 1, and turned face down, so that the bottom card of the 12th waste heap becomes the top card of the re-made stock. No shuffling is allowed.

SPIDER

DOUBLE PACK

There are several variations of Spider. The one described in this article is deservedly considered the best, and, indeed, among the best of all patiences, because it frequently calls for deep analysis. According to Redbook Magazine it was the favourite patience of President Franklin D. Roosevelt.

Forty cards are dealt to the table in four overlapping rows of ten cards each: the first, second and third rows face

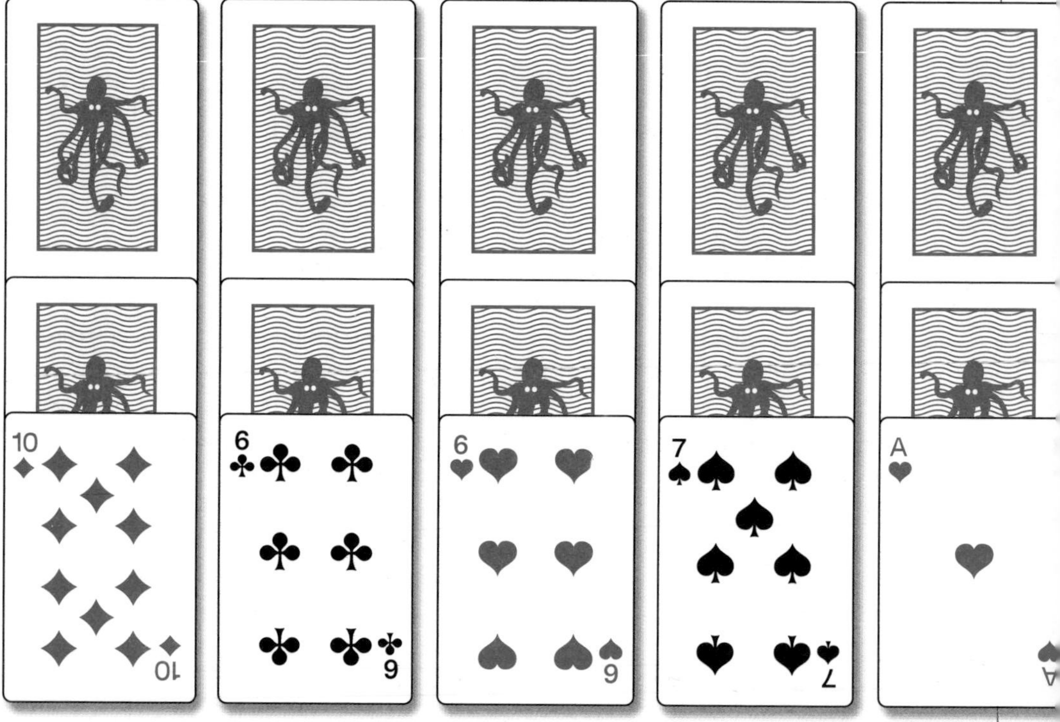

downwards, the fourth row face upwards, as in the illustration below.

Foundation cards are not played to the centre. The game is to build within the layout descending suit sequences on the eight Kings to the Aces. A completed sequence is discarded, so that the game is won when the table is cleared of all cards.

The cards at the bottom of the columns may be packed in descending sequences irrespective of suit and colour, and when a card is moved from one column to another the face-downwards card immediately above it is turned face upwards and becomes available for play.

In the diagram any of the three sixes may be packed on the ♠ 7 and the ♦ 9 may be packed on either of the tens. Two cards will thus be exposed.

When all the cards have been moved from a column, the space may be filled by any exposed card or sequence.

After all possible moves have been made, and all the available spaces filled, ten cards are dealt from the stock, face upwards, one to the bottom of each column, overlapping the cards in position.

Play is continued in this way until the stock is exhausted. The last deal from the stock will, of course, be of only four cards.

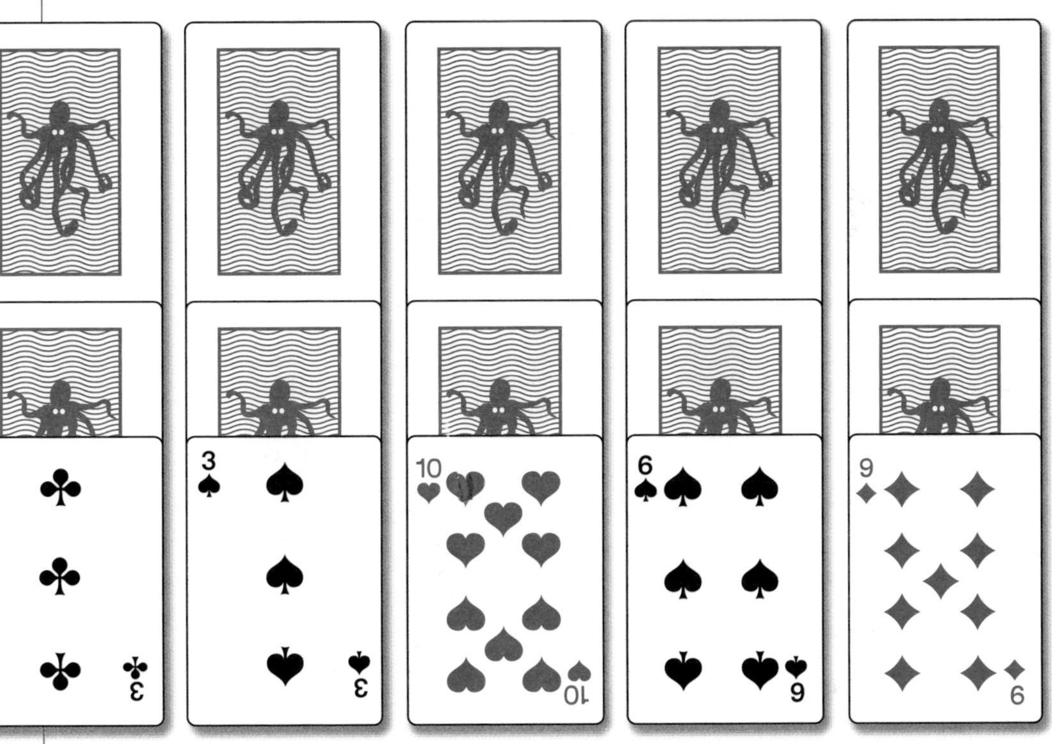

SULTAN

DOUBLE PACK

Sultan, sometimes, but rarely, known as Emperor of Germany, is a two-pack patience that calls for some skill if it is to be successful.

The eight Kings and one ♥ A are removed from the pack and arranged on the table as shown in the illustration overleaf. With the exception of the central ♥ K they serve as foundations to be built up in suit sequences to the

Queens, the Aces ranking between the Kings and the 2s.

On each side of the foundations, deal a column of four cards, as shown in the illustration opposite. It is known as the divan, and the cards dealt to it are available to be built on the foundations. When one is played, the space is filled either from the stock or from the waste heap, but need not be filled immediately.

The pack is turned card by card to a waste heap, and may be dealt three times.

Management of the divan is of great importance. The general rule is not to fill a space with a card that is unlikely to be wanted during the immediate deal. If, for example, a foundation is built up to a 7, and both 8s are already buried, the 9s and higher cards should be played to the waste heap, because if used to fill a space in the divan they would be wasted.

TERRACE

DOUBLE PACK

Also known as Signora and Queen of Italy, this is an excellent patience which calls for considerable foresight. Its special feature is that all the blocking cards (the problems you will have to dodge round) are laid out in a line at the beginning.

Shuffle two packs together. Deal out 11 cards in an overlapping line, the 'terrace', so that you can see what they all are. Leave space below them for the eight bases on which you will be building. Below that deal out four cards side by side, then stop and think.

At this stage you must choose one of the four cards. That card and the other seven of the same rank will form the bases for all the building, though you have to wait for the others to appear. The choice will depend on the cards in the terrace.

Having chosen your base card, put it in the building area, fill the gap it occupied from the pack, and deal out another five cards to make a row of nine. These form the working area, where packing is allowed. Continue packing these cards, taking out base cards for building and filling in the gaps until you get stuck, then turn over cards from the pack to start forming a waste pile. When you get to the end of the pack, there is no redeal – if the cards are not all built onto the bases by then you have failed.

Cards are built up on the bases in sequence, alternating red and black cards and increasing, turning the corner from

Terrace soon after the waste pile has been started.

King to Ace to 2 when you reach it. The exposed cards in the working area, the top card of the waste pile and the top card of the terrace are available for building.

Within the working area, packing is done in descending sequence, alternating red and black cards, turning the corner from 2 to Ace to King as necessary. Only one card at a time may be moved – sequences in the working area can only be moved by building – and gaps which appear may only be filled with the top card of the waste pile. Cards from the terrace may not be used for packing - they must be built directly. The only cards available for packing are single cards in the working area and the top card of the waste pile.

The illustration shows a game shortly after the waste pile has been started. Kings were chosen as base cards, and three of them have been found. One of these has been built up to a black 3, getting rid of the first two cards of the terrace in the process. In order to get rid of the next card, the ♣ 9, it will be necessary to find a red 4, a black 5, and so on up to a red 8 (the 5, the 6 and the 8 are already waiting in the working area, so this won't be too difficult). Note that it is illegal to pack the ♥ 8 and ♠ 9 onto the ♥ 10 in the working area, since only one card may be moved at a time.

The art of getting this game of patience to turn out is to work out in advance where the terrace cards are going to go, and not to do any building which does not contribute directly to this aim. For much of the time you will be turning cards from the pack to the waste pile, waiting for some particular card to come up so that you can move the top card off the terrace. While doing this, though, you can prepare a 'reception committee' for the next cards in line down the terrace. It hardly matters how big the waste pile becomes – you will find that it has an almost magical way of disappearing once the terrace has been got rid of. With care this patience can be turned out successfully about half the number of attempts.

THREE BLIND MICE

SINGLE PACK

This is a simple patience which more or less operates itself. This one does not turn out very often (about one time in ten) and has a way of getting stuck very near the end which you may find amusing or aggravating depending on your temperament.

Use a single 52-card pack and deal out ten piles of five cards, overlapping so that you can see all the faces, as shown in the illustration overleaf. All the cards in the seven piles on the left should be placed face up, but the bottom three cards in each of the three piles on the right should be face down. Keep the two odd cards on one side and play them wherever possible.

The object is to build each of the four suits in descending sequence (Queen on King, 8 on 9, etc.) from

Three Blind Mice starting position

King down to Ace. This is done directly by building cards onto each other in suit. For this purpose the card being built onto must be on top of its pile, but the card doing the building can be anywhere except further down the same pile, so long as it is face up. If there are other cards on top of the one being built, they are carried with it.

When one of the 'blind' cards is exposed it is turned over and can join in the play.

Kings may be played into the spaces which arise when one of the ten piles becomes empty.

The illustration shows the start of a game. From here we can put the ♠ Q directly onto the ♠ K, but the ♦ 5 has to wait until the ♦ 6 is exposed.

The building might start with the ♣ 7 being played on the ♣ 8, keeping the ♣ 3 and ♥ A on top of it. This exposes the ♥ 3, so we can put the ♥ 2 (and ♦ 7) on the ♥ 3. Now one of the blind cards is exposed and can be turned over.

WINDMILL

DOUBLE PACK

The game known as Windmill or Propeller gets its name from the layout. Any King is placed face upwards on the table, and two cards are dealt above it, two below it, and two on each side of it, to form a cross (see illustration). The first four Aces that are dealt, whether to the layout or as the stock is turned, are played to the angles of the cross.

The object of the game is to build on the central King a descending, round-the-corner, sequence of 52 cards, regardless of suit and colour, and ascending suit sequences, regardless of suit and colour, on the four Aces to the Kings.

In the layout shown, the ♦ A is played to an angle of the cross, the ♦ Q is built on the ♠ K, and the ♥ J on the ♦ Q. At any time a card may be taken from an Ace foundation and played to the King foundation, but only one card may be taken from each Ace foundation during the building of any one sequence on the King foundation.

The stock is turned to a waste heap, and a space in the layout must be filled from the waste heap, or from the stock if there is no waste heap.

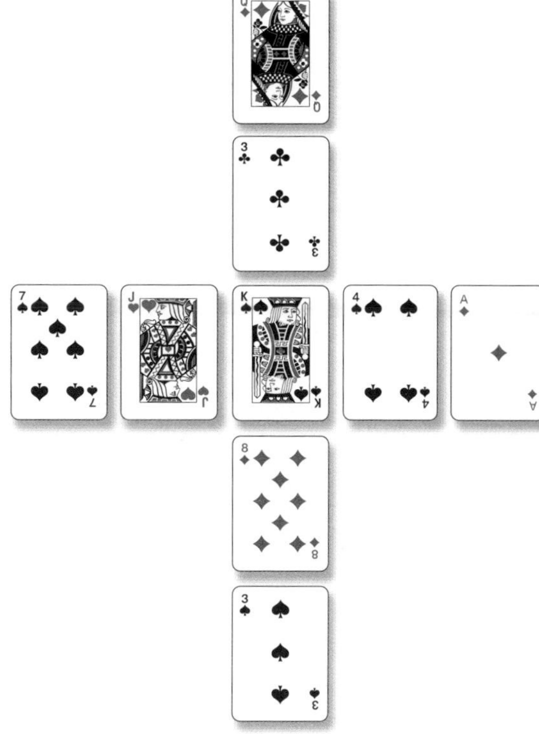

There is no second deal, but when the stock is exhausted, the waste heap may be taken up and the first card dealt. If it can be played to a foundation, the next card is dealt, and so on. The game, however, comes to an end when a card can no longer be played to a foundation.

GLOSSARY

All pastimes have a vocabulary of their own. That of card playing is probably the most extensive, because there are so many different games and most are of obscure origin. This list, therefore, is by no means complete and comprehensive; rather it includes only the words and expressions that are used in this book and, due to limitation of space, those that are self-explanatory and those that most readers may be expected to know are omitted.

ABOVE THE LINE In games of the Bridge family, bonus scores and penalty scores are recorded above a horizontal line across the scoresheet. cf BELOW THE LINE.

ABUNDANCE (ABONDANCE) In games of the Solo Whist family, a declaration to win nine tricks.

ALONE In Euchre, the right of the player who has named the trump suit to play without his partner.

ANTE A compulsory bet made before the deal.

ASSIST In Euchre, a declaration made by the dealer's partner to accept the suit of the turn-up card as the trump suit.

BANCO A bet equal to the amount staked by the banker.

BASTO The ♣ A in Ombre.

BEG In games of the All Fours family, a rejection by the non-dealer of the suit of the turn-up card as the trump suit.

BELLA In Klaberjass, an announcement made by the player who holds the King and Queen of the trump suit, after he has played the second one, allowing him to score 20 points.

BELOW THE LINE In games of the Bridge family, scores for tricks bid and won are recorded below a horizontal line across the scoresheet. cf ABOVE THE LINE.

BETE In Pinocle, failure to make the contract. cf DOUBLE BETE and SINGLE BETE.

BEZIQUE In games of the Bezique family, the ♠ Q (or ♣ Q if spades or diamonds are trumps) and ♦ J (or ♥ J if spades or diamonds are trumps).

BLACK MARIA In games of the Black Maria family, the ♠ Q.

BLITZ In Gin Rummy, winning a game against an opponent who has failed to score.

BOODLE CARDS In games of the Newmarket family, the Ace, King, Queen and Jack, each of a different suit, from another pack, placed in a layout and on which bets are staked.

BOOK In games of the Bridge and Whist families, the first six tricks won by a side, that do not count in the scoring.

BOTTOM LAYOUT In Monte Bank, the two cards from the bottom of the pack placed by the banker face upwards on the table. cf TOP LAYOUT.

BOWER In Euchre, the Jack of a suit. cf LEFT BOWER and RIGHT BOWER.

BOX In Gin Rummy, the score for winning a hand.

BRAGGERS In Brag, the ♦ A, ♣ J and ♦ 9, that serve as wild cards.

BRISQUE In games of the Bezique family, any Ace or 10.

BUILD (1) In Casino, the play of a card to a card in the layout to make up a total that may be taken with another card in the hand. (2) In games of Patience, the play of a card of the same suit on the next one above or below it in rank.

BUY Increasing a bet for the advantage of drawing a card face downwards.

BURY A CARD In Pinocle, discarding face downwards a card from hand.

CACHETTE In Quinto, the widow-hand.

CALYPSO In Calypso, a complete suit, from Ace to 2, in a player's trump suit.

CANASTA In games of the Canasta family, a meld of seven or more cards. cf MIXED CANASTA and NATURAL CANASTA.

CAPOT In Piquet, the winning by one player of all 12 tricks.

CARDS In Piquet, the score for winning the majority of tricks.

CARTE BLANCHE A hand that contains no court card.

CASH Leading and winning a trick with an established card.

CASINO cf GREAT CASINO & LITTLE CASINO.

CENTRE In games of Patience, that part of the table to which the foundation cards are played.

CHECK In Poker, a nominal bet that reserves the right to call or raise if another player bets.

CODILLE In Ombre, one opponent winning more tricks than ombre.

COMBINE In Casino, picking up cards from the layout of the total pip value of a card in hand.

COMET In games of the Comet family, a wild card, usually a 9.

COMMON MARRIAGE In games of the Bezique family, the meld of the King and Queen of the same plain suit. cf ROYAL MARRIAGE.

CONDITIONS In Panguingue, certain melds by making which a player immediately collects chips from all other players.

CONTRA A call which doubles the score for a hand in Skat.

COUP A winning play or bet.

COURT CARD Any King, Queen or Jack.

CRIB In Cribbage, an extra hand formed by the discards of the players.

CUT THROAT A version of what is usually a partnership game in which each player plays for himself.

DIS In Pinocle, the 9 of the trump suit.

DISCARD The play of a card that is not of the suit led nor a trump.

DOUBLE BETE In Pinocle, the penalty suffered by the bidder whose score for melds and cards taken in tricks fails to equal his contract. cf SINGLE BETE.

DOUBLETON An original holding of two cards of a suit.

DUMMY In games of the Bridge family, the partner of the declarer, and the hands he exposes on the table.

ELDER HAND In Piquet and other games for two players, the non-dealer. cf YOUNGER HAND.

ELDEST HAND The player who sits next to the dealer and whose privilege it is to play first. In most games, this is the player to the dealer's left, but in a few games, such as Panguingue, where play rotates anti-clockwise, it is the player to dealer's right.

EUCHRE In Euchre, failure to win at least three tricks.

FACE CARD Same as COURT CARD *q.v.*

FIFTEEN In Cribbage, the play of a card which, with those already played, adds up to fifteen.

FINESSE An attempt to win a trick with a card that is not the best held nor in sequence with it.

FLUSH A hand with all cards of the same suit.

FOLLOW SUIT To play a card of the same suit as that of the led card.

FOOT In Panguingue, the lower half of the stock set aside for use if the HEAD *q.v.* is exhausted.

FOREHAND In Skat and Schafkopf, the player to the dealer's left. cf MIDDLEHAND.

FOUNDATION In games of Patience, a card played to the centre on which a complete suit or sequence must be built.

GATE In Monte Bank, the bottom card of the pack.

GIFT In games of the All Fours family, the point scored by the dealer if he begs and the dealer decides to play.

GIN In Gin Rummy, a hand in which all the cards are melded.

GO In Cribbage, the announcement that a player cannot play without exceeding 31.

GO DOWN or GO OUT Same as KNOCK (1) *q.v.*

GOULASH In Towie, a redeal of the four hands unshuffled and with each hand arranged in suits.

GRAND In Skat, a contract in which the four Jacks in effect form a trump suit of their own.

GRAND SLAM In games of the Bridge and Whist families, the winning of all 13 tricks. cf SMALL SLAM.

GREAT CASINO In Casino, the ♦ 10. cf LITTLE CASINO.

HAND CARDS In Lansquenet, the two top cards of the pack exposed face upwards on the table.

HEAD In Panguingue, the top half of the stock. cf FOOT.

HEEL Same as TALON *q.v.*

HIGH In games of the All Fours family, the score for being dealt the highest trump in play. cf LOW.

HIS HEELS In Cribbage, a Jack turned up as the start.

HIS NOB In Cribbage, the Jack, either in hand or crib, of the same suit as the start.

HOLE CARD In Stud Poker, the first card dealt,

face downwards, to a player.

HONOURS (1) In games of the Bridge family, the Ace, King, Queen, Jack and 10 of a suit. (2) In Whist, the Ace, King, Queen and Jack of a suit.

HUITIEME In Piquet, a sequence of eight cards.

IN HAND In Skat, a contract in which the declarer does not look at the skat.

INTRIGUE In Pope Joan, the Queen and Jack of the trump suit played by the same player.

JACK In games of the All Fours family, the score for winning the Jack of the trump suit.

JACKPOT In Poker, a deal in which a player must hold at least a pair of Jacks to open.

JASZ In Klaberjass, the Jack of the trump suit.

JINX In Spoil Five, an undertaking, by the player who has won three tricks, to win the remaining two.

JOKER An extra card supplied with the standard 52-card pack used in some games as a wild card.

KITTY Same as POOL *q.v.*

KNOCK (1) In games of the Rummy family, signification by a player that all his cards are melded. (2) In Poker, signification by a player that no further bet will be made by him.

LAYING OFF (i) In Gin Rummy, the playing of cards to opponent's melds. (2) In Panguingue the playing of cards to one's own melds.

LAYOUT Cards laid out on the table in a prescribed pattern either for the purpose of placing bets or to be moved in accordance with the rules of the game.

LEAST In Schafkopf, the hand played when no player has offered to be Player, so each plays for himself.

LEFT BOWER In Euchre, the Jack of the same colour as the Jack of the trump suit. cf RIGHT BOWER.

LEFT PEDRO In Cinch, the 5 of the same colour as the 5 of the trump suit. cf RIGHT PEDRO.

LITTLE CASINO In Casino, the ♠ 2. cf GREAT CASINO.

LOO In Loo, failure to win a trick.

LOW In games of the All Fours family, the score made by the player who is dealt the lowest trump in play. cf HIGH.

LURCH In Cribbage, winning a game before the opponent has gone half-way round the scoring board.

MAKER The player who names the trump suit.

MANILLE In Ombre, the ♥ 7 or ♦ 7 if either suit is trumps, the ♠ 2 or ♣ 2 if either suit is trumps.

MARCH In Euchre, winning all five tricks by one side or one player.

MARRIAGE cf COMMON MARRIAGE and ROYAL MARRIAGE.

MATADORES In Ombre, the collective name for the three top trumps - SPADILLE, MANILLE and BASTO.

MATRIMONY In Pope Joan, the King and Queen of the trump suit played by the same player.

MELD A matched set of three or more of a kind or a sequence of three or more of the same suit in consecutive order of rank.

MENEL In Klaberjass, the 9 of trumps.

MIDDLEHAND In Skat and Schafkopf, the player to Dealer's right i.e. the player between FOREHAND q.v. and dealer.

MISERE In Solo Whist, a contract not to win a trick.

MISERY Same as MISERE *q.v.*

MISS In Loo, the widow-hand.

MIXED CANASTA In Canasta, a meld of seven or more cards of which one, two or three cards are wild. cf NATURAL CANASTA.

MUGGINS In Cribbage, an announcement that enables a player to take points that his opponent has overlooked.

NAP A declaration in Nap(oleon) to win all five tricks.

NATURAL CANASTA In Canasta, a °meld of seven or more cards of which none is a wild card. cf MIXED CANASTA.

NON-COMOQUER In Panguingue, a group of Kings or Aces.

NULL In Skat, a contract to take no tricks.

NULLO Same as MISERE *q.v.*

OMBRE In Ombre, the player who plays against the other two players in partnership against him.

ORDER UP In Euchre, the declaration of an

opponent of the dealer accepting the suit of the turn-up card as the trump suit.

PAIR (1) In Casino, the play of a card and taking up as a trick all the other cards of the same rank in the layout. (2) In Cribbage, playing a card of the same rank as the previous one played.

PAIR-ROYAL (1) In Brag, three cards of equal rank. (2) In Cribbage, playing a third card of the same rank as a pair.

PAM In Loo, the ♣ J.

PARTIE In Piquet, a game.

PEDRO cf LEFT PEDRO and RIGHT PEDRO.

PEG In Cribbage, a marker used for scoring on a board.

PINOCLE In Pinocle, the ♠ Q and ♦ J.

PITCH In Auction Pitch, the opening lead that determines the trump suit.

PIQUE In Piquet, the winning of 30 points in hand and play before an opponent scores. cf REPIQUE.

PLAIN SUIT A suit other than the trump suit.

PLAYER In Calabrasella and Schafkopf the player who elects to play on his own against the other two players.

POINT In Piquet, the number of cards held in the longest suit.

POLIGNAC In Polignac, the ♠ J.

POOL The collective amount of players' stakes and fines.

POPE In Pope Joan, the ♦ 9.

POT In Poker, a game in which all the players put up an ante.

PROPOSE In Ecarté, a request by the non-dealer that cards may be exchanged for others from the stock.

PUESTA In Ombre, ombre and one or both of his opponents winning the same number of tricks.

PUNTO In Ombre, the Ace of whichever red suit is trumps.

QUART In Piquet, a sequence of four cards.

QUATORZE In Piquet, any four cards of the same rank higher than the 9.

QUINT (1) In Piquet, a sequence of five cards. (2) In Quinto, the 5 of every suit, and every pair of cards in a suit that totals five.

QUINT ROYAL In Quinto, the Joker.

RAISE In Poker, increasing a bet by putting up more than is necessary to equal the previous player.

RECONTRA In Skat, a call which after a call of Contra q.v. redoubles the score for a hand.

REFAIT In Trente et Quarante, a drawn game.

REFUSE (1) In games of the All Fours family, the rejection by the dealer of a proposal by the non-dealer to make another suit trumps. (2) In Ecarté, the rejection by the dealer of the non-dealer's proposal that cards may be exchanged for others from the stock.

REPIQUE In Piquet, the winning of 30 points in hand alone before opponent scores. cf PIQUE.

REVOKE Failure to follow suit when able to or to play a card in accordance with the laws of the game.

RIGHT BOWER In Euchre, the Jack of the trump suit. cf LEFT BOWER.

RIGHT PEDRO In Cinch, the 5 of the trump suit. cf LEFT PEDRO.

ROB THE PACK In Cinch, the privilege accorded to the dealer of selecting cards from the stock.

ROUND A division of dealing, betting or playing in which each player participates once.

ROUND THE CORNER A sequence of cards in which the highest is considered adjacent to the lowest.

ROYAL MARRIAGE In games of the Bezique family, the meld of the King and Queen of the trump suit. cf COMMON MARRIAGE.

RUBBER Three successive games between the same sides or players: winning two of the three games.

RUBICON Failure of the loser of a game to reach a specified minimum total of points.

RUFF Playing a trump card on the lead of a card of a side suit.

RUMMY In games of the Rummy family, the declaration by a player of all his cards in one turn.

RUN Same as SEQUENCE *q.v.*

RUN THE CARDS In games of the All Fours family, to deal more cards and a fresh turn up after a beg has been accepted.

SACARDO In Ombre, ombre winning more tricks than either of his opponents individually.

SCHMEISS In Klaberjass, an offer to play with the

turn-up card as the trump suit or throw in the hand, as the opponent prefers.

SCHNEIDER In Skat or Schafkopf, to take 90 or more card points in tricks.

SCHWARTZ In Skat or Schafkopf, to take all the tricks.

SEPTIEME In Piquet, a sequence of seven cards.

SEQUENCE Two or more cards of adjacent rank.

SIDE SUIT Same as PLAIN SUIT *q.v.*

SINGLE BETE In Pinocle, the concession of defeat and payment of a forfeit, without playing. cf DOUBLE BETE.

SINGLETON An original holding of only one card of a suit.

SINK In Piquet, omitting to announce a scoring combination.

SIXIEME In Piquet, a sequence of six cards.

SKAT In Skat, the two cards remaining after a deal i.e. the WIDOW *q.v.*

SLAM cf GRAND SLAM and SMALL SLAM.

SMALL SLAM In games of the Bridge and Whist families, winning 12 tricks. cf GRAND SLAM.

SMUDGE In Auction Pitch, a bid to win all four tricks.

SOLO In games of the Solo Whist family, a bid to win five tricks.

SPADILLE In Ombre, the ♠ A.

SPINADO In Spinado, the ♦ A.

SPOIL In Spoil Five, when no player wins three tricks.

SPREAD In Panguingue, a meld.

STAND (1) In games of the All Fours family, to accept the suit of the turn up card as the trump suit. (2) In Vingt-et-Un, to elect to take no further cards.

START In Cribbage, the top card of the cut turned face upwards by the dealer.

STOCK The undealt part of the pack which may be used later in the deal.

STRADDLE In Poker, a compulsory bet of twice the ante.

STRINGER In Panguingue, a sequence.

SWEEP In Casino, taking in all the cards in the layout.

TABLANETTE In Tablanette, an announcement that a player is able to take all the cards on the table.

TAKE-IT In Klaberjass, to accept as the trump suit the suit of the turn up card.

TALON In Piquet and some games of Patience, cards laid aside in one or more packets for later use in the same deal.

TOP LAYOUT In Monte Bank, the two top cards of the pack placed by the banker face upwards on the table. cf BOTTOM LAYOUT.

TRAIL In Casino, the play of a card to the layout by a player who can neither pass, combine, build nor call.

TRIO In Piquet, three cards of the same suit higher than the 9.

TURN UP A card faced after the deal to determine, or propose, the trump suit.

TWIST In Vingt-et-Un, a request to be dealt a card face upwards.

UP CARDS (1) In Gin Rummy, the card turned up after each player has been dealt ten cards. (2) In Stud Poker, a card dealt face upwards.

VALLE CARD In Panguingue, the 7s, 5s and 3s, the melding of which wins chips.

VOID Having no cards of a specified suit.

VOLE In Ecarté, winning all five tricks.

VULNERABLE In games of the Bridge family, being subject to bigger penalties and bonuses after winning a game.

WAIVE The privilege, in some games of patience, to lift a card and play the one under it.

WIDOW Extra cards dealt to the table usually at the same time as the hands are dealt to the players.

WILD CARD A card that the rules of the game permit the holder to specify as representing any card.

YOUNGER HAND In Piquet and other games for two players, the dealer. cf ELDER HAND.

INDEX